Direct Instruction Mathematics

Second Edition

Jerry Silbert
Eugene Public Schools
Eugene, Oregon

Douglas Carnine
University of Oregon

Marcy Stein
University of Washington

Merrill Publishing Company
A Bell & Howell Information Company
Columbus   Toronto   London   Melbourne

Cover Art: Marko Spalatin

Published by Merrill Publishing Company
A Bell & Howell Information Company
Columbus, Ohio 43216

This book was set in Helvetica

Administrative Editor: Ann Castel
Production Coordinator: Jo Ellen Gohr
Cover Designer: Brian Deep

Library of Congress Catalog Card Number: 89–61506
International Standard Book Number: 0–675–21208–1
Printed in the United States of America
1 2 3 4 5 6 7 8 9 - 94 93 92 91 90

Preface

Mathematics instruction is becoming more holistic in nature, stressing the application of mathematics in a variety of contexts. This goal cannot be reached unless students receive careful systematic instruction. In addition, students who succeed take pride in their achievement. Consequently, we have attempted to specify procedures that maximize the likelihood of student success. Movements toward more effective mathematics instruction are definitely needed. National and international evaluations of students as well as evaluations of elementary school teachers have reported serious gaps in students' and teachers' knowledge of mathematics. Moreover, we have received numerous requests from teachers who found mathematics training programs to be inadequate. Teachers were particularly vocal about the lack of specific guidance given in how to deal with students who were having difficulty learning mathematics. The text explains the inadequacies of some instructional programs and provides teachers with the information needed to modify the programs.

Although we have found the procedures suggested in this book effective, we do not claim they are panaceas. First of all, implementing our suggestions will require a great deal of hard work on the part of the teacher. Secondly, we do not claim that our suggestions regarding teaching strategies are the best possible. It is our hope that the systematic procedures recommended here will stimulate the development of even better techniques.

Direct Instruction Mathematics includes these features:

- A description of essential skills and procedures for teaching major skills.
- Procedures for evaluating, selecting, and modifying mathematic programs (especially the addition of explicit strategies and practice exercises) to meet the needs of all students.
- Techniques for effectively presenting lessons, including techniques for pacing tasks, motivating students, and diagnosing and correcting errors.
- Guidelines for individualizing instruction through properly placing students in a program and then moving them at an optional rate through the program.
- Suggestions for classroom organization that maximize the amount of time students spend engaged in math instruction.

The book is organized into two parts: (1) Perspective and (2) Skills and Concepts. The first chapter in the perspective section discusses the philosophy and techniques of direct instruction in general; the second, how these techniques can be integrated into a school mathematics program. The third outlines the scope and sequence of mathematics instruction in the elementary grades. The skills and concepts chapters in the second part are the heart of the book. Each chapter discusses a specific skill area: vocabulary and language skills, counting skills, symbol identification and place value, addition, subtraction, multiplication, division, facts, problem solving, fractions, decimals, percent, measurement, geometry, and study skills. These chapters include suggestions for meaningfully introducing each skill, procedures for teaching specific strategies, and analyses of the major problem types within each skill area. Each chapter also contains a sequence and assessment chart. The sequence is designed to minimize student failure and to provide the practice and review necessary for student mastery. The assessment items can serve as a diagnostic test, and as a basis for constructing short-term goals for Individual Education Plans (IEPs).

Also included in some skills and concepts chapters are descriptions of the ways in which various skills are presented in commercial programs and discussions of how and why these procedures must often be modified if the needs of the hard-to-teach students are to be met. (These discussions will be particularly useful to the increasing number of classroom teachers working with mainstreamed, handicapped students as a result of P.L. 94–142.) Table 1 summarizes how the book might be used by primary, intermediate, and remedial teachers.

At the end of most chapters research findings are summarized. These sections are quite brief because the research on instruction is difficult to interpret. Many studies focus on variables that are not consistently defined from one study to the next, so contradictions in findings cannot be understood. Second, with the exception of research by Brownell and some others, programmatic research has not been conducted. As a consequence, findings are fragmented and lack replications.

Revisions in the Second Edition

Because of the importance of problem solving and word problems in mathematics instruction, our research has focused on teaching word problems. That research is reflected in Chapter 12, which was totally rewritten for this edition. The chapter on basic facts (Chapter 7) was also completely reorganized to make it easier for teachers to apply. Other less extensive revisions were made throughout the book to incorporate feedback from various instructors and students. The research summaries and samples from commercial programs have been updated. Finally, a comprehensive instructor's guide that includes answers to the application items has been prepared.

Acknowledgments

Foremost among the many people to whom we are grateful are the direct instruction teachers who proved that math failure isn't inevitable. We are also grateful to Zig Engelmann, whose melding of logical analysis and empiricism has resulted in the development of numerous, highly effective mathematics programs. Many of the procedures described in this book were derived from the the DISTAR Arithmetic Corrective Mathematics Core Concepts in Mathematics, and the new Math Connections series authored by Engelmann and his colleagues. The effectiveness of these programs was documented by a comprehensive national study, which is summarized in Appendix A. Special thanks goes to Mary M. Gleason, an outstanding colleague, who gave extensive feedback in how to revise the book. Additional ideas have been contributed by our colleagues and students, including Linda Carnine, Bernadette Kelly, Linda Olen, Frank Falco and West Becker. We are particularly indebted to our reviewers, George Brent, Glassboro State College; Eric Jones, Bowling Green State University; Mary M. Gleason, University of Oregon; and Galen Alessi and Dick Schminke, who provided us with invaluable feedback and suggestions. We also appreciate the efforts of Lori McGinty, Kathy Thomas, Debbie Evans, Janet Thomas, Mardi Klotz, Marciana Liquid, Mary Grannon, and Susan Wayne.

Topics of Interest

Contents

Formats for Teaching Major Skills

The secret of education lies in respecting the pupil.

Ralph Waldo Emerson

PART ONE

Perspective

1 Direct Instruction

Many mathematics texts discuss the philosophy and theory of mathematics instruction. Most methods texts provide activities and games involving mathematics. Few, however, deal extensively with the instructional specifics. *Direct Instruction Mathematics* focuses on what teachers can do to maximize the likelihood that students will learn mathematics. The learning theory underlying this book is elaborated in detail elsewhere (Engelmann & Carnine, 1982; Becker, 1987) and cannot be adequately summarized here. A theoretical framework, labeled constructionist by Resnick (1980), does provide a general notion about our assumptions. The term *constructionist* implies that students seek meaning from learning situations. The concepts and skills possessed by a teacher can be transmitted to a passive learner. The learner tries continually to "make sense" out of what a teacher says and does. The way in which teachers organize the learning environment determines how successful learners will be in constructing the meaning that teachers intend to convey. Direct instruction provides a comprehensive set of prescriptions for organizing instruction so that students acquire, retain, and generalize new learning in as humane, efficient, and effective a manner as possible.

The need for effective instruction is growing rapidly. While many variables influence students' acquisition of mathematics, these variables are certainly central: (1) program design, (2) presentation techniques, and (3) organization of instruction, particularly the amount of teaching time. These three variables are all essential ingredients of a successful mathematics program. A well-designed program and a good teacher will not produce significant gains if instructional time is too limited. Similarly, a well-designed program and adequate instructional time will not lead to success if the teacher is not skilled. Finally, adequate time and a skilled teacher will not adequately serve students if the materials are poorly designed.

As will become apparent later in this book, no single type of instructional program, presentation technique, or classroom organization is appropriate at all times. Direct instruction, therefore, takes on different characteristics, depending on the type of student being taught and the objective. Direct instruction, when used with intermediate grade level students at average or above average skill levels, is characterized by a heavy emphasis on student directed independent work. On the other hand, the use of direct instruction with primary level students or with intermediate level students who have encountered difficulty in earlier grades is characterized by a more structured, more teacher-directed environment. Teachers ask many questions, provide immediate feedback and corrections, and praise frequently.

Before describing direct instruction procedures in more detail, we need to consider their application to instructionally sophisticated students. Direct instruction procedures are intended to make learning mathematics easier by breaking down complex tasks into their component skills, teaching these components, and demonstrating to students how the components are combined. This simplification of complex tasks is particularly important for instructionally naive students, but can also accelerate the learning of instructionally sophisticated students if used appropriately.[1] A potential misuse of direct instruction with instructionally sophisticated students results from unnecessarily slowing their speed of learning. Unnecessary practice and redundant explanations waste valuable teaching time. This situation can be avoided by giving an initial assessment. The teacher should provide instruction for only those exercises that students cannot do. In short, instructionally sophisticated students benefit from direct instruction if they are moved through a mathematics program at an optimal rate and are provided no more structure than is necessary.

Instructional Design

To effectively teach mathematics, teachers need to construct the kinds of lessons and to develop the specific teaching procedures that will best meet their students' needs. In addition, teachers often need to be able to modify or supplement certain aspects of commercial programs. This book assists teachers in acquiring these skills. We assume that almost all children can learn mathematics if lessons are designed so that students can readily understand what is being presented. The nine steps below are needed for constructing an effective instructional program:

1. Specify long- and short-term objectives
2. Devise procedural strategies
3. Determine necessary preskills
4. Sequence skills
5. Select a teaching procedure
6. Design formats
7. Select examples
8. Specify practice and review
9. Design progress monitoring procedures

The following discussion outlines the critical aspects of instructional design on which the procedures in this text are based.

---

[1] Instructionally naive students are those students who do not readily retain newly presented information, are easily confused, and have difficulty attending to an instructional presentation for more than a few minutes.

Specify Long- and Short-term Objectives

The first step in designing an instructional program is to specify long-term objectives, i.e., what students are supposed to be able to do when they have completed the program. Based on the long-term objectives, the short-term objectives can be written. These are needed to identify smaller "chunks" of content that must be taught and to provide guidance in writing progress indicators. For teachers to tell when these objectives have been met, performance indicators must be stated as specific, observable behaviors. In a performance indicator, the type of task is specified, along with accuracy and rate criteria. For example, a reasonable performance indicator for single digit addition would be: Given 25 single digit addition problems, a first grader will correctly solve at least 22 in 1 minute with no more than one error. In contrast, an objective stating that students will understand the concept of addition is nonspecific, nonobservable, and therefore, unacceptable.

Devise Procedural Strategies

Whenever possible, instructional programs should teach explicit strategies designed to enable students to work a broad set of examples. The strategies need to be explicit as well as generalizable. Devising explicit strategies is fairly simple for computation problems, but very difficult for application problems, as illustrated by word problems. (See Chapter 12 for examples of such strategies.) This text, while by no means comprehensive, contains procedural strategies for a range of basic mathematics skills that teachers can incorporate into their daily mathematics instruction.

Determine Necessary Preskills

Instruction should be sequenced so that the component skills of a strategy are taught before the strategy itself is introduced. The component skills, therefore, can be referred to as preskills. For example, in order to solve a percent problem such as "What is 23% of 67?" the student must be able to (1) convert percent to a decimal—23% = .23, (2) work multiplication problems with multi-digit factors,

$$\begin{array}{r} 67 \\ \times .23 \\ \hline 201 \\ 134 \\ \hline 15.41 \end{array}$$

and (3) place the decimal point correctly in the product—15.41.

Sequence Skills

The order in which information and skills are introduced affects the difficulty students have in learning them. Sequencing involves determining the optimum order for introducing new information and strategies. Three sequencing guidelines are (1) preskills of a strategy are taught before the strategy; (2) easy skills are taught before more difficult ones; and (3) strategies and information that are likely to be confused are not introduced consecutively.

Within any given area of mathematics, one can predict which problem types will cause students the most difficulty. Generally, the more steps in a strategy and the greater the similarity of the strategy to other previously taught strategies, the more difficult the problem type will be. Teachers should carefully analyze various problem types for their relative difficulty. The need for a careful analysis of problem types can be illustrated by looking at column subtraction. Obviously, problems which require renaming (borrowing) are more difficult than problems that do not require renaming. However, not all problems which require renaming are of equal difficulty. A problem like 3002 – 89 is significantly more difficult than a problem like 364 – 128 because of the difficulty in renaming numbers with zeroes (the 300 in 3002).

Another example of the need for careful analysis occurs when teaching teen numerals. Primary grade teachers are well aware of the problems low-performing students have identifying 11, 12, 13, and 15. What is not as obvious is why students have these problems. Two possible causes are irregularity and the direction of reading (beginning with the digit on the right). Students usually read numerals from left to right, but they must read teen numerals from right to left. For example, when identifying 16, students start with the number represented by 6 on the right before saying the suffix teen. Similarly students read 14 as fourteen not teen four. In addition to this general problem, the numerals 11, 12, 13, and 15 are irregular. While the numeral 16 is read sixteen, and 14 is read fourteen, 15 is not read fiveteen nor is 13 read threeteen. Our sequencing recommendation for symbol identification (not for counting exercises) is to introduce the regular, thus easier teens (14, 16, 17, 18, and 19) before the more difficult ones (11, 12, 13, and 15). Sequencing from easy to difficult

reduces student errors and frustration, which is a major goal of direct instruction.

The third sequencing guideline is to separate the introduction of information and/or strategies that are likely to be confused. The more similar two tasks or symbols are, the more likely students are to confuse them. For example, students are likely to confuse the numerals 6 and 9, which are often written identically except for their relative position. Thus, 6 and 9 should not be introduced consecutively. Likewise, the skip counting series for 6s and 4s are quite similar in that they both contain 12, 24 36 (6, 12, 18, 24, 30, 36 vs. 4, 8, 12, 16, 20, 24, 28, 32, 36). Introducing these series consecutively would be likely to cause confusion on the part of some students.

Sometimes potential areas of confusion are hard to predict. For example, in an earlier edition of *DISTAR Arithmetic I*, the authors introduced the symbol 5 immediately after the symbol 4. They noted that a significant number of low-performing students confused 4 and 5. Upon analysis of the confusion, they realized that the names of the two numerals begin with the same sound—*four* and *five*. In revising the program, the authors separated the introduction of 4 and 5. The number of students developing confusions on these numerals dramatically decreased.[2]

Select a Teaching Procedure

There are three basic types of tasks in mathematics instruction: motor task, labeling tasks, and strategy tasks. The majority of tasks for young children are motor and labeling tasks; later tasks are mostly strategy tasks.

MOTOR TASKS In a motor task, students memorize a series of words (counting or saying a rule) or execute a precise movement (writing symbols). A four-step procedure is used to teach motor tasks: model, lead, test, delayed test. A model is simply a demonstration by the teacher. For example, the teacher models skip counting by saying, "My turn to count by 6s: 6, 12, 16, 24, 30." A lead consists of the teacher's helping the students make the desired response. "Say the 6s with me. Get ready, 6, 12, 18, 24, 30." The lead is repeated until the students

---

[2] *DISTAR Arithmetic I* is an instructional program based on a direct instruction approach. The DISTAR math program was co-authored by Siegfried Engelmann and Doug Carnine (Chicago: Science Research Associates, 1969, 1975, 1989). A new six-level basal mathematics series also based on direct instruction theory is currently in preparation.

appear able to make the response successfully. (The lead may also consist of a physical prompt; e.g., the teacher guides the student's hand as the student writes numerals.)

The test consists of the teacher's asking the students to make the response without any assistance. The delayed test occurs several minutes later, after "interference" in the form of a different task. For example, after teaching students to say the first part of a 6 series (6, 12, 18, 24, 30), the teacher might present an exercise on fractions and then retest the students on the 6 series. If the students are able to respond correctly, the teacher goes on to the next task in the lesson. If the students do not respond correctly, the teacher repeats the model-lead-test steps. Thus, instruction is individualized; lower performers receive extra practice while higher performers go on to other tasks.

LABELING TASKS Labeling tasks are those in which the student must say the word which correctly labels an object (e.g,, saying "four" when shown the symbol 4, saying "triangle" when shown that form, and saying "dime" when shown that coin). In labeling tasks, students are assumed to have the motor skill needed to produce the response. They must just learn when to make the response—say "four" when they see a 4 but not when they see a 5. The procedure for teaching labeling tasks involves three steps: (1) model, (2) alternating test, and (3) delayed test. The model involves the teacher pointing to the symbol, telling the students what it is called, and having the students repeat the label. The teacher then proceeds to the alternating test pattern, alternating between the new example and other previously taught examples. In the alternating pattern, the number of previously taught examples between presentations of the new example gradually increases. The teacher might present the new example, a review example, the new example, two review examples, the new example, then three review examples. For instance, assume x is the new example and a, b, and c are review examples The sequence of an alternating pattern test might look like this: x a x b a x a c b x. (Note that the review examples should not be presented in the same order each time.) The teacher follows the alternating pattern until the students respond correctly to the new example after three or four previously introduced examples are presented. This alternating pattern is very important because it requires the students to remember the response to the new example and to discriminate the new example from other examples. Gradually increasing the intervals

for which students are required to remember the new response builds student retention of the new examples and at the same time minimizes the probability of failure. If a student makes an error, the teacher returns to the beginning of the pattern. The delayed test simply consists of the teacher asking the students to identify the new example later in the lesson. If the students respond incorrectly, as with motor tasks, the teacher returns to earlier steps, in this case, the model and alternating test pattern.

STRATEGY TASKS Strategy tasks are those which require the integration of a series of sequential steps to form a strategy. Strategies are taught by using a model, guided practice, and test procedure.

The model consists of the teacher's demonstrating to the students how to work the problem. This model step differs from that used in teaching motor or labeling tasks; the teacher asks questions that prompt which previously taught component skill to apply at each step.

In the guided practice step, the teacher prompts the students less although she still asks them strategy-based questions as they work the problem. The structured guidance is gradually faded until the students are eventually working problems on their own, which is the test step. This step includes supervised independent work, in which students work problems independently while the teacher carefully monitors their work.

Design Formats

Once the appropriate teaching procedure (motor, labeling, or strategy task) has been selected, formats should be written to use during instruction. A format translates a general teaching procedure into the specifics of what a teacher says and does. A format should also include correction procedures for errors and examples to be presented to the students. Formats must be designed so that teacher explanations are clear and unambiguous; teachers must take care not to use words students do not understand.

One of the most important features of this text is the inclusion of formats for teaching major mathematical skills and concepts. The formats have been carefully designed to present instruction in a clear, concise manner. In designing the formats, a major consideration was to provide consistency throughout the parts in the format. Consistency in teacher wording and explanations fosters student understanding.

As mentioned in the preface, we do not suggest that our formats represent the ideal teaching procedures. It is our hope that the systematic procedures recommended here will stimulate the development of even better techniques. If teachers modify the formats in this book or create their own, they should be careful to maintain consistency and clarity throughout the format.

Some educators might object to the idea that teachers should memorize what are, in essence, scripts. Our response is that preparing and rehearsing formats prior to their use with students allow the teacher, during instruction, to focus full attention on the students. Rather than being distracted by thinking of additional examples or the next steps to present, the teacher can concentrate on monitoring the students' responses, correcting mistakes, and keeping motivation high.

Select Examples

Selecting examples refers to constructing problems that will be presented in formats. The first guideline for selecting examples is to include only problems that students can solve by utilizing the current or a previously taught strategy. For example, if students had just been taught a renaming strategy for solving subtraction problems, the teacher would not give students a problem such as 304 – 87. Since there is a zero in the tens column, this type of problem is more difficult, and new steps need to be taught before it is introduced.

The second example selection guideline is to include not only examples of the currently introduced type but also examples of previously introduced problem types which are similar to the currently introduced problem type. The purpose of including these previously introduced problem types is to provide students with practice in differentiating when to use the new strategy from when to use previously taught strategies. The importance of including this mixture of problem types cannot be overemphasized. Unless previously taught problem types are included, students will forget or misapply earlier taught strategies.

Specify Practice and Review

A critical instructional goal must be to teach skills in a manner that facilitates skills retention over time. Providing practice and review sufficient for skill mastery is an essential aspect of instructional design. Recent research has made clear the relationship between student achievement and mastery learning and sufficient practice and review. If adequate time is not spent teaching and reviewing mathematics skills and concepts, either students will not learn them, or if they do learn them initially, they will not retain them.

Questions concerning the amount of practice and appropriate mastery levels require further research. We can, however, provide these general guidelines, which address the two essential phases of practice identified by Burton (1952): "(a) the integrative phase in which perception of the meaning is developed; and (b) the repetitive, or refining, or facilitating phase in which precision is developed" (p. 126).

1. Provide massed practice until mastery is reached. Mastery is attained when the student is able to work problems accurately and fluently. It is difficult to specify exact fluency criteria for advancement since the speed at which students work problems is contingent in early grades on their motor skills, and in later grades on their knowledge of basic mathematics facts. Therefore, the only area we will specify speed criteria for is facts (see Chapter 7).

2. Provide systematic review. Once students have reached a mastery level, the teacher can gradually decrease the number of problems of that type which appear on daily worksheets. The problem type should, however, never entirely disappear but should be systematically reviewed. In some cases, this will require deliberate inclusion of the problem type at intervals on future worksheets. In other cases, built-in review is naturally provided as the problem type becomes a component skill in a more advanced problem type. For example, as subtraction problems with renaming (borrowing) are mastered, they would be integrated into story problems. Practice in the higher-level skill, solving story problems requiring subtraction with renaming, would then naturally review the earlier skill, subtraction with renaming.

Design Progress Monitoring Procedures

Items selected to monitor student progress should be similar to those selected for instruction, since the assessment should focus on what is taught. The initial assessment is needed to establish which long- and short-term objectives the student has already met. As much as possible, instruction should target those objectives from the assessment that have not yet been met. (The realities of most situations make this difficult to accomplish, because the teacher usually has a number of students to teach at the same time. Although the teacher could give students worksheets based on their individual skill levels, most students do not learn new skills by completing worksheets. Students need to be taught new skills. The problems that result from the heterogeneous abilities of students receive careful attention in this book.)

Student progress should be assessed at regular intervals to determine if students are learning at an acceptable rate. New methods, such as curriculum-based measurement, represent sophisticated approaches to measuring progress.

CURRICULUM-BASED MEASURE-MENT Curriculum-based measurement (CBM) refers to a specific set of systematic procedures developed to help teachers determine whether their students are progressing at an optimal rate. CBM offers an alternative both to informal observations that tend to be inconsistent and to achievement tests that are administered too infrequently to help teachers make instructional decisions. According to Deno (1987), CBM has two distinctive features that separate it from other curriculum-based assessments. First, the recommended procedures possess reliability and validity commensurate with standardized achievement tests; secondly, the procedures are designed to be administered frequently to provide teachers with on-going performance data.

Ideally, CBM materials are derived from the local school curriculum, and peer sampling is conducted to establish local norms. A norm sample is helpful for teachers in determining how close an individual's performance is to that of his/her classmates. The development of CBM procedures generally involves a four-step process (Fuchs, 1987):

1. Identifying a long-range goal—e.g., given a set of computational problems representing fifth grade math curriculum, the student will work a specified number of problems and write a specified number of symbols correctly in 2 minutes.
2. Creating a pool of test items—the local curriculum is the source.
3. Frequently measuring student performance.
4. Evaluating the results—this is the means for determining if instructional changes need to be made.

CBM currently is being used both in regular and special education settings in a variety of ways. The procedures have been used to make decisions regarding initial screening, identification for special services, program planning, progress monitoring and program evaluation. Since it is not within the scope of this book to elaborate on these procedures, we refer the reader to an entire issue of *Exceptional Children* (1985) devoted to curriculum-based assessment, and to work currently being done by Drs. Lynn and Doug Fuchs at Vanderbilt University on computer application of CBM.

Presentation Techniques

The second major aspect of direct instruction involves teacher presentation techniques. How a teacher presents skills significantly affects both the student's rate of learning skills and the student's self-concept. The need to be concerned with developing student self-image while teaching academics has been discussed by Engelmann (1969):

> The sphere of self-confidence that can be programmed in the classroom has to do with the child's ability to "stick to his guns," to have confidence in what he has learned, and to approach school tasks with the understanding that he is smart and will succeed. For a child to maintain such an impression of himself, he must receive demonstrations that these descriptions of himself are valid. If he finds himself failing in school, displeasing the teacher, feeling unsure about what he has learned, he must reevaluate himself and perhaps conclude that he is not a complete success. (p. 68)

As mentioned earlier, different presentation techniques are appropriate for different stages of mathematics instruction. For example, during math instruction in the early grades, direct instruction typically involves more group teaching than independent work. In upper grades the amount of group instruction decreases, and the amount of independent work increases. Another example of how different techniques are used at different times involves diagnosis. The diagnosis of student skill deficits during early math instruction is done by evaluating students' oral responses; in later grades, a diagnosis is often based on an analysis of students' written answers to worksheet exercises.

In general, early primary grade (K through second grade) teachers must be proficient in the variety of presentation techniques needed to maintain student participation in oral question-answer exchanges. On the other hand, intermediate grade teachers must be more skilled in managing students who are working independently. In both cases, however, teachers must convey warmth and active demandingness, two aspects of effective teaching identified by Kleinfeld (1975):

> The first and most important characteristic is the effective teacher's ability to create a climate of emotional warmth that dissipates students' fears in the classroom and fulfills their expectations of highly personalized relationships. The second characteristic is the teacher's ability to resolve his own ambivalent feelings about the legitimacy of his educational goals and express his concern for the students, not by passive sympathy, but by demanding a high quality of academic work. (p. 318)

Teacher presentation techniques may be divided into two main areas. The first area involves those teacher behaviors that maintain a high level of student attentiveness and participation during group instruction. The second area includes those teacher behaviors that ensure students master all skills being presented. We call this second area teaching to criterion.

Maintaining Student Attention

The more attentive the student is during instruction, the higher the probability that the teaching demonstration will be successful. Attentiveness is maintained by structuring tasks to keep students actively involved and by establishing a learning environment that contributes to student motivation.

A discussion of how to foster student motivation would require many pages. Instead of giving a simplified overview, we will refer to several books that discuss this critical topic in depth (Becker, 1986; Paine, 1988; Alberto & Troutman, 1990). Here, we deal solely with how the teacher can structure tasks to keep students involved.

The length of a teacher's explanation or demonstration affects the likelihood that students will be attentive. Teachers should make explanations brief and concise. The more time the teacher spends talking, the fewer opportunities there are for student responses. Teachers working with primary grade and lower-performing, intermediate grade students should structure their presentation so that students are required to respond quite often. Teachers presenting beginning skills might structure lessons so that they usually do not speak for more than 10 to 15 seconds without calling for a student response. Since a teacher cannot call on every individual student at that rate, we recommend, whenever possible, that all students respond, i.e., a group response.

Mathematics instruction, especially at the lower levels, involves many tasks to which there is just one correct answer and, thus, lends itself quite well to unison responding. The advantage of unison responding is that it allows teachers to utilize their time most efficiently. Some educators react to unison responding as an inhuman procedure which produces robots. Our reply on this issue also deals with the question of humanism. Resources allotted to the schools are limited. It would be nice if the average classroom size were 10 students and there were enough specialists for each student who encounters difficulty in learning. Unfortunately this is not the case. The humanistic question is how to use resources most efficiently. Structuring instruction to incorporate unison responding is an attempt to deal with the reality that exists. We realize the dangers inherent in unison responding if it is misused. If used properly, however, unison responding is an effective tool to be used in ensuring that all students receive an education. Some very specific presentation skills are required of the teacher who is calling for unison responses: (1) appropriate use of signals, (2) pacing, and (3) seating arrangement.

SIGNALS A signal is a cue given by the teacher that tells students when to make a unison response. The effective use of signals allows participation by all students, not just the higher performers who, if allowed, tend to dominate the lower-performing students. For example, if a teacher neglects to use a signal when presenting a story problem, higher-performing students are likely to respond long before lower performers have had a chance to organize and produce their responses. As a result, the lower-performing students may learn to copy responses from the other students, or they may just give up. Either result leads to a reduction in the amount of practice these lower-performing students receive. A signaling procedure can avoid this problem.

To signal a unison response, the teacher (1) gives directions, (2) provides a thinking pause, and (3) cues the response. In giving directions, the teacher tells the students the type of response they are to make and asks the question. For example, if presenting an addition fact task, the teacher might say "Listen. Get ready to tell me the answer to this problem: 4 + 6."

After the directions comes the thinking pause. The duration of the thinking pause is determined by the length of time the lowest-performing student needs to figure out the answer. (If one student takes significantly longer to answer than the other students in the group, the teacher should consider providing extra individual practice for that student or placing him in a lower-performing group.) For easier questions (simple tasks involving review of previousy taught skills), the thinking pause may be just a split second, while for more complex questions, the thinking pause may last 5 to 10 seconds. (The formats in this book include the designation *pause, signal* following questions, which requires a pause of several seconds to allow students to figure out the answer.) Carefully controlling the duration of the thinking pause is a very important factor in maintaining student attentiveness and providing students with a successful learning experience.

The final step in the signaling procedure is the actual cue to respond. A cue or signal to respond may be a clap, finger snap, hand drop, touching the board, or any similar type of action. Signals for labeling tasks are discussed in detail in Chapter 6. This procedure can be modified for use with most tasks. On tasks calling for a long thinking pause, the teacher would say "get ready" an instant before signaling. The purpose of saying "get ready" is to let the students know when to expect the signal to respond. Since the length of thinking pauses varies with the difficulty of the question, students do not know when to respond following a pause. Therefore, in order to elicit a group response in which each student has the opportunity to initiate his answer independently of the students next to him, the cue "get ready" is given. This cue is particularly useful for teacher-directed worksheet tasks, since students are looking at their worksheets and cannot see a hand signal from the teacher.

The essential characteristic of any good signal is its clarity. The signal must be given so that students know exactly when they are expected to respond. If a signal is not clear, students will not be able to respond together. The teacher should use the students' behavior to evaluate the clarity of her signals. A repeated failure to respond together usually indicates that the signals are unclear or the teacher has not provided adequate thinking time.

PACING Anyone who has observed young children watching TV shows such as "Sesame Street" or "The Electric Company" can attest to the value of lively pacing in keeping students attentive. Teachers need not put on an elaborate show to foster attentiveness but should be familiar enough with their material to present it in a lively, animated manner and without hesitation.[3] Teachers who are well versed in their materials will not only be able to teach at a more lively pace but will also be able to focus their attention more fully on the students' performance.

Another aspect of good pacing involves the efficient organization of materials. Just as a teacher should be well prepared to present tasks, she should also have clearly thought out the most efficient ways of handling teacher and student materials. A teacher might use colored clips to mark each group's lesson in the teacher's guide and/or student books. Simply being able to locate the appropriate lesson easily and quickly might well save several minutes daily. Arranging student materials so that the teacher can quickly hand them out will also save minutes each day. This may seem trivial, but several minutes saved each day add up, by the end of the school year, to a significant amount of instructional time.

SEATING ARRANGEMENT Lower-performing students should be seated at the front of the room so their responses can be monitored more easily. Teachers can hear and see responses of students seated near the front of the room. The teacher is then better able to assist and, when appropriate, praise those students who are attending and working hard.

Although most math instruction is delivered to an entire class of students, lower performing students learn better when they receive instruction in small groups. For small group instruction in primary grades, we recommend seating the students in chairs, without desks, in a semi-circle. The students face into a wall or corner, with their backs to the rest of the room. The teacher sits facing the group and looking out at the classroom so that he can monitor the rest of the class. Since the students in the group have their backs to the rest of the class, they are less likely to be distracted. Students should be seated close enough to the teacher so that he is able to easily monitor their performance. Lower-performing or distractible students should sit toward the center of the group since they require the most careful monitoring. Figure 1.1 shows a sample seating arrangement.

---

[3] In training new teachers, we found that approximately a half hour of daily rehearsal was necessary to bring teachers to the point where they could present skills at an acceptable pace. This preparation time is needed only at the beginning of the year.

Figure 1.1 Suggested Seating Arrangement. An open circle (O) indicates naive or distractible students. Note that these students are not placed next to each other.

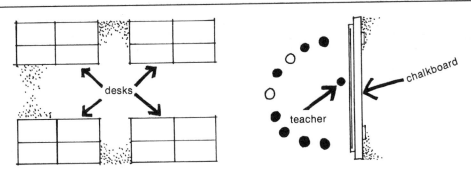

Criterion Teaching

Teaching to criterion occurs in two stages. First, teachers need to present a particular format until all the students in a group are able to answer every question in the format correctly. Second, teachers should present a set of examples until all students can respond correctly to all of the examples in the set. Criterion teaching then is a composite skill which involves appropriate monitoring, correcting, diagnosing, and remedying of problems. Only by teaching to a high criterion can teachers ensure student mastery and retention of the material.

MONITORING Monitoring student performance (determining whether or not the student responds correctly) is rarely a problem when a teacher is working on a one-to-one basis with a student. Monitoring the performance of a group of students, however, requires a great deal of skill, especially when utilizing oral responding. It can be very difficult for the teacher to hear mistakes made by one or two students in a group. So, along with listening to students' responses, the teacher must watch the students' faces. The position of the students' eyes and mouths can tell the teacher a great deal. For example, the teacher should watch the students' mouths to see if they are responding on signal and giving the correct response. The teacher should also watch the students' eyes to see whether they are looking at the appropriate example on their worksheets or at the teacher's visual display. If a student is not looking at the appropriate place, the student may simply be mimicking other students' responses rather than initiating her own answer.

Simultaneously monitoring every student on every unison response is impossible. Consequently, a teacher must systematically switch her attention from student to student, focusing primarily on lower-

performing students. For example, in a group of eight students, where five students seldom have difficulty while three often do, the teacher would watch the lower performers for two or three responses and then shift her attention to several higher performers for a response or two. She would then shift her attention back to the lower-performing students for several responses before briefly monitoring other higher performers. Always returning her attention to the lower-performing students ensures that the teacher monitors them about twice as often as she does the higher-performing students.

Individual tests are a very important monitoring tool because they provide more accurate information than unison responses. With unison responses, a teacher can never be absolutely certain whether or not the student has been copying the responses of other students. An individual test, therefore, indicates much more clearly whether or not the student knows the correct answer. If the student makes a mistake when responding individually, the teacher should provide additional group practice and repeat the individual test later.

The teacher should give individual tests only after all the students in the group appear to be answering correctly during unison practice. Calling on a student individually who has not had enough practice to master the task may needlessly embarrass the student in front of his peers.

Since individual tests are time-consuming, they should not be given to every student after every task. As a general rule, turns should be given to all lower-performing students each time a new or difficult task is presented. Higher-performing students, on the other hand, would be tested less often. Note, though, that any student who has had difficulty on a task should receive more frequent individual turns on that task during the next several lessons.

When presenting tasks that call for written responses, the teacher should devise systems for giving immediate feedback to the students. For example, when working with younger students on tasks such as numeral writing, the teacher should monitor lower-performing students after every response and higher-performing students after at least each third or fourth response. When working with older students, the teacher can either tell students the correct answer or have a higher-performing student write the answer on the board while the other students mark their own papers. She should also walk around the room looking at the students' work so that she can adjust her presentation to their performance and provide immediate corrections when needed.

Students' independent work should be marked daily. Older, more responsible students can often check their own papers using an answer key. With less responsible or younger students, the teacher, an aide, or volunteer should mark the papers. Note also that, ideally, all errors on papers should be corrected by students before the papers are sent home. Requiring students to go back and correct errors helps teachers determine if errors were caused by lack of knowledge or lack of concentration.

The importance of careful monitoring cannot be overemphasized. The sooner the teacher detects a student's skill deficit, the easier it will be to remedy. For each day that a student's confusion goes undetected, the student is, in essence, receiving practice in doing something the wrong way. To ameliorate a confusion, the teacher should plan to spend 2 days reteaching for every day the student's confusion goes undetected. Thus, careful monitoring is a critical component of efficient instruction.

CORRECTING The first step in correcting errors made by students during group instruction is to determine the cause of the error. The teacher must decide if the error results from inattentiveness or from a lack of knowledge.

The cues a teacher uses in judging whether inattentiveness is the cause of the problem are these: (1) where the student is looking and (2) what the student was doing before the question was asked. A student looking away from the board before responding is not likely to be attending.

Teachers must be quite careful in responding to errors that appear to stem from inattentiveness. Negative teacher attention may result in reinforcing the undesired student behavior. To eliminate the possibility of inadvertently encouraging nonattend-

ing, the teacher should praise another student who attends and responds correctly. Later, when the student who originally was not attending is paying close attention, the teacher must be sure to praise him for attending. Letting the student know that he will get attention when he is following directions is essential. If a student makes many errors because of inattentiveness, the teacher must systematically work on increasing the student's motivation to attend. Once again, we refer the reader to the texts mentioned on page 9. Working with the nonmotivated student requires a good deal of teacher skill and understanding. There is no simple formula that will work in all instances.

The correction procedure for errors that are not caused by inattentiveness but result from lack of knowledge depends on the nature of the task. Correction procedures differ for motor, labeling, and problem-solving tasks.

To correct errors that stem from a motor deficit (e.g., writing a symbol or counting), the teacher models the correct response, leads the students until they appear able to respond correctly, and then tests them. The teacher continues the correction until students can make the correct responses several times in a row. The extra practice needed to produce several consecutive correct responses in a motor task is very important in facilitating retention. If students respond 10 times incorrectly and then just once correctly, they are not likely to remember the correct response. Therefore, having students repeat the correct response several times is essential to increasing the probability of retention. *Note that students should repeat the correct response several times consecutively only in motor tasks.*

When presenting a labeling task, the teacher follows the three-step procedure of model, alternating pattern, and delayed test. In labeling tasks the alternating pattern provides for adequate repetition of the correct response. For example, if a student does not respond when asked to identify the numeral 4, the teacher first models the correct response: "This is 4." After modeling, the teacher would alternate between 4 and the other numbers in the task 3, 8, 6, and 5. The teacher might follow this pattern: **4**, 3, **4**, 8, 6, **4**, 5, 6, 3, **4**. The delayed test is given later, possibly at the end of the lesson. The purpose of the delayed test is to help diagnose the severity of the confusion. If the error persists on the delayed test, the teacher knows that more practice must be provided before introducing new information.

If an error occurs when the teacher is presenting a strategy, the teacher usually follows a two-step correction. First, the teacher corrects the specific error, modeling the correct response if necessary, or, preferably, prompting the students by asking questions from the strategy. In the second step, the teacher returns to the beginning of the strategy and presents the entire strategy again. The purpose of returning to the beginning of the strategy after correcting an error is to ensure that the students do not lose track of how all the steps in the strategy are integrated. Returning to the beginning of the strategy is very important when presenting strategies. For example, a student answers the problem:

$$\frac{3}{4} = \frac{\square}{20} \quad \text{by writing} \quad \frac{3}{4} = \frac{8}{20}$$

The correction procedure for this error involves pointing out to the students that to rewrite a fraction without changing its value, the student must multiply it by a fraction that equals one whole (multiplying a number by 1 does not change its value). The teacher then guides the student through critical steps to figure out the fraction that equals one: "Four times what number equals 20? . . . That means the denominator of the fraction we multiply 3/4 by is 5. So what must the numerator be? . . . Why? . . . " These questions prompt students to derive the answer without actually being told the answer.

Correction procedures for errors resulting from inattentiveness and lack of knowledge have been discussed. Two further kinds of errors, both relative to unison responding tasks, can also occur: late responses and failure to respond at all. When a student gives the correct response but answers after the other students have responded, the teacher cannot be sure if the student knew the answer or was simply copying the responses of other students. Likewise, if a student does not respond, the teacher does not know whether the student knows the answer.

Teachers should be careful in handling these situations, generally avoiding making negative comments to the late or nonresponding student. Also, it is important that the teacher attempt to identify the reason for the inadequate response. If there is a reasonable probability that the student needed more time to figure out the response, the teacher should simply repeat the task later, providing the student with a longer thinking pause. However, if the inadequate response appears to be caused by a lack of cooperation, the teacher should reward students who do respond through praise or physical contact (handshake, pat on back). The reward is designed

to make clear to the students that answering correctly is important and will result in teacher attention. As mentioned earlier, some students give wrong answers to elicit attention from the teacher. Rewarding students who respond correctly will help buttress against students' deliberately making incorrect responses for attention and will provide an appropriate model for gaining teacher attention.

A final note on corrections: Teachers must also be careful about the way they word corrections so that they do not inadvertently humiliate a student. Generally, the less said by the teacher during a correction, the better.

DIAGNOSING AND REMEDYING Diagnosis involves determining the cause of a set of errors; remediation is the procedure of reteaching a skill, based on the diagnosis. Note that corrections are quite different from a remediation in that they are administered immediately after an error to a teacher question and require minimal diagnosis, since the teacher knows exactly what question the student missed.

The first decision to make in diagnosing errors is determining whether they are what Alessi calls "can't do" versus "won't do" problems. Won't do problems occur when students have the necessary skills but are careless, do not complete their work, are inattentive, etc. A diagnosis of won't do errors requires a remediation that focuses on increasing student motivation. A diagnosis of can't do problems requires a remediation that focuses on the student's confusion or skill deficit.

The teacher diagnoses errors by examining the missed problems on worksheets and/or by interviewing the students about how they worked problems they missed (Lankford, 1974). As the Elementary School Mathematics Committee said, "Careful analysis of errors through observation and interviews with individual children is essential" (Pincus, Coonan, Glasser, Levy, Morgenstern, & Shapiro, 1975, p. 581).

The basic steps below apply to diagnosing and remedying errors on any type of problem:

1. The teacher analyzes worksheet errors and hypothesizes what the cause of the errors might be.
2. The teacher interviews the student to determine the cause of the error, if it is not obvious.
3. The teacher provides reteaching through board and/or worksheet presentations.
4. The teacher tests the student on a set of prob-

lems similar to the ones on which the original errors were made.

An error can be one of three basic types: a fact error, a component skill error, or a strategy error. Basic facts are the 100 addition and multiplication facts formed by adding or multiplying any two single digit numbers and their subtraction and division corollaries. Sometimes students miss problems solely because of a fact error. Here are examples of such problems:

$$\begin{array}{r} 8 \\ 7\overline{)65} \\ \underline{63} \\ 2 \end{array} \qquad \begin{array}{r} 44 \\ 379 \\ \times\ \ 6 \\ \hline 2268 \end{array} \qquad \begin{array}{r} 8 \\ 2\cancel{9}3 \\ -\ 58 \\ \hline 234 \end{array}$$

Note that in each problem, the student followed the correct sequence of steps for working the problem but missed the problem because of a basic fact error ($8 \times 7 = 63$, $6 \times 9 = 48$, $13 - 8 = 4$).

Component skills are previously taught skills which are integrated as steps in a problem-solving strategy. Component skill errors in the lower grades usually involve a counting or symbol identification error. In the later grades, a much wider range of component skill errors may occur. Below is an example of a fraction problem missed because of a component skill error:

$$\frac{3}{4} + \frac{2}{5} =$$

incorrect: $\dfrac{3}{20} + \dfrac{2}{20} = \dfrac{5}{20}$ *correct:* $\dfrac{15}{20} + \dfrac{8}{20} = \dfrac{23}{20}$

Note that in the incorrectly solved problem, the student knew to convert both fractions to a common denominator but did not know the component skill of rewriting a fraction as an equivalent fraction.

A strategy error occurs when the student demonstrates that she does not know the sequence of steps required to solve the particular problem type. For example, in the following example, the student merely subtracts the denominator from the numerator when instructed to convert an improper fraction to a mixed number:

$$\frac{13}{6} = 7 \qquad \frac{15}{2} = 13$$

This student's performance indicates he does not know the strategy for rewriting improper fractions.

Being able to determine the cause of an error is very important since the choice of a remediation procedure is determined by the cause. If a student misses problems solely because of basic fact errors, the remediation procedure consists of either providing practice on the specific fact errors made or increasing the motivation to perform accurately. If the student misses a certain fact consistently, the remediation must involve practice on that fact. If, however, the student does not consistently miss any one fact but gets the same fact correct in one problem and not in another, the remediation would involve increasing the reward for accurate work. As mentioned earlier, if not motivated, students will often rush through problems, not carefully applying their knowledge.

A component skill error may also result from inattentiveness. Therefore, teachers should not remedy a component skill unless the student makes an error on the component skill several times on the assignment. The remediation procedure initially involves reteaching that particular component skill. When the student is consistently able to perform the component skill, the teacher reintroduces examples of the problem type that was originally missed. For example, when given the following story problem, the student makes the mistake indicated:

Lisa wants to run 515 miles.
If she runs 5 miles a day, how many days must she run?

incorrect:
$$\begin{array}{r} 13 \\ 5\overline{)515} \\ \underline{5} \\ 15 \end{array} \qquad 13 \text{ days}$$

correct:
$$\begin{array}{r} 103 \\ 5\overline{)515} \\ \underline{5} \\ 01 \\ \underline{00} \\ 15 \end{array} \qquad 103 \text{ days}$$

In solving the problem the student was able to translate the words into the correct equation but made a division error when solving the equation. The remediation procedure for this error would involve presenting the format for solving division problems that have a zero in the quotient. The teacher would present the format for 2 consecutive days, or longer if more practice was needed to generate consistently accurate responses from the student. After the student is able to work the component skill correctly, he would again be presented division story problems with a zero in the quotient, which is the type of problem in which the component skill was initially missed. Note that the remediation focuses solely on the component skill missed; the teacher does not have to work on the skill of translating story problems.

If a student misses a problem because of a strategy error, the teacher reteaches the strategy for that particular skill, beginning with the initial, highly structured presentation. Again, a strategy remediation is not called for unless the student misses that strategy several times in the assignment.

Unfortunately, diagnosis and remediation are not as simple as outlined above. Sometimes students will perform inconsistently, making different types of errors or making errors in one example and not in other, similar examples. For example, when given a worksheet including a variety of subtraction problems, with and without renaming, the student performs as in the example below:

a.	b.	c.	d.
35	26	45	57
−14	−18	−32	−19
1	8	13	42

e.	f.	g.
34	26	40
−18	−12	−32
16	14	12

h.	i.	j.
54	20	42
−30	−12	−24
24	8	18

Note that the student missed two problems (d and g) because of strategy errors but solved other problems of the same type correctly (b, e, i, and j). When inconsistency results in a student's performing below a 85% to 90% accuracy level, the remediation procedure should involve providing close supervision in an effort to determine the cause of the errors. If there is no apparent pattern to the errors, increasing the rewards for accurate work (increasing motivation) is essential.

A final note on diagnosis and remediation concerns examining student worksheets. Teachers should pay special attention to review worksheets on which there are just one or two examples of previously introduced problem types. If a student makes a strategy or component skill error when there are just a couple of problems of that type, the teacher should test the student on several more problems of that type to determine if remediation is necessary. For example, if a worksheet contained two subtraction problems requiring renaming and the student failed to rename in one problem, the teacher would test the student on a larger set of subtraction problems to determine if remediation is called for. The test would involve giving the students a worksheet containing a mix of problems including the problem type missed and similar, but earlier introduced problem types. Teachers might prepare a series of worksheets each focusing on a particular problem type, at the beginning of the school year and put them in files for easy accessibility.

Organization of Instruction

The final aspect of direct instruction—organization of instruction—involves testing, grouping, and placing students in instructional groups and organizing instruction in the classroom and throughout the school to ensure effective use of resources, particularly the use of time (Rieth, Polsgrove, & Semmel, 1979; Rosenshine & Berliner, 1978). These topics are discussed in depth in Chapters 2 and 3.

Research

Three distinct areas of research provide support for a direct instruction approach to teaching mathematics: teacher-effectiveness research, research on individual math skills, and research specifically addressing direct instruction.

TEACHER-EFFECTIVENESS RESEARCH Rosenshine (1976), in a review of several teacher effectiveness studies, has discussed teacher behaviors which appeared to produce greater student achievement. "Positive significant results were obtained for direct time, factual questions, teacher positive feedback, supervised study in groups and attention to task. The researcher thought that these results could be placed into a tentative pattern labeled direct instruction." Since Rosenshine's initial work, several other studies have yielded similar results.

As a part of the Beginning Teacher Evaluation Study (BTES), researchers looking for factors related to student success observed how veteran second and fifth grade teachers spent their reading and math instructional time (Denham & Lieberman, 1980). In analyzing the results of this study, the researchers derived a metric called Academic Learning Time (ALT) that could be used reliably to predict student performance. ALT is the amount of time students spend engaged in relevant academic content of a high success rate. Results from the BTES added another component to the previous teacher-effectiveness findings in that not only did students need a higher rate of academic-engaged time to increase achievement, but students needed to be engaged in activities at which they were successful.

The research discussed above is by no means an exhaustive discussion of the teacher-effectiveness literature. However, these studies are representative of that body of research. The majority of teacher-effectiveness instructional studies do contention that a systematic, explicit approach to mathematics instruction, such as the one presented in this text, will lead to improved student performance.

INDIVIDUAL MATH SKILL STUDIES Unfortunately, there are few experimental studies in the literature that compare instructional approaches for specific math skills. Relevant research on isolated skills that is available has been included at the end of each chapter.

DIRECT INSTRUCTION STUDIES Two types of research on direct instruction are available in the literature. There are direct instruction studies on specific math skills: e.g., fractions (Kelly, Gersten & Carnine, in press), facts (Carnine & Stein, 1981) or problem solving (Darch, Carnine & Gersten, 1984). As mentioned above, these and other isolated skill studies are discussed in more detail in each respective chapter. One study, however, is of particular relevance in this section. Kameenui, Carnine, Darch, and Stein (1986) conducted three studies (on subtraction, fractions, and division) to compare systematic direct instruction design principles to a more traditional/basal approach to lesson development. The traditional approach is usually characterized by (1) the use of non-verbal mathematics (e.g., pictures, objects), (2) reliance on an informal, inductive discussion of the concept or strategy to be taught, and (3) the use of personalized, more general correction procedures. In all three studies, the students taught using explicit direct instruction procedures performed better on at least one acquisition measure than the comparison groups. How to develop lessons using direct instruction design principles is the subject of this text.

The second type of direct instruction research consists of evaluations of large scale implementations of direct instruction programs. A federally funded 10-year study called Follow Through evaluated several major approaches to educating low-income, primary grade students (Gersten & Carnine, 1984). (The Follow Through study is discussed in more detail in Appendix A.) In this study, direct approaches were compared with approaches based on the language-experience model, Piaget's stages of learning, child development theory, discovery learning, and open education. The results, as presented by Abt Associates, revealed that students taught by the direct instruction approach consistently outperformed control students on basic cognitive and affective measures.

> The Direct Instruction Model is specific in stating that children participating in the FT program are expected to, on the average, perform at the same level as their middle-class peers by the end of third grade. This goal has largely been achieved . . . When all Direct Instruction sites are grouped and compared with the MAT (Metropolitan Achievement Tests) norms, students on the average are performing at grade level in Reading, Math, and Spelling . . . . In sum, the Direct Instruction Model program is generally effective in raising the achievement of Follow Through children to a level comparable with national norms. (Stebbins, Proper, St. Pierre, & Cerva, 1977, pp. A-168, A-169)

To ascertain whether the effects of the mathematics program were enduring, the later effects of Follow Through were assessed at five diverse sites (Becker & Gersten, 1982). Low-income fifth and sixth graders who had completed the full three years of the Follow Through program (grades 1–3) were tested on standardized achievement tests. Results indicated consistent, significant positive effects for math problem-solving, weaker but significant effects for math concepts, and no significant effects in computation. It appears that students retain some of the generalized problem-solving strategies they are taught and apply them to fifth and sixth grade.

The effectiveness of direct instruction with more advantaged students has also been documented. Guthrie (1977) reported that direct instruction was the only approach in the Follow Through study that produced benefits with both low- and middle-income students.

It is important to emphasize that students in structured programs have outperformed students from other programs, not only in academic areas but also in areas of self-esteem. Rosenshine (1979) found that the two Follow Through programs that produced the highest proportion of significant positive results on the Coopersmith Self-esteem Inventory were both highly structured direct teaching programs. Also, in a study of middle-class students, Solomon (cited in Rosenshine, 1979) found that control and orderliness related not only to achievement gain but also to gain in inquiry skill, creativity, and self-esteem.

2 | Organizing Mathematics Instruction

This chapter outlines specific procedures for organizing mathematics instruction and integrating direct instruction program design and presentation techniques into the classroom setting. The chapter is divided into four sections. The first section discusses how to select materials. The second outlines specific procedures for modifying a commercial program to make it more effective for a broader ability range of students. The third section specifies procedures for initial assessment, including information on placing and grouping students for instruction. The fourth section outlines the important aspects of presenting a unit. These four sections are intended to create a context in which the application of the remaining chapters in the text can be better understood.

Selecting Instructional Materials

The quality of mathematics instructional materials is an important factor in determining not only how quickly some students will learn new skills but also whether some students learn certain skills at all. High-performing students can learn mathematics from a large range of approaches; many middle ability students will also learn from many different types of material but at a slower rate in some programs. Lower-performing students, on the other hand, may not master many important mathematics skills unless carefully designed materials are used.

Types of Mathematics Programs

Three basic types of instructional programs are most frequently used in the schools: the developmental basals, the specific skill programs, and those programs designed especially for lower-performing students.

DEVELOPMENTAL BASALS   At the core of mathematics instruction in most classrooms is the basal developmental mathematics program, which includes sequentially planned student and teacher materials for grades K–6. These programs are developmental in that they are designed for students learning mathematics for the first time. There are about a dozen major developmental basal programs on the market.

Basal programs are usually divided into between 10 to 20 topical units to be presented in a school year. Each unit focuses on a particular set of related skills such as addition, subtraction, multiplication, division, etc. Table 2.1, which contains the contents of three first grade basal workbooks (*Holt School Mathematics*, *Heath Elementary Mathematics*, and *Scott Foresman Invitation to Mathematics*), illustrates this topical organization. The advantage

Table 2.1 Scope and Sequence for First Grade Programs

Unit	Holt	Macmillan	Heath
1.	Sets	Numbers through 5	Numbers through 6
2.	Numbers through 9	Sums through 5	Numbers through 10
3.	Subtraction (first number 5 or less) & addition (sums of 5 or less)	Subtraction, first number through 5	Geometry (circles & squares, rectangles & triangles, paths, segments, curves, closed figures)
4.	Numbers through 50	Geometry (ball, can, box, circle, rectangle, square)	Subtraction & addition of numbers to 6
5.	Subtraction & addition through 6	Numbers through 10	Place value (numbers to 100)
6.	Subtraction & addition through 8	Sums through 10 (three addends)	Subtraction & addition (through 10)
7.	Numbers through 100	Measurement & geometry	Measurement
8.	Fractions (1/2, 1/3, 1/4), time (half-hour & hour), money (through quarter)	Subtraction, first number through 10	Subtraction & addition (through 12)
9.	Subtraction & addition through 10	Addition & subtraction	Fractions (1/2, 1/3, 1/4 of a set and region)
10.	Geometry (sphere, cylinder, cone, cube, square, triangle) & measurement (centimeter, inch, liter, cup, kilogram, pound)	Numbers through 99	Subtraction & addition (two digit numbers—no regrouping)
11.	Subtraction & addition through 12	Sums through 99 (no sequencing)	Subtraction & addition (through 18)
12.	Subtraction & addition through 18	Measurement	
13.		Subtraction, first number through 99 (no regrouping)	
14.		Addition & subtraction (sums through 18)	

to the teacher in using the basal programs is their comprehensiveness. The typical basal program includes, in one form or another, nearly all the skills in the scope and sequence of elementary mathematics instruction. However, major weaknesses can be found in most basal programs: first, a lack of specificity in instructions for the teacher, and second, an inadequate amount of practice and review for students to develop mastery. Regarding the first weakness, lack of specificity, the teacher's guides of most basal problems contain general direction for the teacher using terms such as *explain* or *discuss* rather than providing the teacher with carefully stated directions on how to present skills and correct student errors.

The second weakness, inadequate practice and review, results in part from the spiral curriculum design employed in their construction. In the spiral curriculum, one or two units devoted to a particular topic are presented each year. For example, a unit on fractions is usually included in each math book from the first grade to the sixth. Each year the concepts introduced become more complex. In the first grade book, simple fraction drawings might be introduced; in the third grade, adding fractions; in the fourth, equivalent fractions, etc. The problem with the spiral design has been that relatively little review of a skill is provided once the unit is completed. Although recent editions of the basal programs have given more emphasis to review, they still often do not provide adequate practice. Several practice examples of a new skill may appear for just three or four lessons even though many students may require weeks of practice to develop mastery. Because of the lack of specific strategies and adequate practice and review, basal series require substantial modifications to become effective tools for teaching instructionally naive students. The problems with basal programs result in part from the publishers' failure, despite the money invested in production, to systematically test program components for their effectiveness. Morris Kline, in writing about the integration of new math ideas into programs, said:

No large-scale testing of the quality of the modern mathematics program has been undertaken. At present the amount of effort devoted to assessing properly the claims of proponents of modern mathematics is negligible in comparison with the claims. The superior understanding which the modern mathematics approach is supposed to provide has not been demonstrated by tests or by any other major objective measure. (pp. 108–109)

Note that this statement was made after many publishers had invested huge sums in producing and marketing modern math programs.

SPECIFIC SKILL PROGRAMS Specific skill programs focus on one related group of skills (e.g., addition, subtraction, fractions, division, multiplication, etc.). Some of these programs are carefully sequenced and planned. Others are simply a collection of worksheets designed to provide extra practice. The advantage of specific skill programs is that they are more likely to provide adequate practice to facilitate mastery of the skill. A disadvantage of such programs is their lack of comprehensiveness. A teacher using only specific skill series would have to provide systematic review of skills from previously taught areas and would have to ensure that students were taught all of the skills in the scope and sequence of instruction required by the school district.

PROGRAMS FOR LOW PERFORMERS The third type of mathematics program is developed especially for the student who is having difficulty or is likely to have difficulty in school. These programs may be marketed as programs for slow learners, remedial programs, or programs for retarded students. Teachers must be very cautious when examining these programs for while some are constructed very well, others have been constructed poorly.

We conducted an analysis to determine the extent to which basal programs and programs for slow learners utilize direct instruction principles, using three mathematics programs: a traditional basal, a program for slow learners, and a program for the retarded. The analysis looked at single digit addition. Each program was evaluated on each of the subskills of addition: equality, symbol identification, various counting skills, relationship between numerals and lines, etc. Each subskill was rated positive, neutral, or negative along several dimensions: whether it was included in the program, whether the teaching procedure was adequate, whether sequencing was appropriate, and whether

practice was adequate. The ratings for each program were summarized as a percentage, which was calculated by dividing the number of neutral and positive ratings by the total number of ratings. The percentages indicated how well a program could be predicted to work with low-performing students. The percentages were 48 for the traditional basal, 16 for the program for slower learners, and 11 for the program for the retarded. Note that the programs designed for the lowest-performing students were judged to be the least effective.

Program Evaluation

When you examine a program, be it a basal, specific skill, or special program, four main areas to critically evaluate are the (a) strategies taught, (b) sequence of skills, (c) example selection, and (d) amount of practice and review.

STRATEGY TEACHING Whenever possible, an instructional program should teach strategies in a clear, concise manner. Explicit strategies for word problems are illustrated in Chapter 12. Except for the SRA Direct Instruction Mathematics programs, explicit strategies for word problems seldom appear in textbooks. Most suggestions are too vague to be of much help; e.g. most programs recommend that students read, analyze, plan and solve but don't give explicit instruction in how to determine the appropriate operation.

Once a strategy is taught, the program should provide a step-by-step transition from explicit teacher-directed instruction to completely independent work. The transition is best accomplished through guided practice, where the teacher asks only a few important questions to prompt the next steps in a strategy and is available to answer students' questions when they need it.

A good strategy teaches only the skill intended without leading to misinterpretations. In teaching beginning addition, for example, most programs use pictures to introduce the skill. Students are usually shown two groups of objects and asked to identify the number of objects in each group. The teacher then "joins" the groups and asks "how many in all?" Next, the students are shown pictures of two groups with the appropriate symbols written above (see Figure 2.1).

Note that in this specific demonstration, the students can work the problem without ever attending to the symbols; they can merely count the objects under the box and write the answer. The difficulty for low-performing students occurs when

Figure 2.1

$$4 \quad + \quad 2 \quad = \quad \square$$

they are subsequently given problems comprised only of symbols: $4 + 2 = \square$. The program assumes that students will either draw objects and then count them or they will remember the answer to the problem. In our experience, this assumption does not hold for instructionally naive students. These students need to be guided through a strategy with a teacher prompting them on what to do at each step. If students have been taught to draw pictures to represent the numerals, then count the pictures, the strategy would have been useful for low-performing students, since it would have given them an explicit procedure they could apply to a variety of problems.

Finally, in well-designed instruction only one strategy is taught for a given skill. For example, in some programs two different algorithms may be presented for working multiplication problems with multidigit factors. Students will first be shown the long form algorithm (example a), then several days later the short form algorithm (example b).

```
                              2 2
   a.   234      b.     234
       ×  7            ×   7
         28            1638
        210
       1400
       1638
```

Teaching more than one strategy for a skill is a common characteristic of many commercial programs. The assumption that the students will better understand the process by being exposed to multiple strategies is prevalent. In actuality, multiple strategies often confuse instructionally naive students and fragment teaching time to the point that no strategy is mastered.

Modification of strategies is a time-consuming task for teachers, especially when the worksheets in a program are all related to the strategy suggested in the teacher's guide. Teaching students a strategy different from that in the text often involves writing new worksheets. Examining teaching strategies is particularly critical when evaluating first grade programs since many tasks involve illustrations. In later grades, a teacher can often use the examples in the student textbook and workbook even after modifying the strategy. In later chapters, we present strategies that can be incorporated into most programs.

SEQUENCE OF SKILLS The sequence in which skills are presented determines in part the amount of difficulty students will have in learning strategies. Skills which are likely to be confused should not be introduced consecutively. Also, preskills should be taught prior to the introduction of strategies that require their application. Many programs do not teach all the necessary preskills. For example, most beginning-level programs assume all students can rote count and have students count objects on the very first lesson. However, some students will need to learn to rote count before they are able to count objects. A program should allow ample time for the students to master the preskills. Most commercial programs that do provide for the teaching of preskills, however, often fail to provide enough practice on the preskill before it is integrated into a strategy.

EXAMPLE SELECTION Problems which appear in students' assignments should be carefully controlled. Only problems which can be solved through application of previously taught strategies should be included. Also, a variety of problem types should be included to teach students to discriminate when the previously taught problem-solving strategies should be applied. After a new problem type is introduced, worksheet exercises should include a mixture of problems including the newly introduced problem type and similar problem types that have been taught previously. For example, after subtracting with renaming (borrowing) is introduced, worksheets should contain problems which do and do not require renaming. On that worksheet, then, students not only practice renaming, but they also practice the skill of discriminating when renaming is appropriate.

Commercial programs often do not include adequate discrimination practice. For example, when renaming is introduced in subtraction in a widely used basal program, 125 of the 127 prob-

Figure 2.2 Instructional Materials Rating Scale

				Poor Excellent
	Program	**Year**	**Area examined**	
I. Strategy				
A. Presentation of the strategy by the teacher is carefully specified to ensure clarity and maintain consistency for related problem types.				1 2 3 4 5
B. Presentation of the strategy is designed for systematic transition from a highly structured presentation to a less structured one.				1 2 3 4 5
II. Sequence				
A. All preskills are taught sufficiently prior to introduction of the strategy to allow for development of mastery of the preskill.				1 2 3 4 5
B. A problem type is not introduced until students have been taught a strategy to solve problems of that type.				1 2 3 4 5
III. Example Selection				
A. A mix of the current and previous type problems is provided.				1 2 3 4 5
IV. Practice and Review				
A. Sufficient numbers of examples are presented to enable students to master new skill.				1 2 3 4 5
B. Sufficient review of skills is included to facilitate retention.				1 2 3 4 5

lems require renaming. This lack of discrimination practice may cause some students to rename every subtraction problem they encounter.

PRACTICE AND REVIEW Adequate practice on new skills should be provided to enable students to develop mastery; adequate worksheet review of earlier taught skills should be provided to facilitate retention.

Programs should specifically indicate the problems to be reviewed. Furthermore, in evaluating a program, the teacher should note the degree to which massed practice is provided immediately after a new problem type is introduced. The more complex the strategy, the longer massed practice should be continued. Teachers should also note the degree to which a systematic review of problem types is provided. After massed practice has enabled students to develop mastery, problems of that particular type should be reviewed periodically; at first, each second day and then gradually less often.

EVALUATION SCALE The four areas of evaluation are summarized in the Instructional Materials Rating Scale in Figure 2.2. This scale was designed to provide guidance to teachers in evaluating commercial programs in areas related to student achievement. When inspecting a commercial program, the teacher using the scale would inspect several major

skill areas: counting, symbol identification, and vocabulary teaching in beginning level programs; addition, subtraction, story problems, and fact learning in first to second grade programs; multiplication, division, fractions, basic facts, story problems, and decimals in intermediate grade materials. Specific factors to consider in relation to each skill area are discussed in each of the subsequent chapters in this text. When examining the way a particular skill area is presented in a commercial program, we recommend that the teacher first read the corresponding chapter in this text, noting relevant variables specific to that area. Then the teacher can look for those variables when rating the program with the Instructional Materials Rating Scale.

In some instances, teachers will have to choose among several programs, none of which the teacher may feel is constructed satisfactorily. When teachers have limited options regarding which programs they may select, they should choose the program which provides the best systematic practice and review of problem types.

This recommendation is based on the fact that the area of practice and review is probably the most time-consuming area to modify. Modifications often involve the construction of *daily* student worksheets, a task similar to writing a complete program. On the other hand, if a program provides adequate practice on various types of problems, a teacher could replace complex or confusing strategies suggested in the program with clearer, more direct strategies that generalize to a wide range of problems.

Modifying Commercial Programs

Many commercial programs will need some degree of modification to make them suitable instructional vehicles for lower-performing students. This section provides specific guidance in making these modifications. The modifications should be made before the teacher uses the program, ideally during a summer workshop.

As mentioned earlier, most basal programs are divided into 10–20 units, each focusing on a particular skill area. A specific skill program can be considered a unit since it focuses on one skill area. The five steps outlined below are designed to help teachers closely examine a unit and make appropriate modifications. Teachers should keep in mind that the performance levels of their students determine the need for making the modifications. Extensive modifications are usually needed for low-performing students who require careful teaching and adequate practice for successful learning.

Five Steps in Modifying a Unit

1. Prioritize the objectives of the unit and set mastery levels.
2. Select problem-solving strategies.
3. Construct teaching formats for the major skills (and for preskills when necessary).
4. Select practice examples.
5. Design worksheets or select pages of the text to provide review of previously taught skills.

PRIORITIZING THE OBJECTIVES If the program has not already done so, the teacher must specify the objectives of the unit, i.e., determine exactly which problem types are presented in the unit. To do this, the teacher first examines each page in the student textbook and workbook and lists the specific problem types found in the unit. Teachers can use the Instructional Sequence and Assessment Charts found at the beginning of most chapters as guides in identifying problem types. Identifying specific problem types is very important. Teachers should take care not to assume (as do some instructional programs) that because students have learned a problem-solving strategy for a specific problem type, they will always be able to generalize the strategy to related problem types. For example, students who have been taught a strategy in column addition for renaming in the ones column and tens column will not necessarily be able to apply the strategy to examples that require renaming in the tens and hundreds columns. Likewise, students may be able to work a problem when vertically aligned but not be able to work the same problem when rewritten horizontally.

After determining the problem types presented in the unit, the teacher must then decide which problem types to delete, delay teaching, or add to the unit. Our general recommendation for teachers of low-performing students is to initially concentrate instruction on the most essential grade level skills. Only when students have mastered all the essential skills should the teacher present instruction in less essential skill areas. In judging the degree to which a skill is essential, the teacher must consider the following:

1. How often the student will apply the skill in the future.
2. Whether or not the skill is a prerequisite for more advanced problem types and related skills.

Once the teacher has determined what problem types students should be able to work at the conclusion of the unit, the teacher must decide on mastery levels for the various problem types. Two factors must be considered when defining mastery: accuracy and speed.

The minimally acceptable accuracy level depends on the nature of the skill. Relatively simple tasks which are components for several more advanced problems should be practiced until students develop 95–100% accuracy. For example, a teacher should provide practice on basic addition facts such as 6 + 3, 8 + 5, and 9 + 2 until the student can accurately respond to any basic fact question. Likewise, exercises in rounding off should be continued in mass until the student can perform with 95–100% accuracy. On problem types which require the application of a multi-step strategy, the minimum accuracy level may be somewhat lower than 95%. Unfortunately, we have no experimental data on which to base recommendations. Our recommendation is that teachers provide supervised practice until students reach an 85–90% accuracy level for worksheet assignments containing a mix of problem types that require multi-step strategies.

A speed criterion also depends on the relative complexity of the problem type and the students' motor skills. As a general rule, we recommend that for each fact computation in a problem, the teacher allow about 2–3 seconds. For example, in working the problem 7 × 243, a teacher would set a speed goal of 10–15 seconds since five fact computations (7 × 3, 7 × 4, 28 + 2, 7 × 2, and 14 + 3) are needed to work the problem. The exact speed criterion will depend on the students' knowledge of basic facts. The criterion is faster for students who have mastered basic facts and slower for those who have not.

Again, let us point out the need for further research in this area. There is presently scant experimental data on how quickly students should work problems. However, there is little doubt that fluency is important, Students who work problems with relative fluency are more likely to retain strategies over a longer period of time.

SELECT STRATEGIES As mentioned earlier, developmental basals, in an apparent attempt to develop conceptual understanding, often simultaneously introduce two or more alternative problem-solving strategies for the same skill. Rather than developing a conceptual foundation, the introduction of alternative problem-solving strategies confuses many students. When using a program that presents alternative strategies, select just one of the strategies to teach students.

In deciding which strategy to select, keep two factors in mind: (1) the relative efficiency of the strategy, and (2) the similarities of the strategy to the strategy taught by other teachers in the school. The first factor is central to direct instruction: Students should be taught strategies they can learn relatively easily and can apply to a range of related problems, which implies they understand the strategy. The second factor calls attention to the need for continuity from grade level to grade level in teaching procedures. Many students will have difficulty in mathematics if they are taught a different strategy each year. Each chapter in this book outlines recommended strategies for major skill areas. The strategies sometimes represent a compromise between what we consider to be ideal and what is likely to be used by a majority of teachers.

CONSTRUCT FORMATS A format translates a general teaching procedure into specific teacher and student behaviors. Formats should reflect a carefully designed progression, beginning with a teacher demonstration of the strategy and followed by teacher-guided worksheet practice, worksheet practice characterized by less teacher direction, supervised worksheet practice, and finally independent work.[1] Throughout Chapters 4–20 are formats to teach various math skills. To see what a format looks like, turn to Figure 8.5. This format illustrates the first four stages: Part A, the structured board presentation; Part B, the structured worksheet; Part C, the less structured worksheet; and Part D, supervised practice. In this format the teacher introduces students to the steps in adding two numbers with a demonsration on the blackboard. In the structured worksheet presentation, the teacher guides students in applying the strategy to problems on their worksheets. In the less structured worksheet presentation, the teacher provides systematically less guidance. During supervised practice, the teacher closely monitors students as they work problems on their own, providing only corrective feedback. Supervised practice is continued until students develop accuracy. As mentioned earlier, accuracy is reflected by the low incidence of student errors. Attaining a high level of accuracy does not, however, guarantee fluency. Therefore, once students attain accuracy, massed independent practice on the specific skills should be maintained until students are fluent as well as accurate in their worksheet performance.

The number of days it takes to make a transition from the structured stage to the independent stage is dependent on the relative complexity of the problem type. If a new problem type involves a simple extension of a previously taught strategy, the stages can be covered in 2 days. If a new, complex strategy is being taught, approximately 6 to 10 days may be required for the transition. For example, column addition with a two digit and one digit number

$$
\begin{array}{r}
34 \\
+\ 9 \\
\hline
\end{array}
$$

is introduced after problems containing two digit numbers

$$
\begin{array}{r}
34 \\
+19 \\
\hline
\end{array}
$$

have been taught. The absence of a tens number in a problem like

$$
\begin{array}{r}
34 \\
+\ 9 \\
\hline
\end{array}
$$

---

[1] Though a well-constructed format is critical in teaching low-performing students certain mathematics skills, how the teacher presents the format also is essential to its effectiveness as a teaching tool. As previously discussed, teachers should practice formats prior to teaching students so that during the actual teaching session, the teacher can concentrate on student performance. Teachers should become familiar enough with the formats so that they are able to present the format using any of the relevant example types. The preparation required for an effective presentation is time-consuming. However, the improved student performance that results from preparation time is obvious.

Figure 2.3 Example Pattern

Day	Part A Structured Board Presentation Problems	Part B Structured Worksheet Problems	Part C Less Structured Worksheet Problems	Part D Supervised Practice Problems	Part E Independent Practice
1	3	2			
2	1	3			
3–4		2	3		
5			4	4	
6–till accurate				8–10	
Till fluent					8–10

can be confusing for some students. However, if they know the strategy for adding two digit numbers, most students can usually progress through all four stages of the format for the new problem type in 2 days. On the other hand, most students would not be able to learn to work division problems with two digit divisors

$$23\overline{)947}$$

in such a short time. For that division skill, 6 to 10 days would probably be required to progress to the last stage. The actual time requirements for moving through the four stages for a particular skill are determined by students' learning rates. Some students will cover the four stages for division with two digit divisors in 4 days, whereas other students might take 3 weeks or more.

Each format specified in this book includes a chart estimating the number of days to be devoted to each stage and the number of problems that should be presented each day. The chart from Figure 8.5 is reproduced in Figure 2.3. Under the column labeled *Day* are numbers representing the days on which the format is being taught. For example, 1–2 under lesson days stand for the first and second day the format is introduced. On day 1, five examples are presented—3 using Part A and 2 using Part B. On day 2, four examples are presented—1 with Part A and 3 with Part B. Note that on day 2, the teacher presents only one problem on the board but guides the students through 3 worksheet problems. Note that at the bottom of the first column are the phrases "until accurate" and "until fluent." We suggest providing supervised practice until students develop accuracy (85–90% level). For some students, this may require 1 or 2 days of practice while for others it may require a longer period of time. The students' performance determines how long massed supervised practice is provided. Likewise, after the students develop accuracy, we suggest

providing massed independent practice until they develop fluency. Again the students' performance determines for how many lessons the massed independent practice continues. (The questions of what to do when just one or two students in a group have not reached an acceptable accuracy level while others have is discussed on pages 37–38.)

SELECT PRESENTATION EXAMPLES Many commercial programs do not include sufficient numbers of examples in their initial presentations to enable students to develop mastery. Also, they rarely provide an adequate mixture of problem types to enable students to discriminate when to apply the various strategies. Teachers, therefore, must be prepared to construct worksheets to supplement the number of practice examples in the students' textbooks.

The charts at the beginning of each format suggest the number of problems to be presented daily. The examples indicated for the structured board and structured worksheet parts of the format would be limited to problems of the current type. The purpose of these parts is to teach the problem-solving strategy for the new problem type.

The number of problems depends on the relative complexity of the problem type. Since problems requiring more steps are more time-consuming, fewer problems can be presented. For example, when introducing division problems such as

$$2\overline{)12} \qquad 5\overline{)30} \qquad 9\overline{)36}$$

which require few steps, about 10 problems could be assigned. However, when presenting more complex division problems such as

$$25\overline{)372} \qquad 48\overline{)1432}$$

only 4 to 6 problems would be provided.

The less structured worksheet presentation and supervised practice parts of a format call for a mixture of the currently introduced problem types and previously introduced types. The purpose of presenting students with a variety of problems is twofold. First, after students learn the steps in a given problem-solving strategy, they must learn to discriminate when it is appropriate to apply the strategy. Without carefully designed worksheet practice, lower-performing students tend to apply the last strategy they have learned to all related problems on a worksheet. For example, after some students learn a subtraction strategy for double borrowing in problems with the zero in the tens column

$$\begin{array}{r} \overset{29}{\cancel{30}}4 \\ -\ 19 \\ \hline 285 \end{array}$$

they might apply the strategy inappropriately to all subtraction problems containing zeroes in the tens column, whether renaming is necessary or not.

$$\begin{array}{r} \overset{29}{\cancel{30}}4 \\ -\ 24 \\ \hline 270 \end{array} \qquad \begin{array}{r} \overset{29}{\cancel{30}}4 \\ -\ 13 \\ \hline 281 \end{array}$$

The second reason for including various problem types is to provide the review necessary for students to maintain mastery of the previously taught skills. Without systematic review, low-performing students, in particular, will forget and/or confuse earlier taught strategies. A discussion of example selection guidelines is provided for each format in the book. The guidelines will enable teachers to generate examples over the course of time the format is being presented.

PROVIDE REVIEW Many commercial programs do not provide adequate review to facilitate retention of skills. Intensive practice on a new problem type should be provided so that students develop both accuracy and fluency. After mastery is achieved, problems of that type need no longer appear in mass on every worksheet. However, systematic review of skills should be provided. Teachers can provide this review by selecting problems from various pages in the basal text and workbook, by selecting worksheets from supplementary programs, or by preparing their own worksheets. An example of a teacher-made worksheet to provide review on previously introduced skills appears in Figure 2.4. The worksheet is one made by a fourth grade teacher late in the school year. The problems in the worksheet are numbered to facilitate workchecks in which students mark their own papers.

Initial Assessment

Following the selection, evaluation, and modification of a program, teachers should prepare to assess their students. At the beginning of the school year, we recommend that classroom teachers divide students into instructional groups and place these groups at an appropriate lesson in the instructional program. The following discussion covers recommendations for testing, grouping, and placing students in programs.

Testing

The two tests used to help group and place students are the placement test and the diagnostic test.

PLACEMENT TESTING The placement test should contain a representative sample of problem types from the mathematics program being used. Although many programs contain their own placement test for the purposes of grouping and placing students, some programs do not. Also, some programs may contain tests that are inappropriate because they omit essential skills and assess too many nonessential skills. Therefore, we have provided an alternative testing package designed to provide a maximum amount of information in a relatively short period of time. Keep in mind that the purpose of the placement tests is solely to provide a basis for initially grouping students and determining the appropriate level at which to begin instruction.

The six tests appear in Figure 2.5. The tests include items on addition, subtraction, multiplication, division, place value, story problems, fractions, decimals, and percent items. Level A tests problem types usually taught in kindergarten and the first part of first grade; Level B covers skills taught in mid- and late first grade. Level C covers second grade skills, and so on. Since the tests are administered in the beginning of the year, students are tested on the skills taught in the preceding grade, except of course for students who are entering school for the first time. First graders would be given Level A; second grade students are tested on Level B; third graders, on Level C; fourth graders, on Level D; fifth graders, on Level E; and sixth graders and junior high students, Level F. If the teacher has reason to suspect that the student may be performing below grade level, she can administer a lower level test to the student. The Level A and B tests are

Figure 2.4 Student Review Worksheet

Name _____   Date _____

1.

   7)2135

2.

   204
   × 37

3.

   4002
   - 86

4.

   3742
   1856
   +3928

5.

   $\frac{5}{9} + \frac{2}{3}$

6.

   $\frac{3}{4} \times 8$

7.

   $3\frac{2}{5} - 2$

8.

   $\frac{3}{4} = \frac{\square}{20}$

9.

   5 × 135

10.

   9010 - 328

11.

   52 × 87

12.

   314 - 9

13. Jill earned 1,085 points in May.
    Ann earned 1,036 points in May.
    How many points did they earn altogether?   _____

14. Sarah scored 184 points this season.
    If she scored 8 points each game, how many games did she play?   _____

15. Dina ran 3 2/5 miles on Monday and 5 4/5 miles on Tuesday. How many more miles did she
    run on Tuesday than on Monday?   _____

16. Jack read 3/4 of an hour each night.
    How many hours will he read in 12 days?   _____

17. a. What is the sum of 5 and 3?   _____
    b. What is the difference of 5 and 3?   _____
    c. What is the product of 5 and 3?   _____

18. How many inches in 4 feet?   _____ _____

19. Three pounds equal how many ounces?   _____ _____

20. Jane has 2 quarters, 3 dimes and 2 nickels.
    How many cents does she have altogether?   _____ _____

---

designed to be administered individually, since they contain beginning level skills, many of which require oral responses. An aide or parent volunteer could be trained to assist the teacher in giving the test. Note that there are tester directions and record forms for Level A and B tests. A copy of the record form would be made for each student tested. Levels C through F are designed to be administered to students as a group. The teacher merely hands out the tests and instructs the students to work all the problems they can. In administering the test, the teacher should not impose a time limit. Also, the teacher should help students read any words they are unable to decode. The teacher should keep the students' work as a formal record of their entry skills.

DIAGNOSTIC TESTING Teachers who work exclusively with low-performing students will have to write Individual Education Programs (IEPs) for each

student they serve, Therefore, these teachers often need to conduct more thorough initial testing.

Chapters 5–20 contain instructional sequence and assessment charts arranged by grade level for the critical skills covered in each chapter. The sample items in these seqences can be used to construct a more thorough test that can be used in setting up IEPs for the students.[2]

Grouping Students

The teacher would administer the placement test during the first days of the school year. Student performance on the beginning of the year placement test is used to group students.[3] After administering the placement test, the teacher should record stu-

---

[2] © 1990 Merrill Publishing Co. Permission granted for noncommercial reproduction of the tests in Figure 2.5.
[3] The grouping and placing procedures for kindergarten and first grade students taking the Level A test are discussed in Chapter 3.

Figure 2.5 Placement Tests

LEVEL A
For Beginning Kindergarten and
First Graders

TESTER INSTRUCTIONS

I. Counting Skills

    1. Counting by 1s

       Instructions
       "I WANT YOU TO COUNT FOR ME. START AT 1. COUNT AS HIGH AS YOU CAN." Stop student at 20 or when student leaves out or mixes the order of more than two numbers. If student makes an error in counting, give the student another chance to count. Tell student to start again at 1.

       Recording
       Write the highest number said correctly by student on either attempt.

    2. Counting Lines

       Instructions
       a. Point to the lines in box *a* below.
           "LOOK AT THESE LINES.
           I WANT YOU TO COUNT THEM AND TELL ME HOW
           MANY LINES THERE ARE."
       b. Repeat with box *b*.

       Recording
       If student counted lines correctly, write +.
       If student counted only some of the lines correctly, write
       the number counted correctly.

    3. Drawing Lines

       Instructions

       Give student pencil and paper.
       a. "DRAW THREE LINES.
           HOW MANY LINES ARE YOU GOING TO DRAW? DRAW THEM."
       b. Repeat a with six lines.

       Recording
       Write + if correct or write number of lines drawn and counted correctly.

II. Symbol Skills

    1. Numeral Identification

       Instructions
       Point to each numeral below and ask, "WHAT IS THIS?"

       4 2 6 7 3 8 5 9 10

       When the student misses three in a row, stop testing symbol identification and test symbol writing.

Measurement items use U.S. customary units, such as feet and pounds. However, metric units can be substituted for customary units. Chapter 18 discusses teaching procedures for both customary and metric units.

Figure 2.5 cont'd

   Recording
   Write a + in the box next to each numeral identified correctly.
   Write NR for no response. If a student says an incorrect number, write the number the student said.

2. Numeral Writing

   Instructions
   Give student pencil and paper.
   a. "WRITE THE NUMERAL 4."
   b. Repeat step a with these numerals:

   2   6   7   3   8   5   9   10

   Recording
   Write a + for any numeral drawn correctly.

   Write a + even if numeral is drawn backward; i.e.   Ɛ

   However, write a *b* (for backward) next to the plus.
   Stop testing when students miss three in a row and go to Part III.

III. Math-related Language Concepts

1. More-Less

   Instructions
   a. Tell me which number is *more*, 5 or 7.
   b. Tell me which number is *more*, 8 or 3.

   Recording
   Write + for each question answered correctly.

RECORD FORM—LEVEL A

Student Name _____

Date of Test _____

Tester _____

I. Counting.

   1. Counting by 1s—highest number counted to ☐
   2. Counting Lines
      4 lines ☐   7 lines ☐
   3. Drawing Lines
      3 lines ☐   6 lines ☐

II. Symbol Skills

   1. Identification   4 ☐   2 ☐   6 ☐   7 ☐   3 ☐   8 ☐   5 ☐   9 ☐   10 ☐

   2. Writing   4 ☐   2 ☐   6 ☐   7 ☐   3 ☐   8 ☐   5 ☐   9 ☐   10 ☐

III. Math-related Language Concepts

   more-less
   5 or 7 ☐   8 or 3 ☐

Figure 2.5 cont'd

LEVEL B
For Beginning Second Graders

TESTER INSTRUCTIONS

I. Symbol Skills

1. Symbol Identification—Teens and Tens

Point to each numeral below and ask,
"WHAT NUMBER?"

14 17 13 15 12 11
26 48 35 52
50 30 21 41

Recording
Write + next to each numeral identified correctly.
Write the number said for each numeral identified incorrectly.
(Stop testing when student misses three in a row and go to II.)

II. Counting Skills

Instructions
1. "I'LL SAY A NUMBER. YOU SAY THE NUMBER THAT
   COMES NEXT; 39. WHAT COMES NEXT?"
   Repeat step 1 with 69, 49.

Recording
Write a + next to each numeral for which student responds correctly.
Write the number said for each incorrect response.

Recording for III, IV, V
Write + if correct; write student's response if incorrect.
Stop testing in a section when student misses two problems in a row.
Proceed to next section.

III. Operations

Written Presentation of Operations

1. Give students pencil and point to problems on record form.
   "WORK THESE PROBLEMS AND WRITE THE ANSWERS."

IV. Story Problems

1. "LISTEN. SAM HAD 3 HATS (pause 1 second).
   HE GOT 2 MORE HATS. HOW MANY HATS DID
   HE END WITH? LISTEN AGAIN.
   SAM HAD 3 HATS (pause 1 second).
   HE GOT 2 MORE HATS.
   HOW MANY HATS DID HE END WITH?"

2. "NEW PROBLEM: ANN HAD 5 TOYS (pause 1 second).
   SHE GAVE AWAY 2 OF THE TOYS.
   HOW MANY TOYS DID SHE END WITH?"
   (Repeat story one time.)

3. "NEW PROBLEM: JACK HAS 4 EGGS (pause 1 second).
   HE BUYS 3 MORE EGGS. HOW MANY EGGS DOES HE END
   WITH? LISTEN AGAIN. JACK HAS 4 EGGS (pause 1 second).
   HE BUYS 3 MORE EGGS. HOW MANY EGGS DOES HE END WITH?"

Figure 2.5 cont'd

4. "NEW PROBLEM. JANE HAD 7 PENCILS (pause 1 second).
SHE LOST 3 OF THE PENCILS. HOW MANY PENCILS DID
SHE END WITH? LISTEN AGAIN. JANE HAD 7 PENCILS
(pause 1 second). SHE LOST 3 OF THE PENCILS.
HOW MANY PENCILS DID SHE END WITH?"

V. Multi-digit addition (no renaming)

1. Point to problems on record form. "WORK THESE PROBLEMS."

RECORD FORM—LEVEL B

I. Symbol Identification

| 14 | | 17 | | 13 | | 15 | | 12 | | 11 | | 26 | |

| 48 | | 35 | | 52 | | 50 | | 30 | | 21 | | 41 | |

II. Counting Skills

39 ☐   69 ☐   49 ☐

III. Operations

$6 + 3 = \square$ $7 - 4 = \square$ $5 + \square = 8$

$\begin{array}{r} 8 \\ +4 \\ \hline \end{array}$ $\begin{array}{r} 9 \\ -5 \\ \hline \end{array}$ $3 + \square = 5$

IV. Story Problems

1. 3 hats, gets 2 ☐
2. 5 toys, gave away 2 ☐
3. 4 eggs, buys 3 ☐
4. 7 pencils, lost 3 ☐

V. Multi-digit Addition

$\begin{array}{r} 24 \\ +32 \\ \hline \end{array}$ $\begin{array}{r} 56 \\ -24 \\ \hline \end{array}$ $\begin{array}{r} 47 \\ +21 \\ \hline \end{array}$ $\begin{array}{r} 78 \\ -32 \\ \hline \end{array}$

LEVEL C
For Beginning Third Graders

1. $\begin{array}{r} 1 \\ 3 \\ +2 \\ \hline \end{array}$ 2. $\begin{array}{r} 37 \\ +48 \\ \hline \end{array}$ 3. $37 + 6 = \square$ 4. $39 - 4 = \square$ 5. $\begin{array}{r} 247 \\ +315 \\ \hline \end{array}$

6. $\begin{array}{r} 39 \\ -14 \\ \hline \end{array}$ 7. $\begin{array}{r} 54 \\ -18 \\ \hline \end{array}$ 8. $\begin{array}{r} 60 \\ -15 \\ \hline \end{array}$ 9. $\begin{array}{r} 382 \\ -137 \\ \hline \end{array}$ 10. $5 \times 4 = \square$

11. $2 \times 6 = \square$ 12. Write the fraction   13. ___ minutes after ___

Figure 2.5 cont'd

14. Sam had 15 cats. He got some more cats.
    He ends with 19 cats. How many more cats did he get? ☐ cats
15. Jack has 16 cats and 3 dogs. How many pets does he have? ☐ pets
16. Jill has 26 dollars. Jim has 12 dollars less than Jill.
    How many dollars does Jim have? ☐ dollars
17. Jim has 2 dimes and 2 nickels.
    How many cents does Jim have? ☐ cents
18. One foot equals how many inches? ☐
19. Write seven hundred fifteen _____
20. Write four hundred eight _____

LEVEL D
For Beginning Fourth Graders

1. 374
   +261

2. 3,761
   +1,854

3. 342 + 7 + 14 = ☐

4. 423
   - 17

5. 3,529
  -1,872

6. 203
  - 84

7. 35
  × 4

8. 47
  × 3

9. 5 × 24 = ☐

10. $\frac{4}{7} - \frac{2}{7} = $ ☐

11. How many inches in 2 feet? ☐ inches
12. Bill had 15 apples, 3 bananas, and 27 oranges. How many pieces of fruit did Bill have? ☐ pieces
13. Sam had 423 apples. He sold 58 apples. How many apples does he have left? ☐ apples.
14. Jim had a quarter. He spent 17 cents. How many cents does he have left? ☐ cents
15. Jack is 25 years old. His uncle is 8 years younger than Jack. How old is Jack's uncle? ☐ years old
16. Circle five thousand and six.
    5,060   506   5,600   5,006
17. Circle four thousand and twenty.
    4,200   420   4,020   4,002
18. What time is it?

    ____half past 4
    ____a quarter to 4
    ____a quarter to 5
    ____a quarter after 4

19. Jim has a quarter, a dime and 4 pennies. How many cents does Jim have? ☐ cents
20. Jill has 5 cans of worms. There are 4 worms in each can. How many worms does Jill have? ☐ worms

21. 4 × ☐ = 24   22. 3)18̄   23. 9)36̄   24. 5)19̄   25. 4)15̄

Figure 2.5 cont'd

LEVEL E
For Beginning Fifth Graders

1. $3,486 + 92 + 486 = \Box$ 2. $8,003 - 2,632 = \Box$

3. $1,000 - 863 = \Box$ 4. $\begin{array}{r} 40,206 \\ -\ 4,138 \end{array}$ 5. $\begin{array}{r} 406 \\ \times\ 7 \end{array}$

6. $\begin{array}{r} 43 \\ \times 39 \end{array}$ 7. $\begin{array}{r} 534 \\ \times\ 78 \end{array}$ 8. $9 \times 423 = \Box$

9. $2\overline{)135}$ 10. $6\overline{)249}$ 11. $24\overline{)82}$

12. $46\overline{)138}$ 13. $4\frac{3}{5} - 2\frac{1}{5} = \Box\frac{\Box}{\Box}$ 14. $\frac{2}{5} = \frac{\Box}{15}$

15. $\frac{6}{8} = \frac{\Box}{4}$ 16. $\frac{3}{4} - \frac{1}{2} = \frac{\Box}{\Box}$ 17. $\frac{3}{4}$ of 8 equals

18. There are 15 classes in Adam's school. There are 30 children in each class. How many children in Adam's school? $\Box$ children

19. Jane has 84 cents. She wants to buy pencils which cost 7 cents each. How many pencils can she buy? $\Box$ pencils

20. In March, Bill had 3,426 stamps in his stamp collection. Bill wants to have 5,000 stamps. How many more stamps does Bill need? $\Box$ stamps

21. Jill had $100. She bought a shirt that cost $8.65. How much money does she have left?

22. How many minutes in 4 hours? $\Box$ minutes

23. Tim has 60 cents. Pencils cost 9 cents each. How many pencils can Tim buy? $\Box$ pencils

24. Seventy-two inches equals how many feet? $\Box$ feet

25. Write 9 thousand and forty _____

Figure 2.5 cont'd

**Level F
For Beginning Sixth Graders or
Junior High Students**

1. Write this number:
   six million four hundred thousand _____

2. Write this number:
   Eight hundred thirty thousand _____

3. 2.14
   × .7

4. Round off this number to the nearest whole number:
   7.83 _____

5. Round off this number to the nearest tenth:
   8.693 _____

6. $7\overline{)2835}$

7. Work this problem; convert your answer to a mixed number.
   $\frac{4}{5} + \frac{3}{5} =$

8. 284
   ×346

9. $7\overline{)42.91}$

10. 3869
    1868
    +4285

11. $47\overline{)1325}$

12. $35\overline{)714}$

13. 7.1 − 3.45 =

14. $9\overline{).36}$

15. 8 + .34 + 7.02 =

16. $\frac{3}{4}$ of 12 =

17. $\frac{3}{4} - \frac{2}{3} =$

18. $8 - 3\frac{1}{2} =$

19. Jill is a carpenter. She makes $8.75 every hour she works. She works 45 hours. How much does she earn? _____

20. Bill bought a piece of material which was 1 yard long. He cut off 1 foot and 3 inches. How much material does he have left? _____

21. Mrs. Adams is going to take a trip to see her daughter who lives 2,000 miles away. If Mrs. Adams drives 50 miles an hour, how many hours will she have to drive? _____

22. Jack weighs 38 3/4 pounds. He is 7 1/4 pounds lighter than his brother. How much does Jack's brother weigh? _____

23. James had 10 dollars. He bought a pen for $3.46 and a book for $1.83. How much does he have left? _____

24. There are 26 phones on each floor of an office building which is 48 floors high. How many phones altogether in the building? _____

25. Jack worked 3 hours and 40 minutes on Monday and 4 hours and 25 minutes on Tuesday. How many more minutes did he work on Tuesday than on Monday? _____

Figure 2.6 Sample List of Placement Test Scores

Teacher <u>Smith</u>   Grade <u>5</u>   Test Form Given <u>E</u>

Student	Number Correct	Student	Number Correct
1	0	16	12
2	3	17	16
3	4	18	16
4	4	19	16
5	4	20	17
6	6	21	18
7	6	22	18
8	7	23	18
9	7	24	19
10	7	25	19
11	7	26	19
12	8	27	19
13	8	28	19
14	8	29	25
15	8	30	25

dent performance on a summary sheet like the one in Figure 2.6. Students should be listed according to the number of problems correctly answered on the test, with the students who scored lowest listed first. The teacher then uses this list as a basis for forming groups. As mentioned previously, we strongly recommend that students be grouped homogeneously for instruction to maximize instructional efficiency and student participation.

Prior to actually dividing students into groups, the teacher should decide on the number of instructional groups that she is able to teach per day. In the primary grades, since all students (even high performers) require a significant amount of teacher directed, closely supervised instruction, a class should be divided into two or three instructional groups. On the other hand, in the intermediate grades, students performing at grade level can be placed in relatively large groups (20–25 students) since they are more instructionally sophisticated and do not need as much constant monitoring and immediate feedback. An exception, of course, is made for students performing below grade level.

The teacher should group the lowest-performing students first. If one or two students score significantly lower or higher than the rest of the class (see students 1, 29, and 30 in Figure 2.6), they should be grouped with students from another class who are performing at a comparable level. Wherever possible, teachers should make use of cross-class grouping to provide the best possible placement for students. Also, in constructing groups, the teacher should remember that, if possible, the group of low performers should be the smallest group in the class. This group is kept small so that each student can receive more individual attention from the teacher.

After constructing the group comprised of the lower-performing students, the teacher looks for cut-off scores that would result in homogeneous grouping for the remaining students. For example, in Figure 2.6 students 17–28 would form a group. Next, the teacher needs to make decisions about "borderline" students, those students whose test scores place them between a higher and lower group (see student 16 in Figure 2.6). Before grouping these students, the teacher should examine their placement tests more closely to determine the types of errors they made. If several errors on a student's test were caused by mistakes in basic facts, the teacher should consider placing the student in the higher group, If, on the other hand, the student's errors indicated a lack of problem-solving strategies, he should be placed in the lower group.[4] Examples of the two types of errors are illustrated below:

Fact Errors

```
  1            1                              64
 46           69           24             5)372
+27          +35          ×37               35
 74          103          161               22
                          720               20
                          881
```

Strategy Errors

```
                                            10
 46           69           24             5)372
+27          +35          ×37                5
613          914         72168               2
```

[4] See pages 13–14 for further discussion of fact versus strategy errors.

A final, but still very important, topic involves regrouping. In grouping students, it is important to keep in mind that a student's initial test performance should never be the sole determinant for the student's group placement for the entire school year. The other major determining factor is the student's performance in the group. If the teacher discovers a student learns new skills more quickly than the rest of his group, the teacher should consider moving the student into a higher-performing group. Similarly, if the teacher discovers that one student consistently makes more errors than the other students in her group, the teacher would consider placing that student in a lower-performing group. Regrouping should be done during the first week or two of instruction. The earlier the regrouping, the easier it is for students to transition from one group to another.

Placing Students in a Program

A student should be placed in an instructional program at a point as close to his ideal instructional level as possible. That is, a student must have previously mastered all skills introduced up to that point in the program and not have mastered the majority of skills introduced after that point. Placing students appropriately in a program is very important. Placing students at a level too high may result in their encountering much failure; placing students at a level too low is inefficient and may lead to discipline problems as students become bored. Teachers working with students on a one-on-one basis can determine a starting lesson by testing skills in the order in which they are introduced in an instructional program. They continue testing until a skill deficit appears, and then teach the student this skill. Teachers working with groups of students will find placing a group of students at a starting lesson more difficult since no two students, especially in the upper grades, are likely to have developed mastery on an identical set of skills. Teachers must select a starting lesson which will not be too low for the higher performers in the group nor too high for the lower performers. The first decision facing classroom teachers using a basal program is whether a group should be placed in the materials designated for the students' grade level. Teachers can begin by giving the appropriate placement test in Figure 2.5.

During the first days of school, kindergarten and first grade students should be given the Level A placement test on page 27. Initial groupings can be made on the basis of how many numerals students can identify and write. Students who can identify and write nearly all numerals can be given the Level B test to determine the extent of their knowledge. Second grade students would be given Level B, etc. Our general recommendation (assuming the placement test includes problem types taught during the previous grade) is to place students in their respective grade level material if they can work between 60 and 80% of the problems in the placement test.

Students who perform above an 80% level on the placement test should be given the placement test for the next grade level. If students get between 60 and 80% of the items on that test correct, the teacher may want to consider placing the students in books for the next higher grade level. Teachers should exercise caution, however, in placing students in advanced material. Students often need time to develop fluency in applying basic facts and problem-solving strategies, Therefore, they should be placed in a higher-grade level of a basal program only if they work problems on the placement test quickly as well as accurately.

Groups with many students who score below a 60% level on the initial placement test for their grade level may need to be placed in a lower grade level book, or in special remedial materials. Again, caution must be exercised. Some students may perform quite poorly the first day or two of school, but with a week or two of practice improve significantly. Therefore, for students scoring poorly on the placement test, the teacher should spend about a week or two attempting to reteach how to work problems similar to those missed on the initial test. Following the tutoring, the teacher should readminister the test. If, after this time, students can get 60% or more of the items on the placement test correct, they can be placed in their grade level text. The group, though, would require very careful instruction and close monitoring throughout the school year.

Students who, after a week or so of tutoring, are still unable to perform at a 60% level on the placement test may need to be placed in material from a lower grade level or in remedial material. See the section on remedial instruction (pages 47–49) for a discussion regarding these students.

Presenting a Unit

Once teachers have prepared materials and grouped and placed students, they can begin presenting units from the program. Presenting a unit from a basal series or a specific skill program involves (a) administering a pretest of the skills in that unit, (b) presenting the daily lessons that make up the units, and (c) progressing at an optimal rate.

PRETESTING Before presenting a unit, the teacher will need to construct and administer a pretest. Administering a pretest is helpful in several ways. Pretesting prevents the teacher from either overlooking a prerequisite skill that needs to be taught or spending instructional time on skills students have already mastered. In addition, the pretest can be used as a post-test to measure students' skill acquisition after the unit has been completed.

The pretest for a specific unit should include the following:

1. Problem types in that skill area that had been taught in the preceding grades
2. The preskills required to solve the new problem types taught in the unit
3. Examples of the new problem types presented in the unit

Problem types taught in earlier grades are included so that the teacher can identify any deficits which should be remedied before more difficult problems are introduced. Generally, items should be drawn from the two previous grades. The preskills and problem types from the current unit are included so that the teacher can determine where instruction should begin, i.e., whether the teacher needs to teach the preskills and/or what problem types require direct instruction.

Two or three problems of each type should be tested. The Instructional Sequence and Assessment Charts at the beginning of Chapters 5–20 provide a bank of pretest items the teacher can draw from. These charts include a sequential list of problem types with several illustrative problems listed for each type. A fifth grade teacher about to teach a multiplication unit, for example, would construct a test which included all the multiplication problem types on the Instructional Sequence and Assessment Chart introduced in grades three through five. The teacher would copy these problems onto a ditto, run off copies, and give these copies to the students to work. Note that these charts do not include every problem type students will encounter. Any problem types not listed on the charts, but to be included in the unit, should be added to the test.

A record form that can be used to record student performance on pretests appears in Figure 2.7. The students' names would be listed in the first column. Across the top of the form are spaces for the problem types. Each box is divided into two parts, one to record student performance on the pretest and one to record student performance on the post-test. The teacher would record student performance by writing a + if the student got all the problems of a particular type correct and a − if the student missed any of the problems of that type.

After testing the students, the teacher must decide with which problem type to begin instruction. As a general guideline, we recommend beginning instruction with the earliest problem type failed by more than one-fourth of the students in the group. Starting at this point would allow the teacher to make efficient use of group instructional time, since the teacher would be presenting material that is new to a significant proportion of the students in the group. However, teachers must be extremely cautious in following this procedure. A teacher must remember that he is responsible for seeing that each student receives the instruction necessary for mastering important skills. Therefore, when first presenting a unit, he needs to plan on working individually with the students who missed earlier problem types. The extra instruction should continue until those students have caught up with the rest of the group.

Presenting Daily Lessons

A daily mathematics lesson includes three basic parts: (1) teacher presentation of skills, (2) independent seatwork, and (3) a workcheck.

TEACHER PRESENTATION The teacher presentation usually lasts from 15 to 30 minutes. Less time is required by intermediate students functioning at grade level; more time with younger students and intermediate students functioning below grade level. Instructional time is filled with one or both of the following activities:

1. *Remediation of previously taught skills.* The teacher should remedy any of the previously taught skills or problem types with which several of the students had difficulty. If only one or two students experience difficulty, the teacher should work with these students individually, independent of group instructional time. Student performance on the independent worksheets should serve as a basis for planning remediation exercises. Remember, whenever a student's performance is below 85–90% on two consecutive review worksheets, or the

Figure 2.7 Pretest Record Form

Unit _____

Pretest Date _____

Post-test Date _____

Student Names	Problem Type																			
	Pre	Post	Pre	Post	Pre	Post	Pre	Post	Pre	Post	Pre	Post	Pre	Post	Pre	Post	Pre	Post	Pre	Post

student misses several examples of a specific problem type, a remediation procedure is called for. The remediation procedure usually calls for reteaching one of the worksheet exercises of the relevant format (i.e., structured worksheet presentation, less-structured worksheet, etc.).

2. *Presenting new skills.* The teacher presents the skills currently being introduced. The presentation may involve presenting problems on the board, guiding students through working problems on worksheets, merely supervising students working on their own, or a combination of the above activities.

A more detailed overview of daily lessons during the beginning and later stages of instruction appears in Chapter 3.

INDEPENDENT SEATWORK Independent seatwork refers to the exercises which students complete without assistance at a time other than the teacher-directed instructional time. Exercises for independent seatwork can include workbooks or textbooks, assignments, problems written on the board, dittoed worksheets prepared by the teacher, or activities designed to be carried out with peers. Part of the independent seatwork exercise should include massed practice on the most recently introduced problem types. The other part of the seatwork exercises should include a variety of earlier introduced problem types. As a general rule, we recommend that students be assigned exercises which require 20–30 minutes to complete. Teachers working with older intermediate grade students can assign these worksheets as homework.

A WORKCHECK A workcheck is a specified time for correcting the work students complete independently and inspecting worksheets to determine skills which might require remediation during instructional time. Students' work must be checked daily if they are to receive feedback in the most efficient manner. The sooner a student's weakness or deficit can be identified, the easier it is to remedy. At the same time, the longer a student practices doing something the "wrong" way, the more difficult it is to correct.

Teachers of younger students will find it most efficient to mark papers themselves. Teachers of older students have several alternatives: Higher performing students may mark papers, students can mark their own papers, or the teacher can conduct a group workcheck, in which he reads the answers and the students mark their own papers.

An important part of any workcheck is having students rework the problems they missed on the completed independent assignment. Watching students rework problems helps teachers determine the cause of the student errors. If a student is consistently able to correctly rework problems which he missed, the teacher can assume that lack of motivation is a likely cause of the errors. If, on the other hand, the student is not able to rework the missed problems, the teacher knows that there is a specific skill deficit which requires a remedy.

Progressing at an Optimal Rate

A critical teaching skill is the ability to move a group at an optimal rate. A rate is optimal when a teacher spends no more instructional time on a skill than is necessary for students to develop accuracy. Generally, students can be said to have developed accuracy when they can answer correctly 85-90% or more of the problems on a worksheet containing examples both of the currently introduced type and examples of previously introduced types, with no assistance from the teacher.

Ideally, a teacher should work on a problem type until all students in a group have achieved this accuracy criterion. However, a teacher should not significantly delay the progress of the majority of students because just one or two students are having difficulty. At the same time, the teacher has a responsibility to see that all students achieve success.

Students who consistently require additional time to master new skills should be considered for placement in a lower group. If an alternate placement is not possible, arrangements for some type of tutoring should be made.

3 Scope and Sequence

This chapter presents an overview of the scope and sequence of math instruction in the elementary grades. It is divided into two sections. The first section deals with skills usually taught to students just entering school (kindergarten or first grade). The second section deals with the skills taught in the second through sixth grade.

We devote a disproportionate amount of attention to the beginning months of instruction because this is a crucial time. Well-executed instruction during these months can facilitate student success in later grades. Unfortunately, in most textbooks, relatively little attention has been devoted to integrating the teaching of the various beginning level skills into a coordinated program.

In addition to discussing the scope and sequence of instruction, this chapter discusses issues relevant to each stage. For the beginning stage, we look in depth at commercial programs. For the later stage, we discuss how to establish a remedial program of instruction. Finally for both stages, we provide a description of how daily lessons can be constructed to facilitate optimal progress by students.

Kindergarten and Early First Grade

This section overviews the scope and sequence of beginning mathematics instruction and is pertinent for those school personnel who are or will be working with preschool, kindergarten and first grade students.[1] The major skills taught during kindergarten and the early part of first grade appear in the skill hierarchy chart in Figure 3.1. On the left side of the chart are lesson numbers, 1 through 150, listed in intervals of 10. The skill falling in the area to the right of the first 50 lessons are the ones normally taught in kindergarten. The skills across from the next 90 lessons (50–140) are those normally presented in the early months of first grade. Each box represents a particular skill area. By noting the lesson number in line with the bottom of the box, the reader can determine when that skill is introduced. Likewise, by finding the lesson number across from the top of the

---

[1] An important question concerning beginning mathematics is whether direct instruction should begin in kindergarten or in first grade. This question is of particular importance for students entering school with relatively few math-related skills.

We recommend that direct instruction in a small group setting begin in kindergarten. Even though kindergarten students may not progress as rapidly through a program as first grade students will, they will receive a substantial head start. They will enter first grade with a set of math skills they would not otherwise have had. This recommendation is particularly important for teachers working with students from lower socio-economic environments. These students must learn skills as quickly as possible so that they may, in later grades, be able to take place next to their more advantaged peers.

A note of caution: Lower-performing kindergarten students are quite naive. Thus, instruction must be carefully planned and implemented. The wording in a teacher's explanation must be carefully controlled, demonstrations must be clear and unambiguous, and careful practice and review provided. Teachers must also present lessons in a manner which fosters a positive attitude toward mathematics.

Figure 3.1 Skill Hierarchy for Beginning Mathematics Instruction (Kindergarten and First Grade)

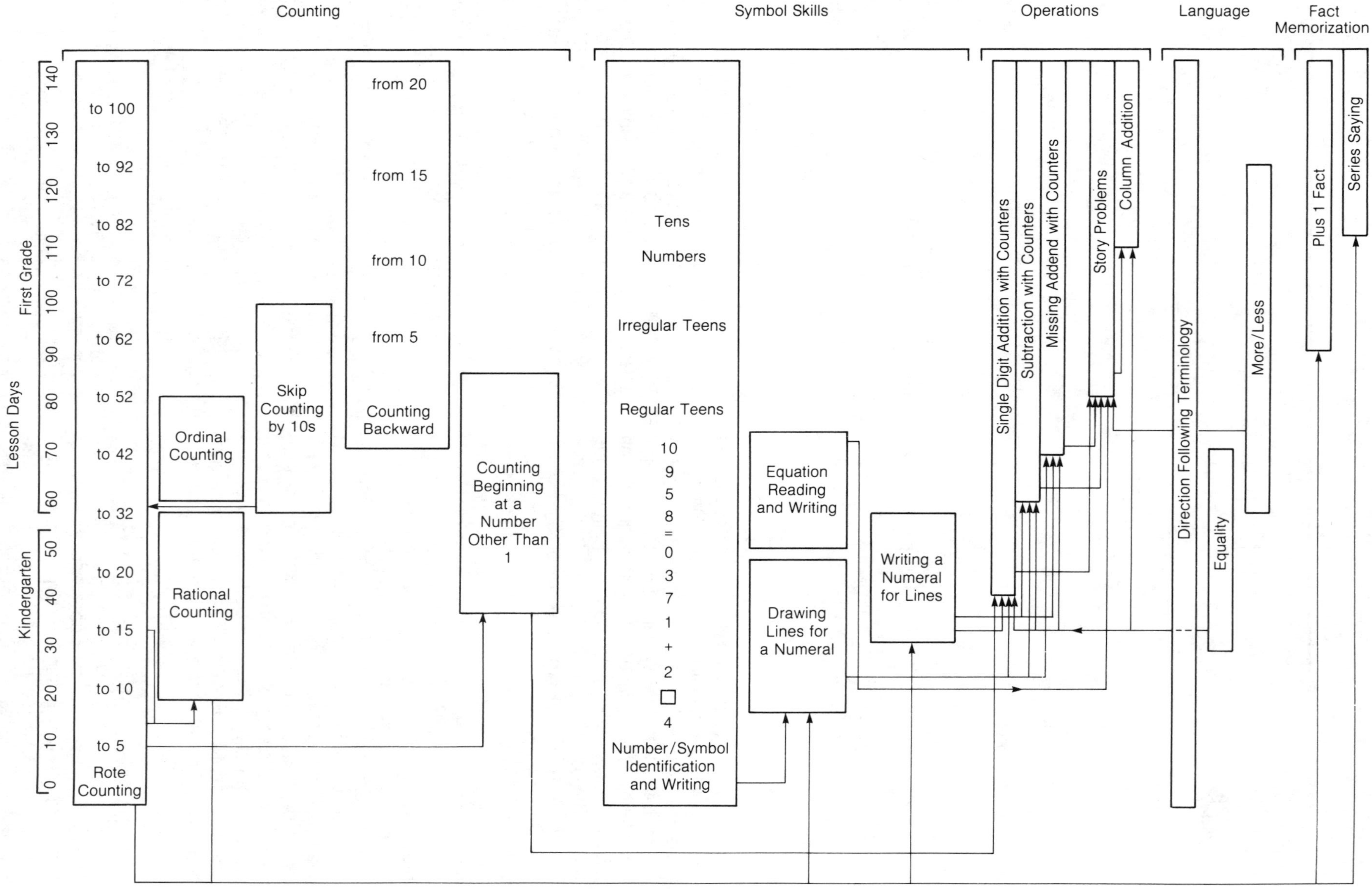

box, the reader can determine when instruction on a specific skill ends. Note that when instruction on a specific skill ceases, the skill is incorporated into a strategy for a later skill. For example, the equality rule is incorporated into addition, subtraction, and missing addend problems. The relationship between equality and these other skills is shown by the arrow from the equality box to the boxes for the other skills.

All the arrows extending to and from boxes indicate which skills are prerequisite skills for more advanced skills, as in the case of equality. Note the numerous interrelationships. Student success in a later introduced skill is nearly always contingent on mastery of symbol identification and writing, counting groups of objects (rational counting), writing symbols to represent lines, and equality.

Note also on the chart that skills are divided into five main areas: counting skills, symbol skills, operations, language skills, and fact skills. Below is a summary of each of the areas presented in the beginning mathematics part.

Counting Skills

Counting skills include the following:

1. Rote counting, in which the students are simply taught to memorize the sequence of consecutively ordered numbers starting at 1
2. Rational counting, which involves coordinating rote counting with the touching of objects
3. Counting beginning from a number other than 1 (e.g. 5, 6, 7, 8), which is a critical component skill for teaching rote counting to higher numbers
4. Counting backward, which is a component skill for one type of subtraction strategy
5. Ordinal counting, in which students are taught to count objects saying first, second, third, fourth, etc., instead of 1, 2, 3, and 4
6. Skip counting by 10s, which is also a component skill for teaching rote counting to higher numbers

Symbol and Place Value Skills

Here are the symbol and place value skills presented in beginning mathematics:

1. Identifying and writing numerals 0–10 and symbols used in equations (i.e., +, −, □, =)
2. Drawing the specified number of lines for a numeral and writing the appropriate numeral for a given set of lines

3. Identifying and writing numerals for teen numbers
4. Identifying and writing two-digit numbers 20–99
5. Reading and writing equations (6 + □ = 8 is read 6 plus how many equals 8—a preskill for solving story problems.)

Language Skills

The language skills stressed in beginning mathematics include the following:

1. The equality principle—an equation involves ending with the same number on both sides of the equals sign. This is a key concept introduced in beginning instruction. Initial addition and subtraction strategies focus on the equality principle.
2. The meaning of the terms *more* and *less*. These terms appear in many story problems.
3. Following directions skills and mathematics-related vocabulary like *next*, the *following*, etc.

Operations

During early mathematics instruction, students are taught to solve simple addition and subtraction problems by using counters to represent the quantities expressed by numerals. We recommend the use of lines as counters because they are easy to use, always accessible, and leave a permanent record of the student's work that makes diagnosis and remediation possible. Students are taught equality concepts and how they are applied to problem-solving strategies. First, students are taught to solve simple addition and subtraction problems by making the appropriate number of lines under the first numeral in the equation:

$$6 + 3 = \Box$$
$$\text{|||||}$$

Then the students either write more lines if the problem is an addition or cross out lines if the problem involves subtraction:

$$6 + 3 = \Box \qquad 6 - 3 = \Box$$
$$\text{|||||} \quad \text{|||} \qquad \cancel{\text{|||}}\text{||}$$

Next the students count the number of lines on the left side of the equal sign and make an equal number of lines under the box on the other side of the equal sign:

$$6 + 3 = \Box \qquad 6 - 3 = \Box$$
$$\text{|||||} \quad \text{|||} \quad \text{|||||||} \qquad \cancel{\text{|||}}\text{||} \quad \text{|||}$$

Finally the students count the number of lines under the box and write the appropriate numeral. Note that the equality concept—you must end with the same number on both sides of the equal sign—is the cornerstone for solving problems.

In the strategy for solving missing addend problems like $4 + \square = 6$, students apply the equality and line-drawing skills they learned earlier for addition by making the sides equal and then filling in the missing numeral.

These initial addition, subtraction, and missing addend strategies are designed to teach a fundamental understanding for the relationship equality has to all basic operations. After students have developed accuracy in applying these strategies they are presented with a new strategy in which they need not make lines for each numeral: in working addition problems, the students merely write lines to represent the amount being plussed, then begin counting with the number in the first group. For example, in solving $6 + 3 = \square$, the students write

$$6 + 3 = \square$$
$$\text{III}$$

then count 6, 7, 8, 9 and write 9 in the box.

Teaching these less cumbersome strategies serves as a transition to the more abstract state in which students work problems without using any physical objects to represent quantities.

Story Problems

Story problems require the student to use addition or subtraction skills to determine the answer to a lifelike situation involving quantities. The story problems introduced initially would be relatively simple ones in which the verb clearly indicates whether the problem requires plussing or minusing. For example, in this problem—Bill had 7 apples. He ate 3 apples. How many does he have left?—the verb *ate* clearly indicates the problem is a subtraction problem. Students are taught to translate problems phrase by phrase to the equation: $7 - 3 = \square$.

Facts

Fact learning refers to the process in which students are taught to mentally compute the answer to the 100 addition facts formed by two single digit addends. Early exercises in this area are designed to teach students the relationship between counting and facts. Students first learn to figure out plus 1 facts by saying the next number in the counting sequence; 8 follows 7 so $7 + 1 = 8$. Later exercises teach students to say a series of related facts:

$$6 + 1 = 7, 6 + 2 = 8, 6 + 3 = 9$$

After students learn the relationship between facts and counting exercises, various activities to facilitate memorization are introduced. Note that fact memorization exercises are introduced after students have mastered the concept of addition through the equality-based counter exercises.

Commercial Programs

Young children are more readily confused than older students due to their relative naivete. Instruction for young students, especially those who come into school with few academic skills, must be quite carefully structured. Unfortunately, many programs designed to teach beginning level skills do not provide ample directions to the teacher in how to present skills in a clear, concise manner. The programs are weakest in the lack of attention given to teaching basic numeration skills (counting and numerical identification). Teacher's guides often contain vague directions rather than specific suggestions.

Teachers must be particularly cautious in evaluating programs labelled readiness programs. The readiness components of the basal programs we examined provided neither clear demonstrations nor adequate practice and review skills. An example of a program construction according to the principles espoused in this text is *DISTAR Arithmetic 1* (Engelmann & Carnine, 1989).[2]

Constructing Daily Lessons

Groups composed of students who know relatively few math skills (i.e., cannot rote count past 15 or identify at least six numerals) should not be placed in a traditionally constructed first grade basal program. We strongly recommend placing these students in a program such as DISTAR, which carefully teaches the critical beginning level skills.

Teachers unable to obtain an instructionally sound program for teaching beginning skills will have to modify the program they are to use. When constructing daily lessons for beginning level instruction, teachers should follow several guidelines:

1. Tasks from several skill areas should be presented in each lesson. Each lesson should include (a) counting tasks, (b) symbol identification and writing tasks, and (c) language tasks.

---

[2] Teachers should examine DISTAR to see what a highly systematic mathematics programs for beginning skills looks like.

During the first weeks of instruction, about 5 to 10 minutes might be spent on each area. When students can rote count to ten and can count objects, teachers can incorporate the equality based operations into the lessons. The Skill Hierarchy in Figure 3.1, along with the specific sequencing suggestions in later chapters, is useful in determining when to introduce new skills.

2. Lessons should be constructed in a manner likely to keep student attentiveness high. Do not spend too long on a drill task. Instead of a 10 minute drill on rote counting, two or three shorter exercises should be scattered throughout the lesson. Group sessions should begin with exercises that are relatively easy for the children. Arrange lessons so that difficult tasks are followed by relatively simple tasks. Figures 3.2 and 3.3 illustrate what daily lessons would look like at an early phase and late phase of the beginning stage.

Primary and Intermediate Grades

This section is for teachers working with primary and intermediate grade students. A general overview of the skills introduced in late first grade through sixth grade appears in the Skill Hierarchy in Figure 3.4. Note that there are 11 main areas of instruction: basic fact memorization, counting and place value skills, column addition and subtraction, column multiplication, column division, story problems, fractions, decimals and percent, measurement, geometry, and study skills. The arrows on the chart indicate the relationship among skill areas. Note that basic facts and place value are preskills for column operations which, in turn, are preskills for story problems. Likewise, fraction skills are preskills for decimal and percent. The interrelationship of skill areas is stressed to illustrate the need for a systematically coordinated approach to math instruction. When presenting skills from one area, the teacher must consider which preskills from other

Figure 3.2 Daily Lesson—Third and Fourth Week of Instruction

Teacher-directed Lesson

Oral Tasks
  Rote counting (two 3 minute sessions)
  Language skills (5 minutes)e.g., same number
  Numeral identification (two 3 minute sessions)

Worksheet Tasks
  Drawing lines for a numeral (3 minutes)
  Equality exercises (5-7 minutes)
  Numeral writing (3-5) minutes
  Tracing and copying new numerals (3-4 minutes)

Independent Worksheet

  Tracing and copying previously introduced numerals

Figure 3.3 Daily Lessons—Midway through Beginning Stage

Teacher-led Tasks

Oral Tasks
  Rote counting (3 minutes)
  Identifying teen numerals (3-4 minutes)
  Equation reading (3-4 minutes)
  Skip counting by tens (2-3 minutes)

Worksheet Exercises
  Supervised practice on subtraction problems (10 minutes)
  Writing teen numerals (3-4 minutes)

Independent Worksheet Exercises
  Addition problems—10 problems
  Writing a numeral for lines—4 examples
  Copying numerals—4-5 lines

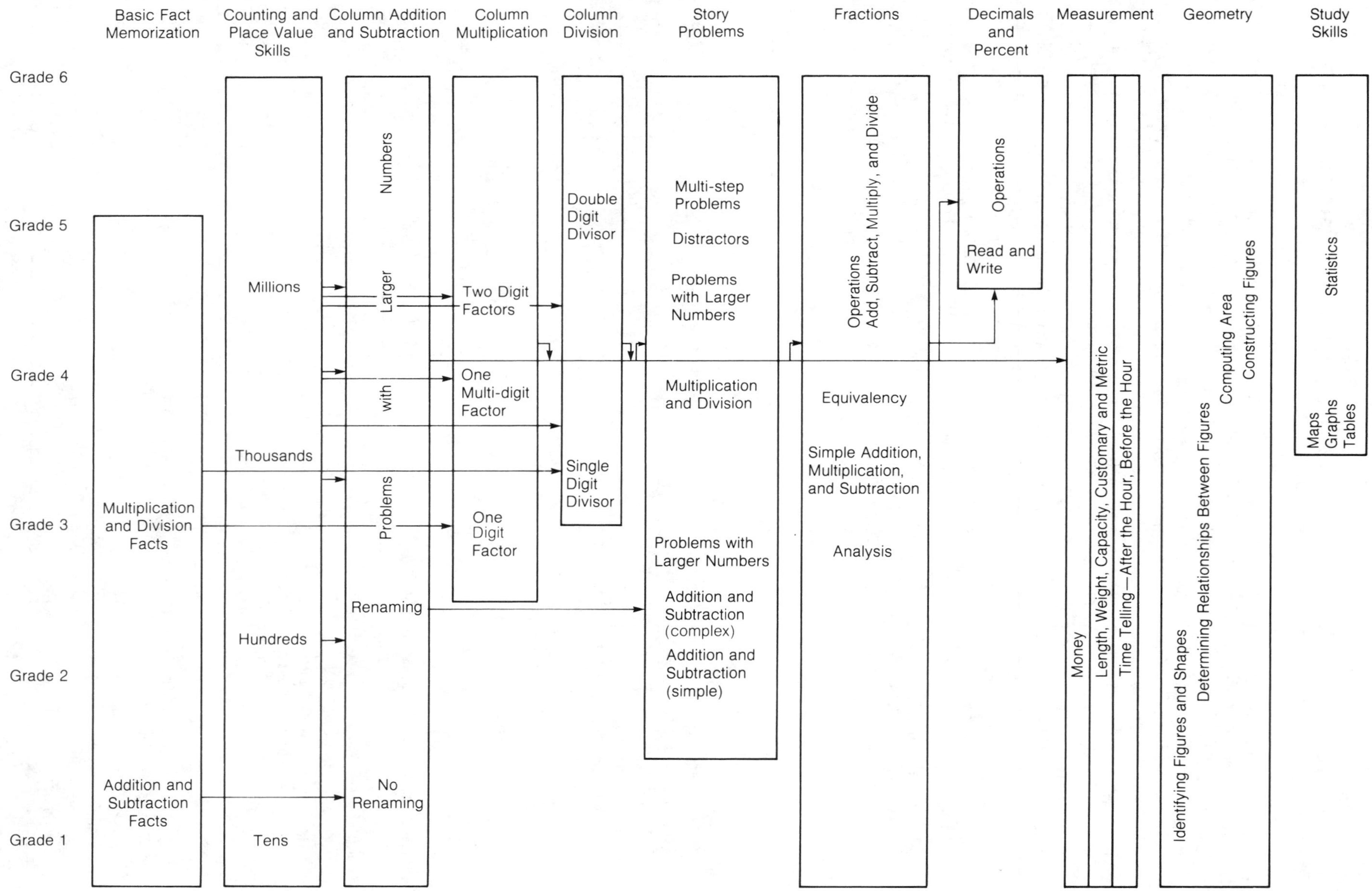

Figure 3.4 Skill Hierarchy for Elementary Mathematics Instruction

areas are relevant. A summary of the main areas of instruction in the primary and intermediate grades follows.

Basic Facts

Facts include (a) the 100 addition problems which can be formed by adding two single digit numbers and the 100 subtraction facts which are the corollaries of the addition facts and (b) the multiplication problems which can be formed by multiplying two single digit numbers and the division facts which are the corollaries of the multiplication facts. Mastery of basic facts is critical if students are to develop fluency in working problems. The negative attitudes many children have about math can be traced to not having mastered basic facts. Unfortunately, the need to provide students with the adequate practice to develop mastery of this critical preskill has not received significant emphasis either in teacher training textbooks or in the teacher's guides of commercial programs. Little mention is given in either source to the specifics of facilitating mastery of basic facts. An entire chapter (Chapter 7) of this text is devoted to basic facts. Incorporating daily fact memorization exercises is one of the most significant modifications teachers must make in supplementing the instruction provided in commercial programs. At least 10–15 minutes daily should be devoted to exercises which facilitate fact memorization until students master all basic facts.

Counting and Place Value Skills

These skills were first introduced in the beginning stage. Instruction in these critical component skills is continued throughout the intermediate grades. In second grade, students learn to count and read and write hundreds numerals. In third grade, thousands numbers are introduced.

Column Addition and Subtraction

These problems can be divided into two main areas: problems which require renaming (carrying or borrowing) and problems which do not require renaming. Problems which do not require renaming are introduced first. Problems involving renaming are introduced after students have learned the place value skills needed to identify and write multi-digit numerals. Initial renaming problems include two digit numbers. As students learn to read and write larger numbers, problems with these

numbers are presented. The bulk of renaming is taught in second and third grade.

Multiplication and Division

These skills are introduced in two stages, as in the case for addition and subtraction: (a) introducing the concept and (b) multi-digit operations. After the concept has been introduced with semi-concrete objects and students have learned 30–40 basic facts, multi-digit problems are introduced. Multi-digit multiplication problems can be divided into two groups. First are those problems in which one of the factors (numbers being multiplied) is a one digit number and the other a multi-digit number (e.g., 7 × 35). Second are problems in which both factors are multi-digit numbers (e.g., 37 × 46). Problems with a one digit factor are introduced in the third grade while problems with only multi-digit factors are introduced in fourth grade.

Multi-digit division problems can also be divided into two groups. First are problems in which the divisor is a one digit number (e.g., 342 ÷ 7). Second are problems in which the divisor is a two digit number (248 ÷ 37).

Story Problems

During the beginning stage, only relatively simple story problems that lend themselves to a phrase-by-phrase translation to an equation are presented. For example, Jack had 6 friends. He made 3 more friends. How many friends does he have now? This problem can be translated to the equation 6 + 3 = □. In second grade, a variety of addition and subtraction story problems which do not lend themselves to a phrase-by-phrase translation are introduced. For example, there are 7 girls, 2 play on the basketball team. How many do not? Students are taught to determine what type of operation is called for by determining whether or not the largest quantity referred to in the story is given. If the largest quantity referred to is given, the problem calls for subtraction: There are 7 children, 3 are boys. How many are girls? The largest quantity, children, is given. If the largest quantity is not given, the problem calls for addition: There are 7 boys and 3 girls. How many children? The largest quantity, children, is not given.

Multiplication and division problems are unique in that they deal with equal-sized groups. Multiplication story problems are introduced when students have mastered the various types of addition and subtraction problems and have learned some basic multiplication facts. Division problems are introduced when students can work multiplication, addition and subtraction problems accurately. As students learn to solve equations with larger numbers, these larger numbers are integrated into story problems. While a second grade problem might involve the numbers 25 and 34, a fifth grade story problem might involve the numbers 3,205 and 1,942. Story problems also become more difficult when distracting information is added and when more than one operation is required.

Story problems, as with basic facts, are quite often not given sufficient emphasis in commercial programs. Teacher's guides do not give specific suggestions to teachers on what to do if the students have difficulty. Also the number of problems included in the programs is often inadequate for lower-performing students to develop mastery. Teachers must be prepared to create their own units focusing on story problems. Chapter 12 discusses procedures for teaching story problems.

Fractions

Fractions are usually introduced in late first or second grade. Initially, fraction instruction focuses on analysis skills in which students are taught to differentiate between whole units and parts of a unit, what the numerator and denominator of a fraction signify, and how to read fractions. Simple addition and subtraction problems involving fractions with like denominators are usually introduced in third grade.

In fourth grade, after students have learned basic multiplication facts, equivalent fractions

$$\frac{2}{3} = \frac{4}{6}$$

and various types of conversions are presented:

$$3\frac{1}{4} = \frac{13}{4} \qquad 2\frac{1}{2} = \frac{5}{2}$$

The equivalent fraction skill and the conversion skill are component skills for more complex problems with fractions that have unlike denominators and for reducing fractions and multiplying and dividing fraction problems, which are all introduced during fourth and fifth grade.

Decimals

Decimals are in fact another form of expressing a particular type of fraction (i.e., fractions with a denominator of 10 or any multiple of 10: 100, 1,000,

etc.) and are introduced only after students have mastered basic fraction skills. Students are first taught to read and write decimal and mixed decimal numbers, then solve equations with decimals and mixed decimal numbers.

Measurement

Measurement skills discussed include the topics of money, time, length, weight, and capacity. Topics related to money include these:

1. Determining the value of a group of coins
2. Counting change
3. Knowing decimal notation for money
4. Learning consumer skills

Telling time is presented in three stages. First, students are taught a strategy for figuring out the time and expressing it as minutes after the hour. Second, after students have mastered minutes after the hour, they are taught alternate ways of expressing time as after the hour: using a colon (8:40), quarter past, half-past. Third, students are taught a strategy for expressing time as minutes before the hour.

The measurement skills related to length, weight, and capacity include these:

1. Learning units for measuring
2. Using instruments
3. Learning equivalencies between basic units
4. Converting quantities from one unit to another unit
5. Performing operations

Geometry

Geometry objectives center upon the following:

1. Identifying various figures
2. Determining relationships between figures
3. Computing area of a figure
4. Constructing figures using a compass and/or protractor

Instruction in geometry begins in first or second grade and continues through sixth grade.

Study Skills

An understanding of mathematics is often required to comprehend material from other content areas such as science, social studies, or health. Mathematics in content area material often appears in the form of graphs, charts, map reading skills, and statistics. Teaching procedures for all of these topics are usually introduced in third grade.

Calculators

The question of when to introduce the calculator is one which is sure to be debated vigorously over the next decade. When the calculator is introduced, teachers should be sure to provide clear models of its various functions. Although using a calculator is relatively simple, students are currently still expected to be able to compute. Until that expectation changes, teachers will need to continue teaching computation strategies.

Remedial Instruction

Remedial instruction refers to instruction for students in late first through sixth grade who are performing below grade level or who are progressing at a rate which, if continued, will result in their functioning below grade level.

General Guidelines

Here are relevant guidelines for establishing remedial programs:

1. Provide extra instruction
2. Start the extra instruction as soon as a deficit appears
3. Use well-trained personnel
4. Move students through the instructional program as rapidly as possible
5. Motivate the students to achieve
6. Coordinate special help and classroom activities

The more deficient a student is in mathematics, the greater the amount of instruction the student should receive. As a general guideline, we recommend a student receive an extra 15 to 30 minutes daily of direct instruction for each year the student is below grade level. Thus, a student 2 years below grade level might receive about 1 hour of instruction each day. A student performing several years below grade level will need an enormous amount of practice to catch up with his peers.

The sooner the remediation begins, the more likely it is that the student can be helped. Helping a second grader overcome a 1 year deficit is much easier than helping a fifth grader overcome a 3 year deficit. Younger students not only have less to make up but also tend to have better attitudes, because they have not failed for as long a time.

The more severe the student's deficit, the more careful the instruction must be. Until fairly recently, students in need of remedial help were often sent to volunteers or other untrained personnel. Unfortunately, remedial students, more so than other students, need the help of the most highly trained professionals, who can carefully and consistently identify and correct serious confusions. This is not to say that volunteers cannot be helpful. Volunteers can perform very useful services like drilling the students on math facts. However, they should not assume larger responsibilities unless they receive training and are monitored.

A student with serious skill deficits needs to progress through a program as quickly as possible. Since a remedial student is already behind, she must progress at a rate of more than 1 year for each year of instruction in order to reach grade level. If the student gains only 1 year for each instructional year, she will never reach grade level. To facilitate maximum student progress, the teacher must be very selective in determining how she uses her time. She should present activities which have a direct relationship to the student's skill deficits.

A second way to facilitate maximum student progress is to present two or more skills from unrelated areas concurrently. Instead of presenting one unit at a time (e.g., first addition, then fractions, then story problems, etc.), the teacher presents exercises from two unrelated skill areas at the same time. Problem-solving strategies from different skill areas can be taught concurrently as long as the strategies are not similar. For example, multiplication may be taught at the same time simple fractions are being taught. Likewise, time telling and story problems might be taught at the same time. Obviously more time than normal will have to be devoted to math instruction to allow for the concurrent introduction of units. This extra time is warranted when one considers the importance of mathematics not only in everyday life but also as a prerequisite for future success in school.

Motivation is critical to the success of any remedial effort. The more highly motivated a remedial student is, the greater the student's progress and success. Unmotivated students rarely receive the full benefit of increased instructional time, careful teaching, and a well-designed program. Yet remedial students are often unmotivated, and understandably so. Being in a failure situation every day with few signs of progress has definite effects on student self-image.

First and foremost in establishing motivation is providing a program in which students can succeed. This occurs when students are placed in a soundly constructed instructional program. After they are shown that they are succeeding, their attitudes and motivation will begin to change.

The second critical variable is giving students a goal to work toward. Sometimes it will involve a point system or contract stating that they will receive a certain grade, privilege, or prize for reaching a certain performance level. If a point system or contract is used, it must be carefully designed so that earning the grade or privilege is neither too hard nor too easy. The grade or privilege must be a functional reward, which means that the student will indeed work for it, and the student's daily successes must be clearly tied to his progress toward the grade or privilege. Page 9 includes references to several texts which provide in-depth discussions on establishing motivation.

The final consideration for remedial students is coordination of instruction. In most schools, specifically trained teachers are available to augment regular classroom instruction. The instruction provided by the classroom teacher and by the specialist must be carefully coordinated. The teacher and the specialist should both be teaching the student the same strategies. For example, it would be inappropriate for the classroom teacher to be teaching one multiplication algorithm, while the specialist was teaching another. Likewise, the amount and sequence of information being presented to the student should be carefully controlled. Conflicting approaches overload students with too much information and confuse and frustrate them. Also classroom teachers should not feel that their responsibility for teaching math is abrogated because a student is receiving instruction from a specialist outside the classroom. Lower-performing students generally need more practice to master skills than do average students. The specialist should be providing practice and instruction that supplements and does not replace the instruction provided by the regular classroom teacher. Finally, careful instruction must be continued after special help ceases. Balow (1965) found that while remedial instruction was effective, severe academic disabilities were not corrected by short-term intensive treatment, but need continual attention.

Commercial Programs for Remedial Students

The guidelines for selecting instructional programs for remedial students are basically the same as those specified on pages 17–22 for judging any instructional program. However, teachers should consider also the degree to which the program is geared to the interest level of the older student.

Unfortunately, no comprehensive program designed especially for intermediate remedial grade students is presently being distributed by major publishers; however, many specific skill programs are being distributed, for example, *Corrective Mathematics* by Carnine and Engelmann (1981).

Developing a Remedial Program

Our recommendation for teachers working with older students is to construct their own math curriculum by using a combination of specific skill programs and teacher-made units. The teacher would try to obtain instructionally sound specific skill programs or specific skill programs that require relatively little modification to be instructionally sound. As mentioned earlier, the adequacy of practice and review is the critical factor to consider in judging whether a program can be modified relatively easily. Teacher-made units would be constructed only when no suitable commercial material is available. Constructing worksheets is quite time-consuming, particularly for more advanced skills. Thus, if at all possible, we recommend using commercially prepared materials.

After obtaining these specific skill programs, the teachers for several grade levels would meet and develop an instructional sequence for their respective grade levels, deciding which problem types to introduce at particular grade levels. The Instructional Sequence and Assessment Charts at the beginning of Chapters 5–20 can aid teachers in identifying problem types. Remedial programs should initially focus on more essential skills.

After determining the skills to be introduced in each grade level, the teachers would develop a sequence for introducing the skills. Remember, a key to accelerating student progress is to introduce skills from nonrelated areas concurrently. Another factor to consider in developing a sequence is to begin the grade level sequence with numeration skills (counting and place value) since numeration skills are prerequisite for many mathematical operations.

Figure 3.5 shows a scope and sequence developed by several teachers in planning a remedial program for students functioning between late first and fifth grade levels. The sets (1, 2, 3, 4, . . .) represent periods of time, the length of which depend on how long it takes students to learn the new skills. The skill areas to be worked on in each set are specified. Next to each skill area designation is a code number representing the specific problem type. The code numbers correspond to the code numbers used in the Instructional Sequence and Assessment Charts at the beginning of the respective chapters in this text.

Figure 3.5 can be used by teachers working on a tutorial basis with individual students or small groups of students. The teacher would use a test-teach-test model. The teacher would test the student on the performance indicators specified for each problem type starting at the beginning of the sequence. Teaching would be done when the student's performance on a test indicates a skill deficit.

Basic Facts

One of the most critical areas to consider when planning a program for remedial students is basic facts. Many remedial students will not have memorized basic addition, subtraction, multiplication, and division facts. Some students will be able to figure out facts rather slowly while others will have much difficulty, making an unacceptably high number of errors. Priority must be placed first on developing accuracy in figuring out basic facts and later on facilitating memorization of the facts. Problem-solving strategy teaching must be coordinated with fact instruction. However, instruction on strategies should not be delayed until students have memo-

Figure 3.5 Remedial Sequence

Set	Skill Area	Problem Type	Description
1	Counting		Skip counting by 10s
	Counting		By 1s to 99
	story problems	1	Phrase by phrase
2	Place value		Numeral identification and writing through 99
	Addition	1	No renaming
	Subtraction	1	No renaming
3	Counting	2a	Counting by 1s to 999
	Addition	2a	Three single digit numbers
	Fractions	2a, b	Diagrams
4	Place value	2a, b, c, d	Reading and writing hundreds numbers
	Counting	2b	Skip counting by 2s
	Measurement	2a	Length
5	Place value	2e, f	Column alignment
	Addition	2b, c, d, e	Renaming
	Counting	2b	Skip counting by 5s
	Measurement	2b	Weight
6	Counting	2b	Skip counting by 9s
	Story problems	2a	Classification
	Fractions	2c	Reading fractions
7	Counting	2b	Skip counting by 25s
	Multiplication	2b	One digit factors
	Story problems	2b	Complex action
	Fractions	2d	More, less, equal to 1
8	Subtraction	2a	Renaming—tens numbers
	Counting	2b	Skip counting by 4s
	Story problems	2c	Comparison
	Measurement	2c	Capacity
9	Fractions	2e	Adding and subtracting
	Money	2b, c	Value of group of coins
	Multiplication	2c	Missing factor
10	Time telling	2a	Minutes after the hour
	Subtraction	2b	Hundreds numbers
	Counting	2b	Skip counting by 7s
	Story problems	2d	Three numbers

Figure 3.5 cont'd.

Set	Skill Area	Problem Type	Description
11	Fractions	2f	Multiplying
	Counting	3a	by 1s to 9,999
	Measurement	3d	Ruler: nearest 1/2 inch
12	Place value	3a, b, c, d	Reading and writing numbers through 9,999
	Addition	3a	Complex facts
	Counting	2b	Skip counting by 3s
	Time telling	2b	To the nearest minute
13	Place value	3e	Column alignment—thousands
	Addition	3b, c, d, e	Renaming
	Story problems	3a	Multiplication
	Counting	2b	Skip counting by 8s
14	Subtraction	3a, b	Renaming—complex
	Time telling	2c, d	With colon
15	Subtraction	3c, d	Renaming with zero
	Fractions	3a	Mixed numbers
	Counting	2b	Skip counting by 6s
16	Multiplication	3b, c, d	One multi-digit factor
	Story problems	3b	Multiplication
	Measurement	3e	Ruler: nearest 1/4
17	Division	3a, b, c	Single digit quotient
	Fractions	3b, c	Add and subtract mixed numbers
	Story problems	3c	Division
18	Story problems	3d, e	Larger number problems
	Money	3b	Decimal notation
	Subtraction	3e, f	Problems with thousands
19	Story problems	3f, g, h	Division
	Time telling	3a	Minutes before
	Study skills	3a, b, c	Graphs
20	Counting	4a	10,000-999,999
	Addition	4a	Complex addition facts—sum over 10
	Multiplication	4a, b, c	One digit factor times three digit factor
21	Symbol and place value	4a	Read and write 10,000-999,999
	Division	4a, b, c	Single digit division—two digit quotient
	Addition	4a	Complex addition facts—sum over 20
	Money	4a, b	Decimal notation
22	Addition	4b	Addition three two digit numbers—sum over 20
	Division	4d, e, f, g	Single digit divisor—multi-digit quotient
	Fractions	4a	Rewriting fractions as mixed numbers
23	Measurement	4a	Conversion—length
24	Measurement	4b	Ruler: nearest 1/8
	Fractions	4e	Story problems
25	Symbol and place value	4b	Reading and writing through 10 million
	Multiplication	4d	Two double digit factors
	Fractions	4f, g	Equivalent fractions
	Fractions	4h	Find lowest common multiple
26	Subtraction	4a, b, c, d, e	Problems with zeroes
	Division	4h	Rounding off to nearest ten
	Fraction	4i, j	Add fractions with unlike denominators—also compare

Figure 3.5 cont'd.

Set	Skill Area	Problem Type	Description
27	Addition	4c	Adding three to five multi-digit numbers
	Division	4i	Double digit divisor
	Fraction	4k	Story problems—add and subtract
28	Multiplication	4e	Two digit times three digit factor
	Division	4j	Double digit divisor—estimated quotient incorrect
	Fractions	4l	Factors
29	Measurement	4c	Adding and subtracting—renaming required
	Subtraction	4f	Six digit numbers
	Story problems	4b, c, d	Multi-step
30	Study skills	4a	Mean
	Money	4c, d, e	Purchasing
	Fractions	4m	Greatest common factor
	Measurement	4d	Area
31	Decimals	4a, b, c, d	Read and write: tenths and hundredths
	Measurement	4e	Story problems
	Fractions	4n	Reducing to lowest terms
32	Decimals	4e, f, g	Add and subtract
	Fractions	4p	Add, reduce, convert to mixed number
	Study skills	4b	Maps
33	Place value	5a	Reading and writing millions
	Subtraction	5a, b	Problems with zeroes
	Story problems	5a	Multi-step
34	Multiplication	5a, b	Three digit factors
	Story problems	5b	Multi-step
	Decimals	5a, b	Thousandths
35	Fractions	5a, b	Adding and subtracting
	Decimals	5c, d	Multiplying
	Study skills	5a, b, c	Complex graphs
36	Fractions	5c	Adding and subtracting three fractions
	Decimals	5e	Rounding off decimals
	Study skills	5d	Tables
37	Fractions	5d	Multiplying
	Decimals	5f, g	Dividing by whole numbers
	Story problems	5c	Multi-step
38	Decimals	5h	Rounding off
	Fractions	5e, f, g, h	Dividing
	Percent	5a	Convert % to decimal
39	Decimals	5i, j	Dividing
	Percent	5b	Multiplying
	Story problems	5d	Multi-step
40	Decimals	5k, l	Converting fractions
	Percent	5c	Story problems
41	Decimals	5m, n	Multiplying by 10 or 100
	Measurement	5a	Metric units
	Percent	5d	Converting decimal to percent
42	Decimals	5o, p	Dividing by decimal
	Decimals	5q	Converting decimal to fraction
	Measurement	5b	Metric conversions
	Percent	5e, f	Converting fraction to percent

rized all basic facts, since memorizing the facts may require months or years of practice. Our basic recommendation for teachers is to first work with students to develop accuracy in figuring out basic addition and subtraction facts. Then work on memorizing multiplication and division facts and finally on memorizing addition and subtraction facts.

Teachers will find that most remedial students use their fingers to count out addition and subtraction facts. The initial remediation will focus solely on ensuring that students accurately use an effective finger strategy (see pages 249–250 for more specifics). Most students will require no more than several weeks instruction before they become accurate in figuring basic addition and subtraction facts. During these first weeks, the teacher should also introduce various skip counting series to facilitate future multiplication fact memorization. After students have developed accuracy in figuring basic addition and subtraction facts, they should be started on memorization exercises with multiplication. When the students have memorized multiplication and division facts, the teacher goes back and presents memorization exercises for addition and subtraction facts. (Specifics for implementing basic fact programs can be found in Chapter 7.) The reason we recommend presenting memorization exercises on multiplication facts before addition facts is that while students can use their fingers to figure out addition and subtraction facts, they cannot do so for multiplication facts. Also, since knowledge of multiplication facts is a prerequisite skill for most advanced arithmetic (fraction reduction, decimals, percent, measurement, etc.),

the teacher who first works on multiplication facts will be able to present these advanced skills sooner.

Teachers should test students' knowledge of basic facts during the first week of school. We recommend administering a test including all 100 basic multiplication facts, and a test including all 100 basic addition facts. The facts are written on a worksheet. The students are instructed to work all the problems they can and raise their hands when they finish. The teacher uses a stop watch to time the students, recording the time it takes each student to finish the page. The timing is done to measure a student's relative fluency. This testing will help teachers make decisions in grouping students and planning the remedial program.

Daily Lessons

The daily lesson during second through sixth grade includes teacher-directed presentation, independent seatwork, and the workcheck. A sample lesson appears in Figure 3.6. Note the inclusion of exercises to teach skills from two unrelated areas, division and fractions. Also note the inclusion of the basic fact exercises. Remember basic fact memorization should be part of every daily lesson until the student has memorized all basic facts. Older students who do not know their basic facts should receive extra daily practice. Also note that the worksheet for independent seatwork includes a review of problem types mastered in previous lessons as well as intensive practice on recently introduced problem types, which students can solve accurately but need more practice to develop fluency.

Figure 3.6   Sample Lesson

Presentation

   5–10 minutes on division with two digit divisors, structured worksheet (4 problems)
   10–15 minutes on adding fractions with unlike denominators, structured board (3
         problems) and structured worksheet (3 problems)
   10–15 minutes on fact memorization.

Independent Seatwork

   Intensive practice on division problems (one digit divisors, with zeroes in the quotient—
      eight problems), measurement conversions (customary units—eight problems)
   Review of previously mastered material
   Addition and subtraction problems with renaming (4 problems)
   Multiplication problems—multi-digit factors (4 problems)
   Fraction analysis (2 problems)
   Numeral reading and writing (4 numbers)
   Story problems (4 problems)
   Equivalent fractions (4 problems)

Workcheck

PART TWO

Skills and Concepts

4 | Teaching Vocabulary and Language Skills

Vocabulary and language skill instruction may be divided into two areas: (a) the language of instruction and (b) mathematics-related vocabulary and language skills.

Language of Instruction

The language of instruction refers to the terms commonly used in directions given by teachers. For example, a teacher might say any of the following:

1. Find the counter under the last numeral.
2. Touch the small triangle in the first column.
3. Find the biggest number in the second row.

These directions assume that students understand the meaning of the words *counter, under, numeral, triangle, column, biggest, second,* and *row.* Unfortunately, some students enter school knowing few of these terms, and they may have difficulty following the teacher's direction and comprehending his explanations.

Describing procedures for teaching basic vocabulary and language skills such as prepositions, pronouns, attributes, etc., is beyond the scope of this book (see page 60 for a discussion of commercial programs that teach such skills). A screening test to spot beginning students whose language and vocabulary skills may require remediation has been developed.[1] This screening test should be administered early in the year. Students whose performance on the screening test indicates they have a limited knowledge of common terms should (a) be placed in a mathematics program in which the wording in teacher explanations is carefully controlled and (b) receive supplementary language instruction.

Math-related Vocabulary and Language Skills

Math-related vocabulary and language skills include the following:

1. Terms used to describe characteristics of objects (e.g., *square, oval*)
2. Terms used to describe relationships between objects (e.g., *parallel, similar, near*) and relationships between groups of objects (e.g., *equal, more/less*)
3. Terms used to describe numbers in an operation (e.g., *sum, addend, factor*) and the operations themselves (*add, compare*)

---

[1] *Basic Language Concepts Test* by Siegfried Engelmann, Dorothy Ross, and Virginia Bingham (Chicago: SRA, 1981).

4. Classification (e.g., There are 6 boys and 4 girls in Mr. Jones' class. How many students are in his class? Alice has 4 dogs and 3 cats. How many pets does she have?)

Most math textbooks address vocabulary issues only by listing important terms at the beginning or end of each chapter. However, Jackson and Phillips (1983) demonstrated that student math achievement increased when brief vocabulary-oriented instructional activities were integrated daily into mathematics curriculum.

Sequence of Instruction

Vocabulary terms that appear in formats to teach math skills should be taught prior to the introduction of the format. For example, in the equality rule—we must end with the same number on this side and the other side of the equal—the terms *end with*, *side*, *equal*, *same*, and *other* are used. The meanings of these terms should be taught prior to the introduction of the equality rule.

On the other hand, terms which label the numbers in an operation (e.g., *sum*, *divisor*, *numerator*, *denominator*) need not be taught until after that operation is presented. For example, the terms *difference*, *subtrahend*, and *minuend* would not be introduced when subtraction is initially taught. They would be taught in the late primary or intermediate grades after students had mastered most subtraction problem types.

Vocabulary Teaching Procedures

The procedures used to teach vocabulary are especially critical for teachers working with instructionally naive students. Teaching vocabulary to average and above average students is relatively easy because these students have a good understanding of language and already have a sizeable vocabulary. Young, instructionally naive students, on the other hand, often will not know many common words, will have difficulty repeating statements of more than four or five words, and often will be confused by demonstrations that are not absolutely clear.

Vocabulary can be taught orally in three ways: modeling only positive and negative examples, using synonyms, or giving definitions. Here is an example of modeling a positive example: The teacher holds a meter stick under a line on the chalkboard and says, "This line is 1 meter long." The teacher

then models a negative example, holding the meter stick under a different line on the board and saying, "This line is not 1 meter long." Modeling positive and negative examples is used mostly with 5- and 6-year olds, when verbal explanations of a new word would include words students do not understand. For example, when teaching "1 meter," the teacher would not say "A meter is 100 centimeters." The second procedure for vocabulary teaching, using synonyms, is used when a student knows a word(s) that can be used to explain the meaning of a new, unknown word. For example, a student knows the word *over* but does not know *above*. Instead of introducing *above* through modeling positive and negative examples, the teacher just tells the student that *above* means *over* and then tests the student on positive and negative examples to make sure he understands the synonym.

The third method for teaching new vocabulary, giving definitions, is used when students have adequate language to understand a definition and when the concept is too complicated to be explained through a synonym. The teacher constructs a definition by specifying a small class to which a new word belongs and then telling how the word differs from other members of the class. For example, a simple definition of *numerator* might be the top numeral in a fraction. After telling students the definition, the teacher presents positive and negative examples to test the students' understanding of the definition: The teacher presents fractions and points to the numerator asking, "Is this the numerator?"

Since definitions require knowledge of all the words in the definition, this vocabulary teaching method is used only after students have developed a basic vocabulary. Below is a more in-depth overview of these three vocabulary teaching procedures.

Teaching Vocabulary through Modeling Positive and Negative Examples

The basic procedure for teaching vocabulary by modeling involves three steps:

1. Modeling positive and negative examples of the new word
2. Testing the students on their mastery of the examples
3. Presenting examples of the new word along with examples of other previously taught words

Review should be cumulative. Newly introduced words should be reviewed heavily at first, appearing daily for at least three or four lessons and then less

Figure 4.1

STEP 1 Teacher models, presenting six to eight examples, half of which are positive examples and half, negative examples.

$\bigcirc\ ()\ \bigcirc\ \bigcirc\ \bigcirc\ \bigcirc\ \bigcirc$

"This is an oval." or "This is not an oval."

STEP 2 Teacher tests with yes-no question presenting positive and negative examples until the students make six consecutive correct responses.

"Is this an oval?"

STEP 3 Teacher tests by asking for names of various geometric forms which have been previously taught. The teacher presents examples until students make six consecutive correct responses. Teacher alternates between oval and other objects: oval, circle, oval, triangle, square, oval, circle, square, triangle, oval.

"You tell me square, triangle, oval, or circle."

---

frequently, every other day for a week or two, and intermittently thereafter. As is the case in introducing all skills, the rate at which vocabulary words are introduced is dependent on the students' mastery of previously introduced words. Figure 4.1 illustrates the use of modeling to teach the concept *oval*.

PRESENTATION When modeling, examples must be presented at a rapid enough rate to keep students' attention. The teacher should present the examples in a lively fashion, stressing key words: "This is an oval. This is not an oval." When testing, the teacher must present the task until students are able to respond correctly to a group of at least three positive and three negative examples (six in all). It is only after students can make consecutive correct responses to all the positive and negative examples that a teacher can tentatively conclude that the students understand the new word.

EXAMPLE SELECTION The most important aspect of teaching vocabulary through modeling is selecting a set of appropriate examples. A set of examples is appropriate only if it is capable of teaching the student the meaning the teacher intends to present. When a student fails to understand a word being taught through modeling, it is more often than not because of inappropriate examples.

A set of examples may be inappropriate because it causes students to learn an interpretation other than the one intended by the teacher; for example, a thick pen and a thick pencil are presented as examples of *thick*. Since both these objects are writing tools, some naive students might interpret *thick* as having something to do with writing rather than with size.

A set of examples may be inappropriate because it is too limited and does not give the student enough information to generalize to other instances of the word. When a baby first learns the word *dog*,

the baby may think the word refers solely to the dog in his house. Only through further experiences does the child learn to expand his definition of *dog* to a whole set of dogs, many of which are quite different in appearance. To provide the opportunity for the same kind of learning to take place in the classroom, a teacher must provide enough positive examples of a new word to enable the student to respond to a full range of positive examples. When presenting *oval*, the teacher should include ovals of different sizes and positions to ensure proper generalization.

Selecting three to six examples that show different types of positive examples is the first step in constructing a set of examples for use in modeling. If only equilateral triangles were presented to exemplify triangle, the student might think that only equilateral triangles are triangles. Therefore when presenting examples to teach a concept such as a triangle, the teacher might use this set of positive examples:

Students see that triangles can be of various sizes.

In addition to positive examples, an appropriate set of examples should also include negative examples. The purpose of the negative examples is to rule out incorrect generalizations. For each positive example, a negative example that is as similar as possible to the positive examples should be included in the set. The positive and negative examples will form a pair. Each pair of examples can be referred to as a minimally different pair. The purpose of using minimally different pairs is to focus student attention on the characteristics that determine whether or not an example is positive. The use of minimally different pairs is illustrated in the example below for teaching the triangle:

		This pair signifies that a triangle cannot have four sides
		This pair indicates that three sides must be straight
		This pair indicates that a triangle cannot have only two sides
		This pair shows that a triangle must have all three sides joined

Teaching Vocabulary with Synonyms

Teaching new vocabulary through synonyms is similar to the procedure of modeling examples, except that the teacher first equates a new word (*huge*) with a known word(s) (*very big*) rather than modeling examples. The teacher would give the synonym ("Here's a new word, *huge*. *Huge* means very big.") rather than modeling examples ("This is huge. This is not huge.") Next, just as in the second step of the modeling format, the teacher tests with a set of positive and negative examples of the new word and asks the students to say "huge" or "not huge." Third, the teacher provides practice in applying several recently taught synonyms: "Is this huge? Is this damp? Is this tiny? Find the one that is huge." The purpose of this review is to build retention. Without this drill, some students will not remember the synonyms for new words. The amount of practice the teacher provides depends on student performance. In general, a new word should appear daily for several consecutive lessons and then every other day for the next few days. Thereafter, the amount of review decreases.

PRESENTATION The format in Figure 4.2 illustrates synonym teaching with the word *subtract*.

The major steps include the teacher's presenting the synonym, testing positive and negative examples, and then reviewing the new word and previously introduced words.

EXAMPLE SELECTION The selection of synonyms must be done very carefully. Students must understand the meaning of the familiar word since it is intended to explain the new word. It would be inappropriate to use the term *circular* to explain *round* since most young students will not understand the meaning of *circular*. On the other hand, using the synonym *over* to explain *above* is reasonable since most students know what *over* means. Teachers can find potential words to use for synonyms by referring to a thesaurus.

Teaching Vocabulary with Definitions

The third procedure for teaching vocabulary is through definitions. In constructing definitions, teachers must be concerned with making them understandable to students rather than technically correct. For example, a square might be defined as a four-sided, closed figure in which each side is the same length. Although some might disapprove of this definition, it is adequate to teach the meaning of square to children *if positive and negative examples are also presented*. Definitions are also kept understandable by using only words students know.

Some sample definitions appear below. Note the effort to keep them as understandable as possible.

1. Denominator—bottom number in a fraction.
2. The sum is the answer when you add.
3. Equilateral triangle—triangle with equal sides.

Figure 4.2 Format for Synonym Teaching

TEACHER	STUDENTS
1. State the new word and the equivalent familiar word and then test. "HERE IS A NEW WORD. SUBTRACT. SUBTRACT MEANS MINUS. WHAT DOES SUBTRACT MEAN?"	"Minus"
2. Present positive and negative examples until the students make six consecutive correct responses. Examples are not repeated in the same order. Write 4 + 2 on the board. "DO WE SUBTRACT IN IN THIS PROBLEM?" Pause. Repeat step 2 with 8 - 3, 5 + 5, 6 - 2, 4 - 1, 4 + 1.	"No"
3. Review new word and other words until students answer all questions correctly. "WHAT DOES ADD TELL US TO DO?" "WHAT DOES SUBTRACT TELL US TO DO?"	"Plus" "Minus"

Figure 4.3 Format for Teaching Vocabulary with Definitions

TEACHER	STUDENTS
1. State the new word and its definition and have students say definition. "A SUM IS THE ANSWER WHEN YOU ADD. WHAT IS THE SUM?" Signal.	"The answer when you add."
2. Present positive and negative examples. Write 4 - 1 = 3 and point to 3. "IS 3 A SUM?" "HOW DO YOU KNOW?" Write 2 + 1 = 3 and point to 3. "IS THIS A SUM?" "HOW DO YOU KNOW?" Continue presenting examples until the students answer six consecutive questions correctly. (5 − 1, 9 + 2, etc.)	"No" "We aren't adding." "Yes" "It is the answer when you add."
3. Review word previously introduced. "WHAT IS THE DIFFERENCE OF 5 AND 2?" Pause, signal. "WHAT IS THE SUM OF 5 AND 2?" Pause, signal.	"3" "7"

Examples used to teach vocabulary by definitions must be carefully controlled. Just as in modeling, both positive and negative examples should be used, including minimally different instances. Figure 4.3 illustrates definition teaching with the word *sum*.

Equality

The addition and subtraction strategy problems presented to beginning level kindergarten or first grade students should be based on the equality principle, which can be introduced once students can count a group of 10 objects.

Research has shown that the context in which the equality concept is taught influences whether elementary children understand the relational nature of the term "equals" (Baroody and Ginsburg, 1983). Many people have attributed children's difficulty with this concept to maturational or developmental limitations. However, Baroody & Ginsburg demonstrated that if equality is introduced first in a context other than addition (e.g., 4 = 4; 6 ≠ 2), students experience less difficulty understanding that equals means "the same as."

Equality can be taught by presenting a functional definition and a series of positive and negative examples. The definition is functional in that it describes a condition that must be met for the equality principle to apply. *We must end with the same number on this side and the other side of the equal sign.* Figure 4.4 includes a format for introducing equality. This format should be presented during the beginning stage before addition is introduced. The format includes three parts. In Part A, the teacher

introduces the equal sign and equality rule. In Part B, the teacher demonstrates instances when the equality rule applies and does not apply. Diagrams like the one below in which lines are written inside two adjoining circles are written on the board.

The teacher leads the students in determining whether or not an equal sign would be drawn between the circles. Part C is a less structured worksheet exercise similar to Part B. Note that in Parts B and C students are asked to say the rule. Saying the rule may be quite difficult for lower-performing students. To ease this difficulty, the teacher might first model, lead, and test, saying just the first half of the rule: *We must end with the same number.* Lower performers may need 5 to 10 corrected repetitions. After several days, the teacher would provide practice in saying the last half of the rule and then the entire rule.

More-Less

The terms *more* and *less* are important because of their frequent use in teacher directions and in several types of application problems: e.g., Jill has 18 apples. Jim has 13 apples more. How many apples does Jim have? Instructionally naive students may not have an accurate understanding of these important terms. Teachers can check students' understanding of these terms by asking students which is more: 7 or 3, 5 or 9, 2 or 6. Students not able to respond correctly should be taught the meaning of *more* and *less*. More-less would be taught several weeks prior to the introduction of story problems.

The term *more* may be taught by equating it with the term *bigger than*. The teacher would write two piles on the board, one pile with five balls, one with two balls. All the balls in each pile would be the same size.

The teacher has the students count the number of balls in each pile and write the appropriate numeral under each pile. The teacher then asks which pile is bigger and models the statement, "Five is bigger than two." The term *more* is then introduced as a synonym for *bigger*. The teacher says five is bigger than two, so five is more than two.

(This exercise is an example of a synonym which is not technically correct. *Bigger* obviously could not be used to describe the relative height of piles of different sized objects. However, the teacher need not go into a long explanation about the multiple meanings of *bigger*.) The term *less* could be introduced several weeks later.

A similar procedure could be used to teach *less*. *Not bigger* is introduced and then *less* is taught as a synonym for *not bigger*. The introduction for *not bigger* starts out the same as the introduction for *bigger*. Rather than asking which pile is bigger though, the teacher asks, "Is this pile bigger?" about each pile. For the pile that is not bigger, the teacher says, "Yes, this pile is not bigger. Two is less than five." After several models, the teacher can present number pairs and ask, "Which is less, nine or two?" Once students know *more* and *less*, a new kind of task is possible. "Is six more or less than nine?"

Figure 4.4   Format for Equality Introduction

Days	Part A Structured Board Presentation Problems	Part B Less Structured Board Problems	Part C Less Structured Worksheet Problems	Part D Supervised Practice	Part E Independent Worksheet Problems
1-2	1	4			
3-6		4	6		
6-7			2	4	
8-9			1		6

PART A: Structured Board Presentation

TEACHER   **STUDENTS**

Write on board: (| | | | |)   =   (| | | | |)

1. Point to equal sign. "THIS IS AN EQUAL SIGN. WHAT IS THIS?"   "Equal"

2. "HERE'S A RULE: WE MUST END WITH THE SAME NUMBER ON THIS SIDE (point to left side of equal) AND ON THE OTHER SIDE OF THE EQUAL."

3. Point to left side. "LET'S SEE IF WE END WITH THE SAME NUMBER ON THIS SIDE AND ON THE OTHER SIDE."

4. Point to left side. "COUNT THE LINES ON THIS SIDE AS I TOUCH THEM." Point to each line as students count.   "1, 2, 3, 4, 5"

5. "HOW MANY DID WE END WITH ON THIS SIDE?"   "5"

6. "SO WE MUST END WITH 5 ON THE OTHER SIDE." Point to right side.

7. "LET'S COUNT THE LINES." Point as students count.   "1, 2, 3, 4, 5"
   "DID WE END WITH 5?"   "Yes"
   "SO THE SIDES ARE EQUAL. WE ENDED WITH THE SAME NUMBER ON THIS SIDE AND THE OTHER SIDE."

Figure 4.4 cont'd

PART B: Less Structured Board Presentation

TEACHER   **STUDENTS**

Write on board: (| | | |)   (| |)

1. "LISTEN TO THE EQUAL RULE: WE MUST END WITH
   THE SAME NUMBER ON THIS SIDE AND ON THE OTHER
   SIDE OF THE EQUAL. SAY THE EQUAL RULE."
   Repeat rule with students until they can say it without
   assistance.

2. "LET'S SEE IF THE SIDES ARE EQUAL."

3. Point to left side. "HOW MANY DO WE END WITH
   ON THIS SIDE?" Pause, signal.   "4"

4. Point to right side. "HOW MANY DO WE END WITH ON
   THIS SIDE?" Pause, signal.   "2"

5. "DO WE END WITH THE SAME NUMBER ON THIS SIDE
   (Point to right side.) AND THE OTHER SIDE (Point to left
   side.)?"   "No"

6. "ARE THE SIDES EQUAL?"   "No"

7. "THE SIDES ARE NOT EQUAL, SO I DON'T WRITE AN
   EQUAL SIGN."

   Repeat 1-7 with several examples, half equal and half
   unequal. Give individual turns to several students.

PART C: Less Structured Worksheet

Give students worksheet with these problems:

a. (| | | |) (| |)   d. (| | |) (| |)

b. (| | |) (| | |)   e. (| | |) (| | | |)

c. (| |) (| | | |)   f. (|) (|)

1. "TOUCH PROBLEM a."

2. "SAY THE EQUAL RULE."   "We must end with the same
                                                  number on this side and the other
                                                  side of the equal."

3. "COUNT AND SEE IF THE SIDES ARE EQUAL." Pause. "ARE
   THE SIDES EQUAL?"   "No"

   TO CORRECT: Point to left side. "COUNT THESE LINES.
               TELL ME HOW MANY YOU END WITH." Point to
               right side. "COUNT THESE LINES. TELL ME
               HOW MANY YOU END WITH. DID YOU END
               WITH THE SAME NUMBER ON THIS SIDE AND
               THE OTHER SIDE?"

4. "DO YOU WRITE IN AN EQUAL?"   "No"

5. If answer to 3 is yes, "WRITE THE EQUAL."
   Repeat steps 1-5 with remaining problems.

Commercial Programs

Most basal math programs provide for teaching critical vocabulary and language skills. Unfortunately, the procedures for teaching these skills and the practice and review provided are usually inadequate for instructionally naive students. Programs for beginning students are particularly weak. For example, in the kindergarten level of *Holt School Mathematics* (1985), only one lesson is devoted to teaching the preposition *over*. The initial teaching activity suggested in the teacher's manual directs the teacher to:

B. To recognize over (above) and under (below)

4. Play "Where is it?" Have the children who are playing the game sit in chairs and close their eyes. One child is chosen to be "It" and to approach each child in turn from the back. "It" holds a crayon either over the child or under the chair and asks, "Where is it?" The seated child guesses where (over or under). If correct, this child becomes "It" and the other sits in the chair.

5. Discuss the position of objects in the classroom; for example, the bookcase is under the picture frame, the clock is over the cabinet, the lights are over their heads, and the floor is under their feet.

6. Use a long piece of yarn to divide the bulletin board in half horizontally. Direct the children to draw pictures to show over and under; for example, an umbrella over a person or a dog under a chair. Instruct the children drawing "over" pictures to color the thing that is over, red. Tell the children drawing "under" pictures to color the thing that is under, blue. Display the "over" pictures above the yarn and the "under" pictures below it.

Such an exercise might be fine for a student who already understands the concept *over*. It will not teach the concept to a more naive student.

For instructionally naive students to succeed in math, we recommend using a vocabulary or language program to supplement the instruction in most commercial math programs. Ideally, the language instruction should not take place during the time allocated for math instruction. We recommend 20–30 minutes' daily language instruction for instructionally naive students.

Unfortunately, space is not available in this book to provide detailed guidelines on how to design the language instruction. Since a teacher's time is so valuable, we suggest using a commercial language program to provide this instruction. When selecting a language program, teachers should spend most of their time examining how the programs teach skills, rather than determining what skills are taught, since most programs cover basically the same content. Teachers should look at individual lessons, noting the formats and examples used. The wording in the formats should be simple and direct. The examples, as mentioned earlier, are critical. Example selection is the key to teaching vocabulary effectively. Note if positive and negative examples are provided. If the program does not provide adequate examples, it will probably not be effective with instructionally naive students.

After looking at the way in which several tasks are constructed, teachers should look at 5 to 10 consecutive lessons, noting how many times each new skill or word is reviewed. The purpose is to determine the adequacy of initial practice and review. If a new skill or word is not reviewed, many students will not learn it. Programs with inadequate review are difficult to modify.

An example of an effectively constructed program designed to teach basic vocabulary and language skills is the *DISTAR Language Series*. The program begins by teaching simple vocabulary (e.g., words like *big*, *red*, *in*, *on*) and expressive language tasks (e.g., teaching students to say statements like "The ball is not big") and proceeds gradually, eventually teaching complex reasoning and inference skills. *DISTAR* is unique in the careful attention given to systematic review and practice.

Vocabulary teaching in later grades in most commercial programs is characterized also by inadequate practice and review. Therefore teachers must be prepared to significantly supplement the number of vocabulary exercises.

5 | Counting

Terms and Concepts

Set A collection of concrete or abstract objects.

Cardinal Number What people usually speak of as a number. The cardinal number of a set is the number that identifies the number of elements or members of a set.

Numeral The symbol representing a cardinal number.

Rote Counting Refers to the child's ability to say number names in sequence but does not include object counting, the ability to say one number for each object.

Rational Counting Counting to determine the cardinal number of a set, i.e., object counting; sometimes called one-to-one correspondence.

Ordinal Numbers Numbers associated with the notion of position, e.g., first, second, third.

Manipulatives Concrete objects that students can hold or handle.

Skip Counting Refers to saying every nth number in the counting series: e.g., in skip counting by 2s, students say every second number: 2, 4, 6, 8; for 8s, every eighth number: 8, 16, 24.

Skill Hierarchy

Counting skills are not only important in themselves, but are also important prerequisite skills for many problem-solving strategies. The skill hierarchy chart in Figure 5.1 lists the major counting skills: rote counting, rational counting, counting from a number, skip counting, and ordinal counting.

Rote counting refers to the ability to say number names in sequence (e.g., 1, 2, 3, 4, 5, 6, etc.). During first grade, students are taught to count up to 99; in second grade, through 999; in third grade, in the thousands. Rote counting requires a great deal of practice.

Rational counting refers to the act of coordinating counting with the touching of objects to determine the quantity of a particular set. Rote counting is a prerequisite skill for rational counting. Students should be able to say numbers in sequence before they are expected to coordinate saying numbers with touching objects. Thus, we recommend that students be able to rote count to 10 before rational counting is introduced. The initial rational counting exercises involve counting a group

Figure 5.1 Skill Hierarchy

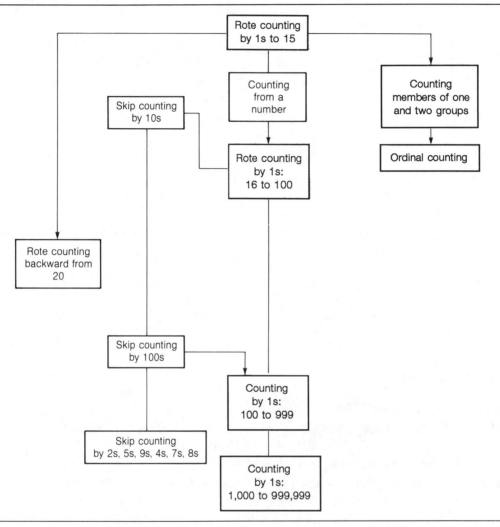

of objects. Later exercises involve counting two groups of objects. This latter counting skill is a prerequisite skill for early addition strategies.

Counting from a number is also a component skill of addition. In counting-from-a-number tasks, students begin with a number other than 1, e.g., begin with 6 and then count 7, 8, 9. In an addition problem like 6 + 3, students would say 6 for a few seconds and then count markers for the second addend: *sssiiixxx*, 7, 8, 9.

Skip counting refers to counting in which the students say multiples of a base number, e.g., when counting by 5s students say 5, 10, 15, 20, 25, 30, etc. The purpose of teaching skip counting by 10s is to facilitate teaching rote counting to higher numbers. From skip counting, students learn that 40 follows 30; therefore, they more easily learn to say 40 after 39. Similarly, they learn to say 50 after 49, 60 after 59, etc.

Skip counting by multiples of 10 (10, 20, 30, 40, 50, 60, 70, 80, 90) is taught after students can rote count to 30. Skip counting by 2s and 5s is taught later in first grade. Other skip counting series are taught in second and third grade, Learning the skip counting series in early grades also facilitates learning basic multiplication facts. Skip counting by 2s three times yields 6; 3 × 2 also yields 6.

Ordinal counting (counting associated with position, as in first, second, third, etc.) is introduced when the students have mastered rational counting. Ordinal counting is taught because of the common use of ordinal numbers in teacher directions, e.g., "Touch the third problem."

Note that counting instruction forms a major component of first grade instruction and should be continued in second and third grades. The Instructional Sequence and Assessment Chart for counting skills appears in Figure 5.2.

Figure 5.2 Instructional Sequence and Assessment Chart

Grade Level	Problem Type	Performance Indicator
K-1	Counting by 1s beginning at 1; counting through 20	Verbal test: teacher asks students to count to 20
K-1	Counting a group of objects	Teacher writes four lines, asks how many lines. Repeat with seven lines, five lines.
K-1	Counting two groups of objects	Teacher writes ||||| |||| and asks how many lines all together?
K-1	Counting by 1s, beginning at 1, counting through 30	Verbal test: teacher asks students to count to 30.
K-1	Ordinal counting first through tenth	Verbal test: teacher draws 10 lines on board, asks students to touch third line and seventh line.
K-1	Skip counting by 10s 10–100	Verbal test: teacher asks students to count by 10 to 100.
K-1	Counting backward from 10 to zero	Verbal test: teacher asks students to count backward from 10 to zero.
K-1	Counting by 1s from 1 through 100	Written test: write the number which comes next: 26, _____ , _____ , 29, _____ 46, _____ , _____ , 49, _____
K-1	Skip counting by 2, 5	Fill in the missing numerals: 2, 4, 6, __ __ __ __ __ __ __ 5, 10, 15 __ __ __ __ __ __ __
2a	Counting by 1s 100 to 999	Write the numeral which comes next: 349_____ 299_____ 599_____ 699_____ 499_____ 704_____ 889_____ 509_____
2b	Skip counting	Fill in the missing numerals: 9 18 27 __ __ __ __ __ __ __ 4 8 12 __ __ __ __ __ __ __ 7 14 21 __ __ __ __ __ __ __ 3 6 9 __ __ __ __ __ __ __ 8 16 24 __ __ __ __ __ __ 6 12 18 __ __ __ __ __ __ 100 200 300 __ __ __ __ __ __
3a	Counting by 1s 1,000 to 9,999	Write the numeral which comes next: 3,101_____ 2,529_____ 5,499_____ 7,308_____ 3,999_____ 7,999_____
4a	Counting by 1s 10,000 to 999,999	Write the numeral which comes next: (Similar to above)

Introducing the Concept

The goal of counting is for students to be able to count objects and events in the world around them. This means that students must become proficient in working with manipulatives.

The teaching procedures for the major counting skills appear in this section. The skills are listed in their relative order of introduction. Rote counting by 1s to 30 is discussed first. Rational counting is discussed next. Rational counting would be introduced when students can rote count to about 10. Thereafter, daily lessons would include both rote and rational counting exercises. After students learn to count one group of objects, they count two groups of objects and determine the total quantity. Next, procedures for teaching students to count from different numbers, to ordinal count, to rote count between 30 to 100, to rote count between 100 and 999, and to skip count are discussed.

Although the ultimate goal is for students to count objects, very early teaching is most efficient with pictures of objects. Teachers are better able to monitor student performance during group instruction if the students are touching and counting pictures. As soon as they are proficient in object counting skills, students should apply their skills to different types of manipulatives in many different settings. In contrast, handing out blocks to each child and ensuring that students handle them appropriately takes much more time. Many low-performing students will learn to count manipulatives more quickly by first receiving focused instruction on counting pictures of manipulatives.

Rote Counting by 1s to 30

On the first day of instruction, the teacher tests the students to determine how high they can rote count without error. The teacher tests each student individually simply by telling the child to count as high as he can. The teacher records the highest number each student counts. With students who cannot count beyond 5, the teacher begins instruction with a task in which she models, leads, and tests on counting to 5. A format for introducing counting appears in Figure 5.3. For students who can count to 5 or beyond, the teacher concentrates on teaching students to respond as a group and does not introduce new numbers. The teacher provides practice in teaching students to count at a lively pace. She uses a model-lead-test presentation, first modeling how fast she wants the students to count. Counting at a lively pace helps keep students attentive and makes remembering the number sequence easier. Initially, the teacher should establish a counting speed that is slightly faster than one number per second. In future lessons as the students become more proficient, rate should be increased to two numbers each second and a half.

Counting at a lively pace will be difficult for lower performers and will require lots of practice. Some students may need 15 to 20 trials before being able to say a new part of the counting

Figure 5.3   Format for Introducing Rote Counting (Numbers 1-12)

TEACHER	STUDENTS
1. "I'M GOING TO COUNT AND END WITH 5. WHAT AM I GOING TO END WITH?"	"5"
"MY TURN." Pause. "ONE, TWO, THREE, FOUR, FIVE. I COUNTED AND ENDED WITH 5."	
2. "NOW YOU'RE GOING TO COUNT WITH ME. WE'RE GOING TO END WITH 5. WHAT ARE WE GOING TO END WITH?"	"5"
"GET READY COUNT: ONE, TWO, THREE, FOUR, FIVE."	"1, 2, 3, 4, 5"
Repeat leading students until they appear able to respond on their own. Before each repetition say, "AGAIN, GET READY. COUNT." Saying these words is important since it gives the students an instant to catch their breath and prepares them to repeat the sequence.	
3. "ALL BY YOURSELVES YOU'RE GOING TO COUNT AND END WITH 5. WHAT ARE YOU GOING TO END WITH?"	"5"
"GET READY, COUNT."	"1, 2, 3, 4, 5"
"WHAT DID YOU END WITH?"	"5"
4. Repeat step 3 several times then call on individuals.	
5. Delayed test: Later in the lesson, repeat steps 3 and 4.	

sequence correctly. If teachers provide adequate repetition during the first weeks of instruction, they will find that they save time in later weeks.

When students can count familiar numbers at a lively pace, the teacher introduces new numbers in the counting sequence. The performance of the group determines which new numbers are introduced. The teacher notes the lowest number correctly counted to by any members of the group and adds the next two or three numbers in the counting sequence. If a student counts to 11 on the pretest, the new part would be 11, 12, 13 (the last number said correctly on the pretest, 11, and the next two numbers, 12 and 13). The format for introducing new numbers in the counting sequence appears in Figure 5.4. The teacher first models counting from 1 to 13, then models just the new part, 11, 12, 13 (see step 1 in Figure 5.4). In step 2, the teacher leads the students in saying the new part. When introducing new numbers, during both the model and lead (steps 1 and 2), the teacher should emphasize the new numbers by saying them in a loud voice. A loud voice is used so that students are always hearing a correct answer. When the students appear able to say the new part by themselves, the teacher tests (step 3), then has them say the entire counting series from 1 through the new part (step 4). The students should repeat the counting sequence until they say it correctly several times in a row. Providing sufficient practice for students to count correctly several times is important to facilitate retention. In

step 5, individual students count by themselves. Step 6 is the delayed test, to help the students remember the new numbers.

The teacher presents tests to several students individually at the beginning of the next day's lesson to determine whether new numbers can be introduced. If the students count correctly, the teacher introduces several new numbers. If the students make errors, the teacher repeats the format with the previously introduced numbers.

When presenting a counting task, the teacher must be quite careful not to give the students inappropriate cues. For example, some teachers have a tendency to count quietly when students are supposed to be counting alone (steps 4 and 5). Sometimes teachers just move their lips. This movement cues the students on the next number to say and precludes them from initiating their own responses. If teachers find a number of students who have no trouble counting in groups but cannot perform the task on an individual test, it is a sign that the teacher might be providing "extra help" during group instruction.

Teachers must also be careful in making corrections. If students fail to stop at the appropriate number, the teacher models the correct response emphasizing the number ended with. "I am going to count and end with 6—*end with 6*: "1, 2, 3, 4, 5, 6. I counted and *ended with 6*." If students leave out a number (counting 1, 2, 3, 4, 6) they should be stopped immediately and the teacher should model

Figure 5.4 Format for Introducing New Numbers

TEACHER	STUDENTS
1. Model. "I'M GOING TO COUNT AND END UP WITH 13. WHAT AM I GOING TO END UP WITH?" "YES, 13. LISTEN. 12345678910 11 12 13." (Quickly count to 10 and then emphasize 11, 12, 13.) "LISTEN TO THE NEW PART: 11 12 13."	"13"
2. Lead. "WHEN I DROP MY HAND, SAY THE NEW PART WITH ME. TEEEEENNNN." Drop hand and respond with students. "11 12 13. AGAIN TEEEEENNNN." Drop hand. "11 12 13." This step is repeated until students respond correctly with the teacher several times in a row.	"11, 12, 13"
3. Test. "SAY THE NEW PART ALL BY YOURSELVES: TEEENN." Signal. TO CORRECT: Return to step 2.	"11, 12, 13"
4. Test on whole sequence. "NOW YOU'RE GOING TO COUNT AND END UP WITH 13. WHAT NUMBER ARE YOU GOING TO END UP WITH?" "STARTING AT 1. GET READY, COUNT."	"13" "1, 2, 3, 4, 5, 6, 7, 8, 9, 10, 11, 12, 13"
5. Call on individuals for step 4.	

the "hard part" by saying four numbers, beginning two numbers before the missed number (3, 4, 5, 6). Next the teacher leads the students on the hard part, tests them on the hard part, then has them begin counting again from 1.

The teacher should be quite careful when making this correction. If a counting error is corrected inappropriately, students may become quite confused. The mistake teachers should avoid is saying the skipped number after the student has made the error. For example, the student says "1, 2, 3, 4, 6," and the teacher says "5." What the student hears is "1, 2, 3, 4, 6, 5." The teacher can avoid this mistake by saying "stop" when a student makes an error and then modeling the whole hard part. The teacher should repeat a rote counting exercise until students can respond correctly to the entire series three times in a row. Sometimes students will make errors several times before responding correctly. If the teacher does not provide more practice on responding correctly, students are less likely to remember the correct sequence the next day.

Mastering rote counting will require lots of practice for lower-performing students. One way to prevent students from becoming frustrated while practicing counting is to spend just 2 to 3 minutes on rote counting tasks at any one time but present counting tasks several times during a lesson. This distributed practice is better than spending 10 to 15

minutes on counting all at once, because when a counting task is too grueling, students will stop trying and just respond randomly until the task is over. Also, counting practice should not be restricted to the instructional time allotted for arithmetic. The teacher can have students practice counting when they are lining up for recess, just before they go to lunch, during opening exercises in the morning, or during the last 5 minutes of class. These extra few minutes of practice during the day will be reflected through increased retention of newly taught numbers. Finally, the teacher should treat counting as a fun exercise. One way this can be done is to incorporate game-like activities into counting exercises. For example, having students count one time with their hands on their knees, the next time with hands on their heads, etc.

Rational Counting: One Group

Rational counting requires coordinating touching objects one at a time, as each is counted, and finally indicating the number for the group. Remember, the ultimate goal is for students to count manipulatives. Early instruction is done with pictures because it is more efficient; less time is consumed. The intent is to establish counting skills as quickly as possible and then have the students apply them to manipulatives throughout each day. The preskill for rational

Figure 5.5 Format for Rational Counting

PART A: Structured Board—Teacher Points and Students Count

TEACHER	STUDENTS
Draw four lines on the board.	
1. "MY TURN. EVERY TIME I TOUCH A LINE, I COUNT. WATCH." Touch lines at 1 second intervals. "1, 2, 3, 4. WHAT NUMBER DID I END WITH?" Repeat step 1 with seven lines.	"4"
2. Draw six lines on the board. "EVERY TIME I TOUCH A LINE YOU COUNT." Point to left of line. "GET READY." Touch lines from left to right at 1 second intervals as students count.	"1, 2, 3, 4, 5, 6"
TO CORRECT: If students make counting errors, count with them. Repeat task until students can respond correctly without assistance. If students count before you touch a line, tell them "WATCH MY FINGER. WHEN I TOUCH A LINE, YOU COUNT."	
3. "WHAT NUMBER DID WE END WITH?"	"6"
4. "SO, HOW MANY LINES ARE THERE?"	"6"
5. Repeat steps 2-4 with three lines, then seven lines. Give individual turns to several students.	

Figure 5.5 cont'd

PART B: Structured Worksheet

Sample worksheet items:

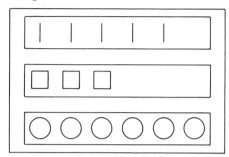

1. Model. Hold up a worksheet, point to a group of objects and say "WE'RE GOING TO COUNT ALL THE OBJECTS. WATCH ME COUNT." Touch objects from left to right and count "1 2 3 4 5. WATCH ME COUNT AGAIN." Touch objects from right to left and count "1 2 3 4 5."

2. Lead. "EVERYONE, HOLD YOUR FINGER OVER THE FIRST PICTURE." Check to see that all students are pointing to but not touching the appropriate picture. "EACH TIME I CLAP, YOU TOUCH AN OBJECT AND SAY THE NUMBER. GET READY." Clap one time per second. Count with students while monitoring their touching.   "1 2 3 4 5"

3. Test. "ALL BY YOURSELVES. YOU'RE GOING TO COUNT THE PICTURES. HOLD YOUR FINGER OVER THE FIRST PICTURE." (Check) "GET READY." Clap one time per second.   "1 2 3 4 5" "HOW MANY LINES ARE THERE?"

4. Repeat steps 2 and 3 with other examples. Give individual turns to several students.

counting is rote counting. The initial exercises in rational counting can begin when the students can rote count to 10. Initially, rational counting involves coordination of the action of touching an object and saying a number in the counting sequence. This coordinated action is often referred to as one-to-one correspondence. The format (Figure 5.5) has two parts. In Part A, the teacher touches lines as the students count and then asks what number they ended with. The teacher must use very clear signals when touching the lines. In Part B, the students count illustrations of objects on their worksheet. The objects in the illustrations in Part B should be placed about a half-inch from each other so that the students won't become confused about which object they are touching. Note that the students are to begin the task by pointing at, not touching, the first object. The teacher signals by saying "Get Ready," pausing, and then clapping. If the students are already touching the first object, they might touch the second object when they hear the clap. The teacher

claps at about 1 to 1 1/2 second intervals. The teacher should not go too fast as too quick a rate may result in coordination errors. The cadence should be kept very predictable so that students do not make unnecessary errors.

Monitoring student performance is particularly critical in this format. Since coordinating touching and counting is the key behavior, listening to the students count is not sufficient. The first days the skill is taught the teacher must repeat the task enough times to enable him to watch each student touch some objects as the student counts. Monitoring at the very start of the task is also important. If students do not begin at the first picture, they will make mistakes. Note that during step 1 of Part B the teacher demonstrates that counting can be done from left to right or right to left. However, to facilitate monitoring, the students should always count from left to right.

Students may make coordination or rote counting errors. If a student makes a coordination error, saying the number before touching a line, the teacher tells the student to count only when the student touches a line. The teacher then repeats the task, saying "Go back to the first object and point to it." The teacher checks to make sure students are pointing and then repeats the task. As with all corrections in early counting instruction, after an error is made a student should repeat the task until she performs it correctly several times in a row. If a student has a lot of difficulty coordinating counting and pointing, the teacher can slow the cadence to a clap each 2 seconds and prompt the student by taking the student's hand, counting with her, and moving the student's index finger from object to object. The teacher might need to repeat this procedure at least three times before testing the student by having her touch and count the objects without assistance. If students make many rote counting errors (e.g., counting 1 2 3 5 6), the teacher should delay rational counting and provide extra practice on rote counting. Exercises in counting objects on worksheets should be done daily for several weeks. After students can quickly and accurately count lines and pictures of objects, they should be given manipulatives to count. Initially, the objects can be arranged in a row, which makes counting manipulatives easier. Counting objects in rows is like counting pictures in rows. After students can count objects in rows, objects should be placed randomly. The teacher would model, lead, and test counting. Students should learn to count objects that are not lined up for them.

Rational Counting: Two Groups

Counting two groups of lines is introduced when students are able to count a single group of six to eight lines. The format for counting two groups of lines teaches the students the function of the word *all* and prepares them for addition. When students first add, they count two groups of lines—all the lines. The format for counting two groups of lines appears in Figure 5.6. In Part A, the teacher draws two groups of lines on the board and has the stu-

Figure 5.6   Format for Counting Two Groups of Lines

Day	Part A Structured Board Presentation Problems	Part B Structured Worksheet Problems
1-3	3	
4-8	2	3
9-15		4

PART A: Structured Board Presentation

TEACHER	STUDENTS
1. Write on board: | | | | | | | | "HERE ARE TWO GROUPS OF LINES." Touch the first group. "HERE ARE THE LINES IN THE FIRST GROUP." Touch the second group. "HERE ARE THE LINES IN THE SECOND GROUP."	
2. "LET'S COUNT THE LINES IN THE FIRST GROUP." Touch as students count. "HOW MANY LINES IN THE FIRST GROUP?"	"1 2 3 4 5" "5"
3. "LET'S COUNT THE LINES IN THE SECOND GROUP." Touch as students count. "HOW MANY LINES IN THE SECOND GROUP?"	"1 2 3" "3"

4. "NOW LET'S COUNT ALL THE LINES. YOU COUNT THE
LINES IN THE FIRST GROUP AND THEN YOU KEEP ON
GOING AND COUNT THE LINES IN THE SECOND GROUP."
Touch as students count.
 	
  TO CORRECT: "WATCH ME COUNT ALL THE LINES."
        Point and count. "YOUR TURN. COUNT
        ALL THE LINES." Touch as students count.
 	
  "HOW MANY LINES IN ALL?"
	"1 2 3 4 5 6 7 8"
	
	"8"

5. Repeat steps 1-4 with | | | | | then | | | | | | |	

Figure 5.6 cont'd

PART B: Structured Worksheet

TEACHER   **STUDENTS**

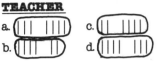

1. "TOUCH CIRCLE a." Check.

2. "TOUCH THE LINES IN THE FIRST GROUP. I'LL CLAP. YOU
   COUNT THE LINES IN THE FIRST GROUP. PUT YOUR
   FINGER OVER THE FIRST LINE. Pause while students place
   finger over first line. "GET READY." Clap at 1 second
   intervals. "HOW MANY LINES IN THE FIRST GROUP?"   "3"

3. Repeat step 2 with the second group.

4. "NOW YOU'RE GOING TO COUNT ALL THE LINES. START
   COUNTING WITH THE FIRST GROUP. PUT YOUR FINGER
   OVER THE FIRST LINE." Pause while students put finger
   over first line. "GET READY" Clap at 1 second intervals.
   "HOW MANY LINES IN ALL?"   "7"

   Call on individual students.

5. Repeat steps 1–4.

---

dents count and tell how many lines in the first group, in the second group, and finally in both groups. Part B is a worksheet exercise in which the students count two groups of lines on their worksheets. Note the schedule at the top of the format. It suggests how many days each part of the format should be presented (left column) and the number of examples presented daily (middle and right columns). The use of this schedule is discussed on pages 23–24 of Chapter 2. Remember the schedules listed are approximations. Higher-performing students may need fewer days and fewer examples. Conversely, lower-performing students may need more.

The error students are likely to make in Part A occurs when they are asked to count all the lines. After counting the lines in the first group, a student is likely to say "one" for the first line in the second group instead of continuing to count. To correct, the teacher models and tests students on that step, and then repeats all the steps. For example, if in counting the lines in this diagram IIII II the student counts 1 2 3 4, 1, the teacher models counting, saying "When we count all the lines, we keep on counting. My turn: 1 2 3 4 5 6." The teacher then tests the students on counting all the lines and then repeats the format from the beginning.

Counting from Different Numbers

Counting from numbers other than 1 saves time when teaching rote counting to higher numbers. For example, in teaching students to count 38, 39, 40,

the teacher would model and test from 36 (36, 37, 38, 39, 40) rather than modeling and testing counting from 1. If students can start at numbers other than 1, teachers can focus on the relevant parts of number sequences. A second reason for teaching counting beginning at a number other than 1 is that this counting skill is a component skill of the early addition strategy. Students solve a problem such as $4 + 3 = \square$ by saying 4 for the first group and then counting each line in the second group: 5, 6, 7.

Figure 5.7 includes a format for teaching students to count beginning at a number other than 1. This format would be introduced when students can rote count to about 15. The format contains two parts. The first part teaches students the meaning of the term *get it going*. (When the teacher says "Get it going," the student is to say the designated number verbally, holding it as long as the teacher signals, e.g., 4 is said "fffooourrr.") The signal used is quite different from signals used in other rote counting tasks. To prompt the students to say the number for a longer time, the teacher signals by moving her hand from side to side.

The students are to begin saying the number as the teacher begins the signal (moving her finger) and to stop saying the number when the teacher stops the signal (dropping her hand). The purpose of the get-it-going signal is to better enable the students to respond in unison.

Figure 5.7 Format for Counting from Numbers Other Than 1

Days	Part A Get-It-Going	Part B Counting
1-2	3	2
3-8		3

PART A: Get It Going Signal

TEACHER

1. Model. "GET IT GOING MEANS TO SAY A NUMBER AS LONG AS I MOVE MY FINGER."

2. Hold up hand. "MY TURN. I'M GOING TO GET 4 GOING." Move hand in circular motion saying "444." After several seconds, drop hand and stop saying 4.

3. Repeat step 2 with 6 and 9.

4. Lead. "LET'S DO IT TOGETHER. WE HAVE 4. HOW MANY DO WE HAVE?"
"GET IT GOING." Signal.
Repeat step 4 with 8 and 2.

5. Test. "YOU HAVE 5. HOW MANY DO YOU HAVE?"
"GET IT GOING." Signal.
Repeat step 5 with 7 and 3.

STUDENTS

"4"
"fooouuurrr"

"5"
"fiiivvve"

PART B: Counting from a Number

1. "WE'RE GOING TO GET IT GOING AND COUNT. MY TURN. WE HAVE FOUR. GET IT GOING." Signal by moving hand in circular motion. After 2 seconds, drop hand. "4444, 5, 6, 7, 8 STOP." Count at a rate of about two numbers a second.

2. "GET IT GOING AND COUNT WITH ME. YOU HAVE 4. HOW MANY DO YOU HAVE?"
"GET IT GOING." Begin signal. "FOUUR."
After about 2 seconds drop hand. "FIVE SIX SEVEN EIGHT."

"4"
"foouurr"
"5, 6, 7, 8"

3. "ALL BY YOURSELVES. YOU HAVE 4. GET IT GOING."
Begin signal; after 2 seconds drop hand.
Say "STOP" after children say "8."

"444, 5, 6, 7, 8"

4. Repeat steps 1-3 with 7, then 3. Give individual turns with 7, 4, or 3.

The teacher should present a set of at least three examples each time Part B is presented. Initially, the examples should all be less than 10. The exercise is repeated until students respond correctly to the entire set, which increases the likelihood that they can generalize the skill to other numbers. Responding correctly to the entire set also implies that if a mistake is made on one example, the teacher repeats all the examples until the students can respond to them consecutively with no errors. Students will need several repetitions before they will master the entire set. However, if a high criterion is maintained initially, the amount of practice needed to master subsequent sets will be reduced.

Sometimes students make the error of starting over at 1: "fooouuur 1 2 3 4." The teacher corrects by modeling and then leading the students several times with an emphasis on the first counted number. However, if the students continue to have problems, the teacher can introduce a procedure where he counts quickly from 1 to the get-it-going number and then signals for the students to respond on the next number: "I'll start counting and when I signal, you count with me: 1 2 3 fooourr (signal) 5 6 7 8 9." The teacher responds with students several times, then tests. After the students begin responding correctly to several consecutive examples, they no longer need the prompt of beginning the sequence at 1.

Ordinal Counting

Ordinal counting involves saying the number associated with relative position; first, second, third, fourth, fifth, sixth. Ordinal counting is introduced only when students can rote count to 20 and can tell the cardinal number for a group. How many lines in the group? A model-lead-test procedure is used to introduce ordinal counting. A way the teacher might introduce ordinal counting is to draw a picture of four children racing and explain the children are having a race. The teacher points to the student in front, saying "first," then to each succeeding student, saying "second, third, fourth," etc. The teacher then models and tests on ordinal counting and on questions about specific objects. For example, the teacher points to the third person and asks, "Show the child who is third."

Counting by 1s from 30 to 100

The procedure for counting by 1s from 30 to 100 should demonstrate the relationship between each tens grouping, i.e., each decade has a sequence in which the numerals 0, 1, 2, 3, 4, 5, 6, 7, 8, 9 appear in the ones column: 4<u>0</u>, 4<u>1</u>, 4<u>2</u>, 4<u>3</u>, 4<u>4</u>, 4<u>5</u>, 4<u>6</u>, 4<u>7</u>, 4<u>8</u>, 4<u>9</u>. Two preskills related to counting higher numbers are rote counting beginning at a number other than 1 (e.g., starting at 5 and counting 6, 7, 8) and skip counting by 10s (10, 20, 30, 40, 50, 60, 70, 80, 90, 100), which is discussed later in the chapter.

The format for counting numbers from 30 to 100 is basically the same as that in Figure 5.4 for introducing new numbers in the early counting sequence, with these modifications. First, the new part would begin at a 10s number ending in 7 and continue through the next 10s number ending in 2 (27, 28, 29, 30, 31, 32, or 47, 48, 49, 50, 51, 52).[1] Second, instead of testing the students on counting from 1, the teacher has them count from a number approximately 10 to 20 numbers lower than the new part. These example selection procedures are illustrated in Figure 5.8.

The first exercises would teach students to count from the thirties to the forties. Counting from the forties to the fifties, etc., would be introduced several days later or whenever students master the lower numbers.

After students practice counting to a new decade for 2 days, the examples are changed each ensuing day to ensure generalizability. For example, students might count from 27 to 42 one day, from 25 to 47 the next, and from 27 to 49 the next.

Counting between 100 and 999

Students are usually taught to count 100 through 999 during second grade. First, students are taught to count by 100s from 100 through 1,000. The 100s skip counting series is usually quite easy for students to learn, requiring only a few days of practice. Once students can count by 1s through 99 and by 100s from 100 through 1,000, the teacher can introduce counting by 1s in the 100s numbers. A three-stage procedure is used. First, the teacher has students count within decades. The teacher uses a model-lead-test procedure on four to five sets of

---

[1] Starting at a higher number (e.g., 8 or 9) gives students too little time to prepare for transition to the next decade. Starting at a lower number makes the task too time consuming.

Figure 5.8 A Sample Selection Procedure for Counting by 1s from 30 to 100

TEACHER	STUDENTS
1. Model, lead, test beginning with numbers ending in 7. "MY TURN TO COUNT FROM 37. THIIRRTTY SEVVENN, 38, 39, <u>40</u>, 41, 42. COUNT WITH ME. 37. "GET IT GOING." Signal.	"Thiirrtty sevvenn, 38, 39, 40, 41, 42"
"COUNT BY YOURSELVES. 37. GET IT GOING." Signal.	"Thiirrty sevvenn, 38, 39, 40, 41, 42"
2. Test counting from a number 10 lower than 37. "LET'S COUNT FROM 27. GET IT GOING." Signal.	"Twenntty sevvenn, 28, 29, 30, 31, 32"
Clap or tap foot to set tempo for counting. Say "STOP" when students say "42."	"...42"

examples each day. Examples similar to the follow-ing would be presented daily until students demon-strate mastery:

3$\underline{5}$0, 3$\underline{5}$1, 3$\underline{5}$2, 3$\underline{5}$3, 3$\underline{5}$4, 3$\underline{5}$5, 3$\underline{5}$6, 3$\underline{5}$7, 3$\underline{5}$8, 3$\underline{5}$9
7$\underline{2}$0, 7$\underline{2}$1, 7$\underline{2}$2, 7$\underline{2}$3, 7$\underline{2}$4, 7$\underline{2}$5, 7$\underline{2}$6, 7$\underline{2}$7, 7$\underline{2}$8, 7$\underline{2}$9
4$\underline{4}$0, 4$\underline{4}$1, 4$\underline{4}$2, 4$\underline{4}$3, 4$\underline{4}$4, 4$\underline{4}$5, 4$\underline{4}$6, 4$\underline{4}$7, 4$\underline{4}$8, 4$\underline{4}$9
8$\underline{6}$0, 8$\underline{6}$1, 8$\underline{6}$2, 8$\underline{6}$3, 8$\underline{6}$4, 8$\underline{6}$5, 8$\underline{6}$6, 8$\underline{6}$7, 8$\underline{6}$8, 8$\underline{6}$9

The objective of the second stage is making the transition from one decade to the next. An example set would include several series extending from a number with 5 in the ones column to the next number in the counting sequence that has 5 in the ones column. Examples similar to those below would be presented daily until students demon-strate mastery. Lower-performing students may require about 2–3 weeks practice.

325, 326, 327, 328, 329, 3$\underline{3}$0, 331, 332, 333, 334, 335
785, 786, 787, 788, 789, 7$\underline{9}$0, 791, 792, 793, 794, 795
435, 436, 437, 438, 439, 4$\underline{4}$0, 441, 442, 443, 444, 445
115, 116, 117, 118, 119, 1$\underline{2}$0, 121, 122, 123, 124, 125

The third stage concentrates on the transition from a hundreds series to the next hundreds series. The example set would include several series extending from a hundreds number ending with 95 to the next number in the counting series which has a 5 in the ones column. A daily lesson might include these ex-amples:

495, 496, 497, 498, 499, $\underline{5}$00, 501, 502, 503, 504, 505
295, 296, 297, 298, 299, $\underline{3}$00, 301, 302, 303, 304, 305
795, 796, 797, 798, 799, $\underline{8}$00, 801, 802, 803, 804, 805
595, 596, 597, 598, 599, $\underline{6}$00, 601, 602, 603, 604, 605

Review can be provided through written work-sheets in which the teacher writes a number on a worksheet with 10 spaces across from it. The stu-dents are to fill in the next 10 numbers.

Skip Counting

Skip counting refers to counting each number of a specified multiple. When a student skip counts by 5s, the student says "5, 10, 15, 20, 25, 30, 35, 40, 45, 50," etc. When skip counting by 8, the students says "8, 16, 24, 32, 40, 48, 56, 64, 72, 80." Throughout this book, we will refer to skip counting as saying the count-by series. Knowledge of the count-by series for multiples of 2, 3, 4, 5, 6, 7, 8, 9, and 10 serves as an important component skill for the memorization of basic multiplication and division facts. Students should learn to count 10 numbers for each series (except 5s): 2 to 20, 3 to 30, 4 to 40,

6 to 60, etc. Students should count by 5 to 60 since telling time involves this skill.

The first count-by series to be introduced should be the 10s since knowledge of this series is a component skill for rote counting to 100. Counting by 10s is introduced when students can rote count by ones to about 30, usually several months into first grade. The next count-by series, the 2s, might not be introduced until several weeks later. Thereaf-ter, a new series may be introduced when students are able to say each of the previously introduced series accurately and fluently. Students are fluent on a specific series when they can say the series within 8 seconds.

We suggest teaching the count-by series cu-mulatively in the following sequence: 10, 2, 5, 9, 4, 25, 3, 8, 7, 6. This order is designed to initially separate those count-by series that contain many of the same numbers. For example, the circled num-bers in the 4 series also appear in the 8 series:

4 ⑧ 12 ⑯ 20 ㉔

Therefore, the introduction of the 4 and 8 series are separated by two other dissimilar series.

Separating similar series helps prevent errors in which students switch series. Switching series, a common count-by error, involves counting by one number and switching to another number after saying a number common to both series. For ex-ample, students may begin counting by 4s and switch to 8s when they come to 16, 24 or 32 (e.g., 4, 8, 12, 16, 24, 32, 40). The chances of students' making that error are reduced when the series are not introduced consecutively. Therefore, the recom-mended sequence for teaching count-bys can make learning the series easier.

The count-by format includes three parts (see Figure 5.9). Part A demonstrates to students that they end up with the same number whether they count by 1s or count by another number and that counting by a number other than 1 can save time. Part A would be presented just for the first lessons in which count-by 2s and 5s are taught. Part B is designed to teach students to memorize the various count-by series.

The teacher uses a model-lead-test proce-dure: saying the numbers of the new series by himself, saying the numbers of the new series with the students, and finally having the students say the numbers themselves. Part C of the count-by format includes a review of previously introduced count-by series. Two or three previously taught series would be reviewed daily.

Figure 5.9 Format for Count-by

Series	Days	Part A Introducing the Concept Problems	Part B Structured Board Presentation Problems	Part C Review Problems
2 & 5	1	1	1(step 1 only)	
	2	1	1(step 1 only)	
	3-6		1 (steps 2,3,4 only)	2 series
3, 4, 6, 7, 8, 9	1		1(step 1 only)	
	2-6		1 (steps 2,3,4 only)	2 series

PART A: Introducing the Concept

TEACHER

Draw 10 lines in groups of two on the board: || || || || ||

1. "LET'S FIND OUT HOW MANY LINES WE HAVE. I'LL TOUCH AND YOU COUNT."
"HOW MANY LINES ARE THERE?"
Write 10 next to the last group.

2. "NOW I'LL SHOW YOU A FAST WAY TO COUNT THOSE LINES." Circle each group of two lines with finger. For each group, ask "HOW MANY LINES IN THIS GROUP?" After asking about all five groups, ask "HOW MANY LINES ARE IN EACH GROUP?"
"WHEN WE COUNT GROUPS OF 2, WE COUNT LINES THE FAST WAY."

3. "LET'S FIGURE OUT THE NUMBERS WE SAY WHEN WE COUNT BY 2. COUNT THE LINES IN THE FIRST GROUP."
Point to each line as students count.
"YES, THERE ARE TWO LINES, SO I WRITE 2 ABOVE THE FIRST GROUP." Write 2 above first group.
"COUNT THE LINES IN THE FIRST AND SECOND GROUPS."
"YOU COUNTED FOUR LINES SO FAR, SO I'LL WRITE 4 ABOVE THE SECOND GROUP." Write it.
Continue to have the students count each successive group from the beginning, writing the appropriate numeral above each group. When the students have finished, the lines should look like this:

2 4 6 8 10
|| || || || ||

4. "NOW YOU KNOW WHAT NUMBERS TO SAY WHEN YOU COUNT BY 2. LET'S COUNT THE LINES AGAIN, BUT THIS TIME WE'LL COUNT BY 2." Point to each numeral as students count.

5. "HOW MANY DID YOU END UP WITH WHEN YOU COUNTED BY 2?"
Point to the 10 written, next to the last group. "HOW MANY DID YOU END UP WITH WHEN YOU COUNTED THE REGULAR WAY?"
"SEE, THE FAST WAY REALLY DOES WORK."

STUDENTS

"1, 2, 3, 4, 5, 6, 7, 8, 9, 10"
"10"

"2"

"1, 2"

"1, 2, 3, 4"

"2, 4, 6, 8, 10."

"10"

"10"

Figure 5.9 cont'd

PART B: Structured Board Presentation

TEACHER	**STUDENTS**

1. Note: This step is used only the first day a new series is introduced. "TODAY WE'RE GOING TO LEARN TO COUNT BY 6. MY TURN: 6, 12, 18, 24, 30. SAY IT WITH ME, GET READY." Signal. "6, 12, 18, 24, 30."   "6, 12, 18, 24, 30"
Lead students until they appear able to say series without help.
"SAY THE 6s BY YOURSELVES. GET READY." Signal.   "6, 12, 18, 24, 30"
Steps 2 and 3 are used after the first part of a new count-by series has been introduced.

2. Test previously introduced part.
"LET'S COUNT BY 6 TO 30. GET READY." Signal.   "6, 12, 18, 24, 30"
TO CORRECT: Model, then lead the students until they can recite the series by themselves with no errors.

3. Model, lead, test new part.
"HERE'S THE NEW PART: 24, 30, 36, 42. SAY THE NEW PART WITH ME. GET READY." Signal.   "24, 30, 36, 42"
Repeat until students appear able to say series without help.
"SAY THE NEW PART BY YOURSELVES. GET READY." Signal.   "24, 30, 36, 42"
Give individual turns to several students.

4. Model, lead, test from beginning of series.
"I'LL COUNT BY 6 TO 42. LISTEN:
6, 12, 18, 24, 30, 36, 42.
SAY IT WITH ME, GET READY." Signal.
"6, 12, 18, 24, 30, 36, 42."   "6, 12, 18, 24, 30, 36, 42"
Respond with students until they appear able to respond without help.
"BY YOURSELVES. COUNTING BY 6 TO 42.
GET READY." Signal.   "6, 12, 18, 24, 30, 36, 42"

PART C: Review

"LET'S SAY SOME COUNT-BY SERIES WE'VE LEARNED BEFORE." Have students say previously learned count-by series. After reviewing a series, have students say new series again.

The first day a new count-by series is introduced, the teacher presents the first three to five numbers in the series. Teachers working with more naive students would introduce just the first three numbers of a series, while teachers working with more sophisticated students might introduce the first five numbers. For example, the first day the count-by 9 series is presented to a group of lower performing students, the teacher would just introduce the first three numbers of the series: 9, 18, 27. On the other hand, a teacher working with higher performing students might present the first five numbers of the series: 9, 18, 27, 36, 45. Teachers working with average students might introduce a whole series in several days while teachers working with lower-performing students may expect the students to require about 2 weeks to master a series.

On the second day of instruction on a series, the teacher tests the students on the part of the series taught the previous lesson. If the students make an error, the teacher repeats the model-lead test procedure from step 1 of Part B. If the students know the part of the series previously taught or require just a couple of practice trials to say the previously taught part correctly, the teacher introduces the next several numbers of the count-by series. The new part includes the last two familiar numbers and the next two or three numbers in the series. For example, students have been previously taught 9s to 36: 9, 18, 27, 36. The new part would include 27 and 36, the last two numbers from the previously taught part, plus the next two numbers in the series, 45 and 54. The teacher uses a model-lead-test procedure first on 27–54 and then on the series from the beginning.

As with any rote counting task, adequate repetition must be provided for student mastery. A teacher may have to lead lower-performing students 5 to 10 times through a series until they are able to say it fluently without errors. When leading students, the teacher should initially use a loud voice, particularly when saying difficult parts of a counting sequence. The purpose of using a loud voice is to ensure that all students are hearing the correct response and to prevent them from cueing on students who may be responding incorrectly. A brisk rhythm should be established by the teacher tapping his foot or clapping his hands to make mastering the series easier. The numbers in a series should be said at a rate slightly faster than a number a second, i.e., saying 9, 18, 27 . . . 90 in about 8 seconds.

Corrections for skip counting errors follow the model-lead-test procedure. When the teacher hears an error, he stops all the students, models the hard part (the two numbers just before the missed number and the one number following the missed number), leads the students on the hard part several times, tests the students on the hard part, and then has them say the entire series from the beginning. For example, if students count "8, 16, 24, 32, 40, 48, 54," the teacher stops them as soon as he hears 54 instead of 56. Next he models, leads, and tests on the hard part: 40, 48, 5̲6̲, 64. After students perform acceptably on the test of the hard part, the teacher has the students begin counting with 8.

A new series is introduced only when students know all the previously introduced series. Teachers should expect students to initially develop confusion when a series similar to one previously taught is presented. When the 6 series is presented, the teacher may find that students make errors on the 4s series. Both series include 24. A student might count 4, 8, 12, 16, 20, 24, 30, 36, 42, switching from the 4s to 6s at 24. With adequate practice, this confusion can be ameliorated. Practice on previously taught series can also be provided through worksheet exercises in which the students write out the count-by series.

Research

More recent research in the area of counting has focused on the acquisition of different rote counting skills and the application of those skills to problem-solving. Specifically, several studies have examined the shift students make from concrete counting (i.e., counting objects or pictures representing addition statements) to mental counting whereby students count on from the first addend (e.g., 4 + 2 = "four, five, six"). While some of these studies look at the developmental shift (Baroody, 1987), others have investigated instruction in a counting-on strategy as well. Interestingly, Secada, Fuson and Hall (1983) found that their assessment procedure alone has induced a shift to counting-on for some students and their brief instruction (lasting one session) was successful in teaching the skill to seven of eight children in the instructional group. The impact of this shift from concrete counting to mental counting on either students' subsequent math fact skills or problem-solving skills has yet to be investigated, however.

Students vary greatly in the amount of practice they require to master basic counting skills. Staats, Brewer, and Gross (1970) taught counting skills to preschoolers who could not count to 5. A mean of 238 trials over 22.6 sessions was required to teach the students to count five objects, The students were then taught to rote count beyond 5. One child learned to count beyond 5 to 12, a second to 13, a third to 15, and a fourth to 20. Mean training time for the extended rote counting was 3 hours and 19 minutes spread over 37 sessions. We've found that once low-performing kindergarten students learn to count to 10, they need, on the average, 70 corrected repetitions spread over several weeks to learn to count to 15. In contrast to the extensive training required for the preschoolers, Hendrickson (1979) reported that in testing a group of entering first graders, he found that all could count to 10; 95% could count 5 blocks; and 85% could count 12 blocks. The findings illustrate the broad range of student skills and instructional needs in an area as seemingly simple as counting.

In studying the counting and symbol skills of moderately retarded students (mean age of 12 years), Spradlin, Cotter, Stevens, and Friedman (1974) identified the relative difficulty of several different skills. Numeral matching was easiest; pointing to a numeral when a number was stated was of intermediate difficulty; identifying numerals was hardest, e.g., teacher points to 6 and asks, "What is this?" Being able to identify numerals did not imply that students could count. Often students who could identify numerals could not rote count.

Spradlin et al. (1974) found that rote counting was very difficult for students, especially when they were told at which number to stop (e.g., "Count to 7"). Although numeral identification was not correlated with counting skill, stopping at the appropriate number did correlate with being able to count objects correctly. In rational counting tasks, children counted pictures and manipulatives equally well. However, counting out a subset was easier when the objects or picture were in a row:

**** would be easier to count than **
                                     **

Overall, the data suggest that numeral and counting skills are to some extent independent. However, after students master the skills, they can readily use them; e.g., once students can identify numerals and count to a given number, they can count out a set of objects when shown a numeral.

Application Items: Counting

1. A student counts "5, 6, 7, 9." Immediately after the student says "9," the teacher says "8" to correct him. What is wrong with this correction? What should the teacher say and do?

2. In counting from 1–10, a student makes an error at 8. The teacher models the hard part and has the student say it. The student says it correctly. Is this correction sufficient? Tell why.

3. Two days ago you introduced rote counting to 16. At the beginning of the lesson you test the students, and they can count to 16. What would you do that day? What would you do if they couldn't count to 16?

4. The teacher tells the students to count to 45; a child counts correctly until 39 then says 50. What is the correction?

5. When counting this group of lines: I I I I I, a student ends with 8. What are two possible causes of the error? How would the correction procedures differ?

6 Symbol Identification and Place Value

Terms and Concepts

Number Actually is cardinal number. Identifies the number of members in a set.

Numeral A symbol used to represent a number.

Place Value The system by which the value of a digit is determined by the position it occupies relative to the decimal point.

Expanded Notation A numeral written as a sum in which each digit's value is expressed as an addend, e.g., in 342, the digits 3, 4, and 2 are written as the addends 300 + 40 + 2.

Column Alignment Writing numerals one above the other so that the units, tens, and hundreds positions are in columns: 32 + 426 is written

$$\begin{array}{r} 32 \\ +426 \\ \hline \end{array} \quad \text{not} \quad \begin{array}{r} 32 \\ +426 \\ \hline \end{array}$$

Skill Hierarchy

Symbol identification and place value may be divided into three major areas: (a) reading and writing numerals, (b) column alignment, and (c) expanded notation. The skill hierarchy in Figure 6.1 illustrates the specific skills within these areas. Note in Figure 6.1 that numeral identification (reading and writing the numerals zero through 10) is the foundation of the hierarchy. A subcategory which also falls into the class of foundation skills involves numeration matching exercises in which the student must write either the numeral which corresponds to the number of members in a group or vice versa:

These numeration tasks integrate counting and symbol skills.

Place value concepts are introduced through the remaining instructional activities: reading and writing teen numbers, hundreds, thousands and millions numbers; expanded notation; and column alignment. In reading multi-digit numbers, students translate each digit into a value according to its position and then identify the entire numeral. For example, in reading 58, students must note that 5 represents five 10s and five 10s is read as 50. Eight

Figure 6.1 Skill Hierarchy

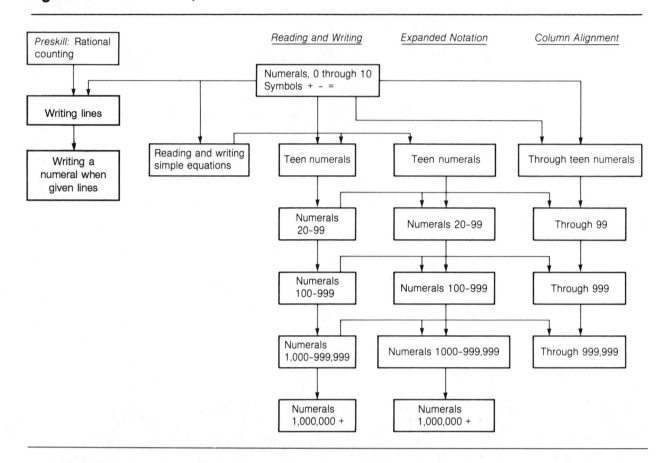

$$342 = 300 + 40 + 2$$

1s is read as 8. The students then put the parts together and identify 58 as "fifty-eight." Writing numerals requires the reverse operation—breaking a number into parts rather than putting parts together. When students are told to write 58, they break the number into parts: 50 and 8. Fifty is represented by a 5 in the tens column; so students write that part. The eight is represented by an 8 in the ones column; so students write that part. In summary, to read numerals, students determine the value of each part and then put the values together. To write numerals, students break the number into parts and write the digit representing each value.

The introduction of expanded notation and place value parallels reading and writing numbers. For example, when teachers see that students can read and write hundreds numbers, they introduce column alignment problems with hundreds numbers:

342 + 8 is rewritten as 342
+8

and then expanded notation problems dealing with hundreds numbers:

Figure 6.2, the Instructional Sequence and Assessment Chart, lists specific skills, indicating their relative order of introduction. Note that many of the tasks in kindergarten and first grade require teachers to test students individually. In later grades, only tasks requiring students to read numerals need be tested individually.

Introducing the Concept

This section deals with skills normally taught during kindergarten and early first grade. These skills are prerequisites for the equality-based strategies that provide a conceptual understanding of addition and subtraction. The skills, listed in the order they are discussed in this section, are

1. Numeral identification (zero through 10)
2. Numeral writing (zero through 10)
3. Symbol identification and writing (+, −, □, =)
4. Equation reading and writing
5. Numeral and line matching

Figure 6.2 Instructional Sequence and Assessment Chart

Grade Level	Problem Type	Performance Indicator
K-1	Reading numerals zero through 10	Read these numerals: 4, 2, 6, 1, 7, 3, 0, 8, 5, 9, 10
K-1	Writing numerals zero through 10	Write these numerals: 4, 2, 6, 1, 7, 3, 0, 8, 5, 9, 10
K-1	Writing a numeral to represent members of a set	□　　□ ‖‖　‖‖‖
K-1	Writing members of set (lines) to represent a numeral	□　　□ ＿＿＿　＿＿＿
1a	Reading teen numbers	Read these numerals: 15, 11, 13, 12, 17, 19, 14, 16, 18
1b	Writing teen numbers	Write these numerals: 15, 11, 13, 12, 17, 19, 14, 16, 18
1c	Reading numbers from 20 through 99	Read these numerals: 64, 81, 44, 29
1d	Writing numbers from 20 through 99	Write these numerals: 47, 98, 23, 72, 31
1e	Column alignment Rewriting horizontal addition and subtraction problems	$85 + 3 = $ ＿＿＿ $4 + 25 = $ ＿＿＿ $37 - 2 = $ ＿＿＿
1f	Expanded notation	$63 = $ ＿＿ $+$ ＿＿ $92 = $ ＿＿ $+$ ＿＿
2a	Reading and writing numbers between 100 and 999 except those with a zero in the tens column	Read: 320, 417, 521 Write seven hundred fifteen ＿＿＿ Write four hundred thirty-six ＿＿＿ Write three hundred fifty ＿＿＿
2b	Reading and writing numbers between 100 and 999 with zero in tens and ones column	Read: 300, 800, 200 Write four hundred ＿＿＿ Write six hundred ＿＿＿ Write nine hundred ＿＿＿
2c	Reading and writing numbers between 100 and 999 with zero in tens column only	Read: 502, 708, 303 Write four hundred eight ＿＿＿ Write seven hundred two ＿＿＿ Write three hundred three ＿＿＿
2d	Rewriting horizontal equations; one number is a hundreds number	$305 + 8 + 42 = $ ＿＿＿ $428 - 21 = $＿＿＿ $31 + 142 + 8 = $＿＿＿
2e	Expanded notation with hundreds numbers	$382 = $ ＿＿ $+$ ＿＿ $+$ ＿＿ $417 = $ ＿＿ $+$ ＿＿ $+$ ＿＿ $215 = $ ＿＿ $+$ ＿＿ $+$ ＿＿
3a	Reading and writing thousands between 1,000 and 9,999 with no zeroes in hundreds or tens column	Read:　3,248　7,151　1,318 Write five thousand three hundred fourteen ＿＿＿ Write two thousand six hundred forty-three ＿＿＿ Write one thousand one hundred forty-one ＿＿＿

Figure 6.2 cont'd

Grade Level	Problem Type	Performance Indicator
3b	Reading and writing thousands numbers between 1,000 and 9,999 with zero in hundreds, tens and ones columns	Read: 3,000 7,000 2,000 Write four thousand _____ Write eight thousand _____ Write six thousand _____
3c	Reading and writing thousands numbers between 1,000 and 9,999 with a zero in hundreds column	Read: 7,025 8,014 2,092 Write five thousand seventy-two _____ Write one thousand forty _____ Write six thousand eighty-eight _____
3d	Reading and writing thousands numbers between 1,000 and 9,999 with a zero in the hundreds and tens column	Read: 4,008 2,002 1,009 Write six thousand eight _____ Write nine thousand four _____ Write five thousand two _____
3e	Column alignment: Rewriting horizontal problems	$35 + 1,083 + 245 =$ _____ $4,035 - 23 =$ _____ $8 + 2,835 =$ _____
4a	Reading and writing all thousands numbers between 10,000 and 999,999	Read: 300,000; 90,230; 150,200 Write two hundred thousand _____ Write ninety thousand four hundred _____ Write one hundred thousand two hundred _____
4b	Reading and writing numbers between 1 and 9 million	Read: 6,030,000; 5,002,100; 1,340,000 Write seven million _____ Write seventy million, eighty thousand _____ Write twelve million, six hundred thousand _____

5a	Reading and writing numbers between 10 and 999 million	Read: 27,400,000
		    302,250,000
		    900,300,000
		Write: ten million _____
		Write: forty million two hundred
		    thousand _____

Remember, though, that the early lessons taught to an instructionally naive student will include tasks from several skill areas. The concurrent introduction of skills is illustrated in Figure 3.2.

Numeral Identification

Numeral identification tasks begin when students can rote count to 8. Introducing numeral identification is delayed until after students can rote count to 8 in order to avoid confusion between counting and numeral identification. Students who enter school knowing how to count can begin learning numerals immediately.

The sequence in which numerals are introduced is important. A basic guideline in sequencing the introduction of numerals is to separate similar-looking numerals and similar-sounding numbers. Students are likely to confuse 6 and 9 because they look so much alike; likewise, students may have difficulty discriminating 4 from 5 since they sound alike (both begin with the /f/ sound). Therefore, a good sequence of introduction would separate both pairs of numbers by several lessons. One possible sequence for introducing the numerals 0 through 10 is 4, 2, 6, 1, 7, 3, 0, 8, 5, 9, 10. Note the separation of 6 and 9; 1, 0, and 10; 4 and 5. This sequence is included as an example, and is not the only sequence that can minimize student errors.

A second sequencing guideline is to introduce new numerals cumulatively. A new numeral is not presented until a student has demonstrated mastery of the previously introduced symbols. Teachers working with students who enter school with little or

Figure 6.3 Format for Introducing New Numerals

Day	Step 1	Steps 2 and 3
1	1	0
2-3	0	1

Note: This format is used with each new symbol. In this example, we assume that the numerals 1, 4, 6, and 2 have been introduced and the numeral 7 is being introduced.

TEACHER	STUDENTS
Write on board: 7 2 4 6 7 7 1	
1. Model and Test. Point to 7 and say "THIS IS A SEVEN. WHAT IS THIS?" Touch 7.	"7"
2. Discrimination Practice. "WHEN I TOUCH IT, TELL ME WHAT IT IS." Point to 2, pause 1 second, then touch 2. Repeat step 2 with these numerals: 7, 2, 7, 6, 1, 7, 2, 1, 6, 7, etc.	"2"
3. Individual Turns. Ask individual students to identify several numerals.	

no previous knowledge of numerals can generally introduce new symbols at a rate of one new symbol each three to five lessons.

The format (see Figure 6.3) for introducing new numerals to students consists of a model, in which the teacher points to the numeral and tells the students the name of the numeral; a test, in which the teacher asks the students to identify the new numeral; and discrimination practice, in which the teacher asks students to identify the new numeral and previously introduced numerals.

The teacher first writes a set of numerals on the board. The new numeral is written several times. Each of the previously introduced numerals is written once. The new numeral is written several times to ensure that the student keys on the appearance of the numeral rather than its position on the board. The most important part of the introduction is the discrimination practice in step 2 of the format. Note that the presentation of the numeral follows an alternating pattern: new numeral, one previously introduced numeral, new numeral, two previously introduced numerals, new numeral, three previously introduced numerals, etc. The time the student has to remember the new numeral is gradually increased by adding more familiar numerals. This pattern is designed to help students better remember a new or difficult numeral. Individual turns are given after the teacher presents the discrimination practice.

If, when giving an individual turn, a student misidentifies or does not respond, the teacher iden-

tifies the numeral and uses the alternating pattern, focusing on that numeral and previously identified numerals.

A clear point and touch signal is essential for clear presentation of this format. The features of a good point-touch signal are illustrated in Figure 6.4. When signaling, the teacher points under the numeral (not touching the board), making sure that no student's vision is blocked by any part of the teacher's hand or body. After pointing under the numeral for 1–2 seconds, the teacher signals by moving her finger away from the board and then back toward it, touching under the numeral. The out and in motion is done crisply with the finger moving away from the board (about 6 inches) and then immediately back to the board. When the finger touches below the numeral, the students are to respond. The out and in motion should be done the same way every time it is used. Any hesitation or inconsistency makes unison responding difficult because the students cannot tell when they are supposed to respond.

Pacing is extremely important for an effective presentation. As a general rule, the teacher should point to a numeral for a second or two, then signal. After the students respond, the teacher should confirm the response ("Yes, this is a 6") or make a correction ("This is a 6. What numeral?"). Then the teacher immediately points to the next number in the task, pauses a second or two, then signals. When pointing to numerals that have been newly in-

Figure 6.4   Point, Out, In and Touch Signal

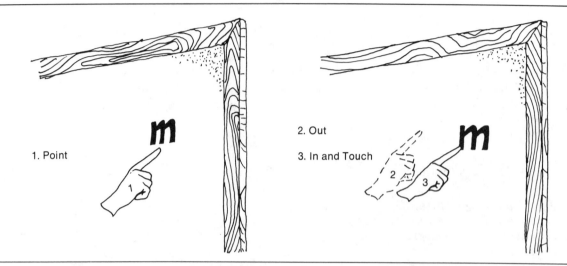

1. Point

2. Out

3. In and Touch

troduced or ones that have caused students diffi-culty in the past, the teacher might initially pause 3–4 seconds before signaling. The primary goal of good pacing is to give students a great deal of practice, with feedback, in a short amount of time.

As with rote counting, the numeral identifi-cation tasks are more efficiently taught if presented for 3–5 minutes at several different times during the lesson rather than in one long session. Numeral identification can also be practiced at various times of the day. Many teachers make cardboard numerals and put them on a bulletin board or wall in the room. The teachers then ask the students to identify the symbols during early morning exercises, before going to recess or lunch, etc. The practice provided by these brief tasks, interspersed throughout the day, can make a great difference in how quickly low-performing students learn to identify symbols.

Numeral Writing

Numeral writing is an important skill in itself and also reinforces numeral identification. As a general rule, a new numeral can be introduced into numeral writing exercises several lessons after it first ap-pears in a numeral identification format. There are three basic stages in teaching students to write single digit numerals:

1. Tracing numerals written on worksheets
2. Copying numerals
3. Writing numerals as the teacher dictates them

As noted in symbol identification, symbols are intro-duced cumulatively. For instructionally naive stu-dents, this may mean they'll be ready to practice writing a new numeral every three to five lessons. For example, students might be able to identify and write symbols according to the schedule on the bottom of the page.

For worksheet tracing exercises, we recom-mend that dots be used to prompt the students where to begin writing the numeral. Two dots would be used for the numeral 4, since it requires two separate strokes. A large dot indicates where the first stroke begins. A small dot is written where the second stroke begins:

During the first several lessons, the teacher leads the students through tracing, instructing them to put their pencil on the big dot, make the line by following the dashed line, then to put their pencil on the small dot (if there is one) and follow that dashed line. The teacher monitors the students quite care-fully, modeling and, if necessary, moving the stu-dents' hands to help them make the lines. The students say the name of the numeral each time they write it.

Lesson	11	12	13	14	15	16	17	18	19	20	21	22	23
Identi-fication	4				2					6			
Writing			4				2					6	

When the students are able to trace a numeral without assistance, the teacher introduces copying. In initial copying exercises, dashed lines and dots appear for the first numeral but only dots for the remaining numerals:

• . • . • . • .

When students can do this exercise, a more sophisticated copying exercise is introduced in which no dots or dotted lines are used as prompts. The students should practice writing each numeral at least 10 to 20 times each day for the first week the symbol is introduced. The number of repetitions can be gradually reduced as student performance improves.

The third and final stage of numeral writing includes numeral dictation exercises in which the teacher says a number, and the students write the numeral. Some students find dictation exercises quite difficult because they not only have to remember what a numeral looks like but also how to write it. The prerequisites for introducing a numeral in dictation exercises are being able to identify and copy the numeral.

In a numeral dictation exercise, the teacher follows the same alternating pattern used in numeral identification tasks. For example, let's say that students have learned to write 4, 2, 6, 1; 7 is being introduced in a dictation exercise. The teacher says "write a 7, write a 4, write a 7, write a 6, write a 1, write a 7, write a 4, write a 2, write a 6, write a 7." The worksheet on which the students are to write the numerals should have blank spaces or boxes large enough to write each symbol in.

Monitoring and pacing are both important presentation behaviors for numeral dictation. The teacher should check the responses of all low-performing students after each numeral is written. The responses of higher-performing students can be checked after every second or third numeral. As soon as the last student has finished writing a symbol, if no mistakes were made, the teacher should dictate the next numeral. Too much time between tasks can result in off-task behavior.

The correction procedure for errors involves a model-test-alternating test procedure. The teacher shows the students how to write the numeral, has the students copy it, and then alternates between having students write the missed numeral and other numerals.

Teachers must be careful in setting reasonable criteria for neatness. Students with little prior writing experience may require many months of practice

before they consistently write numerals neatly. The teacher should gradually increase criteria for legibility and neatness. Remember that in initial exercises, writing a reasonable facsimile of a numeral is the critical student behavior. If a student writes a number backward, the teacher says, "Good. That's a 4, but here's how to write it." The teacher writes the numeral. Note that the correction is made in a positive manner.

Symbol Identification and Writing

The symbols for plus, minus, equal sign, and empty box are taught with the same procedures as for numerals. An empty box can be introduced as "how many." Introducing a box as *how many* facilitates reading equations; e.g., $6 + 5 = \square$ is read: Six plus five equals how many?

Introduction of the various symbols should be interspersed throughout the lessons in which numerals are introduced. The first symbol would be introduced after several numerals; subsequent symbols would be introduced after each group of several numerals.

Equation Reading and Writing

Equation reading is a prerequisite skill for problem solving and fact-learning tasks. Students must be able to read an equation fluently if they are to be able to derive the answer and see its relationship to other equations.

Children may have difficulty reading a problem such as $6 - 3 = \square$ even though they can identify each symbol in isolation. When they read a problem, they must chain the numerals and symbols together, which requires some practice.

Equation reading is introduced when the students know enough numerals and symbols for the teachers to create equations. Students should be able to identify the numerals almost instantaneously prior to introducing equation reading. If students have not received adequate practice to quickly identify numerals when they appear in isolation, they will have much difficulty reading equations. Because the procedure for teaching reading equations is quite straightforward, a format is not included. The teacher would follow the model-lead-test procedure. The teacher writes several equations on the board:

$$4 + 3 = \square \qquad 7 - 3 = 4$$
$$8 + 5 = \square$$

The teacher models reading the first equation at a rate of about a numeral or symbol each second.

(Reading at a faster rate should be avoided initially since it may encourage guessing or imitating responses of other students.) The teacher then responds with the students as they read the statement. Lower-performing students may need 10 or more trials. When the students appear able to read the statement by themselves, the teacher tests the group and then individuals. The same model-lead-test procedure is used with each statement. Equation reading would be practiced daily for several weeks. It can be discontinued when addition is introduced since the addition formats begin with the students reading an equation. The rate at which students read statements would be increased gradually.

Equation writing involves the students' writing an equation dictated by the teacher; e.g., "Listen: Four plus three equals how many? Say that . . .Write it." Equation writing is introduced when the students can read equations with relative ease and are somewhat fluent in writing numerals and symbols, i.e., being able to write most numerals within 2–3 seconds after the teacher says the numeral in a dictation exercise.

The format for equation writing (see Figure 6.5) involves the teacher's saying a statement, the students' repeating the statement at a normal rate, then repeating the statement at a slow rate (a word each 2–3 seconds), and then finally writing the statements. The purpose of having students say the statement slowly is to buttress against students' forgetting the latter part of the statement as they are writing the earlier part.

A common error is writing a numeral or symbol out of order. As soon as the teacher notices an error in a written equation, she points to each symbol while saying the correct statement. For example, if a student writes 6 + □ = 2 for 6 + 2 = □, the teacher says, "Listen: 6" and points to 6; says "plus" and points to +; says "2" and points to □ and immediately says, "This is not 2; let's try the problem again." The teacher has the student cross out or erase the problem, then repeats the statement, has the student say the equation, and then tells the student to write the equation.

Numeration Tasks: Numeral and Line Matching

There are two types of numeration tasks. The first starts with symbols. The student identifies a symbol and then writes the appropriate number of lines; e.g., the student identifies the numeral 2 and then

Figure 6.5 Format for Equation Writing

TEACHER	STUDENTS
1. Give students paper and pencil.	
2. "YOU'RE GOING TO WRITE A PROBLEM. FIRST YOU'LL SAY IT. LISTEN. SIX PLUS TWO EQUALS HOW MANY? LISTEN AGAIN. SIX PLUS TWO EQUALS HOW MANY? SAY THAT." TO CORRECT: Respond with students until they can say the statement at a normal rate of speech.	"Six plus two equals how many?"
3. "NOW WE'LL SAY IT THE SLOW WAY. EVERY TIME I CLAP, WE'LL SAY A PART OF THE STATEMENT." Repond with students. "GET READY." Clap. "SIX." Pause 2 seconds; clap. "PLUS" Pause 2 seconds; clap. "TWO" Pause 2 seconds; clap. "EQUALS" Pause 2 seconds; clap. "HOW MANY?" Repeat step 3 until students appear able to respond on their own.	"six" "plus" "two" "equals" "how many"
4. "NOW I'LL CLAP AND YOU SAY THE STATEMENT BY YOURSELVES." Pause. "GET READY." Clap at 2 second intervals. TO CORRECT: Respond with students.	"Six plus two equals how many?"
5. "NOW WRITE THE PROBLEM."	Students write 6 + 2 = □
6. Repeat steps 1–5 with three more equations.	

draws two lines under the 2. The second starts with lines. The student counts the number of lines or other objects and writes the numeral which represents the number, e.g., for the task below, the student writes a 2 in the box.

$$| \quad |$$
$$\square$$

Both tasks are component skills for the equality-based strategies taught to solve addition and subtraction; therefore, they should be taught relatively early in the instructional sequence, after students have learned to identify and write about five numerals and can count objects in a group. Both numeration skills can be introduced within a short period of time, since they are usually easy for students to learn. As soon as the students learn to identify a new numeral, teachers should incorporate it into numeration tasks.

IDENTIFYING A SYMBOL, THEN DRAWING LINES Prior to introducing tasks in which the students draw lines to correspond to a numeral, the teacher may need to provide practice for lower-performing students in simply drawing lines. The teacher would give students a piece of paper with a series of dots about 1/4 inch apart and 1/2 inch above a horizontal line

. . . .
_____

The teacher then models how to draw lines, followed by an exercise in which students write a line each time she claps (at a rate of about a clap each 2–3 seconds).

Students may write crooked lines or crowd them together, e.g., \/\\\/)\\\\\\ . Either error may cause overlapping or crossed lines. The teacher should carefully monitor and correct by modeling and then if necessary, guide the student's pencil as the student makes the lines. When students can draw lines as the teacher claps, the teacher introduces an exercise in which the students also count as they draw lines. When the students can count and draw lines as the teacher claps, exercises with numerals can be introduced.

Figure 6.6 includes the format for teaching students to draw lines for numerals. In the format, students first identify a numeral, state that the numeral tells them to draw a certain number of lines, and then draw the lines. Since most students readily learn this skill, presentations on two to four lessons are often sufficient before including this problem type on independent worksheets.

Note that a "how many" box is included in the teacher presentation because it is easy to learn and because students must know that not every symbol tells them to draw lines.

If students make errors on independent worksheet items, the teacher should test to determine the cause of the error. Did the student identify the numeral correctly? If not, the misidentification caused the error. If the student identified the numeral correctly, the error resulted from a line drawing error, which is corrected by re-presenting the format in Figure 6.6.

COUNTING THE LINES, THEN WRITING A NUMERAL Writing a numeral to represent a set of objects is important in itself and is also an integral part of the strategy to teach a conceptual base for addition and subtraction. After students draw a set of lines for one side of an equation, they must write the numeral for that set. For

$$4 + 2 = \square$$
$$|\,|\,|\,| \quad |\,|$$

students count six lines and write a 6 in the box. The format for writing a numeral for a set of objects (see Figure 6.7) begins with an explanation of the function for the lines under a box. "The lines under a box tell what numeral goes in the box." The students are then told to count the lines under the box and write the numeral for the number they end with. If students have mastered the necessary preskills—rational counting and numeral writing—they will have little difficulty. After presentations for two or three lessons, items of this kind can be included on worksheets as independent activities.

The two mistakes students make on this task are either miscounting the lines or writing the wrong numeral. Often it is not clear by looking at a worksheet how a student derived an answer. In such a situation, the teacher should ask the student to work several items in front of him, counting aloud so that the cause of the error can be identified and an appropriate correction provided. If the student cannot correctly count lines in several problems, the teacher should provide practice on line counting (see Chapter 5). If a student writes the wrong numeral, the teacher needs to provide practice in numeral identification and numeral dictation.

Mistakes involving mechanics like writing a 4 backward as   are not critical. If the teacher can identify the numeral the student has written, the answer is acceptable. The teacher would praise a student who has written the correct numeral but written it backward. After praising the student,

Figure 6.6 Format for Identifying a Symbol Then Drawing Lines

Structured Worksheet

4	6	□	2

TEACHER   **STUDENTS**

1. "EVERYBODY, TOUCH THE FIRST NUMERAL ON YOUR
   WORKSHEET." Hold up worksheet and point to 4. "WHAT
   IS IT?"   "4"
   "A 4 TELLS YOU TO MAKE FOUR LINES. WHAT DOES
   A 4 TELL YOU TO DO?"   "Make four lines."
   "EACH TIME I CLAP, DRAW A LINE AND COUNT."   Students draw lines and count.
   Signal by clapping once each 2 seconds.   "1, 2, 3, 4."
   "HOW MANY DID YOU END UP WITH?"   "4"
   "GOOD."

2. "TOUCH THE NEXT SYMBOL. WHAT IS IT?"   "6"
   "A 6 TELLS YOU TO MAKE SIX LINES. WHAT DOES A 6
   TELL YOU TO DO?"   "Make six lines."
   "EACH TIME I CLAP, DRAW A LINE AND COUNT."
   Signal by clapping once each 2 seconds.   Students draw lines and count.
   "HOW MANY DID YOU END UP WITH?"   "6"

3. "TOUCH THE NEXT SYMBOL. WHAT IS IT?"   "Box"
   "DOES A BOX TELL YOU TO DRAW LINES? NO. A BOX
   DOES NOT TELL YOU TO DRAW LINES.
   DOES A BOX TELL YOU TO DRAW LINES?"   "No."
   "SO ARE YOU GOING TO DRAW LINES?"   "No."

4. "TOUCH THE NEXT SYMBOL. WHAT IS IT?"   "2"
   "WHAT DOES 2 TELL YOU TO DO?"   "Draw 2 lines."
   "DO IT." After students draw lines, say, "GET READY TO
   COUNT THE LINES. GET READY." Signal by clapping
   once each 2 seconds.   "1, 2"
   "HOW MANY DID YOU END UP WITH?"   "2"

Figure 6.7 Format for Writing a Numeral for a Set of Objects

Structured Worksheet

TEACHER   **STUDENTS**

1. "EVERYBODY, HERE'S A RULE: THE LINES
   UNDER A BOX TELL WHAT NUMERAL GOES
   IN THE BOX. GET READY TO COUNT THE
   LINES UNDER THIS BOX."
   Point to the first problem on the worksheet and pause
   while the students point to first line. "COUNT AS I
   CLAP. GET READY." Clap each second.   "1, 2"
   "HOW MANY LINES ARE UNDER THIS BOX?"   "2"
   "SO WHAT NUMERAL ARE YOU GOING TO
   WRITE IN THE BOX?"   "2"
   "WRITE THAT NUMERAL."

2. Repeat step 1 for additional examples.

---

however, the teacher would point out that the numeral is written backward. Some students will need months of practice writing numerals before they consistently write them in the correct form. The teacher should *not* put undue pressure on the students for writing numerals backward.

Place Value Related Skills

Three place value related skills are discussed in this section: (a) reading and writing numerals, (b) column alignment, and (c) expanded notation.

Teaching procedures are discussed for reading and writing each type of number: teens, tens, hundreds, thousands, and millions. The procedures are quite similar for the different number types. In reading numbers, the students identify the number in each column (e.g., two 10s and four 1s), their value (e.g., two 10s equal 20), and combine the values to come up with the entire number (e.g., 20 and 4 equal 24). In writing numbers, students first "expand" the numbers into their component parts (e.g., 24 = two 10s and four 1s) and then write each component. Variations in the teaching procedures are called for with teen numbers and numbers with zero. With teen numbers students say the ones number first (e.g., 16 is read *six*teen, not *teen*six) but write the tens number first (e.g., in writing 16, students write the 1, then the 6). Numbers with zeroes are difficult because students must omit them when reading (e.g., 306 is read three hundred six, not three hundred zero six) but include them when writing, even though the students don't hear the zero. Instructions in reading and writing are carefully coordinated. Students are first taught to read numbers of a certain type then to write numbers of that type.

Reading and Writing Teen Numbers

READING TEEN NUMBERS Reading teen numbers is introduced when the students can read all numerals between zero and 10. Regular teens are introduced before irregular teens. The numbers 14, 16, 17, 18 and 19 are regular teens. The irregular teens are 11, 12, 13, and 15. For example, whereas 14 is pronounced *four*teen, 12 is not pronounced *two*teen, but twelve. Likewise, 15 is not pronounced *five*teen but fifteen.

The format for teaching students to read teen numbers appears in Figure 6.8. It has three parts. In part A, a structured board exercise, the teacher writes a number grid on the board with spaces for

the tens and ones columns. The teacher tells the students that they read one ten as teen and models reading teen numerals. Then the students read them. On the first day of instruction, examples would be limited to regular teen numbers: 14, 16, 17, 18, 19. The next day one irregular teen would be introduced. A new irregular teen would be introduced each day unless students have difficulty with previously introduced teens. When a new, irregular teen fact is introduced, the teacher alternates between the new number and previously introduced numbers (e.g., 13, 14, 13, 16, 18, 13, 17, 14, 19, 13).

Part B is a less structured exercise in which the students read teen numbers with no prompting. Part B would be presented daily for several weeks. Part C is a worksheet exercise designed to reinforce the place value concept. In Part C the students are shown pictures of counters and are instructed to circle the appropriate numeral. After writing teens has been introduced, students can write the appropriate numeral rather than circling it.

WRITING TEEN NUMBERS Writing teen numbers is introduced when students are able to read teen numbers accurately and with a moderate degree of fluency (able to read a group of five teen numbers at a rate of about one each second). As in the procedure for reading teen numbers, regular teen numbers (14, 16, 17, 18, 19) are introduced first, then irregular teen numbers (11, 12, 13, 15). Irregular teens can be introduced about 2 days after regular teens. If students have no or little difficulty, a new irregular teen would be taught each day. Figure 6.9 includes the format for teaching students to write teen numbers. Part A contains a model-test procedure for teaching students to tell the component parts of a teen number: 14 = a 1 for the teen and a 4. Part B is a structured board presentation. The teacher refers to the number grid on the board and writes the digits in the appropriate columns. Part C is a structured worksheet exercise in which the teacher prompts the students as they write numerals. Part D is an independent dictation exercise in which the teacher says teen numbers and the students write them. If students are able to decode (read words) adequately, the dictation exercise can be replaced with a written worksheet in which students write the numerals indicated by written words.

Practice in writing teen numbers would be continued daily for several weeks to facilitate the development of fluency. The number grid would be included in writing exercises only for the first several weeks and then dropped.

Figure 6.8   Format for Reading Teen Numbers

Day	Part A Structured Board Presentation Problems	Part B Less Structured Board Problems	Part C Worksheet Problems
1–4	4	4	
5–6	2	6	
7–8		6	3
9–20			3

PART A: Structured Board Presentation

Write on board:

Tens	Ones
1	4
1	6
1	7
1	8
1	9

TEACHER   **STUDENT**

1. Point to tens column. "THIS IS THE TENS COLUMN."
   Point to ones column. "THIS IS THE ONES COLUMN."

2. "THESE NUMERALS ALL START WITH ONE TEN.
   FOR ONE TEN WE SAY TEEN. LISTEN TO ME READ
   THE NUMERALS."
   Point to 14.   "14."   Point to 18.   "18."
   Point to 16.   "16."   Point to 19.   "19."
   Point to 17.   "17."

3. "YOUR TURN TO READ THESE NUMERALS." Point
   to numerals in random order as students read.

4. Give individual turns to several students to read
   two numerals.

PART B: Less Structured Board Presentation

Write on board: 14

1. Point to 14. "WHAT NUMBER?" Signal.   "14"
   TO CORRECT: Use steps 1 and 2 from Part A.

2. Repeat step 1 with 19, 17, 18, 16.

PART C: Place Value Worksheet

Give students worksheets with problems such as this one:

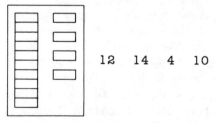

12   14   4   10

1. "LOOK AT THE PICTURE. THE BIG PILE HAS 10
   BLOCKS IN IT. THE SMALL PILE HAS 4 BLOCKS
   IN IT. I'LL COUNT: 10 (pause), 11, 12, 13, 14.
   HOW MANY BLOCKS?"   "14"

2. "THERE ARE 14 BLOCKS. PUT A CIRCLE AROUND
   THE NUMERAL 14."

Figure 6.9   Format for Writing Teen Numbers

Day	Part A Components of Teen Numbers Problems	Part B Structured Board Presentation Problems	Part C Structured Worksheet Problems	Part D Worksheet Dictation Problems
1–3	4			
4	4	4		
5–6		4	4	
7–8			6	4
9–20				6

PART A: Components of Teen Numbers

TEACHER

1. "YOU'RE GOING TO WRITE TEEN NUMERALS. REMEMBER, TEEN TELLS YOU THE NUMERALS HAS ONE TEN. LISTEN: 16. WRITE A ONE FOR THE TEEN AND THEN A SIX. LISTEN: 19. WHAT DO I WRITE FOR 19?"

   "LISTEN: 14. WHAT DO I WRITE FOR 14?"

2. "YOUR TURN: 14. WHAT DO YOU WRITE?"

3. Repeat step 2 with 16, 19, 17, 18.

4. Give individual turns to several students on step 2 or 3.

STUDENTS

"A one for the teen and a 9."

"A one for the teen and a 4."

"A one for the teen and a 4.'

PART B: Structured Board Presentation

Write on board: tens | ones

1. Point to tens column. "THIS IS THE TENS COLUMN. THIS IS WHERE WE WRITE ONE FOR TEEN FOR ONE TEN."

2. "WHAT DO YOU WRITE FOR 14?"
   Write 1 in tens column, 4 in ones column.

   "A one for the teen and a 4."

3. Repeat steps 1 and 2 with 17, 19, 16, 18.

4. Call on students. "READ EACH NUMERAL." Point as students read.

PART C: Structured Worksheet (Dictation)

Students have a worksheet similar to the one below:

    tens | ones
a. _____
b. _____
c. _____
d. _____

1. "TOUCH THE SPACE FOR PROBLEM a. YOU'RE GOING TO WRITE 14. WHAT NUMBER?"

   "14"

2. "WHAT DO YOU WRITE FOR 14?"

   "A one for the teen and a 4."

3. Write 14.

4. "READ THE NUMBER YOU JUST WROTE."

   "14"

5. Repeat steps 1–4 for 16, 19, 14, 17, 18.

Figure 6.9 cont'd

PART D: Less Structured Worksheet (Dictation)

TEACHER	STUDENTS

Give students worksheet with grid.

1. "YOU'RE GOING TO WRITE 14 ON THE FIRST LINE.
   WHAT ARE YOU GOING TO WRITE?"   "14"
   "WRITE 14."
   TO CORRECT: Use steps 1–4 from Part C.
2. Repeat step 1 with 16, 18, 19, 17.

The worksheet exercise in Figure 6.10 contains pictures of a group of 10 objects and several single objects. The students are to fill in numerals in the tens and ones column. This exercise, which reinforces the place value concept, can be introduced after students become proficient in writing dictated numerals.

Reading and Writing Numerals 20–99

READING NUMBERS 20-99 Reading numbers from 20 through 99 is introduced when students can read teen numbers accurately and with modest fluency (reading a group of five teen numbers within 8 seconds). Students should also be able to count by 1s and skip count by 10s to 100 (10, 20, 30, 40, 50, 60, 70, 80, 90, 100). The format for teaching students to read numerals between 20 and 99 appears in Figure 6.11.

Parts A and B utilize piles of 10 blocks to reinforce the place value concept for tens numbers. In Part A (introducing tens place value facts) the teacher draws several piles of 10 blocks. The teacher then tells students various place value facts for tens numbers (nine 10s equals 90) and has the students count by 10s to verify the facts.

In Part B, the teacher uses a model-test procedure to facilitate memorization of the various place value facts for tens numbers. Lower-performing students can be expected to have difficulty with translating two 10s, three 10s, and five 10s, since these are irregular. While four 10s equal forty, and eight 10s equals eighty, two 10s do not equal "twoty" but rather twenty. Likewise, three 10s do not equal "threety" but thirty and five 10s do not equal "fivety" but fifty.

Part C and Part D actually involve reading numbers in the place value grid. In Part C, the teacher instructs students to start reading in the tens column. He asks what numeral is in the tens column and what number that group of 10s equals. Finally the teacher asks what is the sum of that number and the number for the 1s (30 and 5 is 35).

In Part D, students read numerals with no prompting from the teacher. (Note that for the last five lessons in which Part D is used, the grid should not be included.) About a fourth of the examples in Part D should be teen numbers.

In Part E, the student is to select a numeral which represents a group of blocks. The teacher writes diagrams with piles of 10 and individual blocks. The students determine the total by first

Figure 6.10 Teens Numbers Worksheet Activity

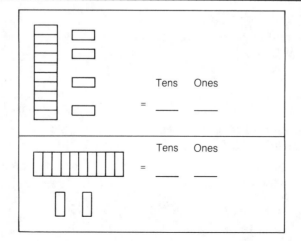

Figure 6.11 Format for Reading Numbers 20-99

Day	**Part A** Introducing Tens Place Value Facts Problems	**Part B** Practicing Tens Facts Problems	**Part C** Structured Board Presentation Problems	**Part D** Less Structured Board Problems	**Part E** Structured Worksheet Problems
1	3	6			
2		6	2		
3		6	6		
4			4	6	
5-8			4	8	
9-20				8	4

PART A (Preskill): Introducing Tens Place Value Facts

Show students diagram like this:

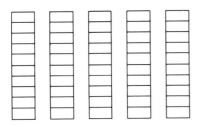

TEACHER

1. "EACH PILE HAS 10 BLOCKS. HOW MANY BLOCKS IN
   EACH PILE?"

2. "COUNT BY 10 EACH TIME I TOUCH A PILE." Touch piles.

3. "HOW MANY BLOCKS IN ALL?"
   "RIGHT, FIVE 10s EQUAL 50." Repeat steps 2 and 3 with
   two 10s and four 10s.

STUDENTS

"10"

"10, 20, 30, 40, 50"

"50"

PART B (Preskill): Practicing Tens Place Value Facts

Erase board.

1. Model. "LET'S PRACTICE WHAT GROUPS OF 10 EQUAL.
   LISTEN. THREE 10s EQUAL 30. WHAT DO THREE 10s
   EQUAL?"
   Repeat with two 10s and five 10s.

2. Test. "WHAT DO TWO 10s EQUAL?"
   Repeat with five 10s, three 10s, six 10s, eight 10s and four
   10s until students can respond correctly to all examples.

3. Present individual turns on step 2.

"30"

"20"

PART C: Structured Board Presentation

Write on board:

tens	ones
4	6

1. Point to tens column. "WHAT COLUMN?"
   Point to ones column. "WHAT COLUMN?"

2. "HOW MANY 10s?"
   "WHAT DO FOUR 10s EQUAL?"

3. "HOW MANY 1s?"
   "WHAT IS 40 AND 6?"
   "SO WHAT DOES THE WHOLE NUMERAL SAY?"
   Repeat steps 1-3 with 52, 38, 93, 81.

"Tens column"
"Ones column"

"4"
"40"

"6"
"46"
"46"

Figure 6.11 cont'd

PART D: Less Structured Board

Write on board:

tens	ones
7	2

1. "WHAT DOES THIS WHOLE NUMERAL SAY?" Pause
2-3 seconds, then signal.　　　　　　　　　　　"72"
TO CORRECT: Point to 7. "WHAT COLUMN IS 7 IN? WHAT
IS SEVEN 10s? WHAT IS 70 AND 2?"

2. Repeat step 1 with 95, 20, 16, 31, 47, 50, 12.

3. Give individual turns to several students.

PART E: Structured Worksheet

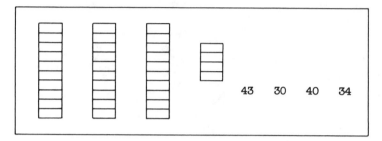

1. "LET'S FIND OUT HOW MANY BLOCKS ARE IN THIS
PICTURE. HOW MANY PILES OF 10s ARE THERE?"　　"3"

2. "WHAT DO THREE 10s EQUAL?"　　　　　　　　　"30"

3. "BUT WE'RE NOT DONE. Point to four remaining blocks.
"WE HAVE TO COUNT THESE BLOCKS." Point to tens group.
"WE HAVE 30 BLOCKS HERE. START COUNTING AT
30 AND TOUCH THESE BLOCKS AS I COUNT. Touch
blocks and count 31, 32, 33, 34.

4. "HOW MANY BLOCKS IN THIS PICTURE?"　　　　　"34"
"PUT A CIRCLE AROUND THE NUMERAL 34."

---

counting the piles of 10. Then they figure out what number the groups of 10 equal (four 10s equal 40). Finally, they count the single blocks (e.g., 41, 42, 43), which assumes the preskill of counting from different numbers.

WRITING NUMERALS FOR 20–99 Writing numerals for 20 through 99 is introduced after students can read these numerals. The format for teaching students to write these numerals appears in Figure 6.12. Parts A and B are preskills. Part A teaches the student to say the composite parts of the number (e.g., 97 is 90 and 7). Part B teaches the students to tell how many 10s in a tens number (e.g., 50 is five 10s). Part C introduces writing numbers from 20 through 99. The teacher says a number and has the students say its component parts. The teacher then asks how many 10s in the tens number and writes the numeral. The teacher then asks, for example, "84 equals 80 and what else?" After the student

says 4, the teacher writes the 4 in the ones column. Part D has the same steps as Part C, except the students write the numerals. Part E is a dictation exercise. The teacher dictates numbers and the students write the appropriate numerals. About a third of the examples in this part should be teen numbers.

Teachers working with remedial students can expect students to have particular reversal problems with numbers ending with 1 (e.g., writing 31 as 13, 71 as 17, or 21 as 12). To remedy reversal problems, the teacher would first present Parts B, C, and D of the writing teens format (Figure 6.9) for one or two lessons. She would concurrently present the writing tens numbers format (Figure 6.12) excluding all tens numbers ending with 1 (e.g., 21, 31, 41, 51). The purpose of excluding the tens numbers ending with 1 is to ensure students' mastery of easier numbers before introducing numbers students typically reverse. After the student writes teen and ten numbers without assistance for several

Figure 6.12 Format for Writing Numbers 20-99

Day	Part A Expanded Notation Problems	Part B Place Value Problems	Part C Structured Board Presentation Problems	Part D Structured Worksheet Problems	Part E Less Structured Worksheet Problems with grid	without grid
1	4	4				
2	2	4	4			
3			6	4		
4			4	6	2	
5				4	6	
6-10					8	3
11-20						8

PART A: Expanded Notation Preskill

TEACHER	**STUDENTS**
1. "EIGHTY-FOUR, SAY THAT."	"84"
2. "EIGHTY-FOUR EQUALS 80 AND 4. WHAT DOES 84 EQUAL?"	"80 and 4"
"WHAT'S THE FIRST PART OF 84?"	"80"
3. "EIGHTY-FOUR EQUALS 80 AND WHAT ELSE?"	"4"
4. Repeat steps 1-3 with 72, 95, 88, 43.	

PART B: Tens Numbers Place Value Facts Preskill

1. "TWENTY HAS TWO 10s. HOW MANY 10s IN 20?"	"2"
2. Repeat step 1 with 60 and 30.	
3. "HOW MANY 10s IN 40?"	"4"
4. Repeat step 3 with 80, 30, 60, 20, 50.	
5. Give individual turns to several students.	

PART C: Structured Board Presentation

Write on board: tens | ones

1. "I WANT TO WRITE SOME BIG NUMBERS. WHEN WE WRITE BIG NUMBERS, WE WRITE THE 10s FIRST. THEN WE WRITE THE 1s. WHAT DO WE WRITE FIRST?"	"The 10s"
"WHAT DO WE WRITE NEXT?"	"The 1s"
2. "LISTEN. 84. WHAT IS THE FIRST PART OF 84?"	"80"
3. "HOW MANY 10s IN 80?"	"8"
"SO I WRITE 8 IN THE 10s COLUMN." Write 8 in the 10s column. "80 EQUALS EIGHT 10s."	
4. "LISTEN: 84 EQUALS 80 AND WHAT ELSE?"	"4"
"SO I WRITE 4 IN THE 1s COLUMN." Write 4 in the 1s column.	
5. "WHAT NUMBER DID I JUST WRITE?"	"84"
6. "HOW MANY 10s IN 84?"	"8"
"HOW MANY 1s IN 84?"	"4"
7. Repeat steps 2-5 with several examples.	

Figure 6.12 cont'd

PART D: Structured Worksheet

TEACHER   **STUDENTS**

Give students the following worksheet:

	tens	ones
a.		
b.		
c.		
d.		
e.		
f.		

1. "TOUCH a. NEXT TO a YOU ARE GOING TO WRITE 79. WHAT ARE YOU GOING TO WRITE?" — "79"

2. "WHAT IS THE FIRST PART OF 79?" — "70"
   "HOW MANY 10s IN 70?" — "7"
   "WRITE 7 IN THE TENS COLUMN."

3. SEVENTY-NINE EQUALS 70 AND WHAT ELSE?" — "9"
   "WRITE 9 IN THE ONES COLUMN."

4. "WHAT NUMBER DID YOU WRITE?" — "79"

5. "HOW MANY 10s IN 79?" — "7"

6. "HOW MANY 1s IN 79?" — "9"
   Repeat step 1-6 with several examples.

PART E: Less Structured Worksheet (Dictation)

Give students worksheet labeled like this:

a. _____

b. _____

c. _____

d. _____

e. _____

f. _____

1. "YOU'RE GOING TO WRITE A NUMERAL ON EACH LINE."

2. "TOUCH LINE a."

3. "YOU'RE GOING TO WRITE 49. WHAT ARE YOU GOING TO WRITE?" — "49"

4. "WRITE 49." — Students write 49

   TO CORRECT: Use steps 2-3 from Part D.

5. Repeat steps 2-4 with 73, 20, 99, 14, 51, 42, 61, 17.

days, the teacher begins working directly on the reversal problem. She presents Part C of the writing teens format (Figure 6.9) with minimally different examples, focusing on ten and teen numbers like 13 and 31, 17 and 71. Part C may have to be presented daily for several weeks to students who are severely confused. Keep in mind that minimally different pairs are used only for remedial students, not for younger students learning the skill for the first time.

Reading and Writing Numbers 100–999

READING HUNDREDS NUMBERS   Reading hundreds numbers is usually taught during second grade. Students should be able to read and write numerals for numbers below 100 prior to the introduction of numbers from 100 to 999. The procedure is very similar to that used for teaching students to read tens numbers. The format for reading hundreds appears in Figure 6.13.

Figure 6.13 Format for Reading Numbers 100-999

Day	Part A Structured Board Presentation Problems	Part B Less Structured Board Presentation Problems
1-2	6	
2-4	4	4
5-20		6

PART A: Structured Board Presentation

TEACHER   **STUDENTS**

Write on board:

huns	tens	ones
5	4	8

1. Point to appropriate column as you say:
   "THIS IS THE HUNDREDS COLUMN.
   THIS IS THE TENS COLUMN.
   THIS IS THE ONES COLUMN.
   TELL ME THE NAMES OF THE COLUMNS."
   Point to the columns starting with hundreds; repeat
   until children are firm.   Students say hundreds, tens, ones

2. "THE FIRST THING WE DO WHEN WE READ A NUMBER IS
   IDENTIFY THE COLUMN THE NUMBER STARTS IN."
   Point to 5 in 548. "WHAT COLUMN DOES THIS NUMBER
   START IN?"   "Hundreds"
   "HOW MANY HUNDREDS DO WE HAVE?" Signal.   "5"
   "WHAT DO FIVE HUNDREDS EQUAL?" Signal.   "500"

3.* Point to 4. "WHAT COLUMN IS THIS?"   "Tens"
   "HOW MANY 10s DO WE HAVE?"   "4"
   "WHAT DO FOUR 10s EQUAL?"   "40"

4.* Point to 8. "WHAT COLUMN IS THIS?"   "Ones"
   "HOW MANY 1s DO WE HAVE?"   "8"
   "WHAT DO WE SAY?"   "8"
   Repeat steps 2-4 until firm.

5.* "LET'S READ THE WHOLE NUMBER. WHEN I TOUCH A
   NUMERAL, YOU TELL ME WHAT IT SAYS."
   Point to 5, pause a second, touch 5.   "500"
   Point to 4, pause a second, touch 4.   "40"
   Point to 8, pause a second, touch 8.   "8"
   TO CORRECT: If children do not respond correctly when
            you touch a number, say "THIS IS THE ____
            COLUMN. HOW MANY _____ DO WE
            HAVE? SO WHAT DO WE SAY?" Then return
            to the beginning of the number.

6. "SAY THE WHOLE NUMBER." Signal.   "548"

7. Repeat steps 2-6 with 697, 351, 874, 932, all written in
   labeled grids.

Figure 6.13 cont'd

"When presenting examples with a 1 in the tens column, the teacher presents these steps instead of 3, 4, and 5 in the format:

3. "WHAT COLUMN IS THIS?" Signal.   "Tens"
"HOW MANY 10S DO WE HAVE?" Signal.   "1"

4. "HOW MANY 1s DO WE HAVE?"   "4"
"WE HAVE ONE 10 AND FOUR 1s, SO WHAT DO WE SAY?" Signal.   "14"

5. "LET'S READ THE WHOLE NUMBER. Point to 5.
"WHAT DO WE SAY FOR THIS?"   "500"
Point to 14. "WHAT DO WE SAY FOR THESE?"   "14"

PART B: Less Structured Board Presentation

Write on board:

huns	tens	ones
4	4	6

1. "NOW WE ARE GOING TO READ THE NUMBERS WITHOUT SAYING THE PARTS FIRST. THIS TIME WHEN I POINT, YOU ARE GOING TO TELL ME THE WHOLE NUMBER."
Point to 446, pause 2–3 seconds, then signal.
TO CORRECT: Repeat steps 2–6 from Part A.

2. Repeat step 1 with 249, 713, 321, 81, 720, 740.

3. Give individual turns to several students.

Figure 6.14   Worksheet Exercise for Reading Hundreds Numbers

Circle the correct numeral:

three hundred sixty-two	320	362	360
four hundred eighty-six	48	468	486
two hundred seventy-one	217	270	271
nine hundred thirty-two	729	932	923

In Part A, the teacher introduces the hundreds column, explaining that numerals in that column tell how many hundreds. The teacher then leads students in reading numerals. He points to the digit farthest to the left, asks what column it is in, and then asks what number the digit represents: "What column is 5 in? . . . What do five hundreds equal?" The teacher then does the same for each remaining digit in the numeral. "What column is the 2 in? . . . What do two tens equal? . . . What column is the 6 in? What do six ones equal?" A slight modification of the basic procedure is used for numbers with a 1 in the tens column. This modification appears in a footnote to the format. In Part B, the teacher has the students say the numbers without teacher prompting.

Daily exercises in reading numbers would be continued for several weeks. Thereafter, practice in reading numbers would be incorporated into operations formats in which the first step always involves reading the problem. Practice can also be provided through worksheet exercises like that in Figure 6.14. Obviously, such written exercises would be appropriate only for students able to decode the words.

The sequence in which hundreds numbers are introduced is important. First are hundreds numbers which do not include a zero in the tens column. Numbers with a zero in the tens column are difficult because the student says nothing for the zero. This more difficult type would be introduced in Part A about a week after the easier numbers. A slight modification in the format is required: In step 3 of Part A, the teacher would say "We have zero tens, so we don't say anything when I point to the numeral zero." Also in step 5, the students should not say anything when the teacher points to the zero. For example, for 608, students say 600 when the teacher points to 6, remain quiet when the teacher points to 0, and then say 8 when the teacher points to 8.

When presenting exercises to teach students to read hundreds numbers with a zero in the tens column, the teacher would include several sets like these: 38, 308, 380, 42, 420, 402, 703, 730, 73. Note that in each set there are three minimally different numbers: a tens number and two hundreds numbers. The hundreds numbers include the same numerals which appeared in the tens number plus a zero. In one of the hundreds numbers the zero appears in the tens column and in the other hundreds number the zero appears in the ones column.

WRITING HUNDREDS NUMBERS Students usually have more difficulty learning to write hundreds numbers than to read them. The sequence in which hundreds numbers are introduced in writing tasks is the same as for reading. We recommend that hundreds numbers be introduced in two stages. During the first stage, hundreds numbers with a zero in the tens column should be excluded; 248 is acceptable but 208 isn't. Two hundred eight is troublesome because no tens number is heard. During the second stage, numbers with a zero in either the tens or ones column may be used.

Figure 6.15 includes the format for teaching students to write the first type of hundred numbers (those without a zero in the tens column). In Part A, the teacher presents a verbal exercise in which she has the students tell the component parts of a hundreds number, e.g., 382 = 300 + 80 + 2. Note the wording in steps 3 and 4 of Part A in which the teacher asks the students if they heard a tens

Figure 6.15 Format for Writing Hundreds Numbers

Day	Part A Expanded Notation Problems	Part B Structured Board Presentation Problems	Part C Supervised Practice Problems	Part D Independent Practice Problems
1-2	5			
3-4	3	4		
5-6		6	6	
7-20				10

PART A: Expanded Notation

TEACHER	STUDENTS
1. "COUNT BY 100s. GET READY, COUNT."	"100, 200, 300, 400, 500, 600, 700, 800, 900"
"NOW COUNT BY 10s. GET READY, COUNT."	"10, 20, 30, 40, 50, 60, 70, 80, 90"
2. "LISTEN. 362. DO YOU HEAR HUNDREDS IN 362?	"Yes"
"WHAT HUNDREDS NUMBER?"	"300"
3. "LISTEN. 362. DO YOU HEAR A TENS NUMBER IN 362?"	"Yes"
"WHAT TENS NUMBER?"	"60"
TO CORRECT: Tell answer, return to step 2.	
4. "LISTEN. 362. DO YOU HEAR A ONES NUMBER IN 362?"	"Yes"
"WHAT ONES NUMBER?"	"2"
5. "362 = 300 + 60 + 2. SAY IT WITH ME."	"362 = 300 + 60 + 2"
"SAY IT YOURSELVES."	"362 = 300 + 60 + 2"
6. Repeat steps 2-5 with 428, 624, and 139.	
7. Give individual turns on steps 2-5 to several students.	

Figure 6.15 cont'd

PART B: Structured Worksheet Presentation (Dictation)

Give students a worksheet in which columns and spaces are written as illustrated.

	huns	tens	ones
a.	___	___	___
b.	___	___	___
c.	___	___	___
d.	___	___	___
e.	___	___	___

1. "YOU ARE GOING TO WRITE HUNDREDS NUMBERS. TOUCH THE HUNDREDS COLUMN. TOUCH THE TENS COLUMN. TOUCH THE ONES COLUMN." Monitor responses.

2. "WHAT'S THE FIRST PART OF 648?"   "600"
   "SO WHAT COLUMN DO YOU START WRITING IN?" Signal.   "Hundreds"
   "HOW MANY 100s IN 600?"   "6"
   "WRITE 6 IN THE HUNDREDS COLUMN."

3. "WHAT COLUMN COMES NEXT?"   "Tens"
   "DO YOU HEAR A TENS NUMBER IN 648?"   "Yes"
   "WHAT TENS NUMBER?"   "40"
   "HOW MANY 10s IN 40?"   "4"
   "WRITE 4 IN THE TENS COLUMN."

TEACHER   **STUDENTS**

4. "WHAT COLUMN COMES NEXT?"   "Ones"
   "DO YOU HEAR A ONES NUMBER IN 648?"   "Yes"
   "WHAT ONES NUMBER?"   "8"
   "WRITE 8 IN THE ONES COLUMN"

5. "WE FINISHED. HOW MANY 100s IN 648?"   "6"
   "HOW MANY 10s IN 648?"   "4"
   HOW MANY 1s IN 648?"   "8"
   "READ THE NUMBER YOU WROTE."   "648"

6. Repeat steps 2-5 with 326, 463, 825, 253, 866.

PART C: Supervised Practice

Write these numerals:

a. two hundred sixty-one
b. four hundred eighteen
c. eighty
d. nine hundred sixty-two
e. forty-eight
f. four hundred eighty
g. twelve
h. nine hundred seven
i. forty-one
j. three hundred ninety-seven

huns	tens	ones

1. "THE INSTRUCTIONS TELL YOU TO WRITE THE NUMERALS."

2. "READ THE WORDS. WRITE THE NUMERAL."

3. "WRITE THE NUMERALS."
   TO CORRECT: Use steps 2-4 from Part B.

4. Repeat steps 2 and 3 with the remaining examples.

number. This wording is intended to prepare students for numbers in which there is a zero in either the tens or ones column.

In Part B the teacher guides the students in writing numerals for numbers through 999. For example, in guiding the students through writing 486, the teacher asks students to say the first part of the number (400) and points out that since it's a hundreds number, they start writing the numeral in the hundreds column. The teacher asks how many 100s and has the students write the numeral (4) in the hundreds column. The teacher then asks what column comes next (tens). This question is designed to remind students that they must always write a numeral in the tens column. The teacher has the students say the tens number (80), asks how many 10s in that number (8), and has the students write that numeral (8) in the tens column. The ones column is done next. The students write 6 in that column.

Part C is a supervised practice exercise in which numbers are written as words. The students must write the numerals. Teachers working with students unable to decode well would read the words to the student. Daily practice would be continued for several weeks. A number grid would be incorporated into exercises for the first several weeks, then dropped.

Note that several tens numbers are included in the exercises. The tens numbers are included to reinforce the concept of proper column alignment. The first digit in a tens number is written in the tens column, while the first digit in a hundreds number is written in the hundreds column.

Numbers with a zero in the tens column are introduced in writing exercises after students can accurately write three digit numerals without zeroes in the tens column. For numbers with a zero in the tens or ones column, step 3 in Part B would have to be modified. For example, after the students indicated that they do not hear a tens number, the teacher asks, "So what do we write in the tens column?" "Zero." "Write a zero in the tens column." The teacher then proceeds to step 4.

Examples would be the same as for exercises focusing on reading numbers with a zero in the tens column; minimally different sets such as 902, 92, 920; 48, 480, 408; and 702, 72, 720 should be used.

Reading and Writing Numbers 1,000-999,999

READING THOUSANDS NUMBERS Thousands numbers are usually introduced during third grade.

The format for introducing students to thousands numbers is fairly simple (see Figure 6.16). Students are taught that the numeral in front of the comma tells how many thousands. They read that number, say "thousands" for the comma, and then read the rest of the number. In reading 3,286 they say "3," then "thousands" for the comma, and finally "286."

Students would read 8 to 10 numbers in the format. The sequence in which thousands numbers are introduced should be carefully controlled. We recommend that thousands numbers be introduced in this sequence:

1. Numbers between 1,000 and 9,999 which have any numeral other than zero in each column
2. Numbers between 1,000 and 9,999 which have zero in one or more columns
3. Numbers between 10,000 and 99,999
4. Numbers between 100,000 and 999,999

We recommend not including numbers with zeroes initially, since students may mistakenly develop the misrule that thousands have something to do with the number of zeroes in a numeral rather than the number of places. When numbers with zeroes are introduced, the teacher should pay careful attention to example selection. A fourth of the numbers would have a zero in the hundreds and tens column, a fourth would have a zero in just the hundreds column, another fourth would have a zero in just the tens column, and a final fourth would have no zeroes at all. A sample set might include 2,000, 2,058, 2,508, 2,815; 7,002, 7,020, 7,200, 7,248; and 9,040, 9,400, 9,004, 9,246.

During fourth grade, students should be introduced to thousands numbers between 1,000 and 9,999 that do not have a comma. Reference type materials students encounter will often have thousands numbers written without a comma. In presenting thousands numbers without a comma, the teacher tells the students that when a number has four digits, it is a thousand and then presents a list including a mix of thousands and hundreds numbers.

WRITING THOUSANDS NUMBERS Writing thousands is taught in four stages, just as reading thousands is. During the first stage, all numbers have a digit other than zero in the hundreds and tens column. In the second stage, numbers with a zero in the hundreds and/or tens column are introduced. (The example in Figure 6.17 is from the second stage, numerals with a zero.) Numbers with a zero in the hundreds column are difficult because students may not write the zero. Students will often

Figure 6.16 Format for Reading Thousands Numbers

Day	Part A Structured Board Presentation Problems	Part B Less Structured Board Presentation Problems
1	6	
2-3	6	4
4-20		8

PART A: Structured Board Presentation

TEACHER   **STUDENTS**

1. "WHEN A BIG NUMBER HAS ONE COMMA, THE COMMA TELLS ABOUT THOUSANDS. HERE'S THE RULE. THE NUMBER IN FRONT OF THE COMMA TELLS HOW MANY THOUSANDS. WHAT DOES THE NUMBER IN FRONT OF THE COMMA TELL?"   "How many thousands"
   Write on board: 6,781.

2. "WHAT NUMBER COMES IN FRONT OF THE COMMA?"   "6"
   "SO WHAT IS THE FIRST PART OF THE NUMBER?"   "6 thousand"

3. Point to 781. "GET READY TO READ THE REST OF THE NUMBER." Signal.   "781"

4. "NOW YOU ARE GOING TO READ THE WHOLE NUMBER." Point to 6, then comma, then 781.   "6,781"

5. Repeat steps 2-4 with these numbers: 2,145; 3,150; 5,820; 6,423.

6. Give individual turns to several students.

PART B: Less Structured Board Presentation

Write on board: 3,820

1. "GET READY TO TELL ME THIS NUMBER." Pause several seconds, signal.   "3,820"

   TO CORRECT: Repeat steps 2-4 from Part A.

2. Repeat step 1 with 9,270; 3,174; 3,271; 9,563; 4,812.

3. Give individual turns to several students.

---

write the number four thousand eighty five as 4,85, leaving out the zero in the hundreds column. Often students simply write the numbers they hear: four thousand, eighty, and five. The teaching procedure for writing numbers must be designed to reinforce the place value concept that digits must be written in the thousands, hundreds, tens and ones columns. Writing numbers with a zero in the hundreds or tens column might be introduced about a week after the easier number types are taught. Just as with reading thousands numbers, sets of minimally different examples should be presented in numeral writing exercises, e.g., 4,028, 4,208, 4,218, 4,280; 6,200, 6,002, 6,020, 6,224; 5,090, 5,900, 5,009, 5,994.

Figure 6.17 shows a format for writing thousands numbers. Note that the format is very similar to the writing hundreds format (Figure 6.15). Before students write a number, the teacher tells them to make a long line for the thousands and shorter lines for the hundreds, tens, and ones numbers. The teacher then has the students tell how many thousands and instructs them to write the appropriate numeral. The students then write a comma for the word *thousand*. Note that the comma should be started on the line with a slightly curved downward pointing line. Many students will write the comma in the middle of the line (e.g., 4'326) so that it looks like the numeral 1. The teacher should watch for this error and immediately correct mistakes by modeling where to write the comma. After the comma is written, the teacher repeats the number, asking the students if they hear a hundreds number. If the answer is no, the student writes a zero. The same

Figure 6.17 Format for Writing Thousands Numbers

Day	Part A Structured Worksheet Problems	Part B Supervised Practice Problems
1-2	6	
3-4	4	6
5-15		10

PART A: Structured Worksheet

TEACHER	STUDENTS

Write on board: ———— —— —— ——

1. "THE BIG LINE IS FOR THOUSANDS. THE OTHER LINES ARE FOR THE HUNDREDS, TENS, AND ONES. WRITE LINES FOR THE THOUSANDS, HUNDREDS, TENS, AND ONES ON YOUR PAPER."

2. "LISTEN. 8,024. HOW MANY THOUSANDS?"   "8"
   "WRITE 8 ON THE THOUSANDS LINE. AND WHAT DO YOU WRITE AFTER THE THOUSANDS NUMBERS?"   "Comma"
   "WRITE A COMMA."   Students write comma.

3. "LISTEN. 8,024. YOU WROTE 8 THOUSAND. WHAT DO YOU HAVE LEFT?"   "24"

4. "ARE THERE ANY 100s IN 24?"   "No"
   "SO WRITE ZERO IN THE HUNDREDS COLUMN."   Students write zero.

5. "ARE THERE ANY 10s IN 24?"   "Yes"
   "WHAT DO YOU WRITE IN THE TENS COLUMN?"   "2"
   "WRITE IT."   Students write 2.

   TO CORRECT: "8,024. WHAT TENS NUMBER DO YOU HEAR? HOW MANY 10s IS 20?"

6. "ARE THERE ANY 1s IN 24?"   "Yes"
   WHAT DO YOU WRITE IN THE ONES COLUMN?"   "4"
   "WRITE IT."   Students write 4.

7. Repeat steps 1-6 with 8,204; 8,240 and 6,008; 6,800; 6,080.

PART B: Supervised Practice (Dictation)

1. "NOW YOU ARE GOING TO WRITE SOME NUMERALS WITHOUT HELP."

2. "MAKE A LONG LINE FOR THOUSANDS AND SHORTER LINES FOR HUNDREDS, TENS, AND ONES."

3. "LISTEN. 9,028. WHAT NUMBER?"   "9,028"
   "WRITE 9,028." Monitor responses.

   TO CORRECT: Use steps 2 and 3 from structured part.

4. Repeat step 3 with these numbers: 9,208; 9,280; 8,004; 8,400; 8,040.

procedure is used with the tens and ones column. In Part B the students write numbers without assistance.

Practice in writing thousands numbers should be continued daily for several weeks. Practice can be provided through worksheet exercises similar to those in Figure 6.14 for writing hundreds numbers.

Reading and Writing Millions

Reading and writing millions numbers is usually taught during late fourth and fifth grade. Reading millions can be taught using a procedure similar to that taught for reading thousands. The teacher instructs students to identify millions by examining the number of commas in the number. Students are taught that when two commas appear, the numbers in front of the first comma signify millions, while the numbers in front of the second comma signify thousands. The teacher initially prompts students by having them say the number a part at a time.

For example, in reading the number 8,342,000, the teacher would ask, "How many commas? . . . What does the number in front of the first comma tell about? . . . Say the first part of the number . . .What do the numbers in front of the second comma tell about? . . . How many thousands? . . . Say the whole number . . . "

Example selection for reading millions numbers should include a mix of millions numbers and thousands numbers so that the students receive practice in discriminating what to do when there are two commas versus one comma.

Writing millions numbers is taught by using a quasi-number grid with spaces for each column: ___ ___ ___ ___ ___ ___ ___ . The teacher leads the students through writing the numerals, using basically the same steps as in the format for writing thousands numbers (see Figure 6.17). "Listen. 5 million 203 thousand, 450. How many million? . . . Write 5 in the millions column . . . 5 million 203 thousand. How many thousands? . . . Write 203 in the spaces before the thousands comma . . . Listen, 5 million 203 thousand 450. Write the rest of the number."

Numbers that will be especially difficult for students to write are those with zeroes in either the hundreds or ten thousands columns, like 3,064,800, 2,005,000, or 8,000,124. These numbers are introduced in writing exercises only after the students can write easier numbers. Again, as with thousands numbers, minimally different sets should be used; e.g., 6,024,000, 6,204,000, 6,024, 6,240,000, 6,240. The sets should include a mix of millions and thousands numbers. A great

deal of practice reading and writing millions numbers will be necessary before students develop mastery. This practice should be provided through oral and worksheet exercises over a period of several months.

Column Alignment

Column alignment involves writing a series of numerals so that the appropriate digits are vertically aligned. Column alignment is an important skill because it is a prerequisite for advanced computation and story problems, in which the numbers to be computed do not appear in a column in the story: e.g., "Fred has 4,037 marbles. He gives 382 marbles to his younger brother. How many does he have left?" Column alignment exercises also test students' understanding of place value. For example, students who try to solve the problem about Fred's marbles by writing

$$\begin{array}{r} 4,037 \\ -3\,62 \\ \hline \end{array}$$

not only will arrive at the wrong answer but also have not mastered important place value skills.

Column alignment problems usually involve numerals with different numbers of digits written as row problems. The complexity of these column alignment problems increases as the number of digits increases. At first, problems would involve adding tens and ones numbers (32 + 5 + 14); later, hundreds, tens and ones (142 + 8 + 34); then thousands, hundreds, tens, and ones (3,042 + 6 + 134 + 28).

The strategy we recommend involves rewriting the numbers: the number with the most digits first and the other numbers under that number. The purpose of writing the largest numeral first is to establish the columns. The teaching procedure would involve a simple model-test procedure in a structured worksheet format (see Figure 6.18). The teacher tells the rule about the numeral with the most digits being written first and then guides the students in determining in which column to begin writing the other numerals. The structured worksheet exercise would be presented for several lessons, using about five problems daily. Thereafter, practice on about five problems daily would appear on independent worksheets for several weeks.

Expanded Notation

Expanded notation involves rewriting a number as an addition problem composed of the numerals which each digit represents. For example, the

Figure 6.18 Format for Teaching Column Alignment

Structured Worksheet

```
   a. 42 + 361 + 279              361
                                  279
                              +    42

   b. 79 + 604 + 324
```

<u>**TEACHER**</u>   <u>**STUDENTS**</u>

1. "TOUCH PROBLEM a. I'LL READ IT:
   42 + 361 + 279. PROBLEM a HAS BEEN RE-
   WRITTEN IN A COLUMN. TOUCH THE COLUMN
   PROBLEM. THE LARGEST NUMBER IS ON TOP.
   TOUCH 361. THE SMALLEST NUMBER IS ON
   THE BOTTOM. TOUCH 42. THE 4 IN 42 IS IN
   THE TENS COLUMN."

2. "TOUCH PROBLEM b."   Students touch 79 + 604 + 324.
   "READ THE PROBLEM."   "79 plus 604 plus 324"

3. "WE'RE GOING TO WRITE THE NUMERALS IN A COLUMN
   SO WE CAN ADD THEM. WE WRITE THE LARGEST
   NUMBER FIRST. WHAT'S THE LARGEST NUMBER?"   "604"
   "WRITE IT AND THEN CROSS OUT 604 IN THE ROW
   PROBLEM."   Students write 604.

4. "NOW GET READY TO WRITE 324 UNDER 604. WHAT
   COLUMN DOES 324 START IN?"   "Hundreds"
   "WRITE 324 AND CROSS IT OUT IN THE ROW PROBLEM."   Students write 604
                                                                     324

5. "NOW GET READY TO WRITE 79. WHAT COLUMN WILL
   YOU START WRITING IN?"   "Tens"
   "WRITE 79 AND CROSS IT OUT IN THE ROW PROBLEM."   Students write   604
    ~~79 + 604 + 324~~   324
                                                                         79

6. "HAVE YOU CROSSED OUT ALL THE NUMERALS IN
   THE ROW PROBLEM?"   "Yes"
   "WHAT KIND OF PROBLEM IS THIS?"   "Addition"
   "WRITE IN THE SIGN. YOU'RE DONE WRITING THE
   PROBLEM. NOW WORK IT."

7. Repeat steps 1–5 with four more problems.

---

number 3,428 would be rewritten horizontally as 3,000 + 400 + 20 + 8 or vertically as

```
      3000
       400
        20
   +     8
```

The sequence in which expanded notation problems are introduced parallels the order in which students are taught to read and write numerals: teens, 20–99, 100–999, 1,000–999,999, etc.

The teaching procedure for the verbal component of expanded notation is included in the previously discussed numeral writing formats; e.g., What makes up 16? (see Figure 6.9) and Do you hear a tens number in 382? . . . What tens number? (see Figure 6.15). With this background, students should have relatively little trouble saying a number as an addition problem (354 – 300 + 50 + 4), which is the focus of the structured board presentation (see Figure 6.19). On the structured worksheet, students say numbers as addition problems and then write the problems. Since a less structured format is unnecessary, supervised practice can follow the structured worksheet.

Figure 6.19 Format for Expanded Notation

Day	Part A Structured Board Presentation Problems	Part B Structured Worksheet Problems	Part C Supervised Practice Problems
1-2	4-6		
3-6	4	4	
7 till accurate		1	4

PART A: Structured Board Presentation

TEACHER   **STUDENTS**

1. "LISTEN. 624. SAY THAT."   "624"

2. LISTEN TO ME SAY 624 AS AN ADDITION PROBLEM:
   600 + 20 + 4."

3. "YOUR TURN. SAY 624 AS AN ADDITION PROBLEM."   "600 + 20 + 4"

4. Repeat step 3 with 29, 406, 317, 29, 871, 314.

PART B: Structured Worksheet

1. "SAY 472 AS AN ADDITION PROBLEM."   "400 + 70 + 2"

2. "WRITE 472 AS AN ADDITION PROBLEM."   Students write problem.

3. Repeat steps 1 and 2 with 427, 612, 94, 37, 274, 906, 704.

PART C: Supervised Practice

1. Give students worksheets with problems like these:

   624 = _____ + _____ + _____

   385 = _____ + _____ + _____

   Tell students, "WRITE THESE NUMBERS AS ADDITION PROBLEMS."

Research

As with many other topics discussed in the text, the limited research tends to be of two types: survey and method comparisons. A survey study in place value was done by Smith (1973), who found the most difficult skill to be renaming, e.g., 43 = 30 + 13. In a study of intervention methods, Barr (1978) compared three approaches for teaching the names and concrete representation for two digit numerals. Although the three approaches did not differ in post-test results, a 4-week delayed retention test did show significant differences in the number of correctly worked problems. In the most effective treatment, students counted groups of more than 10 objects by 1s, learned to associate numerals with each group, and then grouped objects in sets of 10 and counted the groups as 10s and the rest as 1s, e.g., 10, 20, 30, 31, 32, 33, 34. During the last two lessons of the 10-lesson program, the students learned that the left digit represented the number of groups of 10s. This procedure is quite similar to the one recommended in the text. In the least effective strategy, the students never counted beyond 10 but immediately grouped objects into sets of 10 and learned that the left digit represented the number of 10s. The treatment of intermediate effectiveness was the same as the most effective treatment except that the students never counted groups by 10s and 1s. These findings were similar to those of Rathmell (1972).

Many math educators today advocate the use of manipulatives to teach initial place value skills. Although no research was available that compared the performance of students taught to use manipulatives with those taught to use more abstract representations, Edge and Ashlock (1982) conducted a study to determine if there were differences in learning and transfer as a result of using a variety of manipulatives versus only one type of manipulative. Most mathematics textbooks do recommend that teachers use a variety of concrete objects to teach place value concepts. The researchers found no significant differences between groups in either learning trends or transfer of learning. Whether one uses several types of manipulatives or only one kind of manipulative to teach place value does not seem to make any difference.

Application Items: Symbols and Place Value

1. The teacher is presenting a task on which the numerals 4, 2, and 5 appear. When the teacher points to 4 and asks "What number?", a student says "5." What is the correction procedure?

2. A child writes a 7 in an empty box over a group of five lines. Tell two possible causes of this error. How could you determine the exact cause? Describe a remediation.

3. During a test of writing numbers, a student writes a 2 as a 5. What would the teacher do?

4. Below is a worksheet item done independently by a child. The item required the student to write the appropriate number of lines to represent a numeral. Note the errors made by the student and describe the probable cause. Describe a remediation.

| 2 | 5 | 6 | 4 | 3 | 7 |

|| |||| |||||| ||||| ||| |||||||

5. When presenting a format in which the students are being taught to read tens numbers, a student identifies 71 as 17. What does the teacher say in making the correction?

6. Two teachers are introducing the reading of hundreds numbers. Below are the examples each included in the lesson. Which set is more appropriate? Tell why.

Teacher A   306   285   532   683   504
Teacher B   724   836   564   832   138

7. A child writes 38 when the teacher says 308. Specify the wording the teacher uses to correct (see appropriate format).

8. The numerals below are representative of various types. Tell the type each numeral illustrates. List the order in which the types would be introduced.

   836; 13; 18; 305; 64; 5,024; 5,321

9. Construct a set of six to eight examples to be used in presenting the specified parts of the following formats.

   a. Format for reading hundreds numbers. Less structured board presentation used when teaching hundreds numbers with a zero in the tens column.

   b. Format for reading thousands numbers. Less structured board presentation with thousands numbers with zeroes in hundreds and/or tens column.

Basic Facts

There are 390 basic facts: 100 addition, 100 subtraction, 100 multiplication, and 90 division. Basic addition facts include all possible combinations in which each of the addends is a whole number under 10. Basic subtraction facts include all possible combinations in which the subtrahend and the difference (a and b in $c - a = b$) are one digit numbers. Tables 7.1 and 7.2 include all the basic addition and subtraction facts.

Basic multiplication facts include all possible combinations in which each of the factors is a single digit number (e.g., in $a \times b = c$, a and b are single digits). Basic division facts include all possible combinations in which the divisor and quotient are single digit numbers (e.g., in $c \div a = b$, a and b are single digit numbers, $a \neq 0$). Table 7.3 includes all basic multiplication and division facts.

Teaching Procedures

Ashlock (1971) outlines three different types of instructional activities designed to teach basic facts: activities for understanding, activities for relating, and activities for mastery. The activities for under-

Table 7.1 Basic Addition Facts

					Addends					
		0	1	2	3	4	5	⑥	7	8	9
	0 +	0	1	2	3	4	5	6	7	8	9
	1 +	1	2	3	4	5	6	7	8	9	10
	2 +	2	3	4	5	6	7	8	9	10	11
	3 +	3	4	5	6	7	8	9	10	11	12
	4 +	4	5	6	7	8	9	10	11	12	13
Addends	5 +	5	6	7	8	9	10	11	12	13	14
	6 +	6	7	8	9	10	11	12	13	14	15
	⑦+	7	8	9	10	11	12	⑬	14	15	16
	8 +	8	9	10	11	12	13	14	15	16	17
	9 +	9	10	11	12	13	14	15	16	17	18

NOTE: Problems are formed by an addend from the column on the left, an addend from the row on top, and their intersection; e.g., the numerals for 7 + 6 = 13 are circled.

Table 7.2 Basic Subtraction Facts

					Subtrahends					
	0	1	2	3	4	5	6	(7)	8	9
1-	1	0								
2-	2	1	0							
3-	3	2	1	0						
4-	4	3	2	1	0					
5-	5	4	3	2	1	0				
6-	6	5	4	3	2	1	0			
7-	7	6	5	4	3	2	1	0		
8-	8	7	6	5	4	3	2	1	0	
9-	9	8	7	6	5	4	3	2	1	0
10-		9	8	7	6	5	4	3	2	1
11-			9	8	7	6	5	4	3	2
12-				9	8	7	6	5	4	3
(13-)					9	8	7	(6)	5	4
14-						9	8	7	6	5
15-							9	8	7	6
16-								9	8	7
17-									9	8
18-										9

Minuends (row labels on left)

NOTE: Problems are formed by a minuend from the column on the left, followed by a subtrahend from the top row, and finally, the difference, which is the intersection; e.g., the numerals for 13 - 7 = 6 are circled.

Table 7.3 Basic Multiplication/Division Facts

÷/×	0	1	2	3	4	5	6	(7)	8	9
0	0	0	0	0	0	0	0	0	0	0
1	0	1	2	3	4	5	6	7	8	9
2	0	2	4	6	8	10	12	14	16	18
3	0	3	6	9	12	15	18	21	24	27
4	0	4	8	12	16	20	24	28	32	36
5	0	5	10	15	20	25	30	35	40	45
(6)	0	6	12	18	24	30	36	(42)	48	54
7	0	7	14	21	28	35	42	49	56	63
8	0	8	16	24	32	40	48	56	64	72
9	0	9	18	27	36	45	54	63	72	81

NOTE: Problems are formed by a number from the column on the left, a number from the top row, and their intersection; e.g., the row and column for the numerals 6 and 7 intersect at 42; these circled numbers form 6 × 7 = 42 and 42 ÷ 6 = 7.

standing involve concrete demonstrations of the operations, similar to those we have included in Chapters 8–11.

Relating activities are exercises designed to teach the relationships among various facts. The primary means of teaching these relationships is through the introduction of fact families. Fact families can be constructed as a series like the +1s (3 + 1, 4 + 1, 5 + 1, etc.), +4s (5 + 4, 6 + 4, 7 + 4, etc.), +doubles (2 + 2, 3 + 3, 4 + 4, etc.), and as sets of three related numbers that generate four facts. Below are examples of fact families constructed from three related numbers:

addition/ subtraction

3, 5, 8
3 + 5 = 8
5 + 3 = 8
8 - 3 = 5
8 - 5 = 3

multiplication/ division

3, 5, 15
3 × 5 = 15
5 × 3 = 15
15 ÷ 3 = 5
15 ÷ 5 = 3

Note how the commutative relationship between each pair of addition facts (3 + 5 = 8 so 5 + 3 = 8) and multiplication facts (3 × 5 = 15 so 5 × 3 = 15) greatly reduces the memorization load for students. Instead of having to memorize each fact individually (5 + 3 and 3 + 5), students can be taught that if they know one fact, they also know the reverse. Instructional procedures based on the commutative principle are discussed later.

Our recommendations for how to group facts into sets of fact families appear in Figures 7.6 through 7.9. These sets form the basis for presenting facts. The relationship formats listed in these figures are discussed after the next section.

Mastery activities are designed to facilitate memorization. The activities we have identified for building mastery require a sequence for introducing facts, coordination of relationship activities with memorization activities, intensive and systematic review, specific performance criteria that define when new facts can be introduced, record-keeping procedures that allow the teacher to monitor each student's mastery of facts, and motivation procedures.

Pretesting

Before beginning instruction in a fact mastery program, teachers should determine where students should be placed in the fact program.

Students who know few facts would start at set A. Students who know more facts would begin at later points. To determine the set at which students might begin, the teacher administers a written pretest that includes the 100 basic facts with the easier facts listed at the top. The teacher allows students 2 minutes, instructing them to work as many problems as they can. Students who answer 30 or more facts in 2 minutes might start at set G. Students who answer 45 or more might start at set M. Students who are able to answer 60 or more facts in the 2-minute pretest might start at set R. Students who answer 85 or more facts probably need not be placed in a fact program for that type of fact.

Relationship Activities

Since the understanding activities Ashlock recommends are presented in the respective operation's chapter, this chapter focuses only on the relationship and mastery activities. The teaching procedures for the relationship activities include (a) exercises with number families based on a series (e.g., 3×1, 3×2, 3×3) and (b) exercises demonstrating inverse relationships between addition/subtraction and multiplication/division (e.g., $4 + 2 = 6$, $2 + 4 = 6$, $6 - 4 = 2$, $6 - 2 = 4$). While the teaching procedures include strategies similar to those in the other chapters, the intent of the strategies in this chapter is different. Although the relationship strategies can be used to derive an unknown answer, their major purpose is to show the relationship among number families so that memorization will be easier. It appears that memorization of related bits of information, as represented by number families, is easier than memorization of random bits of information. Following a discussion of the teaching procedures for relationship activities, mastery activities will be discussed.

Preskill

A preskill for introducing basic addition facts involves teaching students a strategy to figure out plus 1 facts. (Students who know 30 or more facts do not need to receive instruction on this preskill.) Prior to instruction in facts, students have been using representations of concrete objects to solve simple equations. The format for plus 1 facts (see Figure 7.1) not only teaches plus 1 facts but also begins teaching students that numbers are related in systematic ways. Plus 1 facts, which should be introduced in first grade, are taught through the application of this rule: *When you plus 1, you say the next number.* From the rule, students learn that the first addend is systematically related to the sum:

$$6 + 1 = 7 \qquad 9 + 1 = 10$$

To prepare students for the plus 1 rule, the term *next number* is taught in Part A of the format. At first, the teacher counts several numbers, holding the last number for several seconds (e.g., "3, 4, 5, ssiix"). The students say the next number, "7." After presenting several examples in which the teacher says a series of numbers and asks students the next number (step 2), the teacher presents examples in which she says just a single number, not a series of numbers (step 3), and the students say the next number. A common error made by students is that they continue counting rather than stopping at the next number. Teachers should stop the students immediately if they say more than the next number, model saying just the next number, then repeat the same example before presenting additional examples.

Part B should not be introduced until students have mastered the next number skill taught in Part A. In Part B, the teacher presents the plus 1 rule, models several examples, and then tests. As a prompt, the teacher emphasizes the first addend, stretching it out for several seconds, and de-em-

Figure 7.1 Format for Plus 1 Facts

Day	Part A Next Number Problems	Part B Prompted Plus 1 Problems	Part C No Prompt Problems
1-2	6		
3	3	5	
4-5		5	
6		3	3
7-10			6—a 2 second pause between saying the fact and signaling
11-14			6—a 1 second pause between saying the fact and signaling
15-20			6—an immediate signal with no pause after saying the fact

PART A: Next Number

TEACHER
                                                              STUDENTS

1. "WHEN I PUT MY HAND DOWN, YOU SAY THE NEXT NUMBER."

2. Hold up hand. "ONE, TWO, THREE, FOUR, FIIIVE."
   Drop hand.   "6"

   TO CORRECT: "MY TURN. ONE, TWO, THREE, FOUR, FIIIVE (drop hand) SIX."

   "NEW PROBLEM. TELL ME THE NEXT NUMBER: THREE, FOUR, FIVE, SIX, SEEVVEN?" Drop hand.   "8"
   Repeat step 2 with 3, 4, 5 and 7, 8, 9.

3. "WHEN I PUT MY HAND DOWN, YOU SAY THE NEXT NUMBER. SIIIIX." Drop hand.   "7"

   TO CORRECT: "MY TURN; SSSIIIX (drop hand) SEVEN."

   Repeat step 3 with 8, 4, 9, 2, 5. Give individual turns to several students.

PART B: Plus 1 Rule with Stretch Prompt

1. "EVERYONE LISTEN TO THE RULE. WHEN YOU PLUS ONE, YOU SAY THE NEXT NUMBER. MY TURN. FOOOUUR PLUS ONE EQUALS FIVE. EEIIGHT PLUS ONE EQUALS NINE."

2. "GET READY TO TELL ME THE ANSWERS TO SOME PLUS ONE PROBLEMS. REMEMBER TO SAY THE NEXT NUMBER. FIVE PLUS ONE, FIIIVE PLUS ONE EQUALS . . ." Signal.   "6"
   "YES, 5 + 1 = 6."

   TO CORRECT: "LISTEN, 5, WHAT NUMBER COMES NEXT? SO 5 PLUS 1 EQUALS 6."

3. "THREE PLUS ONE. THHREEE PLUS ONE EQUALS?" Signal.   "4"
   "YES, 3 + 1 = 4"
   Present step 3 with examples like the following until students answer all +1 problems in a row correctly: 9 + 1, 7 + 1, 2 + 1, 8 + 1, 4 + 1.

Figure 7.1 cont'd

PART C: Plus 1 Rule without Prompt

TEACHER	**STUDENTS**
1. "REMEMBER, WHEN YOU PLUS 1 YOU SAY THE NEXT NUMBER."	
2. "EIGHT PLUS ONE EQUALS . . ." Pause, then signal. "SAY THE WHOLE STATEMENT."	"9" "8 + 1 = 9"
3. Repeat step 2 with the following examples: 4 + 1, 7 + 1, 5 + 1, 9 + 1.	

phasizes the words *plus one* (e.g., in "ssiiix + 1" the +1 is said quietly so that students can make the 6, 7 counting association).

In Part C, the teacher presents the plus 1 facts without any prompting. The teacher should initially pause 2 to 3 seconds before signaling for a response, so that the students will have time to figure out the answer. After several days' practice, the teacher can decrease the pause to a second. The teacher continues practice on plus 1 facts until the students can respond instantly to any plus 1 problem.

Series Saying

Series saying, one of the major relationship activities, involves the students saying a consecutively ordered set of fact statements. Series saying prompts the counting relationship among facts, as indicated by the circled numerals in the following series:

$$\begin{aligned} ⑥ + 2 &= ⑧ \\ ⑦ + 2 &= ⑨ \\ ⑧ + 2 &= ⑩ \end{aligned}$$

Series saying may be applied in teaching any of the four types of basic facts: addition, subtraction, multiplication, and division. Figure 7.2 includes a series saying format. Although the format illustrates an addition series, the same format can be used to present other types of series.

There are four parts to the series saying format. In Part A, students read the consecutively ordered statements. In Part B, the teacher erases the answers and the students read the statements. In Part C, the teacher erases everything and requires the students to say the series from memory. Part D provides drill on randomly presented facts. The teacher writes the fact questions on the board without the answer. The facts are written in random order (e.g., 7 + 2, 5 + 2, 8 + 2, 6 + 2). The teacher points to each fact, pauses, and then signals the

students to respond. He repeats the facts until the students can respond with a 1 second pause. The facts are written in random order so the students will not memorize the order of the answers.

Reading statements (Part A) in a rapid, crisp fashion is critical for instructionally naive students because they often read statements slowly or inaccurately. If students cannot *read* the series of statements in a crisp, rapid fashion, they will have a great deal of difficulty saying the series from memory and remembering facts during the random drill (Part D). The teacher must provide adequate practice to enable the students to say the series of statements at a fast rate.

The teacher should set a pace for saying the statements so that each statement in the series is said in approximately 2 to 3 seconds (2 seconds for older students, 3 seconds for younger students). There should also be a slight pause, about 1 second, between each statement. The pacing of the task is illustrated in Figure 7.3. The top row indicates seconds elapsed. Across the bottom row are the statements the teacher would say. The same pace should be continued in Parts B and C.

Teachers can expect instructionally naive students to have a great deal of difficulty saying statements at a brisk rate. The correction is to keep leading (responding with the students) at a brisk pace and gradually fade the lead so that the students are saying the statement independently. The teacher must be quite careful to provide the adequate repetition in an enjoyable manner.

Teachers working with lower-performing students may find that several days practice on Parts A and B are needed before continuing on to Parts C and D. Teachers working with higher-performing students may be able to present all parts in a day or two.

The first day that Part D is presented only the first three facts in the series should be presented. A new fact would be included in Part D each of the next 2 days.

Figure 7.2 Format for Series Saying

PART A: Reading Statements

TEACHER   **STUDENTS**

Write on board:

5 + 2 = 7
6 + 2 = 8
7 + 2 = 9
8 + 2 = 10

1. "EVERYBODY, I'LL TOUCH THEM. YOU READ.   "5 + 2 = 7
   GET READY." Point to numerals and symbols in each   6 + 2 = 8
   statement. Repeat step 1 until students can read statement   7 + 2 = 9
   at a rate of a statement each 3 seconds.   8 + 2 = 10"

PART B: Reading Statements with Answers Erased

1. "NOW I'M GOING TO ERASE THE ANSWERS." Erase
   answers. "NOW READ THE STATEMENT AND TELL
   ME THE ANSWER."   "5 + 2 = 7
                                                            6 + 2 = 8
                                                            7 + 2 = 9
   TO CORRECT: Respond with students until they appear   8 + 2 = 10"
        able to respond without assistance.

PART C: Saying Statements

1. "NOW I'LL MAKE IT EVEN HARDER AND ERASE
   EVERYTHING." Erase everything. "GET READY TO SAY
   THE STATEMENTS STARTING WITH 5 + 2." Either clap   "5 + 2 = 7
   or snap fingers to set pace for students to respond.   6 + 2 = 8
                                                            7 + 2 = 9
   Repeat Part C until all students respond correctly and then   8 + 2 = 10"
   present individual turns.

PART D: Random Fact Drill

Write facts in random order on board:

  7   5   6   8
 +2   +2   +2   +2

1. "WHEN I SIGNAL, SAY THE WHOLE STATEMENT
   WITH THE ANSWER."

2. Point to left of 7 + 2, pause 2 seconds, then touch board.   "7 + 2 = 9"

3. Repeat step 2 with remaining facts.

4. Repeat steps 2 and 3 with only a 1 second pause.

5. Repeat step 4 until students can respond to all facts with
   the 1 second pause.

Figure 7.3 Pacing of Series Saying

---

seconds	0	1	2	3	4	5	6	7	8	9

statements   6 + 2 = 8 pause 7 + 2 = 9 pause 8 + 2 = 10

Three Number Fact Families

The other major format designed to demonstrate the relationships among facts is taught through the introduction of three number fact families. These are sets of three numbers from which students can be taught to generate four statements, either addition/subtraction or multiplication/division. For example, given the numbers 3, 4, and 7, students are taught to construct the addition statements $3 + 4 = 7$ and $4 + 3 = 7$. Later students learn to construct the subtraction statements based on the same three numbers: $7 - 4 = 3$, $7 - 3 = 4$.

There are two formats for teaching number families. The first teaches students to use the commutative properties of addition (if $a + b = c$, then $b + a = c$) and multiplication (if $a \times b = c$, then $b \times a = c$). The second teaches students to generate subtraction statements from addition statements and division statements from multiplication statements. The commutative property is extremely important in that it greatly reduces the number of different facts students need to memorize. For every fact that students learn, they can derive the answer to the inverse fact quickly and easily by using the commutative property. For example, if students have memorized that $5 + 3 = 8$, they also know the answer to $3 + 5$. Note that the term *commutative property* is not explicitly taught, just the function of the property.

The first format, which consists of three parts, appears in Figure 7.4. Although the example shown illustrates the commutative property with addition, the same format can also be used to teach the cummutative property of multiplication. In Part A, students are taught how to construct a pair of addition statements from a set of three numbers. For example, given 2, 5, and 7, the students construct $2 + 5 = 7$ and $5 + 2 = 7$. One member of each pair has been previously presented in a series saying format. The second member of each pair is the "reverse fact." For example, if students have been taught the plus 2 facts (e.g., $5 + 2$, $6 + 2$, etc.), the new fact would be the 2+ fact ($2 + 5$, $2 + 6$, etc.). In Part B, the students are verbally tested on the new "reversed" facts. Part C is a worksheet exercise in which the students are given a diagram like this:

$$\Box \quad \boxed{2} \atop \boxed{5}$$

$$\underline{\quad} + \underline{\quad} = \underline{\quad}$$
$$\underline{\quad} = \underline{\quad} = \underline{\quad}$$

and are asked to fill in the sum (called the "big number") and generate two addition statements.

The second format for teaching three number families demonstrates how facts can be related across operations (see Figure 7.5). It is used to generate subtraction facts from addition facts and division facts from multiplication facts. The teacher demonstrates how to generate the subtraction or division statements. For example, after constructing $3 + 4 = 7$ and $4 + 3 = 7$, students are taught to generate the subtraction statements of $7 - 4 = 3$ and $7 - 3 = 4$.

The format for subtraction and division facts includes two parts. Although examples in Figure 7.5 illustrate subtraction, the same format can be used to introduce division facts. In Part A, the teacher demonstrates how three related numbers such as 3, 5, and 8 can generate two subtraction statements. The teacher first has the students add the two smaller numbers (3 and 5), then points out that two subtraction statements can be made. The teacher introduces the rule that *when you subtract, you always start with the big number,* which helps avoid errors like $3 - 8 = 5$. Part B is a worksheet exercise in which the students construct four statements, two addition and two subtraction, from three numbers.

Sequence for Introducing Facts

Basic facts should be introduced in a planned sequence. New sets of facts would be introduced systematically to avoid potential confusion and to facilitate most rapid learning. Figures 7.6, 7.7, 7.8, and 7.9 suggest orders for introducing addition, subtraction, multiplication, and division facts. In each figure there are about 25 sets of facts, each set comprised of three or four facts. The sets are lettered in their order of presentation, i.e., the facts in Set A would be introduced first, followed by the facts in Sets B, C, D, etc. Across from each set of facts is the relationship format recommended for introducing the facts. For example, in Figure 7.7 for subtraction facts, the teacher would present the Set E facts ($6 - 3$, $8 - 4$, $10 - 5$, $12 - 6$) through the three numbers subtraction format. For the $6 - 3$ fact, the teacher would write

in Part A. The teacher writes blanks for only one statement because only one subtraction statement, $6 - 3$, can be generated from the numbers 6, 3, and 3. The teacher would present Part A with

Figure 7.4 Format for Three Number Fact Family: Addition/Multiplication Facts

PART A: Structured Board Presentation

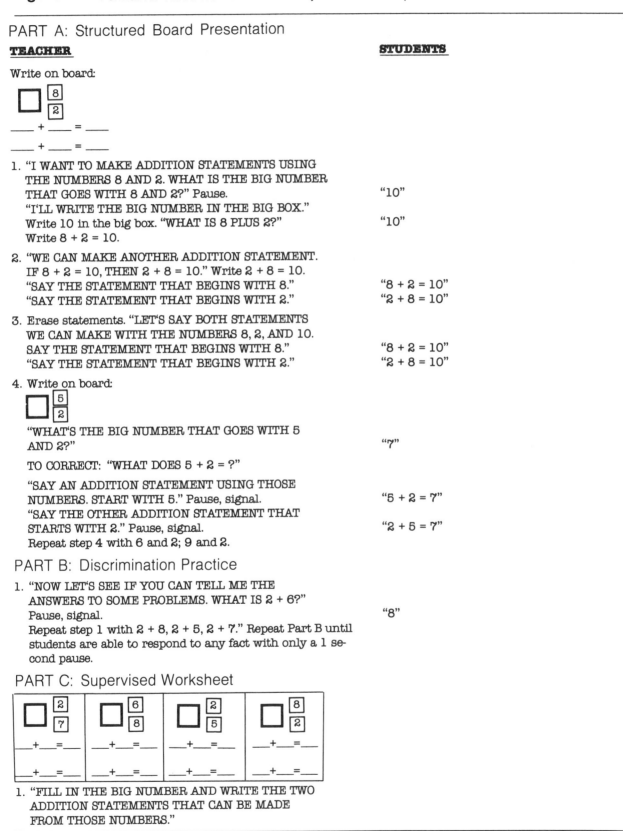

TEACHER	STUDENTS

Write on board:

⬜ 8
     2

___ + ___ = ___

___ + ___ = ___

1. "I WANT TO MAKE ADDITION STATEMENTS USING THE NUMBERS 8 AND 2. WHAT IS THE BIG NUMBER THAT GOES WITH 8 AND 2?" Pause.   "10"
   "I'LL WRITE THE BIG NUMBER IN THE BIG BOX." Write 10 in the big box. "WHAT IS 8 PLUS 2?"   "10"
   Write 8 + 2 = 10.

2. "WE CAN MAKE ANOTHER ADDITION STATEMENT. IF 8 + 2 = 10, THEN 2 + 8 = 10." Write 2 + 8 = 10.
   "SAY THE STATEMENT THAT BEGINS WITH 8."   "8 + 2 = 10"
   "SAY THE STATEMENT THAT BEGINS WITH 2."   "2 + 8 = 10"

3. Erase statements. "LET'S SAY BOTH STATEMENTS WE CAN MAKE WITH THE NUMBERS 8, 2, AND 10. SAY THE STATEMENT THAT BEGINS WITH 8."   "8 + 2 = 10"
   "SAY THE STATEMENT THAT BEGINS WITH 2."   "2 + 8 = 10"

4. Write on board:
   ⬜ 5
        2
   "WHAT'S THE BIG NUMBER THAT GOES WITH 5 AND 2?"   "7"

   TO CORRECT: "WHAT DOES 5 + 2 = ?"

   "SAY AN ADDITION STATEMENT USING THOSE NUMBERS. START WITH 5." Pause, signal.   "5 + 2 = 7"
   "SAY THE OTHER ADDITION STATEMENT THAT STARTS WITH 2." Pause, signal.   "2 + 5 = 7"
   Repeat step 4 with 6 and 2; 9 and 2.

PART B: Discrimination Practice

1. "NOW LET'S SEE IF YOU CAN TELL ME THE ANSWERS TO SOME PROBLEMS. WHAT IS 2 + 6?"
   Pause, signal.   "8"
   Repeat step 1 with 2 + 8, 2 + 5, 2 + 7." Repeat Part B until students are able to respond to any fact with only a 1 second pause.

PART C: Supervised Worksheet

⬜ 2 7	⬜ 6 8	⬜ 2 5	⬜ 8 2
__+__=__	__+__=__	__+__=__	__+__=__
__+__=__	__+__=__	__+__=__	__+__=__

1. "FILL IN THE BIG NUMBER AND WRITE THE TWO ADDITION STATEMENTS THAT CAN BE MADE FROM THOSE NUMBERS."

Figure 7.5 Format for Three Number Fact Family: Subtraction/Division Facts

---

PART A: Structured Board Presentation

| TEACHER | STUDENTS |

TEACHER　　　　　　　　　　　　　　　　　　　　　　**STUDENTS**

Write on board:

☐ ⬚5⬚
⬚3⬚

____ - ____ = ____

____ - ____ = ____

1. "WHAT BIG NUMBER GOES WITH 5 AND 3." Pause.　　　　"8"
   TO CORRECT: "5 + 3 = WHAT NUMBER?"
   Write 8 in box.

2. "WE CAN USE THESE NUMBERS 5, 3, AND 8 TO
   FIGURE OUT SUBTRACTION STATEMENTS. WHEN
   YOU SUBTRACT YOU ALWAYS START WITH THE BIG
   NUMBER. WHAT IS THE BIG NUMBER?"　　　　　　　　"8"
   "I'LL WRITE 8 AT THE START OF THESE SUBTRAC-
   TION PROBLEMS."

3. "EIGHT MINUS THREE, WHAT WILL I END UP
   WITH?"　　　　　　　　　　　　　　　　　　　　　"5"
   "SAY THE FIRST STATEMENT."　　　　　　　　　　　"8 - 3 = 5"
   Write 8 - 3 = 5.
   "EIGHT MINUS FIVE, WHAT WILL I END UP WITH?"　　"3"
   "SAY THAT STATEMENT."　　　　　　　　　　　　　　"8 - 5 = 3"
   Write 8 - 5 = 3.

4. "SAY BOTH SUBTRACTION STATEMENTS."　　　　　　　"8 - 5 = 3
   　　　　　　　　　　　　　　　　　　　　　　　　　　 8 - 3 = 5"

   Repeat steps 1-4 with 3 and 4; 6 and 3.

PART B: Structured Worksheet

Give students worksheets with problems similar to these:

a. 7 ⬚3⬚⬚4⬚ ___ + ___ = ___　　b. 8 ⬚5⬚⬚3⬚ ___ + ___ = ___　　c. 9 ⬚3⬚⬚6⬚ ___ + ___ = ___

(each box followed by:)
____ + ____ = ____
____ + ____ = ____
____ - ____ = ____
____ - ____ = ____

1. "TOUCH BOX a. YOU HAVE TO USE THE THREE
   NUMBERS TO MAKE UP STATEMENTS. FIRST,
   SAY THE ADDITION STATEMENTS."

2. "SAY AN ADDITION STATEMENT THAT STARTS
   WITH 3." Pause, signal.　　　　　　　　　　　　　"3 + 4 = 7"
   "SAY THE OTHER ADDITION STATEMENT."　　　　　　"4 + 3 = 7"
   "WRITE THE ADDITION STATEMENTS."

Figure 7.5 cont'd

TEACHER	**STUDENTS**
3. "NOW WE'LL WRITE THE SUBTRACTION STATE- MENTS. WHICH NUMBER WILL GO FIRST IN BOTH SUBTRACTION STATEMENTS?"	"7"
"SAY THE SUBTRACTION FACT THAT BEGINS 7 - 3." Signal.	"7 - 3 = 4"
"SAY THE SUBTRACTION FACT THAT BEGINS 7 - 4." Signal.	"7 - 4 = 3"
"WRITE THE SUBTRACTION STATEMENTS." Repeat steps 1-3 with remaining examples.	

all four sets of numbers and then present Part B with the four sets of numbers. While the teacher is introducing the new set of facts, memorization worksheet exercises on the previous sets continue.

The relationship exercise, as illustrated with Set G for subtraction, is presented for several days before the facts are introduced into mastery exercises.

In constructing these sequences, three guidelines were followed: (a) easier facts were introduced first, (b) related facts were introduced together, and (c) the reverse of specific series of facts was taught relatively soon after the initial series was presented. These sequences are provided to illustrate just one possible order for introducing facts and are not intended to represent the only or best sequence for teaching facts.

In developmental math programs, addition facts are introduced first, followed by subtraction, multiplication, and division facts. The question of exactly when to introduce subtraction, multiplication, and division facts is a difficult one. More specifically, it is difficult to say whether students should master all of one type of fact before the next type is introduced or whether different type facts should be introduced concurrently using the three number relationship that extends across operations. For example, should subtraction facts be introduced while students are still learning addition facts (and if so, when), or should subtraction facts be introduced only after students have mastered all addition facts? A similar question can be raised about multiplication and division facts as well.

Unfortunately, little experimental research has been done to answer the questions about when to introduce the various fact strands. In our observations of lower-performing students, they have more difficulty when a set of addition facts and the inverse subtraction facts are introduced concurrently. Consequently, we recommend introducing related subtraction or division facts for a particular set a month or more after the original addition or multiplication set has been introduced. More specifically, teachers might begin introducing subtraction facts when the students have learned about half their addition facts. The teacher would then alternate between introducing sets of addition and subtraction. Following this recommendation, teachers would first introduce addition sets A through M, then introduce subtraction set A. Thereafter, the teacher would alternate between addition and subtraction fact sets. Addition Set N would be followed by subtraction Set B, which would be followed by addition Set O, then subtraction Set C, etc.

The question of when to introduce multiplication facts is important. Many students will not have mastered all basic addition and subtraction facts at the time a program calls for the introduction of multiplication. We recommend that multiplication fact teaching begin no later than third grade, even though addition and subtraction facts have not been completely mastered. Knowledge of basic multiplication facts is a critical prerequisite for more advanced operations and, thus, should be mastered no later than fourth grade. Teachers might devote extra time to basic facts for students who have not mastered the basic addition and subtraction by third grade. Two fact sessions might be done daily, one focusing on addition and subtraction facts and one session focusing on multiplication and later division facts.

We recommend that multiplication and division facts be presented to intermediate grade remedial students before addition and subtraction. The reason for this recommendation is that these students are likely to have some type of finger strategy that allows them to compute addition and subtraction facts correctly. (More on the use of fingers appears at the end of the chapter.) On the other hand, they are likely to have no viable strategy for figuring out multiplication and division facts. Teaching multiplication and division facts first

Figure 7.6 Sequence of Addition Facts

Plus 1 Format is fond on page 111.
Series Saying Format is found on page 113.
Three Number Format is found on pages 115–116.

Sets of New Facts	Relationship Format
A 2 + 1, 3 + 1, 4 + 1, 5 + 1	Plus 1 format, series saying
B 6 + 1, 7 + 1, 8 + 1, 9 + 1	Plus 1 format, series saying
C 2 + 2, 3 + 2, 4 + 2, 5 + 2	Series Saying
D 6 + 2, 7 + 2, 8 + 2, 9 + 2	Series saying
E 3 + 3, 4 + 4, 5 + 5, 6 + 6	Series saying
F 2 + 3, 3 + 3, 4 + 3, 5 + 3	Series saying
G 6 + 3, 7 + 3, 8 + 3, 9 + 3	Series saying
H 1 + 2, 1 + 3, 1 + 4, 1 + 5	Three numbers—addition (1, 3, 4) (1, 4, 5) (1, 5, 6)
I 1 + 6, 1 + 7, 1 + 8, 1 + 9	Three numbers—addition (1, 6, 7) (1, 7, 8) (1, 8, 9) (1, 9, 10)
J 2 + 4, 2 + 5, 2 + 6	Three numbers—addition (2, 3, 5) (2, 4, 6) (2, 5, 7) (2, 6, 8)
K 2 + 7, 2 + 8, 2 + 9	Three numbers—addition (2, 7, 9) (2, 8, 10) (2, 9, 11)
L 3 + 4, 3 + 5, 3 + 6	Three numbers—addition (3, 4, 7) (3, 5, 8) (3, 6, 9)
M 3 + 7, 3 + 8, 3 + 9	Three numbers—addition (3, 7, 10) (3, 8, 11) (3, 9, 12)
N 7 + 7, 8 + 8, 9 + 9, 10 + 10	Series saying
O 1 + 0, 2 + 0, 3 + 0 . . . 9 + 0	Series saying
P 0 + 1, 0 + 2, 0 + 3 . . . 0 + 9	Three numbers—addition (6, 0, 6) (7, 0, 7) (8, 0, 8)
Q 5 + 4, 6 + 4, 7 + 4	Series saying
R 7 + 6, 8 + 6, 9 + 6	Series saying
S 4 + 5, 4 + 6, 4 + 7	Three numbers—addition (4, 5, 9) (4, 6, 10) (4, 7, 11)
T 6 + 7, 6 + 8, 6 + 9	Three numbers—addition (6, 7, 13) (6, 8, 14) (6, 9, 15)
U 7 + 4, 8 + 4, 9 + 4	Series saying
V 7 + 7, 8 + 7, 9 + 7	Series saying
W 9 + 8, 8 + 9, 4 + 8	Three numbers—(8, 9, 17) (8, 4, 12)
X 6 + 5, 7 + 5, 8 + 5, 9 + 5	Series saying
Y 7 + 8, 7 + 9, 4 + 9	Three numbers—addition (7, 8, 15) (7, 9, 16) (4, 9, 13)
Z 5 + 6, 5 + 7, 5 + 8, 5 + 9	Three numbers—addition (5, 6, 11) (5, 7, 12) (5, 8, 13) (5, 9, 14)

Figure 7.7 Sequence of Subtraction Facts

Series Saying Format is found on Figure 7.2.
Three Number Format is found on Figure 7.4.

Sets of New Facts	Relationship Format
A 3 - 1, 4 - 1, 5 - 1, 6 - 1	Series saying
B 7 - 1, 8 - 1, 9 - 1, 10 - 1	Series saying
C 4 - 2, 5 - 2, 6 - 2, 7 - 2	Series saying
D 8 - 2, 9 - 2, 10 - 2, 11 - 2	Series saying
E 1 − 0, 2 − 0, 3 − 0, 4 − 0, 5 − 0, 6 − 0, 7 − 0, 8 − 0, 9 − 0	Three numbers—subtraction (1, 0, 1) (2, 0, 2) (3, 0, 3) (4, 0, 4)
F 1 − 1, 2 − 2, 3 − 3, 4 − 4, 5 − 5, 6 − 6, 7 − 7, 8 − 8, 9 − 9	Three numbers—subtraction (1, 0, 1) (2, 0, 2) (3, 0, 3) (4, 0, 4)
G 6 − 3, 8 − 4, 10 − 5, 12 − 6	Three numbers—subtraction (3, 3, 6) (4, 4, 8) (5, 5, 10) (6, 6, 12)
H 5 - 3, 6 - 3, 7 - 3, 8 - 3	Series saying
I 9 - 3, 10 - 3, 11 − 3, 12 - 3	Series saying
J 3 - 2, 4 - 3, 5 - 4, 6 - 5	Three numbers—subtraction (3, 2, 1) (4, 3, 1) (5, 4, 1) (6, 5, 1)
K 7 - 6, 8 - 7, 9 - 8, 10 - 9	Three numbers—subtraction (7, 6, 1) (8, 7, 1) (9, 8, 1) (10, 9, 1)
L 5 - 3, 6 - 4, 7 - 5	Three numbers—subtraction (5, 3, 2) (6, 4, 2) (7, 5, 2)
M 8 - 6, 9 - 7, 10 - 8, 11 - 9	Three numbers—subtraction (8, 6, 2) (9, 7, 2) (10, 8, 2) (11, 9, 2)
N 6 - 3, 7 - 4, 8 - 5, 9 - 6	Three numbers—subtraction (6, 3, 3) (7, 4, 3) (8, 5, 3) (9, 6, 3)
O 10 - 7, 11 - 8, 12 - 9	Three numbers—subtraction (10, 7, 3) (11, 8, 3) (12, 9, 3)
P 14 -7, 16 - 8, 18 - 9	Three numbers—subtraction (14, 7, 7) (16, 8, 8) (18, 9, 9)
Q 8 - 4, 9 - 4, 10 - 4, 11 − 4	Series saying
R 12 - 6, 13 - 6, 14 - 6, 15 - 6	Series saying
S 9 - 5, 10 - 6, 11 - 7	Three numbers—subtraction (9, 5, 4) (10, 6, 4) (11, 7, 4)
T 13 - 7, 14 - 8, 15 - 9	Three numbers—subtraction (13, 7, 6) (14, 8, 6) (15, 9, 6)
U 10 - 4, 11 - 4, 12 - 4, 13 - 4	Series saying
V 14 - 7, 15 - 7, 16 - 7	Series saying
W 17 - 8, 17 - 9, 12 - 8	Three numbers—subtraction (17, 9, 8) (12, 8, 4)
X 11 - 5, 12 - 5, 13 - 5, 14 - 5	Series saying
Y 15 - 8, 16 - 9, 13 - 9	Three numbers—subtraction (15, 8, 7) (16, 9, 7) (13, 9, 4)
Z 11 - 6, 12 - 7, 13 - 8, 14 - 9	Three numbers—subtraction (11, 6, 5) (12, 7, 5) (13, 8, 5) (14, 9, 5)

Figure 7.8 Sequence of Multiplication Facts

Series Saying Format is found on Figure 7.2.
Three Number Format is found on Figure 7.4.

	Sets of New Facts	Relationship Format
A	any problem with a one	Series saying
B	5 × 2, 5 × 3, 5 × 4, 5 × 5	Series saying
C	2 × 2, 3 × 2, 4 × 2, 5 × 2	Series saying
D	2 × 5, 3 × 5, 4 × 5, 5 × 5	Three numbers—multiplication
E	2 × 2, 2 × 3, 2 × 4, 2 × 5	Three numbers—multiplication
F	any problem with a zero	
G	5 × 6, 5 × 7, 5 × 8, 5 × 9	Series saying
H	2 × 6, 2 × 7, 2 × 8, 2 × 9	Series saying
I	6 × 5, 7 × 5, 8 × 5, 9 × 5	Three numbers—multiplication
J	6 × 2, 7 × 2, 8 × 2, 9 × 2	Three numbers—multiplication
K	2 × 0, 3 × 0, 4 × 0, 5 × 0	Series saying
L	0 × 6, 0 × 7, 0 × 8, 0 × 9	Three numbers—multiplication
M	9 × 2, 9 × 3, 9 × 4, 9 × 5	Series saying
N	4 × 2, 4 × 3, 4 × 4, 4 × 5	Series saying
O	2 × 9, 3 × 9, 4 × 9, 5 × 9	Three numbers—multiplication
P	2 × 4, 3 × 4, 4 × 4, 5 × 4	Three numbers—multiplication
Q	9 × 6, 9 × 7, 9 × 8, 9 × 9	Series saying
R	4 × 6, 4 × 7, 4 × 8, 4 × 9	Series saying
S	6 × 9, 7 × 9, 8 × 9, 9 × 9	Three numbers—multiplication
T	6 × 4, 7 × 4, 8 × 4, 9 × 4	Three numbers—multiplication
U	3 × 6, 3 × 7, 3 × 8, 3 × 9	Series saying
V	6 × 6, 6 × 7, 6 × 8, 6 × 9	Series saying
W	6 × 3, 7 × 3, 8 × 3, 9 × 3	Three numbers—multiplication
X	7 × 6, 8 × 6, 9 × 6, 3 × 3	Three numbers—multiplication
Y	7 × 7, 8 × 7, 9 × 7	Series saying
Z	7 × 8, 8 × 8, 9 × 8	Three numbers—multiplication

Figure 7.9 Sequence of Division Facts

Three Number Format is found on Figure 7.4.

Sets of New Facts		**Relationship Format**
A	any number divided by 1	Three numbers—division (8, 1, 8) (4, 1, 4) (7, 1, 7)
B	any number divided by itself	Three numbers—division (3, 1, 3) (9, 1, 9) (8, 1, 8) (2, 1, 2)
C	10 ÷ 5, 15 ÷ 5, 20 ÷ 5, 25 ÷ 5	Three numbers—division (2, 5, 10) (3, 5, 15) (4, 5, 20) (5, 5, 25)
D	4 ÷ 2, 6 ÷ 2, 8 ÷ 2, 10 ÷ 2	Three numbers—division
E	10 ÷ 2. 15 ÷ 3, 20 ÷ 4, 25 ÷ 5	Three numbers—division
F	0 ÷ 1, 0 ÷ 2, 0 ÷ 3, 0 ÷ 4, 0 ÷ 5, 0 ÷ 6, 0 ÷ 7, 0 ÷ 8, 0 ÷ 9, 9 ÷ 3	Three numbers—division
G	4 ÷ 2, 6 ÷ 3, 8 ÷ 4, 10 ÷ 5	Three numbers—division
H	30 ÷ 5, 35 ÷ 5, 40 ÷ 5, 45 ÷ 5	Three numbers—division
I	12 ÷ 2, 14 ÷ 2, 16 ÷ 2, 18 ÷ 2	Three numbers—division
J	30 ÷ 6, 35 ÷ 7, 40 ÷ 8, 45 ÷ 9	Three numbers—division
K	12 ÷ 6, 14 ÷ 7, 16 ÷ 8, 18 ÷ 9	Three numbers—division
L	18 ÷ 9, 27 ÷ 9, 36 ÷ 9, 45 ÷ 9	Three numbers—division
M	8 ÷ 4, 12 ÷ 4, 16 ÷ 4, 20 ÷ 4	Three numbers—division
N	18 ÷ 2, 27 ÷ 3, 36 ÷ 4, 45 ÷ 5	Three numbers—division
O	8 ÷ 2, 12 ÷ 3, 16 ÷ 4, 20 ÷ 5	Three numbers—division
P	54 ÷ 9, 63 ÷ 9, 72 ÷ 9, 81 ÷ 9	Three numbers—division
Q	24 ÷ 4, 28 ÷ 4, 32 ÷ 4, 36 ÷ 4	Three numbers—division
R	54 ÷ 6, 63 ÷ 7, 72 ÷ 8, 81 ÷ 9	Three numbers—division
S	24 ÷ 6, 28 ÷ 7, 32 ÷ 8, 36 ÷ 9	Three numbers—division
T	18 ÷ 3, 21 ÷ 3, 24 ÷ 3, 27 ÷ 3	Three numbers—division
U	36 ÷ 6, 42 ÷ 6, 48 ÷ 6, 54 ÷ 6	Three numbers—division
V	18 ÷ 6, 21 ÷ 7, 24 ÷ 8, 27 ÷ 9	Three numbers—division
W	42 ÷ 7, 48 ÷ 8, 54 ÷ 9	Three numbers—division
X	49 ÷ 7, 56 ÷ 7, 63 ÷ 7	Three numbers—division
Y	56 ÷ 8, 64 ÷ 8, 72 ÷ 8	Three numbers—division

will allow the teacher to present a wider range of operations during the school year. After multiplication and division facts are mastered, the teacher would go back and work on addition and subtraction facts.

Coordinating Mastery and Relationship Activities

As a general rule, new sets of facts should be presented in relationship exercises before appearing in mastery exercises. The teacher introduces a set of facts through a relationship exercise and then provides practice to develop mastery on that set of facts. Figures 7.6–7.9 suggest the relationship format to present before introducing each new set of facts. The specific format to present is listed across from the respective set of facts. Remember, the relationship format would be presented for several days before including facts from that set in memorization exercises.

Exercises for Memorizing

Practice to aid memorization of basic facts can be provided in a number of ways: paired drill in which students practice with each other, teacher drill in which the teacher presents facts to a group, worksheet exercises, flash card exercises in which students are given a specific set of facts to study independently, and game activities. Memorization exercises should be cumulative in that newly introduced facts receive intensive practice, while previously introduced facts receive less intensive, but still systematically planned, practice.

Setting Up a Program to Promote Mastery

A program to facilitate basic fact memorization should have the following components:

1. A specific performance criterion for introducing new facts
2. Intensive practice on newly introduced facts
3. Systematic practice on previously introduced facts
4. A record-keeping system
5. A motivation system
6. Adequate time allotment

MASTERY CRITERION We define mastery of a basic fact as the student's being able to respond instantaneously to the fact question. For example, after the teacher asks, "What is 8 + 7?" the student immediately answers "15." Students should practice a new set of facts until they are able to answer each member of the new set and members of previously introduced sets instantaneously.

An acceptable criterion of performance for a verbal exercise, assuming students say an entire statement, would be a rate of a fact each 2 seconds. The criterion for written exercises depends on the students' motor coordination. Specifically, rate criteria should be based on the speed with which students are able to write numerals. Obviously a student who writes numerals slowly will not be able to complete a worksheet as quickly as a student whose motor skills are more developed and is able to write numbers more quickly. Our basic recommendation is that the acceptable rate criterion be set at a rate that is about 2/3 the rate the student is able to write digits. A student's writing ability can be determined by giving a 1 minute timed test. The student would be instructed to write the number 1 through 9 as many times as he could. Several practice trials would be provided before the timing. The student's writing rate is determined by counting up the number of digits written during this 1 minute period. By multiplying that number by 2/3s, the teacher can estimate how many digits a student should write as answers during a 1 minute fact timing. For example, a student who writes 60 digits in 1 minute should write 40 digits in 1 minute as fact answers ($60 \times 2/3 = 40$).

INTENSIVE PRACTICE AND SYSTEMATIC REVIEW After providing intensive practice on new facts, the teacher must provide practice on the new fact set and previously taught facts. Unless earlier introduced facts are systemically reviewed, students are likely to forget them. Inadequate review is the greatest failing in many commercial math programs' treatment of fact teaching.

ALLOTTED TIME The amount of time devoted to fact practice must be adequate. We recommend that teachers allot 10–15 minutes per day for basic fact learning activities. This time allotment is much more than provided for in most classroom schedules. Teachers should keep in mind that work on basic math facts is time well spent. Children who know facts will be able to compute efficiently and are more likely to encounter success in later math-related activities.

RECORD-KEEPING SYSTEM A record-keeping system is needed to monitor student progress so that the teacher knows when to reinforce a student and when a student is ready to progress to the next set of facts. This system should involve a minimum of paperwork so that little time is taken from actual fact practice.

MOTIVATION A motivational system should be integrated within the record-keeping procedure. The motivation system must be carefully designed so that students see a clear relationship between working hard and receiving recognition for their work.

Manageability is an important aspect of any instructional program and is especially important in a fact program. Procedures must be simple. Materials must be easy to prepare, pass out, collect, and score. Teachers cannot follow procedures that consume inordinate amounts of time.

Three Fact Programs

Three examples of fact mastery programs are presented below. The first program is designed for teachers working with groups of relatively homogeneous students: students who are all functioning near the same instructional level. The second program is designed for a teacher working with heterogeneous groups: groups composed of students functioning at different levels. The third system, a flash card system, is designed for one-on-one tutoring in which an adult or a peer tutors a student.

Homogeneous Group Program

The homogeneous group system is designed for teachers working with a group of students functioning at approximately the same level. The basic system consists of the students doing daily exercises on a fact worksheet. In these exercises the teacher first presents a drill in which the students orally practice newly introduced facts. The oral drill is followed by a written exercise on which the students are timed on a worksheet containing a mix of new and previously introduced facts.

MATERIALS The system requires specially prepared sequences of worksheets for each type of fact: addition, subtraction, division, and multiplication. A worksheet would be prepared for each set listed in Figures 7.6–7.9. Each worksheet would be divided into 2 parts. The top half of the worksheets

should provide practice on new facts, including facts from the currently introduced set and from the two preceding sets. More specifically, each of the facts from the new set would appear four times. Each of the facts from the set introduced just earlier would appear three times, and each of the facts from the set that preceded that would appear twice. If this pattern were applied to sets, each containing 4 facts, the top part of the worksheet would have 36 facts: 16 new facts (4×4), 12 facts from the previously learned set (4×3), and 8 facts from the set before that (4×2).

The bottom half of the worksheet should include 30 problems. Each of the facts from the currently introduced set would appear twice. The remaining facts would be taken from previously introduced sets. All previously introduced facts would appear just one time. *Note:* At the beginning of a fact program, students will not know many facts; thus, facts from previous sets may appear several times on the bottom half of the worksheet. Only when 30 facts have been introduced can each fact appear just once. On the other hand, after more than 30 facts have been introduced, review should be planned so that a fact appear at least once every second or third worksheet.

Figure 7.10 is a sample worksheet for introducing facts according to the guidelines for worksheet construction. The new set consists of $5 + 6$, $5 + 7$, $5 + 8$, and $5 + 9$. Each of these facts appears four times in the top half. The previously introduced set includes $7 + 8$, $7 + 9$, and $4 + 9$. Each of these facts appear three times. Finally, the next earlier introduced set included $6 + 5$, $7 + 5$, $8 + 5$, and $9 + 5$. Each of these facts appears twice. The top half of the worksheet has 33 facts. The bottom half of the worksheet includes the four facts from the new set, each written twice, along with previously introduced facts, each appearing just once.

PRETESTING Before beginning instruction, teachers should determine which type of fact to start with (addition, subtraction, multiplication, division) and where students should be placed in that fact program.

Groups with students who know few facts would start at Set A. Students who know more facts would begin at later points. To determine the set at which students might begin, the teacher administers a written pretest that includes the 100 basic facts with the easier facts listed at the top. The teacher allows students 2 minutes, instructing them to work as many problems as they can. Students who correctly answer 30 or more facts in

Figure 7.10 Sample Worksheet

5 +6	8 +5	5 +8	6 +5	7 +9	5 +7	4 +9	5 +6	7 +8	5 +9	7 +9
5 +8	7 +5	5 +7	7 +8	5 +6	5 +8	4 +9	5 +9	4 +9	7 +9	5 +7
8 +5	5 +6	5 +9	6 +5	5 +7	7 +5	5 +8	9 +5	7 +8	5 +9	9 +5

5 +8	6 +4	7 +5	4 +7	5 +6	9 +8	7 +9	5 +9	4 +8	5 +7
8 +9	7 +8	8 +5	5 +6	8 +7	9 +5	7 +7	5 +8	8 +4	4 +9
9 +7	6 +7	5 +9	7 +4	6 +9	4 +6	5 +7	9 +4	6 +5	6 +8

2 minutes might start at set G. Students who answer 45 or more might start at set M. Students who are able to answer 60 or more facts in the 2 minutes pretest might start at set R. Students who answer 85 or more facts probably need not be placed in a fact program for that type of fact.

Obviously a teacher with 10 or more students in a group will have to compromise when selecting a starting point. As a general rule we recommend a point slightly lower than the average starting point for the students in the group.

After determining a starting set that is appropriate for the group, the teacher makes a copy of the worksheet for that set for each student in the group.

GROUP ORAL PRACTICE The teacher begins the lesson with a group drill in which the students orally practice the facts on the top half of the worksheet. The students say each problem in unison as the teacher signals. The teacher begins the lesson by instructing students on the procedure: "When I signal, you'll read the first problem and say the answer. Then you'll touch the next problem and figure out the answer. When I signal again, you'll read that problem and say the answer."

The teacher then instructs the students to touch the first problem. After allowing 2–3 seconds for students to figure out the answer, the teacher says, "Get ready" and signals by clapping her hands. After the students respond, the teacher instructs them to touch the next problem, pauses to let them figure out the answer, then says, "Get ready" and signals. The teacher keeps her talk to a minimum. "Next problem" (pause) "Get ready" (signal) "Next problem" (pause) "Get ready" (signal).

The teacher repeats this signaling procedure with each fact across the first line. The teacher repeats the line until students are able to answer each fact correctly with no more than a 2 second thinking pause. This may take several repetitions of the entire line. The same procedure is repeated with each line on the top half of the worksheet.

TIMED TEST The timed test is done on the bottom half of the written worksheet. The teacher sets a specified time. A minute and 15 seconds would be a realistic goal for intermediate grade students. The teacher allows the students a minute or two to study the bottom half of the worksheet, then tells them to get ready for the test. The teacher tells the students how much time they have and to start. At the end of the specified time, the teacher says "Stop," has the students trade papers, and reads the answers. Students are to mark all mistakes and write the total number correct at the top of the page, then return the worksheet to its owner.

PROGRESSION After the lesson, the teacher inspects the students' papers and records the number of facts each student answered correctly on the written timed drill. In the next lesson the teacher either repeats the same worksheet or presents the worksheet for the next set of facts. The teacher presents the next worksheet if 3/4 or more of the students answered 28 of the 30 facts correctly. The teacher repeats the same worksheet if less than 3/4 of the students answered 28 facts correctly.

Keep in mind that students will likely need anywhere from three days to two weeks to master a set. During this time the teacher should keep doing the relationship exercises for the new fact set and encourage the students.

SUMMARY The advantage of this system is that it allows the teacher to coordinate the presentation of relationship activities and memorization exercises. Also the system makes monitoring the performance of the students relatively easy. The disadvantage of this group system is that it does not allow individual students to progress at optimal rates. Note that if one or two students are performing at a much lower rate than other students in the group, the teacher should provide extra practice for those students.

Heterogeneous Group Program

The heterogeneous group program is designed for teachers working with a group of students in which there are significant differences in students' fact knowledge. The same worksheets used in the homogeneous system would be used in the heterogeneous system.

MATERIALS Prior to the beginning of the school year, teachers should make booklets for each type of fact: addition, subtraction, division, and multiplication. The booklets would consist of the worksheets for each fact set. Two types of booklets should be prepared, one with answers and one without. A booklet is not needed for each student since students will work in pairs. For a class of 30, about 20 of each type would be adequate.[1]

PRETESTING Students may start with different types of facts (addition, subtraction, multiplication, division) and at various sets within a type of fact. Pretesting to determine a starting set can be done in a group setting or individually. In a group setting, the teacher administers a written pretest that includes the 100 basic facts with the easier facts listed at the top.

The teacher allows students 2 minutes, instructing them to work as many problems as they can. Students who answer 30 or more facts in 2 minutes might start at set G. Students who answer 45 or more might start at set M. Students who answer 60 or more might start at set R. Students who are able to answer 85 or more facts in the 2 minute pretest probably need not to be placed in a fact program for that type of fact.

Individual testing will allow for a more precise starting set. To test individuals the teacher uses the sequences in Figures 7.6–7.9. The teacher begins by testing the facts in set A, then set B, and so on. The teacher continues testing until reaching a set in which the student makes 2 or more errors. (Any fact problem that a student can not answer within several seconds should be counted as wrong.) This set would be the students' starting point.

DAILY ROUTINE Students will work in pairs. As a general rule, teachers should pair students who are working near the same level. Each pair of students will have one booklet with answers and one booklet without answers. The worksheet that each student starts on is designated by a colored clip or other similar object. The student with the answer sheet acts as a tutor while the other student acts as the pupil.

The teacher would have each student practice the top half of the worksheet two times. Each practice session is timed. The teacher says, "Get ready, go" and starts a stopwatch; the pupil practices by saying complete statements (e.g., $4 + 2 = 6$) rather than just answers. Saying the entire fact statement makes it easier for the tutor to follow along. If the

---

[1] These fact sheet booklets can be ordered from Douglas Carnine, P.O. Box 10459, Eugene, Oregon 97440.

pupil makes an error, the tutor corrects by saying the correct statement and having the pupil repeat the statement. The teacher allows students a minute and a half when practicing the top part and a minute when practicing the bottom half. After the allotted time, the teacher says, "Stop, switch booklets." The teacher pauses about 10–15 seconds while the students switch booklets and turn to the other student's starting worksheet. The teachers then says, "Get ready, go." The second student now practices. This procedure is repeated twice to the facts on the top half and twice to the facts on the bottom half of the worksheet.

After allowing each student to practice on the top and bottom halves twice, the teacher tells the students to get ready for a test. The test is only done on the bottom half of the worksheet. The teacher says, "Begin" and starts a stopwatch. One student says answers and the other checks. The student who is checking does not interrupt the student being tested but makes a mark for each error. After the minute period, the teacher says, "Stop." The students are to stop answering immediately. The tutor then counts the number of facts not answered which is recorded across from the letter for the respective set of facts on the students's record form (see Figure 7.11 and the discussion under the heading "Record Form"). The students then switch papers, and the procedure is repeated with the roles switched.

The next day the same procedure is followed except that if a student answered all but two of the facts correctly on the previous day's testing, the student goes on to the next worksheet in the se-

Figure 7.11 Student Record Form

Worksheet	Try 1	Try 2	Try 3	Try 4	Try 5	Try 6	Try 7	Try 8	Try 9	Try 10
W										
V										
U										
T										
S										
R										
Q										
P										
O										
N										
M										
L										
K										
J										
I										
H										
G										
F										
E										
D										
C										
B										
A										

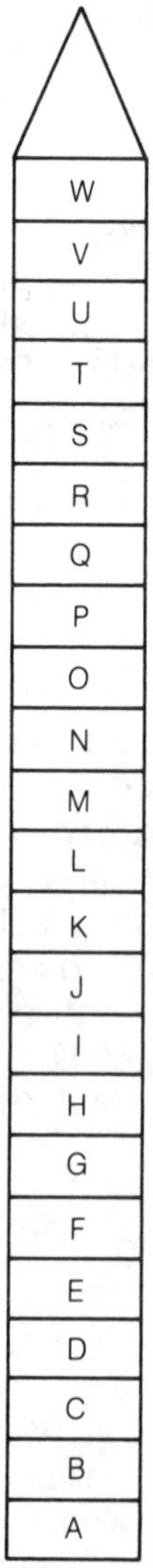

quence. The teacher begins the lesson by having students look at their record form and saying, "If you got no more than two problems wrong yesterday, go on to the next worksheet."

Cooperative behavior on the students' part is essential to make this system work. The teacher should provide strong positive consequences for cooperative behavior among students. Rules for the activity should include (a) talking softly, (b) promptly obeying teacher instructions, and (c) honestly recording performance.

Students may be tempted to cheat, recording inaccurate scores on the test. To guard against cheating, the teacher should listen to students saying the facts during practice. If a student performs quite poorly during practice, an excellent record on testing may be inaccurate. These students should be tested by the teacher to ensure accuracy of the recorded performance.

RECORD FORM A record form that can be used during this exercise appears in Figure 7.11. In the first column, the worksheet letters are listed. Across from each letter are 10 columns. These columns are used to record the number of facts missed on a test. The first day the student does a particular worksheet, the number of facts not answered correctly is written in the first column across from that worksheet letter. The second day, the number is written in the second column across from the worksheet letter, and so on. On the right side of the chart is a progress rocket. Each time the student meets the criterion for a worksheet (two errors or less on 30 problems), the student shades in the space for that worksheet on the rocket. On the next lesson, the student works on the next worksheet in the sequence.

SUMMARY The heterogeneous group program requires extensive preparation by the teacher at the beginning of the school year, because several booklets of worksheets must be made. Also, a good deal of instruction will be necessary to teach students the procedure. The advantage of this system, though, is that once worksheets are prepared and students know what to do, the system provides the individualization needed to allow each student to progress at her optimal rate.

Flash Card System

The flash card system is designed for one-on-one tutoring situations. Only a few materials are required: a testing and recording sheet and flash cards.

The testing and recording sheet (see Figures 7.12–7.15) lists all basic facts in a suggested order of introduction. Note the order is slightly different from that in Figures 7.6–7.9 to avoid students' guessing on the test. Across from each fact are two columns. The first is to record the students' performance on the pretest. The second is to record dates on which a particular fact is introduced.

Flash cards need not be prepared until the teacher determines what facts will be worked on. When making flash cards, the fact and answer would be written on one side of the card, while on the other side only the fact would be written.

PRETESTING The teacher tests the students, beginning with the first fact on the testing sheet and progressing consecutively through the list. The teacher can either say the fact or point to it on the record form, allowing the student to read it. If a student answers a fact within 2 seconds after the teacher asks it, the teacher writes a plus on the record sheet in the test column next to the fact. If the student either answers incorrectly or takes longer than 2 seconds to respond, the teacher puts a minus in the test column. The teacher tests the student on all facts in an area. Note that if the student seems to become frustrated, the teacher can stop testing and continue on a later day.

PREPARING MATERIALS Before beginning instruction, the teacher makes a pile of flash cards. This pile includes 15 cards: 12 should have the facts the student knew instantly on the test, and 3 would be facts the student did not respond to correctly on the test. The 3 unknown facts would be those closest to the beginning of the list.

DAILY INSTRUCTION The teacher does a drill with these 15 cards. Each drill session might last 5–10 minutes. The drill procedure is designed to provide intensive practice on the unknown facts and any facts in the known pile which the student may need more practice on. When practicing, the teacher shows the student a card, and the student is to say the entire statement (e.g., $7 \times 5 = 35$), not just the answer. If the student responds correctly and within 2 seconds or so, the teacher puts the card at the back of the pile.

If the student responds correctly but takes longer than 2 seconds or so, the teacher places the card back two or three cards from the front of the pile. Likewise, if the student responds incorrectly, the teacher tells the student the correct answer and then places the card two or three cards back in the pile. Cards placed two or three back from the front

Figure 7.12 Testing and Recording Sheet: Addition

Student's Name _____

Pretest Date _____

	test	date		test	date		test	date		test	date		test	date
5 + 1			5 + 5			2 + 4			3 + 0			8 + 4		
2 + 1			6 + 6			2 + 8			0 + 7			8 + 7		
4 + 1			5 + 3			2 + 6			0 + 4			9 + 7		
3 + 1			2 + 3			2 + 5			0 + 6			8 + 9		
8 + 1			3 + 3			2 + 7			5 + 4			4 + 8		
6 + 1			4 + 3			2 + 9			7 + 4			9 + 8		
9 + 1			8 + 3			3 + 5			6 + 4			6 + 5		
7 + 1			6 + 3			3 + 9			7 + 6			9 + 5		
5 + 2			9 + 3			3 + 4			9 + 6			7 + 5		
2 + 2			7 + 3			3 + 6			8 + 6			8 + 5		
4 + 2			1 + 6			3 + 7			4 + 5			7 + 8		
3 + 2			1 + 2			3 + 8			4 + 7			4 + 9		
9 + 2			1 + 8			7 + 7			4 + 6			7 + 9		
6 + 2			1 + 4			8 + 8			6 + 7			5 + 6		
8 + 2			1 + 7			9 + 9			6 + 9			5 + 8		
7 + 2			1 + 3			2 + 0			6 + 8			5 + 7		
3 + 3			1 + 9			5 + 0			9 + 4			5 + 9		
4 + 4			1 + 5											

Figure 7.13 Testing and Recording Sheet: Subtraction

Student's Name _____

Pretest Date _____

	test	date		test	date		test	date		test	date		test	date
7 - 1			8 - 4			8 - 5			7 - 7			12 - 4		
3 - 1			12 - 6			7 - 4			5 - 0			16 - 7		
8 - 1			5 - 3			9 - 6			11 - 4			17 - 9		
5 - 1			8 - 3			10 - 9			9 - 4			13 - 4		
9 - 1			7 - 3			10 - 7			10 - 4			12 - 8		
6 - 1			11 - 3			10 - 8			14 - 6			11 - 5		
4 - 1			10 - 3			11 - 9			13 - 6			12 - 5		
9 - 2			12 - 3			11 - 8			15 - 6			15 - 8		
5 - 2			9 - 3			12 - 9			9 - 5			13 - 5		
10 - 2			4 - 3			14 - 7			13 - 7			11 - 6		
4 - 2			6 - 4			18 - 9			10 - 6			16 - 9		
7 - 2			8 - 6			16 - 8			15 - 9			14 - 5		
3 - 2			9 - 8			8 - 0			11 - 7			13 - 9		
8 - 2			7 - 5			6 - 0			14 - 8			12 - 7		
6 - 2			6 - 5			4 - 4			15 - 7			13 - 8		
6 - 3			7 - 6			8 - 8			17 - 8			14 - 9		
10 - 5			9 - 7			2 - 0								

Figure 7.14 Testing and Recording Sheet: Multiplication

Student's Name _____

Pretest Date _____

	test	date		test	date		test	date		test	date		test	date
7 × 1			2 × 4			7 × 2			4 × 9			3 × 6		
1 × 5			5 × 6			2 × 0			3 × 4			3 × 8		
8 × 1			5 × 8			0 × 6			9 × 6			3 × 7		
1 × 3			5 × 7			5 × 0			9 × 8			6 × 6		
9 × 1			5 × 9			0 × 3			9 × 7			6 × 8		
1 × 4			2 × 6			8 × 0			9 × 9			6 × 7		
5 × 2			2 × 8			0 × 4			4 × 6			6 × 3		
5 × 5			2 × 9			9 × 2			4 × 8			8 × 3		
5 × 3			2 × 7			9 × 4			4 × 7			7 × 3		
5 × 4			6 × 5			9 × 3			6 × 9			8 × 6		
2 × 2			8 × 5			4 × 2			8 × 9			7 × 6		
3 × 5			7 × 5			4 × 4			7 × 9			7 × 7		
3 × 3			9 × 5			4 × 3			6 × 4			8 × 7		
2 × 3			6 × 2			4 × 5			8 × 4			8 × 8		
2 × 5			8 × 2			3 × 9			7 × 4			7 × 8		

Figure 7.15 Testing and Recording Sheet: Division

Student's Name _____

Pretest Date _____

	test	date		test	date		test	date		test	date		test	date
8 ÷ 1			6 ÷ 2			35 ÷ 7			27 ÷ 3			32 ÷ 8		
8 ÷ 1			10 ÷ 2			14 ÷ 7			16 ÷ 4			18 ÷ 3		
3 ÷ 3			15 ÷ 3			0 ÷ 9			36 ÷ 4			21 ÷ 3		
8 ÷ 8			20 ÷ 4			40 ÷ 8			54 ÷ 9			24 ÷ 3		
4 ÷ 1			6 ÷ 3			0 ÷ 9			12 ÷ 3			36 ÷ 6		
7 ÷ 1			8 ÷ 4			16 ÷ 8			63 ÷ 9			42 ÷ 6		
9 ÷ 9			30 ÷ 5			0 ÷ 6			24 ÷ 4			48 ÷ 6		
5 ÷ 5			40 ÷ 5			18 ÷ 9			72 ÷ 9			18 ÷ 6		
5 ÷ 1			35 ÷ 5			45 ÷ 9			28 ÷ 4			42 ÷ 7		
6 ÷ 1			45 ÷ 5			0 ÷ 3			81 ÷ 9			49 ÷ 7		
6 ÷ 6			12 ÷ 2			0 ÷ 8			54 ÷ 6			21 ÷ 7		
10 ÷ 5			16 ÷ 2			0 ÷ 4			32 ÷ 4			48 ÷ 8		
20 ÷ 5			14 ÷ 2			0 ÷ 9			32 ÷ 4			24 ÷ 8		
15 ÷ 5			18 ÷ 2			36 ÷ 9			63 ÷ 7			56 ÷ 7		
25 ÷ 5			30 ÷ 6			27 ÷ 9			28 ÷ 7			64 ÷ 8		
4 ÷ 2			12 ÷ 6			12 ÷ 4			72 ÷ 8			56 ÷ 8		
8 ÷ 2													

will receive intensive review. The teacher would continue placing the card two or three places back in the pile until the student responds acceptably (within 2 seconds) four times in a row. At the end of the session, the teacher gives the student the deck of cards, telling the student to practice the cards later in the day and at home.

DAILY TESTING At the beginning of the second session and every session thereafter, the teacher tests the students on the 15 cards worked on the previous day. If the student can respond acceptably (within 2 seconds or so) to every fact, the teacher can take out two cards from the deck. The two cards taken out would have facts that appear closest to the beginning of the list on the testing sheet. Two new cards would be put into the deck, with the next facts students responded unacceptably to on the pretest. The teacher then repeats the drill routine described for the first day. The teacher should write the date these two new facts are introduced on the testing sheet in the second column across from those facts.

Writing the dates new facts are introduced on the record form will avoid problems created by students losing their practice deck of cards. If the practice deck is lost, the teacher can construct a new deck simply by looking at record forms and using the most recently introduced facts to make cards.

Motivation is an important factor. If students practice at home or other times during the school day, their learning rate will most likely be significantly improved. Teachers can encourage students to study by placing a contingency on their performance; e.g., the teacher might say, "If you can say the answers to the 15 cards in the deck in 20–30 seconds tomorrow when we start working, you'll earn 5 minutes extra recess."

Parental Involvement

Parents often would like to help their children at home but are often afraid they will not know what to do, how to do it, or whether they will interfere with what the teacher is doing at school. Fact practice tutoring is a good way to involve parents. Teachers should try to secure a commitment from parents to work with their children on facts at home for about 10 minutes, 3 or 4 days a week. Teachers should ensure that this practice is coordinated with classroom activities. If possible, parents should be invited to a training session. During the training ses-

sion, the teacher would explain the fact system she is using, then go about presenting some specifics of how to work with the child.

The teacher should prepare a tutoring guide for the parents specifying exactly what they are to do and say. During the training session, the teacher would demonstrate the procedure and talk about motivation. The teacher would stress the need for positive reinforcement on the parents' part and for not nagging or deriding the child.

A communication system should be set up to inform parents which facts they should include in the exercises. A weekly letter including the facts to work on might be sent home. As a general rule, parents should provide practice on facts the student has already mastered in class. This is easily arranged if students take their deck of practice cards home.

Additional Practice Activities

Supplemental exercise should be done on facts throughout the day. One practice activity that is fun for students is the fact race. The teacher puts a scorecard on the board with one row for the teacher points and one for the student points:

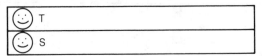

The teacher then states a fact or shows a flash card, pauses a second or two, and calls out a student's name. The teacher then hesitates a second more and says the answer. If the student responds correctly before the teacher says the answer, the students get the point. Note that pausing *before* calling on a student (but after stating the fact) will increase the probability that all students are attending to the question.

The race game can also be modified so that one group of students competes with another group. The teacher divides the class in half, placing an equal number of higher and lower performers in each group. The teacher conducts the game by saying a fact, pausing a second or two, and then calling on a student. The student earns a point for her team if she responds correctly.

Note that the games should be played in a way to avoid embarrassing low-performing students. Rules encouraging appropriate behavior should be discussed before playing the game and enforced during the game. Rules such as "no arguing" or "no complaining" are helpful in playing the game.

During free times, students can play board games in which the students pick a card from a deck of fact flash cards and if they say the fact correctly, they get to hit the spinner and move their man on the board the number of spaces indicated by the spinner.

Remedial Students

On pages 47–53 of Chapter 3 we discussed specific recommendations for intermediate grade remedial students. One suggestion dealt with the students' using their fingers to figure out addition and subtraction facts. Many remedial students will rely on their fingers to figure out facts. Teachers should not initially discourage students from using their fingers since memorizing basic facts may require months and months of practice. Teachers should tell students that eventually they will not have to use their fingers to figure out facts but for the time being, using fingers is fine except during fact memorization exercises. Teachers can expect some lower-performing students to be inaccurate even when using their fingers. These students may be divided into two groups: those who have an effective finger strategy to figure out facts but are careless, and those students who do not have any effective finger strategy.

The errors made by a student will tell whether or not he has an effective finger strategy. Students whose answers are correct about 80–90% of the time, and when wrong are usually just one number off (e.g., 15 − 9 = 5, 8 + 6 = 15, 9 + 7 = 15), probably have an effective strategy but are careless in applying it, counting too quickly or not coordinating counting and moving their fingers. The remediation procedure for these students is simply to provide daily exercises in which a strong reward for accuracy is provided. Students would be given worksheets containing 30–50 basic addition and subtraction facts. The reward should be contingent or the number of problems worked correctly. Daily exercises would be continued until students performed with over 95% accuracy consistently for about a week.

Students who miss more than 20% of basic facts and/or make what seem to be random errors, having answers several numbers away from the correct answer (e.g., 15 − 8 = 4, 8 + 6 = 19, 9 − 3 = 8), are likely not to have an effective strategy to figure out facts. The teacher should watch these students as they work problems in order to determine the students' specific deficits. The teacher would then provide remediation on the specific deficits or, if the students are quite confused, teach a strategy from the beginning. Below are finger strategies, one for addition and two for subtraction, that could be taught to students who by third grade have not developed any effective strategy for figuring out addition or subtraction facts.

For addition, the strategy would involve the following:

1. Noting which of the addends is smaller and putting up that number of fingers (e.g., in 8 + 5 the student puts up five fingers, in 3 + 6 the student puts up three fingers).
2. Counting from the other addend and saying one number for each finger (e.g., in 8 + 3, student puts up three fingers and counts eeighht, 9, 10, 11).

The teacher would demonstrate the strategy with several problems, then provide guided practice by asking, "Which number is smaller? . . . Hold up your fingers . . . Count and figure the answer . . . " Daily supervised practice would be provided until the student performed at a 95% accuracy level for about 2 weeks on a group of about 30–40 random addition facts.

The strategy for subtraction facts would not be introduced until students were proficient in figuring out addition facts. One of two possible finger strategies might be taught for figuring out basic subtraction facts, a counting backwards strategy or an algebra-based counting forward strategy.

In the counting backward strategy, the student puts up the number of fingers being minussed. For example, in 12 − 7 the student puts up seven fingers, says the larger number, then counts backward on each raised finger (tweelvvee, 11, 10, 9, 8, 7, 6, 5). Note that the student does not count a raised finger when saying the larger number.

In the algebra counting strategy, the student counts from the smaller number to the larger number (e.g., to work 11 − 6, the student counts from 6 to 11, putting up a finger each time she counts).

If the student does not have too much difficulty with counting backward, we recommend that the counting backward strategy be taught since the steps in it are basically the same as the addition strategy except for the direction students count. Another advantage of the backward strategy is that students are less likely to become confused when renaming is introduced. Regardless of which strategy is taught, the teacher would provide daily practice on a group of 30–40 random subtraction facts.

Research

Davis, in the *1978 Yearbook of the National Council of Teachers of Mathematics,* integrated research findings on teaching facts with common practice. His suggestions are listed below.

1. Children should attempt to memorize material they reasonably understand.
2. Have children begin to memorize basic arithmetic facts soon after they demonstrate an understanding of symbolic statements.
3. Children should participate in drill with the intent to memorize.
4. During drill sessions, emphasize remembering—don't explain!
5. Keep drill sessions short, and have some drill almost every day.
6. Try to memorize only a few facts in a given lesson, and constantly review previously memorized facts.
7. Express confidence in your students' ability to memorize—encourage them to try memorizing and see how fast they can be.
8. Emphasize verbal drill activities and provide feedback immediately.
9. Vary drill activities and be enthusiastic.
10. Praise students for good efforts—keep a record of their progress.

In addition to these "common sense" suggestions, research on math facts yields two additional recommendations for successful math fact instruction:

1. Students should be taught strategies for memorizing facts.
2. Teachers should provide adequate practice to allow students to achieve both accuracy and fluency.

Fact Strategies

Carnine and Stein (1981) found that students who were taught to apply the statement-saying strategy discussed earlier in the chapter to smaller number facts remembered more facts on a delayed post-test than students who received memorization drill without statement-saying practice. In a second study, which controlled the amount of practice time, students in the statement-saying group learned more facts.

An important aspect of teaching fact strategies involves reorganizing the sequence in which facts are introduced. Thorton (1978) evaluated a strategy for addition facts with bigger numbers. She taught fact pairs, pairs plus 1 (8 + 8, then 8 + 9), related family sets (7 + 7 = 14 and so does 6 + 8: similarly 8 + 8 = 16 and so does 9 + 7), plus 9s, and then the remaining facts. Thorton found that teaching facts in this organized manner resulted in higher post-test scores than unorganized presentations.

Cook and Dossey (1982) compared two approaches for teaching multiplication facts. The order of introduction of the facts varied considerably for the two groups. Results from this study also revealed that teaching related facts promotes more efficient learning than organizing facts according to factor size (0s, 1s, 2s, etc.). Baroody (1985) and Steinberg (1985) found that teaching students thinking strategies and reorganizing the introduction of facts fostered more automatic recall of facts as well.

Practice

Besides teaching strategies, providing practice is a critical component of fact teaching. Carnine and Stein (1981) found that a cumulative introduction of facts, in which previously introduced facts are mastered before new facts are introduced, resulted in quicker mastery of a set of six facts than simultaneously introducing all six facts.

Teaching facts to mastery can be quite time-consuming. Brent (personal communication) found that on the average, primary grade students took 20 8-minute sessions (160 minutes) to learn a set of nine facts (e.g., 1 + 4, 2 + 4, 3 + 4, 4 + 4, 5 + 4, 6 + 4, 7 + 4, 8 + 4, 9 + 4). The average number of digits written at the end of training on a set of facts was 57 per minute with an error rate of about 1 fact.

Pellegrino and Goldman (1987) found that the most efficient way to increase student fluency in solving addition/subtraction facts is to provide considerable amounts of additional fact practice. In an analysis of problem presentation frequency in math textbooks, Ashcraft (1985) discovered that the facts assumed to be stronger in the fact network actually appeared more often in the textbooks, supporting the relationship between practice and mastery.

Today, fact practice is commonly available on computer. To determine the efficacy of computer fact programs, teachers must look at the same components as they would for print programs: Does the program teach fact strategy? How is the presentation of facts sequenced? Is sufficient practice on facts provided? Fushon and Brinker (1985) investigated whether subtraction and division fact practice provided by microcomputers differed from that provided by additional flash card drill. Their results showed a significant increase in fact learning for both treatment groups, but no significant difference between the groups. While using computers may save teachers time in material preparation, the critical variable appears to be the amount of practice provided, not the medium of presentation.

In a study of multiplication facts, Brownell and Carper (1943) concluded that (a) multiplication tables should be taught, (b) the need for concrete devices is not great, and (c) ample drill is necessary.

Another type of research that has been conducted on the four groups of facts concerns relative difficulty. Murray (1939) compared his rankings of relative fact difficulty with those of six other researchers. The findings from the various researchers were similar. A summary of their findings appears in Figure 7.16.

Commercial Programs

Basic Facts

INSTRUCTIONAL STRATEGIES In most programs addition and subtraction facts are taught by emphasizing fact families. In several programs alternative strategies that organize facts differently also are taught. This emphasis on teaching related facts is in keeping with current research on basic fact acquisition.

One caution about initial teaching procedures for addition and subtraction facts, however, involves the use of pictures. While pictures aid students in using a counting strategy to solve computation problems, pictures are a deterrent to memorization; if pictures are available, some students invariably will resort to counting instead of trying to remember the answer. For example, in one program a third of

Figure 7.16

	Subtraction				Multiplication			
Easiest	10 - 1	6 - 2	5 - 4		1 × 1	2 × 1	5 × 1	
	9 - 1	5 - 2	6 - 5		1 × 2	2 × 2	5 × 2	
	8 - 1	4 - 2	7 - 6		1 × 3	2 × 3	6 × 1	
	7 - 1	3 - 2	8 - 7		1 × 4	2 × 4	7 × 1	
	6 - 1	6 - 3	9 - 8		1 × 5	2 × 5	8 × 1	
	5 - 1	5 - 3	10 - 9		1 × 6	3 × 1	9 × 1	
	4 - 1	4 - 3			1 × 7	3 × 2		
	3 - 1	8 - 4			1 × 8	4 × 1		
	2 - 1	6 - 4			1 × 9	4 × 2		
Intermediate	10 - 2	10 - 4	11 - 6		2 × 6	3 × 8	6 × 2	
	9 - 2	9 - 4	10 - 6		2 × 7	3 × 9	6 × 3	
	8 - 2	7 - 4	9 - 6		2 × 8	4 × 3	6 × 4	
	7 - 2	11 - 5	8 - 6		2 × 9	4 × 4	7 × 2	
	10 - 3	10 - 5	10 - 7		3 × 3	4 × 5	7 × 3	
	9 - 3	9 - 5	9 - 7		3 × 4	4 × 6	8 × 2	
	8 - 3	8 - 5	16 - 8		3 × 5	5 × 3	8 × 3	
	7 - 3	7 - 5	12 - 8		3 × 6	5 × 4	9 × 2	
	12 - 4	12 - 6	10 - 8		3 × 7	5 × 5	9 × 3	
Most	11 - 2	14 - 6	15 - 8	13 - 9	4 × 7	6 × 7	8 × 4	9 × 7
Difficult	12 - 3	13 - 6	14 - 8	12 - 9	4 × 8	6 × 8	8 × 5	9 × 8
	11 - 3	16 - 7	13 - 8	11 - 9	4 × 9	6 × 9	8 × 6	9 × 9
	13 - 4	15 - 7	11 - 8		5 × 6	7 × 4	8 × 7	
	11 - 4	14 - 7	18 - 9		5 × 7	7 × 5	8 × 8	
	14 - 5	13 - 7	17 - 9		5 × 8	7 × 6	8 × 9	
	13 - 5	12 - 7	16 - 9		5 × 9	7 × 7	9 × 4	
	12 - 5	11 - 7	15 - 9		6 × 5	7 × 8	9 × 5	
	15 - 6	17 - 8	14 - 9		6 × 6	7 × 9	9 × 6	

the exercises given to students for basic facts practice contain illustrations. For those problems, students need only count the pictures and write the answer, rather than recall the answers from memory. The amount of actual fact practice provided is thereby reduced. Teachers need to remember that if the objective of an exercise is to promote acquisition of facts, then no pictures should be available to students during the activity.

PRACTICE AND REVIEW The most important aspect of any fact program is the provision of adequate practice to develop mastery. A critical part of adequate practice is the cumulative review of previously introduced facts mixed with the presentation of new facts. This type of practice and review is not present in most basals. For example, in the third grade level of one program all basic addition facts are introduced in only three lessons (six student practice pages). Those same facts (sums to 18) are not reviewed until six lessons later when the relationship between addition and subtraction is taught. The program does not pro-vide another opportunity for students to practice addition facts in that level.

Practice provided for learning basic multiplication facts is often less than adequate as well. Basal programs typically teach basic multiplication facts within a single unit. Multiplication facts are introduced most often in sets of common factors, e.g., 3×0, 3×1, 3×2, 3×3, etc. (see Figure 7.17). Note that all the threes facts are introduced at once.

One type of fact practice noticeably absent from the program we examined was fluency practice (i.e., timed fact drills). Whereas programs traditionally address issues of accuracy (number right/number wrong), they have not included exercises whereby students must meet a specified rate criterion as well. For students to be able to recall facts in more complex computation problems, research tells us the students must know their math facts at an acceptable level of "automaticity." Therefore, teachers using these programs must be prepared to supplement by providing more practice as well as by establishing rate criteria that students must achieve.

Figure 7.17

STUDENT OBJECTIVE
To know the multiplication facts for 3.

TEACHING SUGGESTIONS

ACT OUT MULTIPLICATION WORD PROBLEMS WITH MODELS (Materials: counters) Ask the students to use their counters to act out the stories you tell.

"There are 3 wheels on each tricycle. The Baxters have 2 tricycles. How many tricycle wheels do they have?" (6)

"There are 3 tennis balls in each can. Chris has 4 cans. How many tennis balls does Chris have?" (12)

"There are 3 ice-cream cones. Each cone has 3 scoops on it. How many scoops are there altogether?" (9)

"There are 3 puppets in each package. Nancy bought 5 packages. How many puppets did she buy?" (15)

Encourage the students to make up stories.

SKIP-COUNT BY THREES Have students skip-count by threes through 30 (3, 6, 9, 12, 15, 18, 21, 24, 27, 30). As an extension, skip-count backward by threes from 30. (30, 27, 24, 21, 18, 15, 12, 9, 6, 3)

REVIEW ORALLY THE MULTIPLICATION FACTS WITH 3 AS A FACTOR Have students repeat aloud the multiplication facts with 3 as a factor through 3×9 and 9×3.[3]

Source: *Holt Mathematics,* Grade 4 Teacher's Edition (Copyright 1985 Holt Publishing Co., Inc.).

Application Items: Facts

1. Your principal asks you to describe the procedure you are using to facilitate learning basic facts. Assume that you are using the heterogeneous fact program system on pages 125–27. Write a description of the system.

2. The parents of the children in your class want to know why you spend so much time on memorization activities. What would your reply be?

3. Assume you are constructing worksheets for the paired worksheet fact system. You are preparing worksheets for subtraction facts. More specifically, you are now preparing a worksheet for Set U (page 119). (a) List the facts which would appear on the upper half of the worksheet. Next to each fact write how often it would appear on the top half. (b) Describe the guidelines you would use in preparing the bottom half of the student worksheet.

4. You are presenting the relationship format to prepare students for the facts in Set M of the multiplication sequence. Write what you do.

5. You are going to train a volunteer to work with a new student who is not fluent with multiplication facts. Write out directions for a volunteer who will use the flash card card system.

6. Assume the students have learned the basic multiplication facts in sets A through M in fact sequence of this text. Which problems would be appropriate to assign to students and which would not be appropriate?

34	82	34	65	87	48
× 5	× 6	× 9	× 7	× 8	× 2

8 Addition

Terms and Concepts

Addition   Addition is (*a*) the process of combining smaller sets to form a larger set and then determining the total number of the larger set, or (*b*) the union of two disjoint sets. Disjoint sets have no members in common.

Addend   The numbers of the smaller sets in an addition statement (e.g., in 4 + 3 = 7, the addends are 4 and 3).

Missing Addend   A problem type in which students solve for an addend (e.g., 6 + □ = 9).

Sum   The number of the new set formed by combining the smaller sets (e.g., in 4 + 3 = 7 the sum is 7).

Commutative Law of Addition   The sum is the same, regardless of the order in which the numbers are added (e.g., 4 + 3 = 7 and 3 + 4 = 7).

Associative Law of Addition   Any method of grouping may be used to obtain the sum of several addends:

(1 + 2) + 3 = 6 or 1 + (2 + 3) = 6
    3 + 3 = 6 or 1   + 5 = 6

Identity Element for Addition   When any whole number and zero are added, the result is the whole number.

Renaming   Converting a sum of 10 or more to the number of tens groups and the number of units; e.g., 17 is renamed as 10 and 7. In 19 + 28, the sum in the ones column (17) is renamed as 10 and 7 so that the 10 can be written in the tens column. This process had previously been called carrying. When used in addition, renaming is quite similar to expanded notation. In subtraction, a tens number is usually renamed as one 10 and the number of remaining 10s; e.g., 70 is renamed 10 and 60. In a problem such as 74 − 16, the 70 is renamed so that a 10 and the 4 can be combined, allowing a student to subtract a 6 from 14. Six 10s remain in the tens column.

Regrouping The same process as renaming except it is carried out with objects or counters rather than numerals; just as 8 + 4 can be renamed 10 + 2, so I I I I I I I I I I I I can be regrouped I I I I I I I I I I   I I.

Skill Hierarchy

Our discussion of addition is divided into two parts. The first part discusses presenting strategies designed to establish a concrete understanding of the process of addition. These strategies are usually taught to beginning students in kindergarten or first grade. The second part deals with teaching students to work problems at the abstract stage in which the student relies on mental computation rather than on representations of concrete objects. The second stage begins during the latter part of first grade and continues into the upper grades. For purposes of remediation, teachers should not revert to the conceptual introduction but should teach basic facts and the operations specified in the instructional sequence and assessment chart.

Figure 8.1 includes a skill hierarchy designed to help the reader see the relationships between skills taught in the two stages. During the beginning

Figure 8.1 Skill Hierarchy

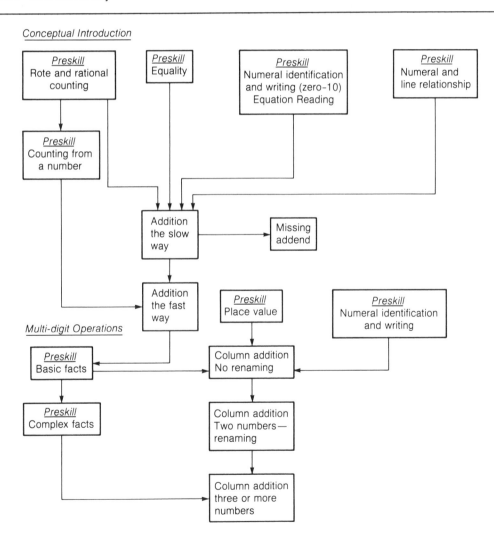

stage, students are taught to solve simple addition problems with concrete or semi-concrete objects representing each addend. For example, when solving the problem 4 + 2, the students are taught to draw four lines under the numeral 4 and two lines under the numeral 2. The students then figure the sum by counting all the lines. Note in the skill hierarchy chart that counting, numeral, and equality preskills must be mastered in order to work these problems. Missing addend problems in which an addend must be computed (e.g., 4 + □ = 7) are also presented during this stage. An understanding of equality is essential to solving missing addend problems.

In the second stage, when multi-digit numbers are added, students work problems without making concrete representations for each addend. A new preskill necessary for solving column addition problems is knowledge of basic addition facts. (The 100 possible combinations of single digit addends are referred to as basic addition facts.)

The ability to accurately and quickly respond to a fact problem is a component skill of all multi-digit problems. Too little attention is usually given to the process by which students learn to memorize basic addition facts. In order to aid the teacher in teaching this critical preskill, we have devoted an entire chapter to teaching basic addition, subtraction, multiplication, and division facts (see Chapter 7).

The first type of column problem involves adding multi-digit numbers in which the sum in each column is less than 10, thus renaming is not required. The problem 36 + 13 does not require renaming, but 36 + 15 does. The next major type of problem involves adding two or more multi-digit numbers in which the sum of one or more columns is greater than 10 and requires renaming. The initial problem in this group would involve adding two double digit numerals like 45 + 37. The sum of 5 and 7, 12, is renamed as one 10 and 2. A 1, for one 10, is written above the 4 and the 2 is written below the 7. Problems with hundreds and thousands numbers are introduced after students have been taught to read and write those numerals. The third major type of problem involves addition of three or more multi-digit numbers. The difficulty of these problems increases as the sum of each column becomes greater. For example, adding 23 + 14 + 32 is not difficult since a sum never reaches 10. On the other hand, in a problem such as 39 + 16 + 27, the sum for the first two numbers is more than 10 (9 + 6 = 15). The student must not only rename but also be able to figure out facts in which a single digit number is added to a two digit number. The sum of the

first two digits in the ones column, 9 and 6, is 15. The students must add 7 to 15 to figure the sum of the ones column. We refer to problems in which a student must add mentally a single digit number to a two digit number as *complex addition facts*. A great deal of practice is necessary for students to master complex addition facts.

Figure 8.2 includes our recommended instruction and assessment sequence. In column one is our numbered designation for the problem type. The number represents the grade level in which this problem type is usually introduced. The letter after the number differentiates one problem type from another within a grade level. In column two is a description of that particular type of problem. In column three are several examples of the problem type that could serve as items on a diagnostic skills test. Remember, for remediation, focus on facts and the skills in Figure 8.2, not skills from the conceptual introduction.

Introducing the Concept

The major objective of initial addition instruction is to develop a conceptual understanding of addition as a union of disjoint sets. Most educators agree that at this stage, demonstrations should involve concrete objects. Math educators recommend a variety of methods for introducing addition. Using the term *sets* and giving demonstrations of joining two sets are suggested in some commercial programs:

Demonstrations through number lines are also suggested:

The direct instruction strategies use lines as semi-concrete objects to represent the members of sets. While nothing is wrong with concrete manipulatives, having students draw lines has several advantages: it graphically demonstrates equality (the same number of lines are on both sides of the equal sign), teachers can more readily conduct instruction with groups of students, and the lines provide a written record of students' strategies, which makes diagnosis easier.

A unique feature of the direct instruction strategies for introducing the addition process is the integration of the equality principle into the strategy.

Figure 8.2 Instructional Sequence and Assessment Chart

Grade Level	Problem Type	Performance Indicator		
1a	Begin fact memorization	See Chapter 7		
1b	Adding a two digit and a one or two digit number; no renaming	35 +21	64 +23	35 + 2
2a	Adding three single digit numbers	1 3 +2	4 4 +3	1 3 +5
2b	Adding two three digit numbers; no renaming	325 +132	463 +124	386 +100
2c	Adding a three digit and a one or two digit number; no renaming	326 + 21	423 + 5	570 + 21
2d	Adding one, two, three-digit numbers; no renaming	4 21 + 2	14 71 + 10	21 14 + 33
2e	Adding two multi-digit numbers; renaming from ones to tens and tens to hundreds	37 +46	48 +14	57 +27
2f	Adding a three digit and a one, two, or three digit number; renaming from ones to tens	247 +315	258 + 13	276 + 8
3a	Complex facts; adding a single digit number to a teen number—sum below 20.	Test students individually; teacher asks: 13 + 3 = 14 + 4 = 12 + 2 =		
3b	Adding two two or three digit numbers; renaming from tens to hundreds	374 +261	83 +43	187 + 81
3c	Adding two three digit numbers; renaming from ones to tens and tens to hundreds	376 +185	248 + 64	437 + 5
3d	Adding three two digit numbers; renaming— ones column totals less than 20.	98 14 +12	39 16 +23	74 24 +12
3e	Adding three or four numbers; renaming from ones to tens and from tens to hundreds—sums of columns below 20.	385 6 24 +120	157 23 245 + 3	8 176 280 + 42
4a	Complex facts; adding a single number to a teen number—sum 20 or over	Test students individually, teacher asks: 16 + 6 = 18 + 8 = 17 + 6 =		
4b	Adding three two digit numbers—ones column totals 20 or more	28 17 +28	29 16 +35	38 18 +15
4c	Adding three, four or five multi-digit numbers; renaming in all or some columns totals 20 or more	892 1486 38 286 + 35	8 4086 85 193 + 242	3856 2488 1932 +1583

It is important that initial strategies demonstrate the application of the equality principle, since a grasp of equality is necessary for success in more sophisticated exercises, e.g., 7 + N = 12.

Making lines for each addend and then counting the lines is referred to as *addition the slow way*. Students draw the appropriate number of lines under each numeral:

$$4 + 2 = \Box$$
$$||||\quad||$$

count the lines, then draw the same number of lines on the other side of the equal sign and write the answer in the box:

$$4 + 2 = \boxed{6}$$
$$||||\quad||\quad||||||$$

By counting the lines one by one and drawing the same number on the other side, the concept of equality is demonstrated. Note that *plus* is used as a verb; students are taught "the plus sign says to count all the lines." Later the term *addition* is introduced; "a plus sign says to add."

Problems with missing addends are introduced after students have demonstrated mastery of initial addition exercises. In solving problems with missing addends:

$$4 + \Box = 7$$
$$||||\qquad|||||||$$

the teacher points out that the sides are not equal. The students must add lines to make the sides equal and then write the numeral representing the number of lines added.

After the students can solve addition and missing addend problems through making lines to represent each numeral, a new strategy, called *addition the fast way*, is introduced. In addition the fast way, students make lines only under the numeral plussed (4 + 2), count the lines beginning

$$||$$

with the first numeral (four, five, six), then write the answer in the box. Addition the fast way represents a transition from the semi-concrete stage in which objects are drawn to represent each member of the set to the stage in which no concrete representations are used. A similar fast way strategy can be taught for missing addend problems.

Addition the Slow Way

Addition the slow way is an important strategy since it is the student's first experience with actually solving a problem. Here are skills which the student should have mastered before addition the slow way is introduced.

1. Identifying and writing the numerals 0–10 and the symbols + = □
2. Equality rule
3. Reading an equation
4. Drawing the appropriate number of lines to represent a numeral
5. Counting the lines in two groups
6. Writing the numeral that represents a set of objects

The format for teaching students to work addition problems the slow way appears in Figure 8.3. In Part A, the teacher works the problem on the board while evoking verbal responses from the students. Circles are drawn around the sides of the equal sign:

$$(5 + 2) = (\Box)$$

to emphasize the concept of side. The steps in the strategy are summarized below:

1. Students read equation, "5 + 2 = how many?"
2. Teacher has students identify equal sign and then gives the equality rule "You must end with the same number on this side of the equal and on the other side."
3. Students draw lines under first addend. (If either addend is zero, the teacher explains that for zero you don't make any lines, so there are no lines to count for zero.)
4. Teacher tells students that the plus sign tells them to count more. So they draw two more lines.
5. Teacher points out that since the problem is a plus problem, they count all the lines in the first group, then keep counting and count the lines in the next group on that side.
6. Students count all lines on that side of the equal sign.
7. Teacher reminds students of equality rule and has students make lines under the box on other side of the equal sign.
8. Students write numeral to represent number of lines.

When presenting Part A, the teacher should repeat a problem until students can correctly respond to all questions. If a student hesitates or responds incorrectly, the teacher should repeat the question, telling the correct answer, then repeat the question again and ask the students to respond.

Figure 8.3 Format for Teaching Addition the Slow Way

Day	Part A Structured Board Presentation Problems	Part B Structured Worksheet Problems	Part C Less Structured Worksheet Problems	Part D Supervised Practice Problems
1	3			
2-3	1	3		
4-5		2	3	
6-7			4	4
8-till accurate				8-10

PART A: Structured Board Presentation

TEACHER

Write on board:

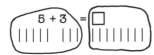

STUDENTS

1. "READ THE PROBLEM."   "5 + 3 = how many?"
2. Point to the equal sign. "WHAT IS THIS?"   "Equal"
3. "LISTEN TO THE EQUAL RULE: WE MUST END WITH THE SAME NUMBER ON THIS SIDE OF THE EQUAL (circle 5 + 3) AND ON THE OTHER SIDE" (circle box).
4. Point to 5. "HOW MANY IN THE FIRST GROUP?"   "5"
   "I'LL DRAW FIVE LINES UNDER THE 5. COUNT AS I DRAW THE LINES." Draw five lines.   "1, 2, 3, 4, 5"
5. Point to + 3. "THIS SAYS PLUS THREE. PLUS TELLS US TO DRAW MORE LINES, SO I DRAW THREE MORE LINES UNDER THE 3. COUNT AS I DRAW THE LINES." Draw three lines.   "1, 2, 3"
6. "WE'VE DRAWN ALL THE LINES ON THIS SIDE. LET'S COUNT AND SEE WHAT WE END WITH. COUNT AS I TOUCH THE LINES." Touch lines.   "1, 2, 3, 4, 5, 6, 7, 8"
   "WHAT NUMBER DID WE END WITH?"   "8"
   "WE MUST END WITH THE SAME NUMBER ON THIS SIDE AND THE OTHER SIDE."
7. Point to 5 + 3. "WE ENDED WITH 8 ON THIS SIDE. SO WHAT NUMBER MUST WE END WITH ON THE OTHER SIDE?"   "8"
   "I'LL DRAW THE LINES. YOU COUNT AND TELL ME WHEN TO STOP." Draw lines under box.   "1, 2, 3, 4, 5, 6, 7, 8, stop"

   5 + 3 = ☐
   |||||| ||| |||||||||

   TO CORRECT: If children don't say stop after 8, keep drawing lines, then say, "WE MADE A MISTAKE. YOU HAVE TO TELL ME TO STOP." Repeat from step 6.

8. "THE LINES UNDER A BOX TELL WHAT NUMERAL GOES IN THE BOX. HOW MANY LINES ARE UNDER THE BOX?"   "8"
   "SO WHAT NUMBER GOES IN THE BOX?"   "8"
   Write 8 in the box. "WHAT DOES 5 + 3 EQUAL?"   "8"
9. "SAY THE WHOLE STATEMENT."   "5 + 3 = 8"
10. Repeat steps 1-9 until students can answer with no errors. Repeat steps 1-10 with several problems.

Figure 8.3 cont'd

PART B: Structured Worksheet

TEACHER   STUDENTS

Sample Worksheet Item:

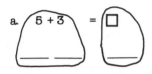

1. "TOUCH PROBLEM a."
2. "READ THE PROBLEM AS I CLAP. GET READY."   "5 + 3 = how many?"
   Clap at 1 second intervals.
3. "HOW MANY IN THE FIRST GROUP?"   "5"
   "MAKE THE LINES."   Students draw five lines.
4. "THE NEXT PART OF THE PROBLEM SAYS PLUS
   3. WHAT DO YOU DO WHEN YOU PLUS 3?"   "Make three more lines."
5. "MAKE THE LINES UNDER THE 3."   Students draw three lines.
6. "LET'S COUNT ALL THE LINES ON THAT SIDE. PUT
   YOUR FINGER OVER THE FIRST LINE." Check.
   "TOUCH AND COUNT THE LINES AS I CLAP." Clap
   one clap per second.   "1, 2, 3, 4, 5, 6, 7, 8"
7. "HOW MANY LINES DID WE END WITH?"   "8"
8. "SO, HOW MANY MUST WE END WITH ON THE
   OTHER SIDE OF THE EQUAL?"   "8".
9. "MAKE THE LINES AND WRITE THE NUMERAL."
10. "WHAT DOES 5 + 3 EQUAL?"   "8"
11. "SAY THE STATEMENT."   "5 + 3 = 8"
    Repeat steps 1-11 with remaining problems.

PART C: Less Structured Worksheet

Give students worksheets with problems.

1. "TOUCH PROBLEM a."
2. "READ THE PROBLEM."   "6 + 3 = how many?"
3. "FIRST YOU MAKE SIX LINES, THEN YOU PLUS 3.
   HOW DO YOU PLUS 3?"   "Make three more lines."
4. "MAKE THE SIDES EQUAL AND FILL IN THE MISS-
   ING NUMERAL." Check.
5. "WHAT DOES 6 + 3 EQUAL?"   "9"
6. "SAY THE STATEMENT."   "6 + 3 = 9"
   Repeat steps 1-5 with remaining problems.

The teacher then would ask questions for the rest of the problem. Following the correction, all the steps from the beginning would be repeated one more time. This last presentation serves as a demonstration of how all the steps fit together.

Part B is a structured worksheet exercise; Part C, a less structured worksheet exercise; and Part D,

a supervised practice exercise. Example selection for all worksheet exercises should include only numerals that students can identify and write. Sums should not exceed 10. On the worksheets, spaces should be left under numerals for students to draw lines. Once the students develop 80–90% accuracy in working the problems, they no longer need supervised practice. Eight to ten problems would appear daily on students' worksheets for several more weeks. Note that on worksheets horizontal bars are drawn below each numeral. These bars are to prompt drawing the lines.

Missing Addend

The strategy discussed in this section teaches students to find the missing addend in a problem like this, $5 + \square = 8$. The strategy is based on the equality rule that "you must end with the same number on both sides of the equal." Students are presented this form of problem to enhance their understanding of the equality principle and demonstrate that the equality principle may be used to solve a variety of problem types.

To solve this simple form of missing addend problems, the students first find the side of the equal sign that tells how many they end with. The teacher then points out that the sides are not equal until the students end with the same number on both sides. The teacher then directs the students to draw lines on the side with the box so that the sides will be equal and to fill in the missing numeral.

Figure 8.4 includes the format for presenting the missing addend strategy. Part A teaches students the component skill of determining the side to start working on. The exercise points out that since a box doesn't tell how many lines to draw, it can't be the side to start on. Parts B and C are structured board and worksheet exercises, respectively. Note that in step 5 of Part B and step 7 of Part C the teacher reminds the students that the lines under a

Figure 8.4 Format for Solving Missing Addends

Day	Part A Side to Start on Problems	Part B Structured Board Presentation Problems	Part C Structured Worksheet Problems	Part D Less Structured Worksheet Problems	Part E Supervised Practice Problems
1-3	6	4			
4		2	3		
5-6			3	6	
7-8				6	4
9-10				6	6
11-till accurate					10-12

PART A: Side to Start On

STUDENTS

Write on the board:

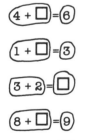

1. "LISTEN. I'M GOING TO TELL YOU SOMETHING ABOUT THE SIDE YOU START WITH. YOU START WITH THE SIDE THAT TELLS HOW MANY LINES TO DRAW. LISTEN AGAIN: YOU START WITH THE SIDE THAT TELLS HOW MANY LINES TO DRAW."

Figure 8.4 cont'd

2. "MY TURN." Point on board to

"CAN I START ON THIS SIDE? NO. HOW DO I KNOW?
CAUSE THE BOX DOES NOT TELL ME HOW MANY LINES
TO DRAW." Point to 6. "CAN I START ON THIS SIDE? YES.
HOW DO YOU KNOW? CAUSE A 6 TELLS HOW MANY LINES
TO DRAW."

3. "NOW IT'S YOUR TURN." Point to

"CAN I START ON THIS SIDE?"   "No"
"HOW DO YOU KNOW?"   "Because a box does not tell how
                                                     many lines to draw."

4. Point to 6. "CAN I START ON THIS SIDE?"   "Yes"
   Repeat steps 1–4 with remaining problems.

PART B: Structured Board Presentation

Write on board:

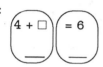

1. "READ THIS PROBLEM."   "4 + how many = 6"

2. "THIS IS A NEW KIND OF PROBLEM. IT DOESN'T TELL US
   HOW MANY TO PLUS. WE HAVE TO FIGURE OUT HOW
   MANY TO PLUS. WHAT MUST WE FIGURE OUT?"   "How many to plus."

3. "WE USE THE EQUAL RULE TO HELP US. THE EQUAL RULE
   SAYS WE MUST END WITH THE SAME NUMBER ON THIS
   SIDE" (point to 4 + □) "AND THE OTHER SIDE OF THE
   EQUAL" (point to 6). "FIRST WE FIGURE THE SIDE WE
   START COUNTING ON." Point to 4 + □. "DO I START
   COUNTING ON THIS SIDE?"   "No"
   "WHY NOT?"   "The box does not tell how many
                                                     lines to make."
   Point to 6. "DO I START COUNTING ON THIS SIDE?"   "Yes"
   "YES. THE 6 TELLS ME TO MAKE SIX LINES." Draw six
   lines under the 6.

4. "WE WANT TO END WITH THE SAME NUMBER ON BOTH
   SIDES." Point to 4 + □. "HOW MANY ON THIS SIDE NOW?" "4"
   "I'LL DRAW FOUR LINES." Draw four lines under 4. "THINK.
   HOW MANY DO WE NEED TO END WITH ON THIS SIDE?"   "6"

   TO CORRECT: "WE WANT TO END WITH THE SAME NUM-
              BER WE END WITH ON THE OTHER SIDE.
              WHAT NUMBER DO WE END WITH ON THE
              OTHER SIDE?"

   "WE HAVE 4. WE WANT TO END WITH 6. COUNT AS I
   MAKE THE LINES. TELL ME WHEN TO STOP." Point to 4.
   "HOW MANY IN THIS GROUP?"   "4"
   "GET IT GOING." Draw lines under box as students count. "444, 5, 6, stop"

   TO CORRECT: If students do not say stop after saying 6, tell
              them, "WE ENDED WITH 6 ON THE OTHER
              SIDE. WE MUST END WITH 6 ON THIS SIDE."
              Then repeat from step 4.

144   Skills and Concepts

Figure 8.4 cont'd

TEACHER	**STUDENTS**

5. "WHAT NUMBER DID WE END WITH?" "6"
   "WE MADE THE SIDES EQUAL. ARE WE GOING TO WRITE
   6 IN THE BOX?" "No"

   TO CORRECT: If children say yes, "WE MUST COUNT THE
   THE LINES UNDER THE BOX TO SEE WHAT
   NUMBER GOES IN THE BOX."

   "THE NUMBER OF LINES UNDER THE BOX TELLS US WHAT
   NUMERAL TO WRITE IN THE BOX. WHAT NUMERAL?" "2"
   Write 2 in box.

6. "4 + HOW MANY EQUALS 6?" "2"
   "SAY THE WHOLE STATEMENT." "4 + 2 = 6
   Repeat steps 1–6 with remaining problems.

PART C: Structured Worksheet

Sample Worksheet Item:

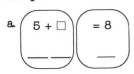

1. "TOUCH PROBLEM a. READ THE PROBLEM." "5 + how many = 8"

2. "TOUCH THE SIDE YOU START COUNTING ON." Students touch side with 8.

3. "MAKE THE LINES UNDER THE 8." Students make eight lines.

4. "TOUCH THE SIDE THAT SAYS 5 PLUS HOW MANY." Students touch the side.

5. "HOW MANY DO WE HAVE ON THAT SIDE NOW?" "5"
   "MAKE FIVE LINES UNDER THE 5."

6. "THINK. HOW MANY DO WE HAVE TO END WITH ON
   THAT SIDE?" "8"

   TO CORRECT: "WE WANT TO MAKE THE SIDES EQUAL.
   WE ENDED WITH 8 ON THE OTHER SIDE SO
   WE MUST END WITH 8 ON THIS SIDE."

7. "TOUCH THE 5. YOU HAVE FIVE LINES SO FAR. MAKE
   MORE LINES UNDER THE BOX SO THAT WE END WITH 8
   ON THAT SIDE." Students draw more lines.
   "HOW MANY DID YOU END WITH ON THAT SIDE?" "8"
   "ARE YOU GOING TO WRITE 8 IN THE BOX?" "No"
   "NO, THE LINES UNDER THE BOX TELL US WHAT NUM-
   ERAL TO WRITE IN THE BOX."

8. "COUNT THE LINES YOU MADE UNDER THE BOX AND
   WRITE THE NUMERAL." Students write 3.
   "5 PLUS HOW MANY EQUALS 8?" "3"
   "SAY THE WHOLE STATEMENT." "5 + 3 = 8"

PART D: Less Structured Worksheet

Give students a worksheet with an equal mix of addition and
missing addend problems.

a.   d.

b.   e.

c.   f. 5 + 3 = □

Figure 8.4 cont'd

TEACHER	**STUDENTS**
1. "TOUCH PROBLEM a. READ THE PROBLEM."	"5 + 3 equal how many?"
2. "TOUCH THE SIDE YOU START COUNTING ON."	
3. "MAKE THE LINES ON THAT SIDE AND GET READY TO TELL ME HOW MANY YOU END WITH." Pause. "HOW MANY DO YOU END WITH?"	"8"
4. "TOUCH THE OTHER SIDE." Pause. "WHAT DO YOU WANT TO END WITH?"	"8"
5. "MAKE LINES TO MAKE THE SIDES EQUAL."	
6. "COUNT THE LINES UNDER THE EMPTY BOX AND WRITE THE NUMERAL."	Students write 8 in the box.

box tell what numeral goes in the box. This prompt prevents errors like 5 + $\boxed{7}$ = 7 in which students write how many on the whole side in the box.

Part D is a less structured worksheet exercise. Worksheets for this part include an equal mix of missing addend and regular addition problems. In Part D, the teacher leads the students through steps designed to teach the students when to apply the missing addend strategy. The teacher then instructs the students to make both sides equal and finally to fill in the missing numeral. Lower-performing students may need a great deal of practice on this part and on the supervised practice part before they can discriminate when and how to apply the regular addition and missing addend strategies. Examples should be limited to problems in which the sum is 10 or less. This limitation is suggested to prevent the tasks from becoming too cumbersome.

When the missing addend is zero, as in 8 + □ = 8, the teacher can use this wording to replace steps 6, 7, and 8 in Part C.

6. "THIS IS A SPECIAL KIND OF PROBLEM. THE SIDES ARE ALREADY EQUAL. 8 ON BOTH SIDES. SO YOU SHOULDN'T MAKE ANY MORE LINES. YOU PLUS ZERO LINES. WRITE A ZERO IN THE BOX."
7. "8 PLUS HOW MANY EQUALS 8?"
8. "SAY THE WHOLE STATEMENT."

Present two problems on the last day that Part C is presented: 8 + □ = 8, 2 + □ = 2. Continue to present problems in which the missing addend is zero in Part D and Part E.

Addition the Fast Way

Addition the fast way (see Figure 8.5) is taught as a transitional step between the strategy in which

students draw lines for each member of the sets represented by each addend and later exercises in which students memorize answers to addition facts. When time for math instruction is limited, teachers can skip addition the fast way and move directly into fact teaching (see Chapter 7). The addition the fast way strategy differs from addition the slow way in that the student only draws lines to represent the addend following the plus:

$$7 + 4 = \Box$$
$$||||$$

When solving the problem, the student starts counting at the number represented by the numeral in the first addend position and then counts the lines (e.g., 7, 8, 9, 10, 11). Then the student writes the numeral representing the sum in the box on the other side of the equal sign. The student does not draw lines under the box. The only new preskill for this strategy is rote counting beginning at a number other than 1.

Addition the fast way would be introduced when students work a mix of addition and missing addend problems with 80–90% accuracy. Teachers can expect some students to have difficulty coordinating counting from a number other than 1 and touching lines. For students who consistently have difficulty with this step, the teacher should present an exercise focusing solely on this compound skill. The teacher might write a series of problems in which the lines are drawn:

$$5 + 3 \qquad 7 + 2$$
$$||| \qquad ||$$
$$3 + 4 \qquad 9 + 5$$
$$|||| \qquad |||||$$

The teacher would model and test counting until the students could do four problems in a row correctly. For example, the teacher teaches 5, saying

Figure 8.5 Format for Teaching Addition the Fast Way

Day	Part A Structured Board Presentation Problems	Part B Structured Worksheet Problems	Part C Less Structured Worksheet Problems	Part D Supervised Practice Problems	Part E Independent Practice
1	3	2			
2	1	3			
3-4		2	3		
5			4	4	
6-till accurate				8-10	

Then begin subtraction introduction (see Chapter 9).   6-10
  Till fluent
Then begin fact memorization instruction (see Chapter 7).

PART A: Structured Board Presentation

TEACHER	**STUDENTS**

Write on board: $5 + 3 = \square$

    ——

1. "I'LL TOUCH AND YOU READ."	"5 + 3 = how many?"
2. "WE'RE GOING TO WORK THIS PROBLEM A FAST WAY. WE DRAW LINES UNDER THE NUMBER AFTER THE PLUS." Point to + 3. "WHAT DOES THIS SAY?"	"+ 3"
"SO HOW MANY LINES ARE WE GONG TO DRAW?"	"3"
"I'LL MAKE THE LINES." Draw three lines under the 3.	
3. "WATCH ME COUNT THE FAST WAY." Touch 5 and then each line. "FIIIIVVVE, SIX, SEVEN, EIGHT. NOW IT'S YOUR TURN TO COUNT THE FAST WAY. HOW MANY ARE IN THE FIRST GROUP?"	"5"
"GET IT GOING . . . COUNT." Touch 5 for 2 seconds then touch each line.	"5555, 6, 7, 8"
4. "HOW MANY DID WE END WITH ON THIS SIDE?"	"8"
"SO HOW MANY MUST WE END WITH ON THE OTHER SIDE?"	"8"
"I'LL WRITE AN 8 IN THE BOX." Write 8 in the box.	
5. "READ THE WHOLE STATEMENT."	"5 + 3 = 8"
Repeat steps 1-5 with 7 + 4, 9 + 5.	

PART B: Structured Worksheet

   $4 + 2 = \square$

   ——

1. Point to 4 + 2 = $\square$. "TOUCH THIS PROBLEM ON YOUR WORKSHEET" Pause. "READ THE PROBLEM OUT LOUD. GET READY." Clap for each symbol.	"4 + 2 equals how many?"
2. "LET'S WORK THIS PROBLEM THE FAST WAY. TOUCH THE NUMERAL AFTER THE PLUS." Pause. "HOW MANY LINES ARE YOU GOING TO PLUS?"	"2"
"MAKE THE LINES UNDER THE 2." Check.	

Figure 8.5 cont'd

3. "TOUCH THE 4 AND GET READY TO COUNT THE FAST
WAY. FOUR. GET IT GOING." Clap as students touch and
count. "COUNT"   "ffoouurrr, 5, 6"

TO CORRECT: Teacher models. "MY TURN ...." If necessary,
moves student's finger as he counts.

4. "HOW MANY DID YOU END WITH ON THE SIDE YOU
STARTED WITH?"   "6"
"HOW MANY MUST YOU END WITH ON THE SIDE WITH
THE BOX?"   "6"
"YES, 6 EQUALS 6. WHAT NUMERAL WILL YOU WRITE
IN THE BOX?"   "6"
"DO IT."

5. "READ THE WHOLE STATEMENT."   "4 + 2 = 6

PART C: Less Structured Worksheet

1. Read problem and determine side. "EVERYBODY, READ
PROBLEM ONE ON YOUR WORKSHEET. GET READY."
Clap for each symbol.   "4 + 3 = how many?"

2. Work problem. "NOW YOU'RE READY TO PLUS LINES AND
COUNT THE FAST WAY. WHAT ARE YOU GOING TO DO?"   "Plus the lines and count the
the fast way."

"DO IT." Check students as they work.

3. "READ THE WHOLE STATEMENT."   "4 + 3 = 7"

"FFFIIIVEEE", then touches each line and counts "6, 7, 8". The teacher would then test by touching 7 and saying "GET IT GOING," and then touching each line.

Example selection criteria for addition the fast way problems are somewhat different than for addition the slow way. Larger numerals can be written in the first addend position since the student no longer has to draw lines to represent that amount. The second addend, however, should usually be below 7 even though an occasional example with 8 or 9 can be presented. Teachers must control the problems so that the sum is represented by a numeral the students have been taught to write.

After students work addition problems the fast way accurately (in Part D), subtraction instruction can begin (see Chapter 9). After students work addition problems fluently (in Part E), memorization of addition facts should begin (see Chapter 7).

Diagnosis and Remediation

This section presents basic procedures for diagnosing and remedying errors in beginning addition. The teacher first decides whether the problem is one of "can't do" or "won't do." In this section, we consider only the "can't do" problems. The basic steps below apply to diagnosing and remedying errors on any type of problem.

1. The teacher analyzes worksheet errors and hypothesizes what the cause of the errors might be.
2. The teacher interviews the students to determine the error, if it is not obvious.
3. The teacher provides reteaching through board and/or worksheet presentations.
4. The teacher tests the students on a set of problems similar to the ones on which the original errors were made.

Once students begin working problems independently using a specific strategy, the errors they make on their worksheets fall into two main categories (fact errors are not possible at this stage because facts are not used nor have they been taught):

1. Component skill errors—those errors that indicate a deficit on one or more of the component skills that make up the strategy
2. Strategy errors—errors indicating problems with the application of the strategy (Strategy errors often are the result of a student's forgetting certain steps in the procedure.)

Our discussion of diagnosis and remediation of each problem-solving strategy will address both types of errors. The similarities of the suggested remediation for each type of error should be noted.

COMPONENT SKILL ERRORS Component skill errors may be made on symbol identification and writing, counting and/or drawing lines (including "get it going" and "count"), and application of the equality rule. When errors are due to component skill deficits, error patterns are more readily apparent. Therefore, a teacher will often be able to determine the cause of these errors by a careful analysis of worksheets. For example, on an addition the fast way worksheet, a student made the following errors:

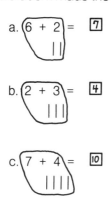

By analyzing the errors made by the student, the teacher would suspect that the student was having trouble coordinating counting from a number or said the number representing the first group while touching the first line in the second group and counted the remaining lines. For example, in problem a the student may have touched the first line under 2 while saying "sssiix" and said "7" when touching the second line.

To remedy a component skill error, the teacher would present an exercise focusing on the component skill for several lessons and firm the student on that skill in isolation before returning to the more advanced problems. For example, to remedy the errors made by the student above, the teacher would present an exercise on just counting. The teacher would focus on that one skill until the student reached a criterion of about 90% correct responses on the examples. Then the teacher would give addition problems to work independently.

Another possible component error involves symbol identification. If a student missed a problem because of numeral misidentification (e.g., calling 6, 9), the teacher would focus on the numeral 6 in numeral identification for several lessons. During this time, the student would not be asked to solve problems including the numeral 6.

STRATEGY ERROR   A strategy error indicates a fundamental lack of understanding of how to sequence the steps in the problem-solving strategy. For example, when watching a student work a

problem using addition the slow way, the teacher notes the student draws lines under each numeral:

$$3 + 6 = \square$$
$$|||\ ||||||$$

but after counting, simply writes the next number in the counting sequence, 10, in the box. This behavior clearly indicates that the student is not employing the strategy.

To remedy a strategy error, the teacher reintroduces the format to the student beginning with the structured board presentation, then progresses to the structured and less structured worksheet presentations. A common strategy error students make when solving problems with missing addends involves adding the addend and sum: 6 + $\boxed{15}$ = 9. Such errors indicate students are not applying the equality principle. The teacher would begin with the structured board presentation, Part B of Figure 8.4, then progress to Parts C and D.

Direct Instruction Procedures for Multi-digit Addition Problems

Column addition problems may be divided into three groups. Simplest are those which do not require renaming:

$$\begin{array}{r} 24 \\ +15 \\ \hline \end{array}$$

Next are problems with two multi-digit addends, and renaming is necessary:

$$\begin{array}{r} 424 \\ +317 \\ \hline \end{array}$$

Most difficult are problems with more *than* two multi-digit addends:

$$\begin{array}{r} 671 \\ 424 \\ +317 \\ \hline \end{array}$$

Students should work column addition problems by using their knowledge of facts. Problems should be constructed from facts the students have been taught.

Problems Not Requiring Renaming

Column addition problems without renaming are usually introduced in first grade after students have learned to read and write numerals for numbers through 99 and are able to figure out mentally about 25 basic addition facts. Remember basic addition facts include all possible pairings in which the addends are single digit numbers (a + b in a + b = c). Students need many months of practice before they have memorized all basic facts. Multi-digit addition problems need not be delayed until students have memorized all basic addition facts. Initial examples, however, should be limited to include the easier basic addition facts. Exercises to help memorize basic addition facts are discussed in detail in Chapter 7.

The procedure for teaching students to work these problems is relatively simple. The teacher has the students read the problem, then points out the place value columns, telling students to first add the 1s and then to add the 10s. Teaching students to always begin working in the ones column buttresses against errors on renaming problems. Although students can begin adding tens numbers when renaming is not required:

$$\begin{array}{cc} 24 & 24 \\ +\underline{12} \text{ then} & +\underline{12} \\ 3 & 36 \end{array}$$

they will have difficulty if they start working problems in the tens column that do require renaming:

$$\begin{array}{cc} 24 & 24 \\ +\underline{17} \text{ then} & +\underline{17} \\ 3 & 311 \end{array}$$

After learning to begin in the ones column, students add the 1s and then the 10s, writing the sum for each column. The teacher asks about the number of 10s rather than the quantity represented by the tens number; that is, for

$$\begin{array}{c} 34 \\ +\underline{21} \end{array}$$

the students indicate they're adding three 10s and two 10s, not 30 and 20; while 3 + 2 is a familiar fact, 30 + 20 is not. Because the teaching procedure is quite simple, we do not include a format in the book for this problem type. A teacher would, however, first use a structured board presentation, then structured and less structured worksheet exercises. The transition from structured board to independent worksheet can be made in about four lessons.

Problems Requiring Renaming

Problems requiring renaming are usually introduced during second grade. Preskills are working addition problems without renaming, mastery in reading and writing numerals, mastery in figuring out basic addition facts, and mastery in expanded notation with teen and tens numbers.

PRESKILL A unique preskill for renaming involves adding three single digit numbers. For example, when adding 10s in

$$\begin{array}{c} 1 \\ 37 \\ +\underline{29} \\ 6 \end{array}$$

the student adds 1 + 3 to get the sum of 4, then adds the sum to 2. Adding three numbers is significantly more difficult for low performers than adding two numbers. When adding three numbers, the student must add the first two numbers, remember the answer, and then add the third number to that sum.

Adding three single digit numbers should be taught several weeks prior to the introduction of renaming problems. The format for teaching students a strategy to solve these problems appears in Figure 8.6. The format contains only three parts: a structured board presentation, a structured worksheet presentation, and supervised practice. Since relatively few steps are involved, a less structured worksheet format is not needed.

The most common error made on this format occurs in step 6, Part A and step 4, Part B, when students are asked to identify the *next* two numbers to be added. Students often respond with the second and third numbers instead of the sum of the first two numbers and the third number; e.g., for

$$\begin{array}{c} 2 \\ 3 \\ +\underline{4} \end{array}$$

students answer 3 + 4 rather than 5 + 4. In Part A, the teacher tries to prompt the correct response by referring to that question as the "hard part." If students do make the error, the teacher must model and test the answer and the repeat the entire problem from the beginning. ("NOW WE'RE ADDING 5 + 4. WHAT ARE WE ADDING NOW? WHAT IS 5 + 4? . . . LET'S DO THE WHOLE PROBLEM AGAIN FROM THE BEGINNING."

There are two example selection guidelines. In about half the examples, the top numeral should be 1 since in most renaming a 1 will be carried to the tens column. Initially, the sum of the three single digits should be 10 or less, so that students will be able to concentrate on adding the three numbers rather than figuring out more difficult basic facts.

INTRODUCING THE PROBLEMS The first type of problem which involves renaming should involve adding a two digit numeral with another one or two digit numeral. Renaming is explained to students by

Figure 8.6 Format for Adding Three Single Digit Numbers

Day	Part A Structured Board Presentation Problems	Part B Structured Worksheet Problems	Part C Supervised Practice Problems	Part D Independent Seatwork Problems
1-2	3	3		
3-4	1	4	5	
4-20 (till fluent)				10

PART A: Structured Board Presentation

TEACHER   **STUDENTS**

Write on board:

```
1     1     3
3     2     1
+2    +4    +6
```

1. "YOU'RE GOING TO LEARN HOW TO WORK A SPECIAL
   KIND OF PROBLEM TODAY. READ THIS PROBLEM."   "1 + 3 + 2"

2. "WATCH ME WORK IT. FIRST I ADD 1 PLUS 3. WHAT DO
   I ADD FIRST?"   "1 + 3"
   "WHAT IS 1 PLUS 3?" Pause.   "4"

3. "1 PLUS 3 = 4. NOW I ADD 4 PLUS 2. WHAT DO I ADD NEXT?"   "4 + 2"
   "WHAT IS 4 + 2?" Pause.   "6"

4. "SO I WRITE THE 6 BELOW THE EQUAL."

5. "LET'S SEE IF YOU REMEMBER. WHAT ARE THE FIRST
   NUMBERS I ADD?"   "1 + 3"

6. "WHAT IS 1 + 3?" Pause.   "4"
   "HERE'S THE HARD PART. WHAT ARE THE NEXT
   NUMBERS I ADD?"   "4 + 2"

   TO CORRECT: If student says 3 + 2, repeat steps 2-6.

   "WHAT IS 4 + 2?" Pause.   "6"
   Write 6.

7. "READ THE PROBLEM NOW."   "1 + 3 + 2 = 6."

8. Repeat with two more examples. Give individual turns to
   several students on steps 1-7.

PART B: Structured Worksheet

Students have worksheets with 10 problems of this type:

```
2     1     5
4     4     2
+3    +3    +2
```

1. "TOUCH PROBLEM ONE. READ IT."   "2 + 4 + 3"

2. "TOUCH THE FIRST NUMBERS YOU ADD." Monitor
   responses. "WHAT ARE THEY?"   "2 + 4"

3. "WHAT IS 2 + 4?" Pause.   "6"

4. "NOW TELL ME THE NEXT NUMBER YOU ADD." Pause.   "6 + 3"
   "YES, 6 + 3."

5. "WHAT IS 6 + 3?" Pause, signal.   "9"
   "WRITE 9 BELOW THE LINE."

6. "READ THE PROBLEM NOW."   "2 + 4 + 3 = 9"

7. Repeat Part B with two more examples.

pointing out that a tens number may not appear in the ones column and, therefore, must be carried to the tens column. For example, leading the students through the problem

$$
\begin{array}{r}
37 \\
+\underline{25}
\end{array}
$$

the teacher asks the students what 7 + 5 equal. After the students say 12, the teacher says, "We have a problem. Twelve equals one 10 and two 1s. We can't have a 10 in the ones column. So, we put the one 10 at the top of the tens column (teacher writes 1 over 3) and the two 1s below the bar" (teacher writes 2 under 5). Figure 8.7 includes the format for introducing renaming.

While Part A focuses student attention on the fact that they cannot have a 10 in the ones column, Part B sets up the chain of steps the students will follow when working problems on their own. The vocabulary used in this format was selected to foster the students' understanding of the operation. For example, under step 4 in Part A, it is important to remind the students that they are adding 10s ("How many 10s do we end with?") so that they remember the values of the numbers and not just think of the numbers as individual numerals. Note that in Part B, step 3, the teacher prompts the students less on determining what 13 equals. Instead of just telling the students that 13 = 10 + 3, the teacher encourages the students to figure out the answer by asking a question from the expanded notation preskill format, "What does 13 equal?" (see Figure 6.19).

A common error made on renaming problems involves carrying the wrong number. For example, in working the problem 37 + 27, the student carries the 4 and writes 1 under the ones column. If the students write the numerals in the wrong places, the teacher should not merely model where to write the numbers but should ask students the critical questions (Part B, step 3) so that they can see where the appropriate places are for each number. After the students correctly answer the questions, the teacher can demonstrate how to put a 10 on top of the tens column.

If a teacher notices that a student hesitates in answering on a particular step, the teacher should say the answer, repeat the question, and have the student respond again. After using this correction procedure, the teacher should then redo the entire problem, saying something like, "Let's do the whole problem again. I bet this time you'll be able to answer every question correctly."

As students learn to read and write larger numbers, renaming problems with these numbers are introduced. First, problems in which students carry a 100 to the hundreds column are introduced. The format for presenting problems in which the students must rename a sum from the tens column would be very similar to the format for renaming a sum from the ones column (Figure 8.7). For example, the students are working this problem: 283 + 185. After asking the students what eight 10s + eight 10s equal, the teacher would say: "We have a problem. Sixteen 10s equal one hundred and six 10s. We can't have a hundred in the tens column, so we put it at the top of the hundreds column (teacher writes 1 over 2) and six 10s here" (teacher writes 6 under answer line in tens column). Problems in which students rename twice, from the ones and then from the tens column, are introduced next. These problems and future problem types will require just a 2–3 day pattern of introduction since once students understand the process of renaming, they ususally have little difficulty generalizing (Overman, 1930). Lower-performing students, however, may need more supervised practice with worksheets containing a mix of problem types.

When presenting the structured board and worksheet parts of a format, the teacher should use only examples of the type being introduced. When presenting the less structured and supervised parts of the format, the teacher should give the students a cumulative review worksheet. Worksheets are designed to provide cumulative review so that previously taught types of problems receive systematic practice. One-third to one-half of these problems should be of the most recently introduced type. The others should be addition problems of previously introduced types and subtraction problems. The problems should be written in random order. Several examples of the new problem type can appear at the beginning of the worksheet. Otherwise, no more than two or three problems of the same type should appear consecutively.

Cumulative review is especially important when introducing renaming. A student cannot be said to have mastered renaming until he can discriminate addition problems which do and do not call for renaming. Addition problems that do not require renaming must be included so that students do not get into the habit of always putting a 1 at the top of the tens column. Likewise, subtraction problems must be included so that the students receive continued practice discriminating addition from subtraction.

An example of a worksheet for a lesson that takes place several days after introducing double carrying (i.e., from ones to tens and from tens to

Figure 8.7 Format for Adding Two Numerals with Renaming

Day	Part A Structured Board Presentation Problems	Part B Structured Worksheet Problems	Part C Less Structured Worksheet Problems	Part D Supervised Practice Problems	Part E Independent Seatwork Problems
1	4	3			
2	2	2	4		
3-4	1	2	6	6	
5-till accurate		1	4	10	
Till fluent					10-20

PART A: Structured Board Presentation

TEACHER

Write on board:

```
 36      48      26
+27     +26     +16
```

1. "READ THIS PROBLEM AS I POINT."

2. "WHAT COLUMN DO WE START WORKING IN?"

3. "WHAT ARE THE FIRST TWO NUMBERS WE'RE GOING TO ADD?"
   TO CORRECT: Point to 6 and 7.
   Repeat step 3.

4. "WE HAVE A PROBLEM. 13 EQUALS ONE 10 AND THREE 1s. WE CAN'T HAVE A 10 IN THE ONES COLUMN SO WE PUT THE ONE 10 AT THE TOP OF THE TENS COLUMN. WHERE DO WE PUT THE 10?"
   Write 1 over 3. "WE WRITE THREE 1s UNDER THE ONES COLUMN. WHERE DO WE PUT THE THREE 1s?" Write 3 under 7.

5. "WHAT ARE THE FIRST TWO NUMBERS TO ADD IN THE TENS COLUMN?"
   "WHAT DOES 1 + 3 EQUAL?" Pause.
   "NOW WHAT TWO NUMBERS WILL WE ADD?"
   "WHAT IS 4 + 2?"
   "HOW MANY 10s DO WE END UP WITH?"
   "WE END UP WITH SIX 10s SO I'LL WRITE SIX UNDER THE TENS COLUMN." Write 6 in the tens column.

6. "WE ARE FINISHED." Point to 63. "WHAT DOES 36 + 27 EQUAL?"
   "READ THE PROBLEM AND SAY THE ANSWER."

7. Repeat steps 1-5 with remaining problems.

STUDENTS

"36 + 27 = how many?"

"The ones column"

"6 + 7"

"13"

"On top of the tens column"

"Under the ones column"

"1 + 3"
"4"
"4 + 2"
"6"
"Six 10s"

"63"
"36 + 27 = 63"

PART B: Structured Worksheet

Students have worksheets with the following problems:

```
 45      57      36      47
+38     +37     +16     +26
```

1. "TOUCH THE FIRST PROBLEM ON YOUR WORKSHEET. READ THE PROBLEM."

2. "WHAT COLUMN DO YOU START WORKING?"
   "WHAT ARE THE FIRST TWO NUMBERS YOU'RE GOING TO ADD?"
   "WHAT IS 5 + 8?" Pause.

"45 + 38 = how many?"

"The ones"

"5 + 8"
"13"

Figure 8.7 cont'd

TEACHER   **STUDENTS**

3. "THERE'S A PROBLEM. WHAT DOES 13 EQUAL?"   "One 10 and three 1s"
   "CAN WE HAVE A 10 IN THE ONES COLUMN?"   "No"
   "SO WHERE DO YOU PUT THE 10?"   "On top of the tens column"
   "WRITE A 1 ON TOP OF THE TENS COLUMN." Monitor
   student responses. "13 EQUALS ONE 10 AND THREE 1s.
   NOW HOW MANY 1s ARE LEFT?"   "3"
   "WRITE THEM UNDER THE ONES COLUMN." Check.

4. "LOOK AT THE TENS COLUMN. WHAT ARE THE FIRST
   TWO NUMBERS TO ADD IN THE TENS COLUMN?"   "1 + 4"
   "WHAT IS 1 + 4?" Pause.   "5"
   "NOW WHAT NUMBERS WILL YOU ADD?"   "5 + 3"
   "WHAT IS 5 + 3?"   "8"
   "HOW MANY 10s DO YOU END UP WITH?"   "Eight 10s"
   "WRITE THE 10s UNDER THE TENS COLUMN." Monitor
   student responses.

5. "YOU'RE FINISHED. WHAT DOES 45 + 38 EQUAL?"   "83"
   "READ THE PROBLEM AND SAY THE ANSWER."   "45 + 38 = 83"

6. Repeat the steps 1-5 with remaining examples.

PART C: Less Structured Worksheet

Give students a worksheet containing problems which involve
renaming and some which do not.

47	53	42	78
+25	+24	-31	+18

78	56	75	26
+21	+36	-23	+43

1. "EVERYONE, READ PROBLEM ONE ON YOUR
   WORKSHEET."   "47 + 25"
   "WHAT TYPE OF PROBLEM IS THIS, ADDITION OR
   SUBTRACTION?"   "Addition"

2. "WHAT ARE THE FIRST TWO NUMBERS YOU ADD?"   "7 + 5"
   "WHAT IS 7 + 5?" Pause, signal.   "12"

3. "DO YOU HAVE TO MOVE A 10 OVER TO THE TENS
   COLUMN?"   "Yes"

4. "NOW WORK THE PROBLEM ON YOUR OWN." Pause.

5. "WHAT DOES 47 + 25 EQUAL?"   "72"

6. Repeat steps 1-5 with remaining problems.

hundreds) appears in Figure 8.8. Note that over one-third of the problems contain double carrying. Of the other addition problems, several involve just carrying from the tens to the hundreds columns, and several involve no carrying at all. About one-third of the problems are subtraction problems.

Three or More Addends

The last major problem type includes those problems with three or more multi-digit addends (see problem types 3d, 3e, 4b, 4c in Figure 8.2). Some of these problems are particularly difficult because

the student is required to mentally add a number represented by a single digit numeral to a number represented by a two digit numeral. For example, note the problems below:

$$\begin{array}{l} 36 \\ 16 \\ +24 \end{array} \Big] 12 + 4 \qquad \begin{array}{l} 47 \\ 24 \\ +13 \end{array} \Big] 11 + 3$$

$$\begin{array}{l} 5839 \\ 2467 \\ 3589 \\ +2849 \end{array} \begin{array}{l} \Big] 16 + 9 \\ \Big] 25 + 9 \end{array}$$

Figure 8.8 Sample Worksheet

376 +277	486 +281	395 -243	495 +235	386 -241
489 +232	37 +28	523 +206	924 -201	924 + 31
372 +472	938 -214	356 +217	284 +382	565 +265
87 +47	87 -47	299 + 91	468 -354	98 +97

Note that in each problem the sum of the first two addends in the ones column is a teen number (12, 11, and 16). The next step in each problem involves adding a single digit number to a teen number (i.e., 12 + 4, 11 + 3, 16 + 9). We call facts in which a single digit number is added to two digit numbers *complex addition facts*. Learning complex addition facts is a critical preskill which takes many months of practice to master. Teachers should begin practice exercises on this preskill after the students know about 50 basic addition facts. For students progressing at an "average rate" in a developmental program that would be some time in early to mid-second grade.

The first type of complex fact introduced would be that in which a single digit number is added to a teen number, and the total does not exceed 19 (e.g., 14 + 3, 15 + 2, 15 + 3, 15 + 4). Figure 8.9 includes a format for presenting this skill. The students learn to transform a complex fact into two simple facts; e.g. students transform 16 + 3 into 10 + 6 + 3, add 6 + 3, then add 10 + 9. Note in the presentation schedule preceding the format that daily practice on this skill would continue for about 30 days to develop fluency.

After students can solve this first type of complex addition fact mentally, they can begin column addition problems involving three or more numbers and requiring renaming. These problems can be introduced with a relatively simple format. The teacher has the students add all the numbers in the ones column. After the sum of the ones column is computed, the students carry the 10 and write the remaining ones under the line. An analogous procedure would be followed with the tens, hundreds, and thousands columns. Note: Examples should be carefully selected so that students do not encounter complex addition facts that have not been previously taught.

The second type of complex addition fact includes facts in which a single digit number is added

to teen number and the sum totals 20 or more (e.g., 16 + 6 = 22, 18 + 7 = 25, 14 + 7 = 21, 15 + 8 = 23). This type of fact would be introduced in late third or early fourth grade. There are 44 more difficult complex addition facts (see Table 8.1). These complex facts can be introduced in sets of two or three facts.

Figure 8.10 includes the format for this more difficult type of complex addition fact. Students transform a fact with a sum over 20 like 17 + 9 into 10 + 7 + 9 and add 7 + 9. Then they add the sum of 16 to 10. In Part A students learn to add the 10 to teens numbers (e.g., 14 + 10, 18 + 10). This skill is used in Part B (e.g., the last step in adding 19 + 3 is adding 10 and 12; the last step for 13 + 8 is adding 10 and 11). Part C provides supervised practice on the new complex facts and those introduced in the previous set.

Part D, an independent worksheet, should include a mix of problems, in half of which the sum is 20 or more and in half of which the sum is less than 20. This mix is needed to prevent students from possibly overgeneralizing and always adding 10 to a complex addition fact (e.g., 14 + 4 = 28). Worksheet exercises to develop fluency in this skill would be similar to those discussed on page 124 of Chapter 7. A set of two or three complex facts would be introduced each several days. The new facts would appear several times on the independent worksheet along with previously introduced facts. Problems should be written horizontally. Instructions on the worksheet should tell students to work the problems mentally. The number of problems increases as more complex facts are introduced.

SELF-CHECKING After students become proficient in working renaming problems with three addends, they should be taught to check their answers. A checking procedure for addition is adding from the bottom digit in each column, assuming the students start with the top digit in each column

Figure 8.9 Format for Complex Addition Facts with a Total Less Than 20

Day	Part A Structured Presentation Problems	Part B Less Structured Presentations	Part C Supervised Practice Problems
1	6		
2-3	2	6	
4-6		6	4
7-30		6	8

PART A: Structured Presentation

TEACHER   **STUDENTS**

1. "I WANT TO ADD 15 + 3 IN MY HEAD."

2. "15 EQUALS 10 + 5. SO WHEN WE ADD 15 + 3 WE ADD
   10 AND (pause) 5 + 3. WHEN WE ADD 15 + 3 WE ADD 10
   AND WHAT NUMBERS?"   "5 + 3"

3. "WHAT IS 5 + 3?" Pause.   "8"
   "WHAT IS 10 + 8?"   "18"
   "SO WHAT IS 15 + 3?"   "18"

4. "SAY THE WHOLE STATEMENT."   "15 + 3 = 18"
   Repeat steps 1-4 with 14 + 2, 11 + 4, 14 + 3, 15 + 3, 12 + 2.
   Give individual turns on steps 1-3.

PART B: Less Structured Presentation

1. "LISTEN: 14 + 3. WHAT DOES 14 EQUAL?"   "10 + 4"
   "SO WHEN WE ADD 14 + 3 WE ADD 10 PLUS WHAT
   NUMBERS?"   "4 + 3"
   "WHAT IS 4 + 3?" Pause.   "7"
   "SAY THE WHOLE STATEMENT."   "14 + 3 = 17
   "WHAT IS 14 + 3?"   "17"

2. Repeat step 1 with 14 + 5, 12 + 3, 16 + 3, 13 + 4, 15 + 3.
   Give individual turns to several students on step 1.

PART C: Supervised Practice

1. "WHAT DOES 11 + 4 EQUAL?" Pause.   "15"

   TO CORRECT: Use step 1 from Part B.
           "SAY THE WHOLE STATEMENT."   "11 + 4 = 18"

2. Repeat step 1 with 17 + 2, 14 + 5, 12 + 6, 16 + 3, 11 + 6,
   13 + 5.
   Give individual turns to several students.

Table 8.1 Complex Addition Facts

Sums greater than 20								Sums less than 20							
1. 11 + 9								11 + 1	11 + 2	11 + 3	11 + 4	11 + 5	11 + 6	11 + 7	11 + 8
2. 12 + 8	12 + 9								12 + 1	12 + 2	12 + 3	12 + 4	12 + 5	12 + 6	12 + 7
3. 13 + 7	13 + 8	13 + 9								13 + 1	13 + 2	13 + 3	13 + 4	13 + 5	13 + 6
4. 14 + 6	14 + 7	14 + 8	14 + 9								14 + 1	14 + 2	14 + 3	14 + 4	14 + 5
5. 15 + 5	15 + 6	15 + 7	15 + 8	15 + 9								15 + 1	15 + 2	15 + 3	15 + 4
6. 16 + 4	16 + 5	16 + 6	16 + 7	16 + 8	16 + 9								16 + 1	16 + 2	16 + 3
7. 17 + 3	17 + 4	17 + 5	17 + 6	17 + 7	17 + 8	17 + 9								17 + 1	17 + 2
8. 18 + 2	18 + 3	18 + 4	18 + 5	18 + 6	18 + 7	18 + 8	18 + 9								18 + 1
9. 19 + 1	19 + 2	19 + 3	19 + 4	19 + 5	19 + 6	19 + 7	19 + 8	19 + 9							

Figure 8.10 Format for Complex Addition Facts with a Total More Than 20

Day	Part A Plus Ten Facts	Part B Structured Board Presentation Problems	Part C Supervised Practice Problems	Part D Independent Worksheet Problems
1-4	6			
5-7	3	3	3	
Each several lessons		3 new facts	6	10-25

PART A: Preskill: plus 10 facts

TEACHER   **STUDENTS**

1. "14 + 10 IS 24. WHAT IS 14 + 10?"   "24"
   "SAY THE STATEMENT."   "14 + 10 = 24"
   Repeat step 1 with 17 + 10, 12 + 10.

2. "WHAT IS 13 + 10?"   "23"
   TO CORRECT: Tell answer. Repeat question.
   "SAY THE STATEMENT."   "13 + 10 = 23"
   Repeat step 2 with 10 + 10, 18 + 10, 11 + 10, 13 + 10, 15 + 10.
   Repeat questions till all are consecutively answered
   correctly.

3. Give individual turns to several students.

PART B: Structured Board Presentation

1. "WHEN WE ADD 15 + 7 WE ADD 10 AND WHAT
   NUMBERS?"   "5 + 7"

2. "WHAT IS 5 + 7?" Pause.   "12"
   "WHAT IS 12 + 10?"   "22"
   "SO WHAT IS 15 + 7?"   "22"
   "SAY THE WHOLE STATEMENT"   "15 + 7 = 22"
   Repeat steps 1 and 2 with 17 + 7, 16 + 5.

PART C: Supervised Practice

1. "WHAT DOES 15 + 7 EQUAL?" Pause.   "22"

   TO CORRECT: "WHEN WE ADD 15 AND 7, WE ADD 10
               AND WHAT?
               WHAT IS 5 + 7?
               WHAT IS 10 + 12?
               SO WHAT IS 15 + 7?"

2. Repeat step 1 with 17 + 7, 16 + 5, 18 + 8, 15 + 5, 17 + 5.

PART D: Independent Worksheet

1. Give students worksheet with mix of complex facts which
   total 20 or more and complex facts which total less than 20.
   "WORK THESE PROBLEMS IN YOUR HEAD. WRITE
   THE ANSWERS."

when they originally work the problem. The teacher introduces checking on a worksheet exercise. Students complete the first problem and the teacher says, "Here's how to check your work to make sure you have the right answer. Start with the bottom number and add up the column. What are the first two numbers? . . . What's the answer? . . . What's the answer for the next two numbers? . . . Is that what you wrote in the answer for ones and at the top of the tens column? . . . Let's start from the bottom again . . . What are the first two numbers you add in the tens column? . . . What's the answer for the next two numbers? . . . Is that what you wrote for the answer?"

Determining whether students check their work is difficult because checking doesn't require any additional writing. An exercise to encourage checking is to give students already worked problems about half of which have incorrect answers. The teacher instructs the students to check the answers and correct mistakes.

Diagnosis and Remediation

As mentioned previously, once the teacher has determined that the errors on student worksheets are not caused by a lack of motivation, the teacher must identify specific skills deficits and provide remediation accordingly. There are three major types of errors—facts, components, and strategy. In the area of addition, the most common errors are facts and their components, renaming errors (either carrying the wrong number or failure to carry), and inattention to the sign in the problem.

FACT ERRORS Fact errors cause most column addition errors. Such errors are sometimes easy to identify, as in the problems below:

a.	b.	c.
1 1	1 1	1
357	228	648
248	744	281
606	971	919

Note that in each problem, the student missed the problem because of a fact error (e.g., in problem a the student wrote 16 for 7 + 8). In some problems, however, teachers will not be able to easily determine if a fact error caused the incorrect answer. For example, in the following problems, the errors could have been caused by failing to add the carried number or by a fact deficit:

d.	e.
1	1
357	228
248	743
595	961

In problem d the student might have incorrectly added 1 + 5 + 4 in the tens column or simply failed to add the carried 10.

In order to determine the specific cause of the errors, the teacher should look for error patterns. For example, in examining student worksheets the teacher should check the problems with errors to see if the same facts were consistently missed. Also, the teacher should utilize the information she has about the student's performance on recent fact worksheets. To confirm the diagnosis, the teacher should observe the student reworking some of the missed problems.

The remediation procedure depends on the nature of the fact errors. If a student consistently misses the same facts, the teacher merely provides extra practice on those facts. On the other hand, some students will be erratic in their performance, answering a fact correctly one time and missing it the next. For such students, the teacher should increase the motivational payoff for working accurately.

A final note on facts concerns teachers' working with older students who rely on their fingers to figure out basic facts. Unfortunately, since lower grade classrooms often do not provide adequate practice on fact mastery, many students may be using their fingers to figure out basic facts. Teachers should be careful in dealing with students who still use their fingers to figure out basic addition facts. They should not forbid the students to use their fingers if that is their only strategy for deriving an answer. Rather, the teacher should ensure that students are using a finger strategy that is relatively efficient and that they use the strategy accurately. Mistakes in finger operations may occur because a student makes errors in counting or does not coordinate putting up his fingers and counting (i.e., the student does not put up a finger for each number counted).

If the cause of the fact errors is determined to be an inappropriate finger strategy, the teacher would devote several minutes each day reviewing that strategy. Keep in mind that correcting a finger strategy deficit is done only with students who have not mastered their basic facts and have no other strategy to use. (See pages 131–32 for more on teaching finger strategy.) In addition to correcting the finger strategy, teachers should spend a great deal of time doing the exercises recommended in the fact chapter to facilitate basic fact mastery so that students can safely abandon the use of their fingers in computation. The ultimate goal of fact remediation is to teach students to master their facts and to stop relying on finger counting altogether.

COMPONENT ERRORS The first component skill deficit involves renaming. Note the errors in the problems below:

$$
\begin{array}{r}
\overset{6}{4}8 \\
+28 \\
\hline
121
\end{array}
\qquad
\begin{array}{r}
\overset{5}{3}9 \\
27 \\
+19 \\
\hline
112
\end{array}
$$

The student carried the 1s instead of the 10s. Errors in which students carry the wrong number are quite serious since they indicate a fundamental misunderstanding of basic place value concepts. A possible remediation exercise for the component skill would involve a set of problems containing boxes where the sum of the ones column and the carried number are to be recorded. For each problem, the teacher would tell the student the sum of the numbers in the ones column, then ask how many 10s and 1s is that sum. The students answer, then fill in the numbers. The remediation set would contain approximately 10 examples that look similar to the following:

$$
\begin{array}{cccc}
\Box & \Box & \Box & \Box \\
68 & 45 & 24 & 86 \\
+19 & +29 & +18 & +67 \\
\hline
\Box & \Box & \Box & \Box
\end{array}
$$

The first three to four examples in the remediation set should all be problems in which renaming is required. However, the examples in the remediation set should contain some discrimination examples in which renaming is not required so that students do not get into the habit of always writing a 1 above the tens column. If students demonstrate place value deficits during the remediation, the teacher may need to reteach the suggested place value format for analyzing a teen or tens number into its component parts (e.g., 16 = one 10 and six 1s, see Figures 6.9 and 6.10). After students are able to do four to six problems in a row filling in the correct numbers (for the structured board presentation—Part B in 6.9, Part C in 6.10), the teacher leads the students through a set of four to six addition problems using Part C of Figure 8.7, then has them do four to six problems with no teacher direction. This remediation procedure is repeated until students' performance on carrying problems is 90% or better.

A component skill deficit similar to carrying the wrong number involves not carrying the 10 at all. Problems in which students fail to carry the 10 look like the following:

$$
\begin{array}{r}
48 \\
+36 \\
\hline
74
\end{array}
\qquad
\begin{array}{r}
32 \\
+19 \\
\hline
41
\end{array}
$$

Since the student wrote the ones number in the appropriate place, it is likely that the student just forgot to carry the 10 to the tens column. The remediation procedure for this error pattern is the same as for the previously discussed error in which the student carried the 1s instead of the 10s. Again, remember it is necessary to individually test students to determine if the errors resulted from a renaming error or from a fact error.

Failure to attend to the sign is the second component skill deficit common to column addition problems. This deficit is characterized by worksheet errors in which the wrong operation is performed:

$$
\begin{array}{r}
342 \\
+131 \\
\hline
211
\end{array}
\qquad
\begin{array}{r}
304 \\
-201 \\
\hline
505
\end{array}
$$

If such errors occur on more than 10% of the problems, a special worksheet should be given including an equal mix of addition and subtraction problems in random order:

$$
\begin{array}{ccccccc}
37 & 28 & 47 & 38 & 47 & 86 & 48 \\
-15 & +13 & +24 & -16 & +25 & -23 & +20
\end{array}
$$

The teacher would present the less structured worksheet exercises (see page 154), instructing students to circle and say the sign before working each problem.

STRATEGY ERRORS Strategy errors are caused by incorrectly carrying out several steps in the strategy. An example of one type of strategy error appears below:

$$
\begin{array}{r}
35 \\
+27 \\
\hline
512
\end{array}
\qquad
\begin{array}{r}
68 \\
+18 \\
\hline
716
\end{array}
$$

This is quite a serious error, indicating the student does not understand the concept of renaming. The remediation procedure for all strategy deficits involves reteaching the format for that particular type of problem. The teacher presents several problems using a structured board presentation, then leads the students through several worksheet problems—structured, then less structured part of the format.

A summary of the deficits common to column addition and the diagnosis and remediation procedures appropriate for each appear in Figure 8.11. Unless otherwise noted, following each remediation procedure the teacher needs to give students worksheets similar to the ones on which the original errors were made in order to test whether the remediation was effective.

Figure 8.11 Diagnosis and Remediation of Addition Errors

Sample Patterns	Diagnosis	Remediation Procedures	Remediation Examples
Fact Errors			

a. 46   253
   +17   +174
   64   447
	Basic fact errors, Student doesn't know the fact 6 + 7.	Emphasize 6 + 7 in fact memorization exercises. See Chapter 7.	

Component Skill Errors			

b. 3   2
   46   53
  +17   +29
   81   91
	Renaming errors. Student carries the 1s to the tens column, writes the 10s in the ones column.	Steps from structured worksheet exercise which focus on renaming. (Figure 8.7, Part B, step 1–3)	10 problems in this form:
			☐ ☐
			69 46
			+36 +29
			☐ ☐

c. 46   25
   +17   +17
   53   32
	Renaming errors. Student forgets to carry.	Same as above.	Same as above.

d. 49   253
   +17   –174
   32   427
	Sign discrimination error. Student subtracts instead of adding, vice versa.	Less structured worksheet exercise. Have students circle the sign before working each problem. (Figure 8.7, Part C, steps 1, 4)	Mix of addition and subtraction problems.

Strategy Errors			

e. 46   253
   +17   +174
   513   3127
	Student does not carry; Writes the entire number in the sum.	Test and/or teach appropriate preskills. Present format beginning with structured board exercise. (Figure 8.7, Part A)	

Research

A fair amount of research on beginning addition has involved trying to determine the strategies employed by school children at different ages and for problems of varying difficulty. In a study of first and second grade children, Houlihan and Ginsburg (1981) found that first grade children consistently used a counting strategy to solve addition problems, while students in the second grade employed both counting and non-counting methods. (The dominant method in second grade, however, was counting-on without concrete objects.) The use of non-counting methods, according to Houlihan and Ginsburg, appeared to vary with addend size.

Carpenter and Moser (1984) replicated and extended these findings in their longitudinal study of first through third grade students when they found that children initially solved simple addition word problems with a count-all strategy, then moved to counting-on and finally employed the use of number facts. However, the data from this study did indicate that children were not entirely consistent in their choice of solution strategies.

Beentjes and Jonker (1987) also found a high degree of inconsistency among both second and third grade students in solving addition and subtraction problems. Ashcraft and Fierman (1982) sought to determine the age at which children shift from counting to memory retrieval. Their data suggest that third grade may be the time of transition, but that even sixth grade students are less efficient in their basic addition fact performance than adults.

Not surprisingly, problems with unknowns in less common positions (e.g., C = a + ☐ or C = ☐ + b) are more difficult (Lindvall, Mauritz & Gibbons,

1978). Research on strategies indicates that students who can read problems correctly (Lindvall & Ibarra, 1980) and have a counting strategy (Jencks & Peck, 1976) are more likely to solve problems correctly. A less expected finding by Sauls & Beeson (1976) was that fourth graders who continue to use a counting strategy, such as fingers, solve problems as quickly and as accurately as students who have memorized their facts, even though the students who still count fingers have lower IQ's and overall levels of mathematics achievement.

In conducting research on common addition errors, the Elementary School Mathematics Committee (Pincus et al., 1975) identified problems in renaming (not carrying, not adding the carried 10, and carrying the wrong digit), subtracting when the smaller digit is on the bottom, and advanced facts like 27 + 7, 39 + 6, etc.

Some research has also been done on teaching strategies. Studies reviewed by Wheatley and Wheatley (1978) suggest that a direct strategy for column addition is quicker than the tens method. In the tens method, students select two digits to add, preferably two that add to 10. In the direct method, the students add the numbers in their order of appearance. The direct method was reported to be 17% faster and of equal accuracy to the tens method.

Commercial Programs

Addition: Regrouping

INSTRUCTIONAL STRATEGIES In most programs students are taught a strategy for regrouping in addition by using bundles of sticks or other manipulatives. The steps in the strategy (with minor variations) in four basals we reviewed are

Step 1 – Add the 1s

Step 2 – "Trade" if equal to 10 or more

Step 3 – Add the 10s

See Figure 8.12 for an example of a page from a basal presentation book.

The strategies for addition with regrouping appear to be straightforward. Our analysis reveals, however, that the programs may not be sufficiently addressing necessary prerequisite skills or providing enough systematic guided practice to ensure student success.

PREREQUISITE SKILLS Often basals attempt to teach the prerequisite place value skills by having students trace numbers already placed in the proper columns. Then students are expected to progress from tracing numbers to independently solving problems. The problem with tracing should be obvious. If the numbers are placed for the students, students do not have to think about where to place them. As a result, some students will have difficulty on similar problems when the prompts are removed.

The remedy to this potential problem is to include intermediate steps in the strategy that require students to identify where they are going to write their answers *before* they write them. Then teachers can correct any errors that occur and prevent error patterns from forming.

A major problem results from the lack of coordination between basic fact teaching and the facts students encounter in regrouping problems. Students do not receive adequate practice to memorize basic facts before they encounter these facts in workbook exercises. Thus students will often use their fingers to figure out the facts. The over-reliance on fingers results in students not receiving a valuable source of practice with facts and hampers students' learning of the concept. The commercial programs which best exemplify the coordination of fact teaching and fact occurrence in regrouping problems are the direct instruction math programs authored by Engelmann and Carnine and published by Science Research Associates.

Figure 8.12

STUDENT OBJECTIVE
To add 2-digit numbers, with regrouping from ones to tens.

TEACHING SUGGESTIONS

Demonstrate 2-digit addition with a model.
(Materials: ones and tens, a Tens and Ones mat for each child) Write an addition problem on the chalkboard. Ask the children to use their ones and tens to show the two sets on their mats.

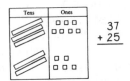

$$\begin{array}{r} 37 \\ + 25 \\ \hline \end{array}$$

Ask them to join the two sets together and if they have more than 10 ones, to trade 10 ones for 1 ten. "Did you make a trade?" Write the little *1* over the *3*. "How many ones were you left with? (2) How many tens do you have now?" (6) Write it.

$$\begin{array}{r} 1 \\ 37 \\ + 25 \\ \hline 62 \end{array}$$

Provide the children with other addition problems to work through with their ones and tens.

READINESS

For students who need help with addition.

Readiness for 141–142

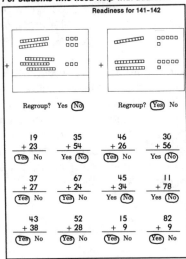

Regroup? Yes (No)   Regroup? (Yes) No

$$\begin{array}{r} 19 \\ + 23 \\ \hline \end{array}$$ (Yes) No
$$\begin{array}{r} 35 \\ + 54 \\ \hline \end{array}$$ Yes (No)
$$\begin{array}{r} 46 \\ + 26 \\ \hline \end{array}$$ (Yes) No
$$\begin{array}{r} 30 \\ + 56 \\ \hline \end{array}$$ Yes (No)

$$\begin{array}{r} 37 \\ + 27 \\ \hline \end{array}$$ (Yes) No
$$\begin{array}{r} 67 \\ + 24 \\ \hline \end{array}$$ (Yes) No
$$\begin{array}{r} 45 \\ + 34 \\ \hline \end{array}$$ Yes (No)
$$\begin{array}{r} 11 \\ + 78 \\ \hline \end{array}$$ Yes (No)

$$\begin{array}{r} 43 \\ + 38 \\ \hline \end{array}$$ (Yes) No
$$\begin{array}{r} 52 \\ + 28 \\ \hline \end{array}$$ (Yes) No
$$\begin{array}{r} 15 \\ + 9 \\ \hline \end{array}$$ (Yes) No
$$\begin{array}{r} 82 \\ + 9 \\ \hline \end{array}$$ (Yes) No

Copymaster S93 or Duplicating Master S93

Ask the children to decide whether or not each problem will require trading (regrouping). Ask them to mark *Yes* or *No*.

141 ▦ **Concrete Materials**

Add ones.
$$\begin{array}{r} 35 \\ + 29 \\ \hline \end{array}$$

Regroup.
$$\begin{array}{r} 35 \\ + 29 \\ \hline 4 \end{array}$$

Add tens.
$$\begin{array}{r} 35 \\ + 29 \\ \hline 64 \end{array}$$

(14 ones)

Add.

$\begin{array}{r}35\\+36\\\hline 71\end{array}$	$\begin{array}{r}48\\+25\\\hline 73\end{array}$	$\begin{array}{r}46\\+29\\\hline 75\end{array}$	$\begin{array}{r}35\\+35\\\hline 70\end{array}$	$\begin{array}{r}13\\+35\\\hline 48\end{array}$	$\begin{array}{r}19\\+45\\\hline 64\end{array}$
$\begin{array}{r}58\\+23\\\hline 81\end{array}$	$\begin{array}{r}32\\+27\\\hline 59\end{array}$	$\begin{array}{r}66\\+19\\\hline 85\end{array}$	$\begin{array}{r}27\\+51\\\hline 78\end{array}$	$\begin{array}{r}75\\+19\\\hline 94\end{array}$	$\begin{array}{r}24\\+67\\\hline 91\end{array}$
$\begin{array}{r}37\\+21\\\hline 58\end{array}$	$\begin{array}{r}46\\+38\\\hline 84\end{array}$	$\begin{array}{r}52\\+46\\\hline 98\end{array}$	$\begin{array}{r}37\\+44\\\hline 81\end{array}$	$\begin{array}{r}83\\+8\\\hline 91\end{array}$	$\begin{array}{r}61\\+9\\\hline 70\end{array}$
$\begin{array}{r}45\\+7\\\hline 52\end{array}$	$\begin{array}{r}67\\+9\\\hline 76\end{array}$	$\begin{array}{r}9\\+32\\\hline 41\end{array}$	$\begin{array}{r}67\\+18\\\hline 85\end{array}$	$\begin{array}{r}41\\+16\\\hline 57\end{array}$	$\begin{array}{r}38\\+27\\\hline 65\end{array}$

Two-place addition, regrouping   (one hundred forty-one) **141**

USING THE PAGES ❧

Discuss the example at the top of page 141. Provide the children with ones and tens. Practice skip-counting by 10. Assign pages 141 and 142.

MENTAL-MATH NOTE ··············

The Shortcut character introduces mental math as well as paper-and-pencil shortcuts. After the children have completed page 142, provide them with oral practice using the shortcut to add 9 to different numbers.

CLASSWORK/HOMEWORK

❧ **Mental Arithmetic**   ❖ **Cooperative Learning Groups**   ◣ **Problem Formulation**

From *Heath Mathematics*, Grade 2 Teacher's Edition, by Walter E. Rucker, Clyde A. Dilley, and David A. Lowry, p. 141. Copyright © 1987 by D.C. Heath and Company. Reprinted by permission.

Application Items: Addition

1. Describe the problem type that each example below represents. List the problems in the order they are introduced. Write the grade level when each type is typically introduced.

a. 462
  +371

d. 84
  +13

b. 35
  16
  +24

e. 348
  +135

c. 46
  87
  +19

f. 368
  +259

2. Below is an excerpt from the independent worksheet to be given to students who have just demonstrated accuracy in solving problem type 2e, adding two two digit numbers, renaming from ones to tens columns. The teacher has made some errors in constructing the worksheet.

   a. Indicate the inappropriate examples.

   b. Identify any omitted problem types that should be included on the worksheet.

Worksheet

a. 462
  +183

b. 75
  +16

c. 141
  +324

d. 38
  +26

e. 582
  + 15

f. 1
  3
  +6

g. 46
  +15

h. 617
  +124

i. 58
  +25

3. At the beginning of the unit, the teacher tested Leslie. Her performance on the performance indicators for problem types 2d-3c appear below.

   Specify the problem type with which instruction should begin for Leslie. Explain your answer.

Performance Indicators

2e. 37   48   57
   +46 +14 +27
    83   61   84

Student: Leslie

2f. 247   258   276
   +315 + 13 + 8
    562   272   284

3a. 13 + 3 = 16
    14 + 4 = 18
    12 + 2 = 14

3b. 374   248   437
   +261 +364 +285
    535   511   652

3c. 276   248   437
   +185 +365 +285
    461   512   622

4. Below are 15 problems which appeared on the worksheets to be done independently by the students in Mrs. Ash's math group. Next to each student's name are the problems missed by the student. For each student, specify the probable cause or causes of the student's errors.

   Describe the remediation procedure. Be specific. For each remediation, indicate the format and the part of that format you would begin remediation with. If no format appears in the book for that problem type, indicate the page in the text that discusses that problem type.

37   364   57   36   48   72   58   57   48   34   514
+26 +212 -23 +22 +28 +26 -32 +34 -24 +26 + 23

Errors: Bill   37   48   Ann   37   48   34   Julie   37   48
              +26   +28   +26   +28   +26   +26   -24
               91   121   513   616   510   11   72

5. The following is an excerpt from the Missing Addend Format (pages 143–46). Student responses are included. Specify teacher wording for the correction required.

Missing Addend Format

PART B: Structured Board Presentation	
TEACHER	**STUDENTS**
Write on board: 4 + $\square$ = 6	
|||| ||||||	
4. "WE WANT TO END WITH THE SAME NUMBER ON BOTH SIDES." Point to 4. "HOW MANY ON THIS SIDE NOW?"	"4"
"THINK. HOW MANY DO WE HAVE TO END WITH ON THIS SIDE?"	"4"

6. Specify a diagnosis and remediation for each of the students listed below.

   a. For each student, describe the probable cause or mistaken strategy responsible for the errors.

   b. For each remediation, indicate the format and the part of that format you would begin remediation with. If no format appears in the book for that problem type, indicate the page in the text that discusses that problem type.

Student A

3 + $\boxed{7}$ = 7   5 + $\boxed{8}$ = 8
/\|\|\| \|\|\|

4 + $\boxed{9}$ = 9   2 + $\boxed{6}$ = 6
/\|\|\|\| \|\|\|\|

Student B

6 + 3 = $\boxed{8}$ 7 + 2 = $\boxed{8}$
\|\|\| \|\|

2 + 4 = $\boxed{5}$ 3 + 5 = $\boxed{7}$
\|\|\|\| \|\|\|\|\|

7. Write the wording the teacher uses in the structured worksheet part in presenting the following problem:

$$162 \atop +283$$

8. Below are worksheets made by several teachers for the less structured part of the format for teaching students to work problems with renaming from the ones to tens columns. Two teachers constructed unacceptable lists. Identify these teachers and tell why each is unacceptable. For the unacceptable lists, specify what could be done to make the list acceptable.

a. | 37 | 37 | 237 | 481 | 374 | 48 | 786 |
     |---|---|---|---|---|---|---|
     | +25 | −25 | + 86 | +110 | −213 | +24 | +346 |

b. | 48 | 78 | 37 | 58 | 73 | 57 |
     |---|---|---|---|---|---|
     | +26 | +25 | + 8 | +24 | +28 | +18 |

c. | 47 | 47 | 385 | 68 | 28 | 74 | 92 | 75 | 342 |
     |---|---|---|---|---|---|---|---|---|
     | +25 | −25 | +214 | +48 | +36 | +23 | −31 | +38 | + 26 |

9 Subtraction

Terms and Concepts

Subtraction The removal of a subset from a set. Subtraction is the inverse of addition.

Subtrahend Quantity to be taken away.

Minuend Original quantity from which an amount will be subtracted.

Difference The quantity remaining after the subtrahend is taken away from the minuend.

Renaming Rewriting a numeral as a greater unit and a lesser unit; e.g., in 75 – 19, 75 is renamed as 60 + 15. Renaming is based on the associative law of addition which states that any method of grouping may be used to obtain the sum of several addends.

Borrowing A term formerly used to describe subtraction with regrouping or renaming.

Regrouping Rearranging a quanitity of *objects* (not numerals) as a greater and lesser than unit; for example, I I I I I I I I I I I I I I I I I I I I I I I I can be regrouped as I I I I I I I I I I I I I I I I I I I I I I I I .

Skill Hierarchy

Subtraction instruction, just as addition instruction, may be divided into two stages (see Figure 9.1). During the first stage, introducing the concept, the teacher presents strategies for solving simple subtraction problems with a one digit minuend, like 9 – 6 = ☐ ; The strategy at this stage involves semi-concrete objects that represent each member in the subtraction problem. The counting, numeral, and equality preskills on the subtraction skill hierarchy are the same as for addition. After subtraction has been taught, problems with a missing subtrahend can be presented. In these problems, all numerals should be below 10 to simplify computation, e.g., 7 – ☐ = 3 and 5 – ☐ = 3. Again the strategy would involve using semi-concrete objects to represent the numerals in a problem. For the purposes of re-

Figure 9.1 Skill Hierarchy

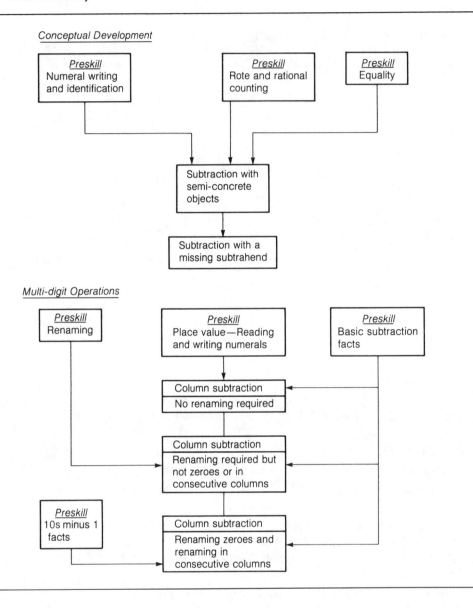

mediation, teachers should not revert to the conceptual introduction but should teach basic facts and the multi-digit operations specified in the Instructional Sequence and Assessment chart.

In the multi-digit operations stage, which usually begins late in first grade, students figure basic facts mentally (without semi-concrete aids). Basic subtraction facts are the 100 possible combinations in which a one digit subtrahend is subtracted from a one or two digit minuend and the difference is a one digit number. Procedures for teaching students to answer and eventually memorize basic subtraction facts are discussed in Chapter 7.

Three basic types of column subtraction problems are included in the multi-digit operations stage (see Figure 9.1). The easiest is the problem in which the subtrahend is smaller than the minuend in each column; renaming is not required:

$$\begin{array}{r} 49 \\ -24 \\ \hline \end{array}$$

In the second type of problem, one or more columns have a subtrahend which is larger than the minuend:

$$\begin{array}{r} 374 \\ -28 \\ \hline \end{array} \qquad \begin{array}{r} 5437 \\ -2859 \\ \hline \end{array}$$

Such problems require renaming or "borrowing":

$$\begin{array}{r} ^{2}^{1} \\ 34 \text{ becomes } \not{3}4 \\ \underline{-15} \underline{-15} \end{array}$$

Students need not have memorized all basic subtraction facts before problems with renaming are introduced. They should, however, know enough facts to allow teachers to provide a variety of renaming problems.

The third type includes more complex column subtraction problems that require renaming. Included are problems with zeroes in the minuend:

$$\begin{array}{r} ^{2}^{9}^{1} \\ 306 \text{ becomes } \not{3}\not{0}6 \\ \underline{-216} \underline{-219} \end{array}$$

$$\begin{array}{r} ^{3}^{9}^{9}^{1} \\ \text{and } 4000 \text{ becomes } \not{4}\not{0}\not{0}\not{0} \\ \underline{-258} \underline{-258} \end{array}$$

and problems with renaming in consecutive columns:

$$\begin{array}{r} 421 6342 \\ \underline{-247} \text{ or } \underline{-4971} \end{array}$$

A more in-depth listing of problems types and when they are usually introduced appears in the Instructional Sequence and Assessment Chart in Figure 9.2.

Introducing the Concept

Subtraction is usually introduced in first grade through demonstrations with semi-concrete objects. A number of alternative demonstrations are suggested in elementary mathematics textbooks. Among these are diagrams using pictures of objects, e.g., 5 – 3 is represented as

and number lines, e.g., 8 – 3 is represented as

This section discusses a strategy that uses lines as semi-concrete objects. It teaches minusing as crossing out; 7 – 4 is represented as

We recommend not presenting subtraction until students have demonstrated mastery of the regular addition strategy. Subtraction may be introduced prior to or after addition problems with missing addends.

Regular Subtraction

In the crossing out strategy, the student first draws the number of lines for the minuend, then minuses by crossing out the number of lines indicated by the subtrahend:

$$6 - 4 = \Box$$

Next the student counts the remaining line, draws the number of lines on the other side of the equal:

$$6 - 4 = \Box$$

and finally writes the numeral representing that set of lines:

$$6 - 4 = \boxed{2}$$

Figure 9.3 shows the format for introducing subtraction. Note that minus is used as a verb, "How many lines are you going to minus?" Since students have already learned to identify the minus sign, they learn that the minus sign tells them to cross out lines. Later the term *subtraction* is introduced and students learn that a minus tells them to subtract.

In parts A and B of the format the teacher presents structured board and worksheet execises focusing solely on the preskill task of crossing out lines and counting the remaining lines. Since line drawing is a fine motor skill, many students in beginning arithmetic instruction may require extensive practice before they become proficient in crossing out the appropriate number of lines. Part C is a structured worksheet exercise in which the teacher leads students as they work entire problems, drawing lines for the first group, crossing out lines for fhe amount to be "minused," counting how many lines they end with, and then applying the equality rule. The minuend in subtraction problems should be 10 or less so that the making-lines task does not become too cumbersome. Part D, the less structured worksheet exercise, is the critical part of the format. The worksheet includes a mix of addition and subtraction problems. Instructionally naive students often have difficulty discriminating which of the two similar problem-solving strategies to use. The format, thus, must provide a great deal of sys-

Figure 9.2 Instructional Sequence and Assessment Chart

Grade Level	Problem Type	Performance Indicator		
1a	Conceptual introduction			
1b	Subtracting a one or two digit number from a two digit number; no renaming	57 -20	45 - 3	28 - 4
2a	Subtracting a one or two digit number from a two digit number; renaming required	54 -18	46 - 9	70 -38
2b	Subtracting a one, two, or three digit number from a three digit number; renaming tens to ones	382 - 37	393 -174	242 - 6
3a	Subtracting a two or three digit number from a three digit number; renaming from hundreds to tens	423 -171	418 - 83	905 -164
3b	Subtracting a two or three digit number from a three digit number; renaming from tens to ones and hundreds to tens	352 -187	724 -578	534 - 87
3c	Tens minus 1 facts	70 – 1 = ☐ 40 – 1 = ☐ 80 – 1 = ☐		
3d	Subtracting a two or three digit number from a three digit number, zero in tens column; renaming from tens to ones and hundreds to tens	503 - 87	504 - 21	700 - 86
3e	Subtracting a three or four digit number from a four digit number; renaming from thousands to hundreds	4689 -1832	5284 -4631	3481 -1681
3f	Subtracting a one, two, three, or four digit number from a four digit number; renaming required in several columns	5342 - 68	6143 - 217	5231 -1658
4a	Subtracting a two, three, or four digit number from a four digit number; a zero in either the tens or hundreds column	4023 - 184	5304 -1211	5304 - 418
4b	Hundreds minus 1 facts	700 – 1 = ☐ 400 – 1 = ☐ 800 – 1 = ☐		
4c	Subtracting a one, two, three, or four digit number from a four digit number; a zero in the tens and hundreds column	4000 -1357	2001 -1453	8000 -4264
4d	Same as 4c except 1,000 as top number	1000 - 283	1000 - 82	1000 - 80
4e	Same as 4c except 1,100 as top number	1100 - 241	1100 - 532	1100 - 830
4f	Subtracting involving five and six digit numbers; renaming	342,523 - 18,534	480,235 - 1,827	38,402 -15,381
5a	Thousands minus 1 facts	5000 – 1 = ☐ 3000 – 1 = ☐ 1000 – 1 = ☐		
5b	Subtracting from a number with four zeroes	80000 - 826	50000 - 8260	10000 - 284

Figure 9.3 Format for Subtraction with Lines

Day	Part A Structured Board (Preskill) Presentation Problems	Part B Structured Worksheet (Preskill) Problems	Part C Structured Worksheet Problems	Part D Less Structured Worksheet Problems	Part E Supervised Practice Problems	Part F Independent Practice Problems
1	3	4				
2	2	3	2			
3			4			
4-5			2	8		
6-7				6	6	
8-till accurate					10-12	
Till fluent						10-12

PART A: Structured Board Presentation—Preskill of Minusing Lines

TEACHER   **STUDENTS**

Write on board: 6 - 2

  | | | | | |

1. "EVERYONE, READ THIS PROBLEM."   "6 - 2"
   "THIS IS A MINUS PROBLEM. WHAT KIND OF PROBLEM
   IS THIS?"   "A minus problem"

2. Point to minus 2. "WHAT DOES THIS SAY?"   "Minus 2"
   "MINUS 2 TELLS US TO CROSS OUT TWO LINES.
   WHAT DOES MINUS 2 TELL US TO DO?"   "Cross out two lines"
   "WATCH ME CROSS OUT TWO LINES." Draw two minuses
   through two lines and count each time,"MINUS 1,
   MINUS 2."

3. "LET'S SEE HOW MANY LINES WE HAVE LEFT. I'LL TOUCH
   AND YOU COUNT."   "1 2 3 4"
   "HOW MANY DID WE END UP WITH?"   "4"
   Repeat steps 1-3 with 7 - 4, 5 - 3.

PART B: Structured Worksheet—Preskill of Minusing Lines

Students have worksheets with four to six problems like this:

6 - 2

| | | | | |

Note that the lines under the first numeral in each problem are
already drawn.

1. "TOUCH PROBLEM a ON YOUR WORKSHEET." Check.
   "READ THE PROBLEM."   "6 - 2"
   "WHAT KIND OF PROBLEM IS THIS?"   "A minus problem"

2. "TOUCH THE FIRST GROUP. HOW MANY LINES ARE IN
   THE FIRST GROUP?"   "6"
   "HOW MANY LINES ARE YOU GOING TO MINUS?"   "2"
   "MINUS THE LINES." Check that students minus two lines.

   TO CORRECT: "WHEN YOU MINUS 2, YOU CROSS OUT
                TWO LINES."

3. "NOW COUNT AND SEE HOW MANY LINES YOU HAVE
   LEFT. Pause. HOW MANY DID YOU END WITH?"   "4"
   Repeat steps 1-3 with remaining examples.

Figure 9.3 cont'd

PART C: Structured Worksheet—Entire Strategy

TEACHER   **STUDENTS**

$5 - 3 = \square$

1. "TOUCH THIS PROBLEM ON YOUR WORKSHEET." Point
   to first problem. "READ THE PROBLEM."   "5 - 3 = how many?"

2. "WHAT KIND OF PROBLEM IS THIS?"   "A minus problem"
   "TOUCH THE FIRST GROUP. HOW MANY LINES ARE
   YOU GOING TO DRAW?"   "5"
   "DRAW FIVE LINES UNDER THE 5."

3. "HOW MANY LINES ARE YOU GOING TO MINUS?"   "3"
   "MINUS THE LINES." Monitor worksheet responses.

4. "NOW COUNT AND SEE HOW MANY LINES YOU END
   WITH. (pause) HOW MANY?"   "2"

5. "SO HOW MANY MUST YOU END WITH ON THE OTHER
   SIDE OF THE EQUAL?"   "2"
   "DRAW TWO LINES AND WRITE THE NUMERAL IN THE
   BOX."

6. "NOW READ THE WHOLE STATEMENT."   "5 - 3 = 2"
   "FIVE MINUS THREE EQUALS HOW MANY?"   "2"
   "SAY THE STATEMENT AGAIN."   "5 - 3 = 2"
   Repeat steps 1-5 with remaining examples.

PART D: Less Structured Worksheet

Give the students a worksheet with an equal mix of addition
and subtraction problems:

a. $4 + 3 = \square$ f. $7 - 0 = \square$

b. $8 - 2 = \square$ g. $8 - 2 = \square$

c. $7 - 5 = \square$ h. $2 + 4 = \square$

d. $5 - 4 = \square$ i. $5 + 3 = \square$

e. $7 + 0 = \square$

1. "THIS WORKSHEET IS TRICKY. IN SOME PROBLEMS
   YOU PLUS AND IN SOME PROBLEMS YOU MINUS. WHEN
   YOU PLUS YOU MAKE MORE LINES. WHAT DO YOU DO
   WHEN YOU PLUS?"   "Make more lines"
   "WHEN YOU MINUS YOU CROSS OUT LINES. WHAT DO
   YOU DO WHEN YOU MINUS?"   "Cross out lines."

2. "TOUCH PROBLEM a. READ IT."   "4 + 3 = how many?"
   "IS THAT A PLUS OR MINUS PROBLEM?"   "Plus problem"
   "WHAT DO YOU DO WHEN YOU PLUS/MINUS?"   "Make more lines."

3. "MAKE THE LINES UNDER THE FIRST GROUP
   THEN PLUS/MINUS."

4. "NOW MAKE THE SIDES EQUAL AND FILL IN THE
   EMPTY BOX."
   Repeat steps 2-4 with the remaining problems.

tematic practice in helping students make this discrimination. The less structured and supervised practice worksheets would also contain an equal mix of addition and subtraction problems. Supervised practice is continued until students can work problems with 80–90% accuracy.

Missing Subtrahend Problems

Missing subtrahend problems (e.g., 7 – ☐ = 3, 8 – ☐ = 1) could be introduced when the students are able to do a worksheet including a mix of addition, regular subtraction, and addition problems with missing addends with 80–90% accuracy. Since the strategy for working this type of problem is relatively difficult to teach—students must circle some lines and cross out the remaining lines—we recommend not presenting the strategy during the beginning stage unless specified by the school district's scope and sequence chart. The missing addend problems provide an ample demonstration of the equality principle.

The strategy for missing subtrahend problems includes the steps shown in Figure 9.4.

A specific format is not included for missing subtrahend problems since many programs do not teach the skill. The format would be similar to that for the missing addend operation. The sides of the equal would be circled. The teacher would begin with an exercise focusing on the mechanical skill of circling lines in a group to form a subset, then crossing out the remaining lines. Problems for an exercise could consist of a numeral followed by a minus sign and an empty box (e.g., 8 – ☐). The teacher could have the students (a) draw lines under the numeral, (b) circle the number of lines indicated by the teacher, (c) cross out the remaining lines, and (d) count up crossed-out lines and write the appropriate numeral in the empty box.

When the students can work this task, the teacher introduces the entire strategy in structured board and worksheet exercises, stressing the equality principle. Finally, the teacher presents a less structured worksheet exercise which includes a mix of subtraction, missing subtrahend, addition, and missing addend problems.

Diagnosis and Remediation

Diagnosis and remediation procedures for beginning subtraction problems are very similar to those discussed for beginning addition problems. The basic steps below apply to diagnosing and remedying errors:

1. The teacher analyzes worksheet errors and hypothesizes what is the cause of the errors.
2. The teacher interviews the students to determine the error, if the cause is not obvious.
3. The teacher provides reteaching through board and/or worksheet presentations.
4. The teacher tests the student on a set of problems similar to the ones on which the original errors were made.

Once students begin working problems independently on their worksheets, their errors usually fall into two main categories:

Figure 9.4

1. Students read problem.	"Seven minus how many equals three?"
2. Students draw lines under minuend.	$\underset{\text{\textbar\textbar\textbar\textbar\textbar\textbar\textbar}}{7}$ – ☐ = 3
3. Students determine the number they must end with on both sides.	
4. Students circle three of the seven lines since they must end end with three to make sides equal.	⦶‖‖‖ 7 – ☐ = 3
5. Students cross out uncircled lines.	⦶‖‖ 7 – ☐ = 3
6. Students count crossed-out lines and write numeral in the box.	⦶‖‖ 7 – 4 = 3

1. Component skill errors that indicate a deficit on one or more of the component skills that make up the strategy.
2. Strategy errors in which steps are omitted, applied in the wrong order, or replaced by incorrect steps. Strategy errors are remedied by reintroducing the structured board or worksheet format. Until the remedy is complete, problems of that type should not appear on the independent worksheets.

COMPONENT SKILL ERRORS Component skill errors are often difficult to diagnose. Note that in this problem the student's error may have resulted from misidentifying 3 as 4 or simply not crossing out the correct number of lines: 9 − 3 = 5.

The teacher can determine the specific cause of errors by looking for patterns. If a student does all problems correctly except those that include the numeral 3, his cause of errors would be the misidentification of the numeral 3. Besides looking for patterns, the teacher can observe students working problems, have the students read each problem, and have them describe what they are doing as they work it.

Once the teacher determines the specific component skill deficit, he works on that specific skill for several lessons. If the skill is one which would cause students to miss many problems (e.g., a skill such as crossing out lines), the teacher would not present any subtraction problems until the students could do the component skill independently. If the component skill is one which causes students to miss just some problems (i.e., numeral misidentification), the teacher excludes subtraction problems with that numeral from independent worksheet assignments until the students demonstrate mastery of that component skill.

A common component skill error, which occurs soon after subtraction appears on worksheets, is adding rather than subtracting and vice versa, e.g., 7 − 3 = 10, 7 + 3 = 4. Teachers can expect most students to make this error occasionally. A remediation procedure is necessary when this type of error occurs frequently (in more than 10% of problems). A remediation procedure is to reintroduce the less structured worksheet format that provides guided practice on discriminating addition and subtraction problems.

Fact Memorization

Students need an understanding of the subtraction operation, which the crossing-out strategy pro-

vides. However, students must learn to memorize the subtraction facts to reduce difficulties in learning multi-digit operations. Fact memorization instruction should begin as soon as students reach the 80–90% accuracy criterion during supervised practice. After students reach the fluency criterion for independent practice, instructional time should be devoted to fact memorization.

Multi-digit Subtraction Problems

This section deals with subtraction problems with multi-digit numbers. The critical component skill of multi-digit problems is renaming (borrowing). Two basic renaming strategies are suggested in mathematics texts. The first, the additive balancing or equal addends method, involves the student's adding a tens unit to both the subtrahend and the minuend. In solving a problem with two digit numbers, the tens unit is added to the ones column of the top numeral while the tens unit is added to the tens column of the bottom numeral:

$$\begin{array}{r} 73 \\ -48 \\ \hline 25 \end{array} \quad \text{becomes} \quad \begin{array}{r} {\scriptstyle 1} \\ 7\overset{1}{3} \\ -5\overset{}{4}8 \\ \hline 25 \end{array}$$

This involves application of the compensation principle for subtraction: The difference between two numbers is unaltered by the addition of the same amount to both terms. In turn, the compensation principle includes the equality principle. Since few students know the compensation principle, and many don't know the equality principle, the equal addends strategy tends not to be understood by most students.

The second method, sometimes called the decomposition or borrowing method, involves renaming the minuend so that a unit from a higher-order column is written in a lower-order column:

$$\begin{array}{r} 73 \\ -48 \\ \hline 25 \end{array} \quad \text{becomes} \quad \begin{array}{r} {\scriptstyle 6\,1} \\ \cancel{7}3 \\ -48 \\ \hline 25 \end{array}$$

Note that the minuend 73 has been rewritten as 60 and 13.

Teaching Prodedure

The direct instruction procedures are based on the borrowing method since this method is used by most teachers in North America. The procedures emphasize knowing when to rename (borrow) and the mechanics of renaming. The conceptual understanding of renaming is also stressed, but in separate exercises from those for teaching the mechanics of working problems. This separation is done to simplify the formats for teaching the mechanics.

Three main groups of problems are discussed: (a) problems which do not require renaming, (b) problems which require renaming and in which the student may "borrow" from the next column, and (c) problems requiring renaming in two consecutive columns, including problems with a zero in the column that must be renamed, thus making the borrowing process more complex.

Column Subtraction—No Renaming

Since column subtraction problems that do not require renaming are taught in basically the same way as addition problems that do not require renaming, we have not included a format. Also, as was the case for addition, we recommend not introducing column problems until students have memorized at least a dozen facts. In working subtraction problems, students subtract in the ones column and then in the tens column. Also, as in addition, students read the number of tens in the tens column, rather than the quantity represented by the numerals: They would say, "three 10s minus two 10s" rather than "30 minus 20."

Subtraction with Renaming

Simple renaming problems include types 2a, 2b, 3a, and 3e from the Instructional Sequence and Assessment Chart in Figure 9.2. Problem type 2a is the first subtraction problem type which involves renaming. It is usually introduced during mid-second grade. The three preskills for this problem type are (a) the place value related skills inherent in reading and writing numerals over 10 (see pages 89–96 in Chapter 6), (b) having memorized at least six facts that can be used for borrowing, i.e., the first number is ten or more (see Chapter 7), and (c) a conceptual understanding of renaming. Figure 9.5 includes a format to teach the concept of regrouping (with objects), which builds a foundation for renaming (with numerals). The format in Figure 9.5 presents a diagram showing several packages, each of which contains 10 objects and several single objects. The teacher then says a story problem that involves giving away some of those objects: "Bill had 34 nails. He wants to give 8 nails to his sister." The teacher points out that to give 8 nails to his sister, Bill will have to open a package of 10. The teacher

erases one pack of 10 nails and draws 10 single nails. The teacher then erases 8 nails and counts the remaining packages and single nails. This format would be presented for several days prior to introducing the renaming format.

The format for introducing the computation for renaming appears in Figure 9.6. The format contains five parts. In Part A, students discriminate when renaming (borrowing) is necessary. Mastery of this discrimination is critical in preventing mistakes in which students subtract the smaller from the larger number regardless of which number is on top (e.g., in 74 – 38 students take 4 from 8). The teacher presents the rule: "When we take away more than we start with, we must rename." This rule is not necessarily intended to be absolutely mathematically correct but is meant to serve as a functional rule to teach the concept. After presenting this rule, the teacher leads students in applying the rule. The teacher points to the top number in the ones column and asks the students how many they are starting with, then points to the numeral below it and asks whether they must rename if they take away that number. Example selection is critical in this format. The teacher must include an unpredictable mix of problems, some requiring renaming and some not.

Part A should be presented for several lessons. The teacher should then test each student individually on a set of about seven problems (e.g., 35 – 28, 45 – 25, 57 – 28, 45 – 27, 74 – 23, 80 – 35, 45 – 20), asking "Do we have to rename in this problem?" The students' performance determines what the teacher does next. If students miss no more than one of the seven problems, the teacher can present Part B, in which the strategy for working problems is presented. If students miss more than one question, Part A would be presented for several more lessons.

Part B introduces the renaming component skill. The teacher explains to the students that they rename by borrowing a 10 and putting it with the ones number. In 75 – 38, they borrow a 10 from the seven 10s and put it with the five 1s. After modeling several problems, the teacher tests students, making sure they can state the steps for renaming.

Parts C and D are structured board and worksheet exercises in which the entire strategy is presented. Part E is a less structured worksheet exercise that includes an equal mix of problems that do and do not require renaming. Part F is a supervised practice exercise. After several days of supervised practice with only subtraction problems, the teacher should put in some addition problems.

Figure 9.5 Format for Teaching Regrouping

TEACHER   STUDENTS

1. Write on board:

10 10 10

"A BOY HAD NAILS. HE HAD THREE PACKAGES WITH
10 NAILS IN EACH PACKAGE AND 4 NAILS NOT IN A
PACKAGE. LET'S FIGURE OUT HOW MANY NAILS HE
HAD IN ALL." Point as you count.
"10, 20, 30, 31, 32, 33, 34."

2. "THE BOY WANTS TO GIVE 8 NAILS TO HIS SISTER.
WE HAVE A PROBLEM. HE CAN'T GIVE 8 NAILS TO HIS
SISTER THE WAY THE NAILS ARE NOW. HE HAS 4 NAILS
AND PACKAGES OF 10 NAILS. HE HAS TO REGROUP
THE NAILS. WHEN WE REGROUP WE PUT A GROUP OF
10 WITH THE 4 NAILS. WHAT DO WE DO WHEN WE
REGROUP IN THIS PROBLEM?"   "Put a group of 10 with 4."

3. "WE OPEN A PACK OF 10 NAILS (erase a group of 10 nails)
AND PUT THE 10 NAILS OVER HERE."
Write: | | | | | |
                                | | | | | |
    10   10

3. "WE STILL HAVE 34 NAILS. THEY'RE JUST IN DIFFER-
ENT GROUPS. WE HAVE TWO GROUPS OF 10 AND A
GROUP OF 14."

"NOW LET'S GIVE 8 AWAY." Erase 8. "LET'S SEE HOW
MANY WE HAVE LEFT. (Point to 6) HOW MANY
HERE? AND TWO 10s EQUAL HOW MANY?"   "6"
                                                 "20"
"WHAT IS 20 AND 6? RIGHT, 26. THE BOY STARTS WITH   "26"
34. HE GIVES AWAY 8 AND ENDS WITH 26."

4. Present one or two more problems.

Note on the chart at the beginning of Figure 9.6 that practice on determining when renaming is required (Part A) continues even after Parts B, C, and D are presented. This extra practice is important in developing fluency.

Supervised practice continues until students can perform with 80–90% accuracy.

Problems requiring renaming become more difficult as the number of digits in the minuend and subtrahend increase. The structured format for presenting each new problem type is quite similar to the wording in the structured format just discussed. For example, when problems involving renaming hundreds are introduced, the teacher would first ask the students to identify what they are starting with and taking away in the tens column and then ask if it is necessary to rename to work the problem. The teacher then leads students through solving the problem. In multi-digit problems that require renaming in several columns, the teacher leads the students through working each column always asking, "What does the column tell us to do? . . . Must we rename?"

The examples for the less structured, supervised practice and independent worksheets should include a mix of the currently introduced and previously introduced problem types. When the first problems requiring borrowing from tens are introduced, about 3/4 of the problems should involve subtraction and 1/4, addition. Of the subtraction problems, only about 1/2 should require renaming. When problems involving borrowing from the hundreds are introduced, 1/2 of the subtraction problems should require borrowing from the hundreds; 1/4, from the tens; and 1/4 should not require borrowing. Some addition problems should

Figure 9.6 Format for Subtraction with Renaming

Day	Part A When to Rename Problems	Part B Steps in Renaming Problems	Part C Structured Board Presen- tation Problems	Part D Structured Worksheet Problems	Part E Less Structured Worksheet Problems	Part F Supervised Practice Problems
1-2	7					
3-4	7	3				
5-6	7		3			
7-8	7		2	4		
9-10				2	6	2
11-till accurate					4	8

PART A: When to Rename

TEACHER

Write on board:
```
 75
-49
```

1. "HERE'S A RULE ABOUT RENAMING WITH SUBTRAC-
TION PROBLEMS: WHEN WE TAKE AWAY MORE THAN
WE START WITH, WE MUST RENAME. MY TURN. WHEN
MUST WE RENAME? WHEN WE TAKE AWAY MORE THAN
WE START WITH. YOUR TURN. WHEN DO WE RENAME?"
Repeat statement with students until they can say it by
themselves.

2. Point to the 5. "WHAT NUMBER ARE WE STARTING WITH
IN THE ONES COLUMN?"
"WE'RE STARTING WITH 5 AND TAKING AWAY 9. MUST
WE RENAME?" Pause and signal.
"RIGHT, WE HAVE TO RENAME BECAUSE WE'RE TAKING
AWAY MORE THAN WE START WITH; 9 IS MORE THAN 5."

3. Write on board:
```
 75
-43
```
"WHAT NUMBER ARE WE STARTING WITH IN THE ONES
COLUMN?"
"WHAT ARE WE TAKING AWAY?"
"MUST WE RENAME IF WE TAKE AWAY 3?" Pause, signal.
"WE DON'T RENAME. WE'RE NOT TAKING AWAY MORE
THAN WE START WITH."

4. Write on board:
```
 38
-27
```
"WHAT ARE WE STARTING OUT WITH NOW IN THE
ONES COLUMN?"
"WHAT ARE WE TAKING AWAY?"
"MUST WE RENAME?" Pause, signal.
"WHY?"

5. Repeat step 4 with these problems:
```
 38    42    42    42
-29   -37   -30   -33
```
Give individual turns to several children.

STUDENTS

"When we take away more than
we start with."

"5"

"Yes"

"5"
"3"
"No"

"8"
"7"
"No"
"We're not taking away more
than we start with."

Figure 9.6 cont'd

PART B: Steps in Renaming

Write on board:

```
 53    75    92
-26   -28   -15
```

1. Point to first problem. "READ THIS PROBLEM."   "53 - 26"
   "THE ONES COLUMN TELLS US TO START WITH 3 AND
   TAKE AWAY 6. WHAT DOES THE ONES COLUMN TELL
   US TO DO?"   "Start with 3 and take away 6"
   "DO WE HAVE TO RENAME?" Pause, signal.   "Yes"
   "RIGHT. WE START WITH 3 AND TAKE AWAY MORE
   THAN 3."

2. "HERE'S HOW WE RENAME: FIRST WE BORROW A 10
   FROM THE FIVE 10s. WHAT DO WE DO FIRST?"   "Borrow a 10 from the five 10s"
   "NEXT WE PUT THAT 10 WITH THE THREE 1s. WHAT DO
   WE DO NEXT?"   "Put that 10 with the three 1s"
   Repeat steps 1 and 2 with the second and third problems.

3. "LET'S GO BACK TO THE FIRST PROBLEM. READ IT."   "53 - 26"
   "WHAT DOES THE ONES COLUMN TELL US TO DO?"   "Start with 3 and take away 6"
   "DO WE RENAME?"   "Yes"

4. "TELL ME HOW WE RENAME. WHAT DO WE DO FIRST?"   "Borrow a 10 from the five 10s"
   "WHAT DO WE DO NEXT?"   "Put that 10 with the three 1s"
   Repeat steps 3 and 4 with the remaining problems.

PART C: Structured Board Presentation

Write on board:

```
 53
-26
```

1. "READ THIS PROBLEM."   "53 - 26"
   "WHAT DOES THE ONES COLUMN TELL US TO DO?"   "Start with 3 and take away 6"
   "DO WE RENAME?" Pause, signal.   "Yes"
   TO CORRECT: "WHAT ARE WE STARTING WITH IN
              THE ONES COLUMN? ARE WE TAKING
              AWAY MORE THAN 3? SO
              DO WE RENAME?"

2. "WHAT DO WE DO FIRST TO RENAME?"   "Borrow a 10 from the five 10s"
   Point to 5. "IF WE BORROW ONE 10 FROM THE FIVE 10s,
   HOW MANY 10s WILL BE LEFT?"   "Four 10s"
   "SO I CROSS OUT THE 5 AND WRITE 4 TO SHOW THAT
   FOUR 10s ARE LEFT." Cross out 5 and write 4.

3. "WE BORROWED A 10. WHAT DO WE DO NEXT?"   "Put the 10 with the three 1s"
   "RIGHT, PUT THE 10 WITH THE THREE 1s." Write 1 in
   front of 3. "NOW WE HAVE 13 IN THE ONES COLUMN.
   FIGURE OUT WHAT 13 MINUS 6 IS." Pause. "WHAT'S
   13 - 6?" Pause, signal.   "7"
   "WE WRITE 7 IN THE ONES COLUMN." Write 7 under the
   line.

4. "THE TENS COLUMN SAYS FOUR 10s MINUS TWO 10s.
   HOW MANY IS FOUR 10s MINUS TWO 10s?" Pause, signal.   "Two 10s"
   "WE WRITE 2 IN THE TENS COLUMN." Write 2 under the
   line.

5. "WHAT IS 53 TAKE AWAY 26?"   "27"
   Repeat steps 1-5 with remaining problems.

Figure 9.6 cont'd

PART D: Structured Worksheet

TEACHER   **STUDENTS**

Give students worksheets with these problems:

```
  92      86      64
 -35     -17     -49
```

1. "READ PROBLEM ONE ON YOUR WORKSHEET."   "92 - 35"

2. "WHAT DOES THE ONES COLUMN TELL YOU TO DO?"   "Start with 2 and take away 5"
   "DO YOU RENAME?" Pause, signal.   "Yes"

3. "WHAT DO YOU DO FIRST TO RENAME?"   "Borrow a 10 from the nine 10s"
   "IF YOU BORROW A 10 FROM THE NINE 10s, HOW MANY
   WILL BE LEFT?"   "8"
   "SO CROSS OUT THE 9 AND WRITE 8 ABOVE IT."   Students cross out the 9 and
   Check papers.   write 8.

4. "WHAT DO YOU DO NOW?"   "Put the 10 with the two 1s"
   "DO THAT. PUT THE 10 WITH THE TWO 1s." Check
   papers. "HOW MANY DO YOU HAVE IN THE ONES
   COLUMN?"   "12"

5. "WHAT IS 12 MINUS 5?" Pause, signal.   "7"
   "WRITE 7 UNDER THE LINE IN THE ONES COLUMN."

6. "LOOK AT THE TENS COLUMN. WHAT DOES THE TENS
   COLUMN TELL US TO DO?"   "Start with 8 and take away 3"
   "WHAT IS EIGHT 10s MINUS THREE 10s?"   "Five 10s"
   "WRITE 5 UNDER THE LINE IN THE TENS COLUMN."

7. "HOW MANY IS 92 TAKE AWAY 35?"   "57"
   Repeat steps 1-7 with remaining problems.

PART E: Less Structured Worksheet

Give students worksheet with a mixture of subtraction
problems which do and do not require renaming:

```
a.  84    b.  95    c.  46    d.  56    e.  78
   -23       -38       - 8       -32       -38

f.  42    g.  34    h.  58
   -26       -26       -52
```

1. "TOUCH PROBLEM a."

2. "READ THE PROBLEM."

3. "LOOK AT THE ONES COLUMN AND GET READY TO
   TELL ME IF YOU NEED TO RENAME." Pause. "MUST
   YOU RENAME?"   "No"
   If the answer is yes, present step 4. If the answer is no, go
   to step 5.

4. "WHERE DO YOU GET THE 10 FROM?"
   "HOW MANY 10s WILL YOU HAVE LEFT?"

5. "WORK THE PROBLEM."
   Repeat steps 1-5 with remaining problems.

Figure 9.7

a. 392 - 81	b. 346 -118	c. 423 -180	d. 728 +324	e. 547 - 83
f. 547 + 38	g. 285 - 84	h. 248 - 58	i. 347 -109	j. 236 - 46

also be included. Figure 9.7 is an example of a worksheet that could be presented after problems requiring borrowing from the hundreds are taught. Note the mixture of problem types: c, e, h, and j require borrowing from hundreds; b and i, from tens; a and g do not require renaming; and d and f are addition.

SELF-CHECKING After students become proficient in working renaming problems, they should be taught to check their answers. A checking procedure for subtraction is adding the subtrahend and the difference. The teacher introduces checking on a worksheet exercise. After the students complete the first problem, he says "Here's how to check your answer to a subtraction problem. Add the bottom two numbers. What's the answer? . . . Is that the same as the top number in the problem? So your answer is correct." To demonstrate why the checking procedure works, teachers should use simple problems like 12 – 8 = 4. The teacher uses the same questions: "Add the bottom two numbers . . . What's the answer? . . . Is that the same as the top number? . . ." With familiar facts, students more readily see that the procedure "makes sense." The same type of exercise suggested for encouraging students to use the addition self-check can be used. Teachers give students a worksheet with some problems worked correctly and some incorrectly. Students are to find the problems worked incorrectly.

Complex Renaming Problems

This group includes problems in which several consecutive columns must be renamed. First we discuss problems which do not include zeroes in the minuend. Working such problems does not involve new skills, just applying the renaming skill in consecutive columns. Errors often occur because students become confused over the crossed-out digits. When the problem

$$327$$
$$-149$$

is worked, the number in the tens column is 11, neither digit of which comes from the original problem:

$$
\begin{array}{r}
2\,11 \\
3\cancel{2}7 \\
-149 \\
\hline
178
\end{array}
$$

An important aspect of the teaching procedure is closely monitoring students as they write on their worksheets. Because of extensive crossing out and rewriting, messiness can cause many errors. Thus, teachers should stress precisely where numerals are to be written.

Students encounter more difficulty with problems that require renaming zero. Types 3d, 4a, 4c, 4d, 4e, and 5b from the Instructional Sequence and Assessment Chart (Figure 9.2) are examples of problems in which a number with a zero is renamed. The basic strategy students are taught is to rename several digits at once. For example, in the problem

$$304$$
$$- 87$$

students treat the three 100s as thirty 10s. By doing this, they rename by borrowing one 10 from the thirty (10s), which is crossed out and replaced with 29:

$$
\begin{array}{r}
2\,9\,1 \\
3\cancel{0}4 \\
- 87
\end{array}
$$

They would follow a similar procedure when working problems containing zeroes in both the tens and hundreds columns:

$$3002$$
$$-\ \ 89$$

The students would treat the 3000 as 300 10s, crossing out the 300, writing 299 in its place and putting a 10 in the ones column:

$$
\begin{array}{r}
2\,9\,9\,1 \\
3\cancel{0}\cancel{0}2 \\
-\ \ 89
\end{array}
$$

This procedure was suggested by Cacha (1975) as a means of simplifying renaming that involved zeroes.

A preskill for solving problem types that involve renaming numbers with zeroes is the tens numbers minus 1 facts, e.g., 60 – 1, 90 – 1, 40 – 1. These facts would be presented about a week prior to introducing problems such as

$$\begin{array}{r} 407 \\ -129 \\ \hline \end{array}$$

The format for teaching tens numbers minus 1 facts consists of two steps. First, the teacher says a tens number (a two digit number ending in zero) and asks the students to indicate what number precedes it. "What number comes before 80?" Second, the teacher introduces the rule that when you minus 1, you say the number that comes just before. Then the teacher has the students apply the rule to a series of examples. The format appears in Figure 9.8. It would be presented for 3–5 days prior to introducing renaming problems with a zero.

Once students have mastered the tens minus 1 preskill, they can be presented with the format for renaming numbers with a zero, which appears in Figure 9.10. The format has three parts. Part A includes a board demonstration by the teacher of how to work the problem. Part B includes steps in which the teacher guides students through solving problems on their worksheets. Part C is a less structured worksheet guide. During the structured board and worksheet exercises, each problem should require renaming. In Part C, the less structured worksheet exercise, students would be presented with a mix of problems—half would require renaming and half would not. For example, a typical worksheet might look like Figure 9.9. In about half of the problems (1, 4, 5, 7, 9, 12, and 15), the numbers in the ones column require borrowing; while in the other half of the problems, borrowing in the ones column is not required. The mix is very important to

prevent students from developing the misrule of always borrowing when they see a zero in the tens column. The importance of a mix of problems on the less structured, supervised practice and independent worksheets cannot be overemphasized. If the examples used are not carefully designed to provide discrimination practice, the students might develop a serious misrule of always crossing out the hundreds number and zero, as in the problem below:

$$\begin{array}{r} 2\,9 \\ \cancel{3}\cancel{0}2 \\ -\ \ 41 \\ \hline 251 \end{array} \qquad \begin{array}{r} 3\,9 \\ \cancel{4}\cancel{0}2 \\ -\ \ 52 \\ \hline 340 \end{array}$$

Problem types become more complex as the number of digits increases, particularly the number of zeroes involved in renaming. In problem type 4c of Figure 9.2, numbers with two zeroes are renamed, as in

$$\begin{array}{r} 3004 \\ -\ \ 86 \\ \hline \end{array}$$

The preskill for this type of problem is hundreds minus 1 facts (e.g., 800 – 1, 300 – 1). The teaching procedure for hundreds minus 1 facts would be basically the same as for tens minus 1 facts.

The teacher presents the structured board and worksheet formats using basically the same wording as in the format in Figure 9.10. The only difference is that the teacher points out that in a problem such as

$$\begin{array}{r} 3004 \\ -\ 128 \\ \hline \end{array}$$

students borrow from 300 10s. "What are you going to borrow one 10 from? What is 300 minus 1? . . . So cross out 300 and write 299." Again, the less structured worksheet exercise would be the critical part of the format. The worksheet should include a mix of problems like that in Figure 9.11.

Figure 9.8 Format for Tens Numbers Minus 1 Preskill

TEACHER	STUDENTS
1. "I'LL SAY NUMBERS, YOU SAY THE NUMBER THAT COMES JUST BEFORE. LISTEN, 60. WHAT COMES JUST BEFORE?" Pause 2 seconds. Signal. TO CORRECT: Tell answer, then repeat the problem.	"59"
2. Repeat step 1 with 30, 80, 40, 70.	
3. "LISTEN. WHEN YOU MINUS 1 YOU SAY THE NUMBER THAT COMES JUST BEFORE. I'LL SAY A PROBLEM, YOU TELL ME THE ANSWER. LISTEN. 60 MINUS 1 IS . . ." Pause, signal. TO CORRECT: Ask, "WHAT NUMBER COMES JUST BEFORE 60?" Repeat step 3 with 30 - 1, 80 - 1, 40 - 1, 70 - 1.	"59"

Figure 9.9

1. 402 − 69	2. 503 −161	3. 305 − 65	4. 302 − 86	5. 504 −128
6. 703 − 42	7. 500 − 36	8. 300 − 40	9. 700 − 4	10. 206 − 36
11. 508 − 32	12. 500 − 26	13. 300 − 20	14. 501 − 61	15. 302 − 48

Figure 9.10 Format for Renaming Numbers with Zeroes

Day	Part A Structured Board Presen- tation Problems	Part B Structured Worksheet Problems	Part C Less Structured Worksheet Problems	Part D Supervised Practice Problems	Part E Independent Practice Problems
1	3				
2	2	4			
3	1	2	6		
4		1	8		
5			4	8	
6-Till accurate				10-15	
Till fluent					10-15

PART A: Structured Board Presentation

TEACHER	**STUDENTS**

Write on board:

    304
   −186

1. "READ THE PROBLEM." — "304 − 186"

2. "WHAT DO WE DO IN THE ONES COLUMN?" — "Start with 4 and take away 6."
"DO WE HAVE TO RENAME?" Pause, signal. — "Yes"

3. "WE HAVE A PROBLEM. WE CAN'T BORROW FROM ZERO 10s. SO WE HAVE TO BORROW FROM THE THIRTY 10s. WE'RE GOING TO BORROW ONE 10 FROM THIRTY 10s." Circle 30 with finger. "WHAT ARE WE GOING TO BORROW ONE 10 FROM?" — "Thirty 10s."
"WHAT IS 30 TENS MINUS 1 TEN?" — "29 Tens."
"SO I CROSS OUT 30 AND WRITE 29 ABOVE IT."

4. "NOW I'LL PUT THE ONE 10 WITH THE FOUR 1s. WHAT IS ONE 10 AND FOUR 1s?" — "14"
"WHAT IS 14 MINUS 6?" Pause, signal. — "8"
"SO I WRITE 8 IN THE ONES COLUMN."

5. "NOW LOOK AT THE TENS COLUMN. HOW MANY 10s ARE WE STARTING WITH NOW?" — "9"
"WHAT IS 9 − 8?" — "1"
"SO I WRITE 1 UNDER THE TENS COLUMN."

6. "HOW MANY 100s ARE WE STARTING WITH NOW?" — "2"
"WHAT IS 2 − 1?" — "1"
"SO I WRITE 1 IN THE HUNDREDS COLUMN."

7. "WHAT IS THE ANSWER TO THIS PROBLEM?" — "118"

Repeat steps 1-7 with these examples: 504 - 327, 602 - 148.

Figure 9.10 cont'd

PART B: Structured Worksheet

TEACHER   **STUDENTS**

```
406        905        403
-287       -626       -248
```

1. "TOUCH THE FIRST PROBLEM. READ IT."   "406 - 287"

2. "WHAT DOES THE ONES COLUMN TELL US TO DO?"   "Start with 6 and take away 7"
   "DO YOU HAVE TO RENAME?" Pause.   "Yes"

3. "CAN YOU BORROW 10 FROM ZERO 10s?"   "No."
   "WHERE ARE YOU GOING TO GET THE ONE 10?"   "From forty 10s"
   "WHAT IS FORTY 10s MINUS ONE 10?"   "Thirty-nine 10s"
   "CROSS OUT THE 40 AND WRITE 39 ABOVE IT." Monitor
   responses. "NOW PUT THE ONE 10 WITH THE SIX 1s."
   Monitor responses.

4. "NOW WORK THE PROBLEM IN THE ONES COLUMN.
   WHAT IS ONE 10 AND SIX 1s?"   "16"
   "WHAT IS 16 MINUS 7?"   "9"

5. "HOW MANY 10s ARE YOU STARTING WITH NOW?"   "9"
   "WHAT IS 9 - 8?"   "1"
   "WRITE IT." Monitor responses

6. "HOW MANY HUNDREDS ARE YOU STARTING WITH
   NOW?"   "3"
   "WHAT IS 3 - 2?"   "1"
   "READ THE WHOLE PROBLEM AND SAY THE ANSWER."   "406 - 287 = 119"
   Repeat steps 1-6 with remaining examples.

PART C: Less Structured Worksheet

```
a. 804     b. 905     c. 609
   -619       -164       -426

d. 605     e. 302     f. 508
   -197       - 42       -349
```

1. "TOUCH PROBLEM a."

2. "READ THE PROBLEM."   "804 - 619"

3. "LOOK AT THE ONES COLUMN AND GET READY TO
   TELL ME IF YOU NEED TO RENAME. (pause) DO YOU
   NEED TO RENAME?"   "Yes"
   If the answer is yes, say, "WHERE DO YOU GET THE 10
   FROM?"   "From eighty 10s"

4. "WORK THE PROBLEM."
   Repeat steps 1-4 with remaining problems.

Figure 9.11

```
a.  3004      b.  3004      c.  3001      d.  7005      e.  7005
    - 289         - 302         -1394         -2101         -2104

f.  7005      g.  6000      h.  6000      i.  4000
    -1149         - 80          - 8           - 50
```

In problems a, c, f, and h, students rename in the ones column. In problems g and i, students rename in the tens column. In problems b, d, and e, students rename in the hundreds column. Teachers can expect students to need a great deal of supervised practice on this type before they reach an acceptable accuracy criterion.

Two additional problem types that may cause students difficulty require borrowing from 10, 100, 1000, or 1100 (problem types 4d and 4e). Problems in which the student must borrow from 10, 100, or 1000 may cause difficulty since the students do not replace each digit with another digit as in

$$799_1$$
$$\cancel{800}4$$

Instead they only replace two of the three digits as in

$$99$$
$$1\cancel{00}$$

Contrast

$$99_1 \qquad 799_1$$
$$\cancel{100}4 \text{ with } \cancel{800}4$$

Without instruction, students may write the nines numbers in the wrong columns:

$$99$$
$$1\cancel{000}$$
$$-\ 193$$
$$\overline{9807}$$

The teaching procedure need not be elaborate. The teacher merely models working several problems and then supervises students as they work the problems.

Diagnosis and Remediation

FACT ERRORS Basic fact errors will usually be obvious. For example, in problems a and b the student has made obvious errors involving the facts 13 − 6 and 12 − 8, respectively.

$$\begin{array}{cc} 3_1 & 4_1 \\ \text{a. } \cancel{4}35 & \text{b. } \cancel{5}28 \\ \underline{-162} & \underline{-186} \\ 2\textbf{?}3 & 352 \end{array}$$

The remediation procedure for fact errors depends on their frequency. An occasional error is remediated by stressing the missed fact in drill exercises. A pattern in which students make several errors on different facts requires a more in-depth remediation procedure. First, the teacher determines the strategy used by the students to derive the basic facts.

This can be done by observing students as they work problems. Teachers may find lower-performing students relying on their fingers. The remediation procedure for such students is discussed in Chapter 7 on facts. Other students may not rely on using their fingers but, nonetheless, may be inaccurate, answering a basic fact correctly in one problem, but incorrectly in the next problem. The remediation procedure for such students involves first working on developing accuracy in computing basic facts. The teacher can do this by giving students a worksheet with about 30 basic facts. A reward contingent on the student's performance should be established. A large payoff should be established for 100% accuracy. For difficult-to-motivate students, a daily reward could be established for improvement over the prior day's performance. After students work these fact worksheets at about 95% accuracy (28 of 30) for several consecutive lessons, this fact exercise can be discontinued. The emphasis of facts should result in improved performance on column subtraction problems. If, however, the student continues making random fact errors in column subtraction problems, the teacher may tentatively consider the problem to be one of motivation and take action to increase student motivation.

STRATEGY ERRORS Errors caused by failure to rename are illustrated below. In problem a, the error is in the ones column. In problem b the error is in the hundreds column.

$$\begin{array}{cc} \text{a. } 342 & \text{b. } 25\cancel{3}4 \\ \underline{-128} & \underline{-1827} \\ 226 & 1307 \end{array}$$

Again, the frequency of the error must be considered before a remediation procedure is planned. An occasional error, occurring no more than in 1 out of 10 problems, needs no extensive remediation. The teacher merely has students rework the problem. More frequent errors of this type require more in-depth remediation, beginning with Part A of Figure 9.6. That part focuses on when renaming is required. The teacher writes several problems similar to the ones missed by the student. The teacher points to each column in a problem, asking if renaming is required to work that column. "Touch the tens column. It says start with 6 take away 4. Must we rename?" This exercise is continued until students can respond correctly to four to five problems consecutively. Next the teacher leads the students through a structured worksheet exercise with several problems (Part D in Figure 9.6), then through less structured worksheet problems (Part E in

Figure 9.6). Finally, the teacher has students work a group of problems as she closely monitors. The set of problems worked on includes a mix of problem types so that the teacher can be sure students are discriminating when renaming is called for. The exercise is continued daily until students perform accurately on independent assignments for several days in a row.

COMPONENT SKILL ERRORS   These errors in the mechanics of borrowing are illustrated below:

a. $\begin{array}{r} {}^{1}\;\; \\ 35 \\ -16 \\ \hline 29 \end{array}$ b. $\begin{array}{r} {}^{6}1 \\ 54 \\ -28 \\ \hline 46 \end{array}$ c. $\begin{array}{r} {}^{2}0\,1 \\ 302 \\ -54 \\ \hline 8 \end{array}$

In problem a, the student forgot to subtract a 10 from the three 10s after borrowing. This error is not uncommon when borrowing is first introduced. For remediation, give students practice rewriting two-digit numerals. Use this wording: "You're going to practice renaming. Touch the first numeral (check). What do you do first to rename this number? Do it. Write a 1 to show one ten. Remember to cross out and write a new number for the first digit." For examples, present a worksheet with these numerals: a. 27 b. 38 c. 71 d. 42.

The error in problem b indicates the student is adding rather than subtracting one 10 when renaming. The remediation procedure begins with the teacher's working on minus 1 facts. The teacher then follows the same procedure as described for problem a.

The error in problem c indicates either that the student is having difficulty with ten numbers minus 1 facts or is confused regarding the strategy to use. The teacher would watch the student work several problems. If the problem relates to tens minus 1 facts, the teacher would reteach tens minus 1 facts (e.g., 60 – 1, 30 – 1, 80 – 1, etc.) from Figure 9.8. When students demonstrate mastery of tens minus 1 facts, they would be presented with the less structured part of the format for that type of problem. If it's a strategy error, the teacher represents the entire format.

A special group of problems which may cause students difficulty are problems with a zero in the ones column of the minuend or subtrahend:

$\begin{array}{r} 60 \\ -34 \\ \hline \end{array}$ $\begin{array}{r} 64 \\ -30 \\ \hline \end{array}$

Students often become confused on problems with zero, answering 70 – 34 as 44 or 74 – 30 as 40. If teachers note errors with this problem type, a special exercise comprised of problems like the ones below should be given. Teachers would first review minus zero facts, pointing out that when you minus zero you end with the same number you start with, then lead students through working the problems. The exercise is continued until students can work the problems with 90% accuracy for several days in a row.

$\begin{array}{r} 60 \\ -34 \\ \hline \end{array}$ $\begin{array}{r} 64 \\ -30 \\ \hline \end{array}$ $\begin{array}{r} 40 \\ -20 \\ \hline \end{array}$ $\begin{array}{r} 43 \\ -20 \\ \hline \end{array}$

$\begin{array}{r} 40 \\ -23 \\ \hline \end{array}$ $\begin{array}{r} 78 \\ -30 \\ \hline \end{array}$ $\begin{array}{r} 70 \\ -38 \\ \hline \end{array}$

A summary of the diagnosis and remediation procedures appears in Figure 9.12.

Research

Research on early subtraction is even more limited than research on addition. Kameenui, Carnine, Darch & Stein (1986) compared a traditional subtraction presentation based on pictures and manipulatives with a direct instruction subtraction counting strategy. Twenty-six first graders with the lowest metropolitan readiness scores from a population of 80 students were tested on counting, symbol identification, and subtraction. Twenty-three students, who had sufficient counting and symbol skills but could not subtract, were randomly assigned to a direct instruction or traditional treatment. The direct instruction students learned the preskill of crossing out a line for each number minused and later were taught the complete strategy. The traditional group was taught according to the procedures specified in the basal mathematics program. In the traditional treatment, students used numbers to describe pictures of subtraction events as well as actual subtraction events. One subtraction event involved students in the class. The teacher asked five students to stand and said, "How many are we starting with?" Next, the teacher told three students to sit down and asked, "How many did we take away?" Then the teacher asked, "How many are left?" Instruction was provided over 7 days, according to the specification of the program used. Each day's instruction lasted 25 minutes. In addition to daily tests on picture and numerical problems, the basal subtraction and the basal unit tests were given. Direct instruction students correctly answered significantly more problems on all three tests. The difference was attributed to the importance of students learning an explicit step-by-step strategy.

Figure 9.12   Diagnosis and Remediation of Subtraction Errors

	Sample Patterns		Sample Diagnosis	Remediation Procedures	Remediation Examples
a.	437 −180	63 −28	Fact error: 13 − 8	Emphasis on 13 − 8 in fact drill.	
b.	34 −18	352 − 71	Component skill: Student did not rename column borrowed from.	You're going to practice rewriting. Touch the first numeral (check). What do you do first to rewrite this number? . . . Do it. Write a 1 to show one ten. Remember to cross out and write a new number for the first digit.	For examples, present a worksheet with these numerals: a. 27 b. 38 c. 71 d. 42
c.	34 −18	72 −36	Strategy: Renaming not done.	Present renaming format starting with Part A, in Figure 9.6.	Examples specified for Figure 9.6.
d.	304 − 21	64 −24	Strategy: Renaming was done unnecessarily.	Same as c	Same as c
e.	63 −48	51 −2	Fact error: Minus 1.	a. Present minus 1 facts b. Present less structured worksheet for the particular problem type.	Mix: some problems require renaming, and some do not. Renaming problems sample all types introduced to date.
f.	35 −14		Component skill: Sign discrimination; student added instead of subtracting.	a. Present less structured part of Figure. Have student circle sign, then work the problem.	Equal mix of addition and subtraction.
9.	304 − 26		Component skill: Problems with zero in tens column; inappropriate renaming.	a. Present tens minus 1 preskill (if necessary). b. Present the format for renaming numbers with zeroes (Figure 9.10)	6-8 problems Examples specified for Figure 9.9
h.	302 − 41	402 − 52	Strategy: Renaming unnecessarily.	Format 9.10, Part C	Example specified for format—see Figure 9.10.

In conducting research on common subtraction errors, the Elementary School Mathematics Committee (1975) identified problems in ignoring the symbol (adding when they should subtract), not renaming (subtracting the smaller from the larger number regardless of position), ignoring the first digit in the top numeral when no digit appeared below it, and not rewriting the larger unit when renaming:

$$
\begin{array}{ccc}
\overset{1}{32} & \text{rather than} & \overset{2}{\cancel{3}}1 \\
\underline{-14} & & \underline{-14} \\
28 & & 18
\end{array}
$$

A study was also conducted to determine the importance of teaching the preskills before introducing the strategy itself (Kameenui & Carnine, 1986). All the students in a second grade classroom were screened to identify students who knew how to subtract single digit numbers but had not learned the renaming skill. The 20 students who were identified as subjects were randomly assigned to either a pretraining or no pretraining group. The pretraining group received instruction on the preskills in Parts A and B of Figure 9.6. Students in the no pretraining group began instruction with the strategy itself (Part C). Instruction for both groups consisted of 10 training sessions. Students in the pretraining group made significantly more correct responses to daily probe measures, which means they mastered the skill more rapidly (x = 8.4 vs. x = 6.9). Differences on the transfer test and maintenance test were not significant. The comparable performance on transfer and maintenance measures suggests that 10 training sessions provided enough practice for all students to become proficient. Had only 5 or 6 training sessions been provided, the differences in probe performance suggest that the preskill group might have scored higher on transfer and maintenance measures.

Commercial Programs

Subtraction: Renaming

INSTRUCTIONAL STRATEGIES As in addition with renaming, most basal programs advocate the use of manipulatives when introducing renaming in subtraction. Interestingly, many programs we examined also include picture representations of the manipulatives on the introductory pages (e.g., pictures of sticks, etc.; see Figures 9.13, 9.14). However, little direction is given to the students on how to work the problems without the manipulatives.

PREREQUISITE SKILLS Most programs identify key prerequisite skills and preteach these skills before the instructional strategy is introduced. However, often the prerequisites are introduced with only a few examples the same day or a day before the strategy instruction. Teachers should allow time for students to master the prerequisites prior to introducing the strategy. Also, they should determine whether *all* necessary prerequisites have been addressed. (See this chapter for a thorough discussion of the preskills to teach before introducing a renaming strategy.)

PRACTICE AND REVIEW Most programs provide an average of 15 to 20 pages of initial practice on two-digit subtraction problems with renaming. While this is an adequate amount of practice initially, little further review of subtraction typically occurs until the next level of the series. This lack of review can be attributed to the spiral curriculum design employed by the majority of math progemas. To maintain student success over time, adequate review on a continual basis must be provided.

Figure 9.13

STUDENT OBJECTIVE

To subtract 2-digit numbers, with regrouping from tens to ones.

TEACHING SUGGESTIONS

Practice subtraction with models. (Materials: tens and ones, Tens and Ones mat) Write

$$\begin{array}{r} 34 \\ -18 \\ \hline \end{array}$$

on the chalkboard. "What should you put on your mats?" (3 tens and 4 ones) "Can you take 8 ones away from your 4 ones? (No) What can you do?" (Trade 1 of the tens for 10 more ones.)

Ask the children to trade one of their tens for 10 more ones. Show them how to record what they have done.

"We took one of the tens to the bank, leaving us with 2 tens."

"We traded the ten for 10 more ones. That gives us 14 ones."

"Now do you have enough ones to take 8 away?" (Yes) Have the children take 8 ones off the mat. "How many ones are left? (6 ones) How many tens should we take away?" (1 ten) Have the children take 1 ten off the mat. "How many tens are left?" (1 ten) On the chalkboard, show the children how to record what they have done.

READINESS

For students who need help with subtraction.

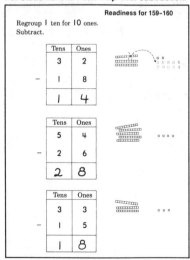

Readiness for 159–160

Regroup 1 ten for 10 ones. Subtract.

Tens	Ones
3	2
– 1	8
1	4

Tens	Ones
5	4
– 2	6
2	8

Tens	Ones
3	3
– 1	5
1	8

Copymaster S96 or Duplicating Master S96

Ask the children to draw the trade, crossing out 1 ten and drawing in 10 ones, and then cross out the amount to be subtracted and write the amount that is left.

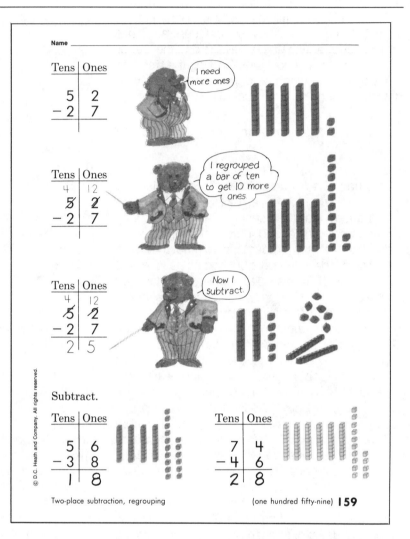

Name _____

Tens	Ones
5	2
– 2	7

I need more ones

Tens	Ones
4	12
5̸	2̸
– 2	7

I regrouped a bar of ten to get 10 more ones.

Tens	Ones
4	12
5̸	2̸
– 2	7
2	5

Now I subtract.

Subtract.

Tens	Ones
5	6
– 3	8
1	8

Tens	Ones
7	4
– 4	6
2	8

Two-place subtraction, regrouping

(one hundred fifty-nine) **159**

USING THE PAGES

Provide the children with tens and ones. Discuss the bear's and the turtle's demonstrations of regrouping on pages 159 and 160. Have the children make check marks by the problems that will require regrouping. A few problems will not require regrouping. Assign the pages.

•••• **ERROR-ANALYSIS NOTE** •••••••••••••

Rather than regrouping the tens, some children may subtract the smaller ones digit from the larger ones digit—for example,

$$\begin{array}{r} 61 \\ -28 \\ \hline 47 \end{array} \quad \text{instead of} \quad \begin{array}{r} 5\,11 \\ 6̸\,1̸ \\ -28 \\ \hline 33 \end{array}$$

Have these children use ones and tens materials. See the Teaching Suggestions.

CLASSWORK/HOMEWORK

Textbook Assignments	Basic	Enriched
all exercises	✔	✔
Keeping Skills Sharp	✔	✔
Optional Materials		
Readiness Worksheet	✔	✔
Basic Worksheet	✔	
Enrichment Worksheet		✔
Creative Problem Solving section 7	✔	✔

▨ **Concrete materials**   ❖ **Cooperative Learning Groups**

Source: From *Heath Mathematics,* Grade 2 Teacher's Edition, by Walter E. Rucker, Clyde A. Dilley, and David A. Lowry, p. 159. Copyright © 1987 by D.C. Heath & Company. Reprinted by permission.

Figure 9.14

STUDENT OBJECTIVES

To subtract any two whole numbers with one regrouping.

To solve word problems using subtraction with regrouping.

TEACHING SUGGESTIONS

Subtract with regrouping. (Materials: ones, tens, hundreds, a place-value mat for each student) Write this subtraction problem on the chalkboard:

$$\begin{array}{r} 54 \\ -28 \\ \hline \end{array}$$

"How many blocks will you put on your mat? (54) How many are you going to take away? (28) Can you take 8 ones from the 4 ones? (No) What can you do?" (Trade 1 ten for 10 ones.)

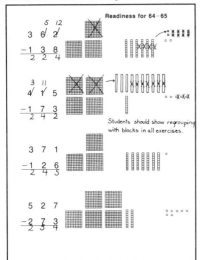

Ask the students to subtract the ones and then the tens. Demonstrate this on the chalkboard.

READINESS

For students who need help with subtraction.

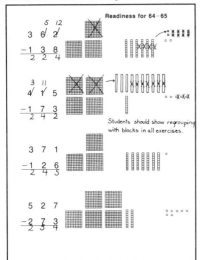

Copymaster S84 or Duplicating Master S84

Draw 3 hundreds, 6 tens, and 2 ones on the chalkboard. We want to take away 138 blocks. There are not enough ones. Cross off 1 ten and draw 10 ones. How many ones do you have now? (12) How many tens do you have now?" (5) Demonstrate how to record this in the example at the left. "Cross off 8 ones. How many ones do you have now? Write *4* in the ones place. Cross off 3 tens. How many tens do you have now? Write *2* in the tens place. Cross off 1 hundred. How many hundreds do you have now? Write *2* in the hundreds place."

In this example, 1 ten is regrouped for 10 ones.

EXAMPLE 1.

Step 1. Not enough ones. Regroup 1 ten for 10 ones.

Step 2. Subtract ones. Subtract tens.

In this example, 1 hundred is regrouped for 10 tens.

EXAMPLE 2.

Step 1. Subtract ones.

$$\begin{array}{r} 426 \\ -152 \\ \hline 4 \end{array}$$

Step 2. Not enough tens. Regroup 1 hundred for 10 tens.

$$\begin{array}{r} ^{3\,12}\llap{\not4}26 \\ -152 \\ \hline 4 \end{array}$$

Step 3. Subtract tens.

$$\begin{array}{r} ^{3\,12}\llap{\not4}26 \\ -152 \\ \hline 74 \end{array}$$

Step 4. Subtract hundreds.

$$\begin{array}{r} ^{3\,12}\llap{\not4}26 \\ -152 \\ \hline 274 \end{array}$$

64

USING THE PAGES

Discuss the examples on page 64. Provide place-value materials for the students who need them. Assign page 65.

••••• *ERROR-ANALYSIS NOTE* ••••••••••••

Some students may regroup when it is not necessary—for example,

 instead of $\begin{array}{r}87\\-26\\\hline 61\end{array}$

Have these students look at exercises 1–15 and find the two exercises that do not require regrouping. (Exercises 7 and 15)

CLASSWORK/HOMEWORK

Textbook Assignments	Basic	Average	Enriched
Exercises 1–32	✓		
Exercises 1–34		✓	
Exercises 6–36			✓
Extra Practice set 15 page 366	✓		

Optional Materials			
Readiness Worksheet	✓	✓	
Basic Worksheet	✓		
Enrichment Worksheet		✓	✓
Excursion Worksheet			✓
Creative Problem Solving section 3	✓	✓	✓

⬛ **Concrete Materials**   ☁ **Mental Arithmetic**

Application Items: Subtraction

1. Below are Mary's and Alex's performances on a set of performance indicators. Specify the problem type with which instruction should begin for each student.

Mary

3a.
$$\begin{array}{r}\overset{3}{4}23\\-171\\\hline 252\end{array}\qquad\begin{array}{r}\overset{3}{4}18\\-\ 83\\\hline 335\end{array}\qquad\begin{array}{r}\overset{1}{2}28\\-137\\\hline 91\end{array}$$

3b.
$$\begin{array}{r}\overset{41}{3}52\\-187\\\hline 245\end{array}\qquad\begin{array}{r}\overset{11}{7}24\\-578\\\hline 266\end{array}\qquad\begin{array}{r}\overset{21}{5}34\\-\ 87\\\hline 567\end{array}$$

3c. 70 − 1 = **69**
    40 − 1 = **39**
    80 − 1 = **79**

3d.
$$\begin{array}{r}\overset{4}{5}03\\-\ 87\\\hline 486\end{array}\qquad\begin{array}{r}\overset{4}{5}\overset{1}{0}4\\-\ 26\\\hline 428\end{array}\qquad\begin{array}{r}700\\-\ 86\\\hline 786\end{array}$$

3e.
$$\begin{array}{r}4689\\-1832\\\hline 3257\end{array}\qquad\begin{array}{r}\overset{41}{5}284\\-4631\\\hline 653\end{array}\qquad\begin{array}{r}3481\\-1681\\\hline 2201\end{array}$$

Alex

3a.
$$\begin{array}{r}\overset{31}{4}23\\-171\\\hline 252\end{array}\qquad\begin{array}{r}\overset{31}{4}18\\-\ 83\\\hline 335\end{array}\qquad\begin{array}{r}\overset{1}{2}28\\-137\\\hline 91\end{array}$$

3b.
$$\begin{array}{r}\overset{41}{3}52\\-187\\\hline 245\end{array}\qquad\begin{array}{r}\overset{11}{7}24\\-578\\\hline 266\end{array}\qquad\begin{array}{r}\overset{21}{5}34\\-\ 87\\\hline 567\end{array}$$

3c. 70 − 1 = **69**
    40 − 1 = **39**
    80 − 1 = **79**

3d.
$$\begin{array}{r}\overset{491}{5}03\\-\ 87\\\hline 415\end{array}\qquad\begin{array}{r}\overset{49}{5}04\\-\ 26\\\hline 478\end{array}\qquad\begin{array}{r}\overset{69}{7}00\\-\ 86\\\hline 614\end{array}$$

3e.
$$\begin{array}{r}\overset{1}{4}689\\-1832\\\hline 3857\end{array}\qquad\begin{array}{r}5284\\-4631\\\hline 1453\end{array}\qquad\begin{array}{r}3481\\-1681\\\hline 2200\end{array}$$

2. Below is an excerpt of the independent worksheet to be given to students who have just demonstrated accuracy in solving problem type 3a. The teacher made some errors in constructing the worksheet.

   a. Indicate the inappropriate examples and specify the problem type.
   b. Identify any omitted problem types that should be included on the worksheet.

a. 524	b. 504	c. 324	d. 533
−186	−328	−192	−261

e. 824	f. 602	g. 523	h. 65
−161	−159	−186	−32

3. Describe the problem type that each example below represents. List the problems in the order they are introduced. Write the grade level when each problem type is typically introduced.

63	353	48	523	346	503
−18	−182	−23	−486	−128	− 87

4. Below are 13 problems which appeared on the worksheet to be done independently by the students in Mr. Dean's math group. Next to each student's name are the problems missed by the student.

   For each student:

   a. Specify the probable cause or causes of the student's error.
   b. Describe the remediation procedure. Be specific (i.e. format part)

4023	4702	8346	342	7304	430
−1857	−2563	−1895	+185	−1286	− 82

2036	3248	3852	402	3826	8306
− 518	−1026	+1624	− 81	− 63	−1243

James

$$\begin{array}{r} \overset{39}{\cancel{402}} \\ -\ 81 \\ \hline 311 \end{array}$$
$$\begin{array}{r} \overset{29}{\cancel{8306}} \\ -1243 \\ \hline 7053 \end{array}$$

Debbie

$$\begin{array}{r} \overset{39\,1}{\cancel{4023}} \\ -1857 \\ \hline 2165 \end{array}$$
$$\begin{array}{r} \overset{6\,9\,1}{\cancel{4702}} \\ -2563 \\ \hline 1138 \end{array}$$

Dylan

$$\begin{array}{r} \overset{79}{\cancel{4702}} \\ -2563 \\ \hline 2239 \end{array}$$

Jack

$$\begin{array}{r} 342 \\ +185 \\ \hline 157 \end{array}$$
$$\begin{array}{r} 3852 \\ +1624 \\ \hline 2228 \end{array}$$

5. Specify the wording the teacher would use in the structured worksheet presentation for the problem

$$\begin{array}{r} 314 \\ -182 \\ \hline \end{array}$$

6. In presenting Figure 9.6, Part A, a board format for introducing renaming problems, the teacher asks for this problem, "Must we rename?" The student says "No." Specify the wording the teacher uses in making the correction.

$$\begin{array}{r} 57 \\ -28 \\ \hline \end{array}$$

7. Below are partial worksheets made by several teachers for the less structured part of the format for teaching students to work problems which require borrowing from the hundreds column. Two teachers constructed unacceptable lists. Identify these teachers and tell why each list is unacceptable. For each unacceptable list, specify what could be done to make the list acceptable.

a.
342	623	483	362	534	235	427	329	427
-181	-182	-193	-181	-184	+132	-193	-152	-121

b.
383	432	342	282	346	425	524	473	392
-195	-150	-186	-195	-138	+132	-187	-197	-161

c.
428	328	526	48	362	364	325	436	329
-368	-209	-385	-29	-182	-148	+132	-214	+142

10 | Multiplication

Terms and Concepts

Multiplication   The process of combining a specific number of sets, each including an equal number of elements, into a single larger set.

Multiplicand   The number of units in each equal set.

Multiplier   The number of sets in the multiplication process.

Factors   The multiplicand and the multiplier in a multiplication problem.

Product   The answer in a multiplication problem. The number designating elements in the combined set of a multiplication problem; i.e., all the equal sets summed together.

Commutative Property   The commutative property for multiplication states that changing the order of two numbers in a multiplication equation does not change the answer. If a and b are whole numbers, then $a \times b = b \times a$; e.g., $3 \times 4 = 4 \times 3$. The commutative property is very helpful in teaching multiplication facts. Once students learn that $3 \times 4 = 12$, they do not need to learn $4 \times 3 = 12$ as a new fact; rather, they can relate 4×3 to the known fact (3×4) and learn the new fact more quickly.

Associative Property   The associative property for multiplication states that if a, b, and c are whole numbers, then $(a \times b) \times c = a \times (b \times c)$; e.g., $(3 \times 2) \times 4 = 3 \times (2 \times 4)$, $(6) \times 4 = 3 \times (8)$, $24 = 24$.

Identity Element   The identity element for multiplication is 1. Any number times 1 equals that number; e.g., $4 \times 1 = 4$, $6 \times 1 = 6$. (The identity element for addition is zero: $4 + 0 = 4$, $6 + 0 = 6$. However, in multiplication a factor of zero results in a product of zero: $4 \times 0 = 0$, $6 \times 0 = 0$.) The identity element for multiplication is often applied in operations with fractional numbers. For example, before students add 1/4 and 1/2, they change 1/2 by multiplying by a fraction equal to 1: $1/2 \times 2/2 = 2/4$. Students substitute 2/4 for (1/2 + 1/4) 2/4 and complete the equation.

Students must realize that multiplying by 2/2 is acceptable only because the fraction equals the identity element for multiplication, which means the value of 1/2 has not been changed. If students do not understand the properties of the identity element for multiplication, they might make this mistake:

$$\frac{1}{4} + \frac{1}{2} = \frac{1}{4} + (\frac{1}{2} \times \frac{1}{2}) = \frac{1}{4} + \frac{1}{4} = \frac{2}{4}$$

Here 1/2 was multiplied by 1/2 to generate an appropriate denominator of fourths, but since 1/2 was not multiplied by a fraction equal to 1, the problem was changed, resulting in an incorrect answer.

Distributive Property The distributive property of multiplication over addition says that if a, b, and c are whole numbers, then

$$a \times (b + c) = a \times (b + c) = (a \times b) + (a \times c)$$

$$3 \times (2 + 4) = (3 \times 2) + (3 \times 4)$$

$$3 \times (6) \quad = \quad 6 \quad + \quad 12$$
$$18 \quad = \quad 18$$

This property is essential to understanding multiplication of multi–digit numbers such as 4 × 27. Expanded notation allows 27 to be rewritten as 20 + 7. The problem 4 × 27 then becomes 4 × (20 + 7), which equals (4 × 20) + (4 × 7). It is also important for later work with fractions, equations, and algebra.

Skill Hierarchy

Our discussion of multiplication is divided into two stages. The first stage involves presenting strategies designed to establish a concrete understanding of the process of multiplication. These strategies are usually taught to students in second grade. The second stage deals with teaching students to work multi-digit problems in which students rely on mental computation rather than on representations of concrete objects. This stage typically begins during third grade and continues into the upper grades.

Figure 10.1 includes a skill hierarchy designed to help the reader see the relationships among skills taught in the two stages. During the beginning stage, a procedure for solving simple multiplication problems with concrete or semi-concrete objects to represent the members in each group is presented. For example, when determining the total in an array such as

```
0 0 0 0
0 0 0 0
0 0 0 0
```

students are shown that they can count by 3, four times and end with 12. When solving the problem, 3 × 4, the students are taught to hold up four fingers for the second factor and then skip count by 3s for each of the four extended fingers: 3, 6, 9, 12. The preskills listed in the Skill Hierarchy Chart include skip counting, numeral skills, and equality. (The teaching procedures for skip counting are discussed in Chapter 5 "Counting.") Students should have mastered at least three skip counting series before multiplication is introduced.

Missing factor problems, in which one factor and the product are given and a missing factor must be computed (e.g., 4 × □ = 12), are also presented during this stage. In the missing factor strategy, students do not know the number of fingers to extend, since the second factor is represented by a box or unknown. For these problems, students hold up a fist and extend a finger every time they skip count, stopping at the product. In 3 × □ = 15 students extend a fist, count 3 extending one finger, count 6 extending a second finger, count 9 extending a third finger, count 12 extending a fourth finger, and count 15 extending a fifth finger. They do not count beyond 15 because they must end with 15 on both sides of the equal sign. Since they extended five fingers, the unknown factor is 5: 3 × □ = 15. The teacher then summarizes by asking how many 3s are in 15. Teachers working with intermediate grade remedial students who have some knowledge of multiplication might not present the finger strategies but might begin instruction immediately with basic fact exercises. Teaching finger strategies for multiplication to older remedial students might result in their developing an overreliance on using fingers rather than memorizing facts.

Figure 10.1 Skill Hierarchy

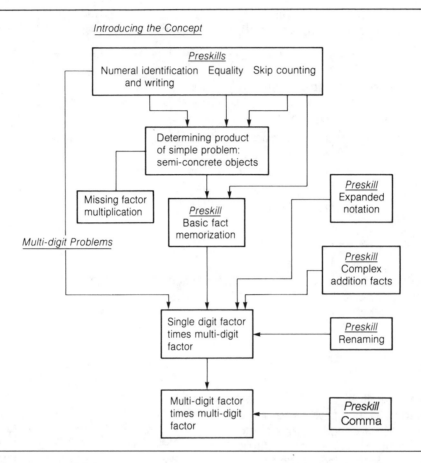

Introducing the Concept

Preskills
Numeral identification   Equality   Skip counting
and writing

Determining product
of simple problem:
semi-concrete objects

Missing factor
multiplication

Multi-digit Problems

Preskill
Basic fact
memorization

Preskill
Expanded
notation

Preskill
Complex
addition facts

Single digit factor
times multi-digit
factor

Preskill
Renaming

Multi-digit factor
times multi-digit
factor

Preskill
Comma

In the second stage, when multi-digit numbers are multiplied, students work problems without holding up fingers for the second factor and using skip counting. Since students do not skip count, a new preskill is implied: knowledge of basic multiplication facts. The 100 possible combinations of single digit factors are referred to as basic multiplication facts. Exercises to facilitate memorization of basic facts can begin a month or so after students have learned to use the count-by strategy to work multiplication problems. (See Chapter 7, "Facts," for a discussion of teaching procedures.) Besides basic multiplication facts, renaming and advanced addition facts (adding a single digit to a multi-digit addend) are also preskills. Knowledge of advanced facts like 72 + 4 is required in many problems with two or more digit factors; in working 95 × 8, students first multiply 5 times 8 and then add the 4 from the 40 to 72, the product of 9 x 8:

$$
\begin{array}{r}
4 \\
95 \\
\times\ \underline{\ 8} \\
760
\end{array}
$$

(See Chapter 8, "Addition," for procedures for teaching advanced addition facts.)

The need for teaching advanced facts can be avoided by presenting a low-stress multiplication algorithm. In the low-stress multiplication algorithm, students write out the complete answer every time they multiply. They don't carry:

$$
\begin{array}{r}
32 \\
\times \underline{24} \\
8 \\
120 \\
40 \\
\underline{600} \\
768
\end{array}
$$

Then they add the products, which seldom involves advanced facts. The major disadvantage of the low-stress algorithm, which is discussed at the end of this chapter, is its limited acceptance in U.S. schools.

Another preskill for multi-digit operations is expanded notation. When students multiply 34 × 7, they should understand that they are multiplying 4 × 7 and 30 × 7, which assumes the expanded nota-

Figure 10.2

$$\begin{array}{r}27\\ \times\ 4\end{array} = \begin{array}{r}20\\ \underline{\times\ 4}\\ 80\end{array} + \begin{array}{r}7\\ \underline{\times 4}\\ 28\end{array} = 108$$

$$20 \times 4 \quad + \quad 7 \times 4$$
$$80 \quad + \quad 28 \quad = \quad 108$$

tion skill of translating 34 into 30 and 4. The role of expanded notation in advanced multiplication operations is illustrated in Figure 10.2.

There are two basic types of multi-digit problems. The first type involves a single digit factor and a multi-digit factor. This type includes problems that do not require renaming and problems that do require renaming. In the easier group, the first product is less than 10 and, thus, renaming is not required; for example, 32×3 does not require renaming in the first product ($2 \times 3 = 6$). Problems in the harder group, like 32×7, require renaming; in $2 \times 7 = 14$ the 10 from 14 is carried. The second major type of problem involves multiplying two multi-digit numbers (e.g., 32×13, 189×43, or 342×179). A more detailed specification of the various multiplication problem types appears in Figure 9.3, the Instructional Sequence and Assessment Chart.

Introducing the Concept

The meaning of multiplication can be conveyed in various ways. Underhill (1981) lists five: sets, arrays, linear models, cross products, and addition. Jerman and Beardslee (1978) suggest that the most common ways of introducing the concept are equivalent sets and cross products. Multiplication as cross products is illustrated for 2×3 in Figure 10.4. Note that the display symbolized by 2×3 contains six pairs of objects as the product and the

display symbolized by 3×5 contains 15 pairs of objects as the product. The product, formed by all possible pairings of two sets, is also called the Cartesian product. Multiplication as equivalent sets is illustrated for 2×3 as

Beginning Multiplication

Single Digit Multiplication

Multiplication with single digit factors can be introduced when students have mastered three count-by series (2s, 5s, 9s) and are able to read and write all numerals between 1 and 99 (see pages 74–77 and 92–95). Single digit multiplication is typically introduced in mid-second grade. The format for teaching it is divided into five parts (see Figure 10.5). Since an equivalent sets representation is easier for students to understand than a Cartesian product, we introduce the multiplication concept in Part A with illustrations of equivalent sets. The students are shown a group of equivalent sets and told they can figure the total a "fast way" when each set has the same number. After verifying that each set has the same number, the teacher demonstrates how to write the problem as a times problem. Next the

Figure 10.3 Instructional Sequence and Assessment Chart

Grade Level	Problem Type	Performance Indicator
1a	Count by 10s to 100 Count by 2s to 20 Count by 5s to 60	
2a	Count by 9s to 90	
2b	One digit times one digit	$2 \times 7 =$ $9 \times 3 =$ $5 \times 6 =$
2c	Missing factor multiplication; both factors are one digit numbers	$2 \times \Box = 8$ $5 \times \Box = 10$ $9 \times \Box = 36$
2d	Count by 4s to 40 Count by 25s to 100 Count by 7s to 70 Count by 3s to 30	
3a	Count by 8s to 80 Count by 6s to 60	
3b	One digit factor times two digit factor; no carrying	$\begin{array}{r} 43 \\ \times\ 2 \\ \hline \end{array}$ $\begin{array}{r} 31 \\ \times\ 5 \\ \hline \end{array}$ $\begin{array}{r} 32 \\ \times\ 4 \\ \hline \end{array}$
3c	One digit factor times two digit factor; carrying	$\begin{array}{r} 35 \\ \times\ 5 \\ \hline \end{array}$ $\begin{array}{r} 43 \\ \times\ 9 \\ \hline \end{array}$ $\begin{array}{r} 17 \\ \times\ 2 \\ \hline \end{array}$
3d	One digit factor times two or three digit factor; problem written horizontally	$5 \times 35 =$ $9 \times 34 =$ $7 \times 56 =$
4a	One digit factor times three digit factor	$\begin{array}{r} 758 \\ \times\ 2 \\ \hline \end{array}$ $\begin{array}{r} 364 \\ \times\ 5 \\ \hline \end{array}$ $\begin{array}{r} 534 \\ \times\ 9 \\ \hline \end{array}$
4b	One digit factor times three digit factor; zero in tens column	$\begin{array}{r} 405 \\ \times\ 3 \\ \hline \end{array}$ $\begin{array}{r} 302 \\ \times\ 5 \\ \hline \end{array}$ $\begin{array}{r} 105 \\ \times\ 9 \\ \hline \end{array}$
4c	One digit factor times three digit factor; horizontal alignment	$352 \times 9 =$ $7 \times 342 =$ $235 \times 5 =$
4d	Two digit factor times two digit factor	$\begin{array}{r} 37 \\ \times 25 \\ \hline \end{array}$ $\begin{array}{r} 26 \\ \times 52 \\ \hline \end{array}$ $\begin{array}{r} 34 \\ \times 25 \\ \hline \end{array}$
4e	Two digit factor times three digit factor	$\begin{array}{r} 324 \\ \times\ 29 \\ \hline \end{array}$ $\begin{array}{r} 343 \\ \times\ 95 \\ \hline \end{array}$ $\begin{array}{r} 423 \\ \times\ 29 \\ \hline \end{array}$
5a	Three digit factor times three digit factor	$\begin{array}{r} 284 \\ \times 346 \\ \hline \end{array}$ $\begin{array}{r} 242 \\ \times 195 \\ \hline \end{array}$ $\begin{array}{r} 624 \\ \times 283 \\ \hline \end{array}$
5b	Three digit factor times three digit factor; zero in tens column of multiplier	$\begin{array}{r} 382 \\ \times 506 \\ \hline \end{array}$ $\begin{array}{r} 320 \\ \times 402 \\ \hline \end{array}$ $\begin{array}{r} 523 \\ \times 703 \\ \hline \end{array}$

Figure 10.4

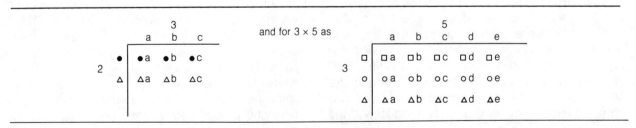

teacher demonstrates how to use skip counting to determine the total. In the final step of Part A, students count the members of the sets one at a time to verify that the answer derived through multiplication is correct. Part A should be included only the first 2 or 3 days the format is presented.

In Part B, students learn to translate a multiplication statement into terms that indicate how the problem is to be solved. For example, in initial problems, the multiplication sign (×) is read as "countby." Students are taught to read the multiplication statement 5 × 2 = as "countby 5, two times." By reading the statement this way students know exactly what to do to derive an answer. "Count by 5, two times" tells them to extend 2 fingers for the number of times they skip count and then to skip count by 5s. After several weeks, students learn to read problems in the conventional manner; e.g., 4 × 3 is read 4 times 3.

When reading multiplication problems in Part B, students begin with the multiplication sign saying "count by" and then say the first number, 5 × 3 is read "count by 5, three times." Since translating multiplication problems differs from reading addition or subtraction problems where students read in a strict left to right order, multiplication problems require a slightly different signal. The teacher should point under both the numeral and the times sign when having students translate problems. With low-performing students, the teacher may even need to point under the sign first, then point to the first number to emphasize that the times sign is read before the numeral.

In Part C, the teacher guides students in solving several multiplication examples in a structured board presentation. First, students read and translate a problem. They hold up the appropriate number of fingers. Then the teacher models the skip counting while touching each extended finger. Next the students skip count each time they touch an extended finger. Finally, the students work three new problems without any teacher modeling.

Part D is the structured worksheet presentation. The teacher has the students extend the appropriate number of fingers, identify the skip counting number, and then work the problem. Part E is the less structured worksheet part of the format where students work a set of problems on their own with the teacher carefully monitoring their performance. After students develop accuracy, they are given 5 to 10 problems daily in independent worksheet exercises.

When having the students count and touch their fingers in step 2, Part C, the teacher must be sure that students coordinate saying the numbers with touching their extended fingers. Low performers may say the first number in the skip counting series before touching the first extended finger; in 2 × 5 students may say "two" and then when they touch their finger, count 4, continuing to count 6, 8, 10, 12. The correction for this error is a model, a lead in which the teacher actually guides the student's hand to coordinate touching and counting, and then a test in which the student touches and counts alone. The teacher should then present a series of examples for the students to practice only the touching and counting and not the entire sequence of steps in Part C. Instead of presenting all the steps, the teacher would tell the student the problem and how many fingers to hold up and then have the student touch and count. For example, the teacher would present a series of examples using this wording: "You're going to count by 5, three times. Hold up three fingers. Good. Now count by 5. Remember to touch each finger as you count by 5."

There are two example selection guidelines: First, example selection should be coordinated with count-by instructions. The first digit in the multiplication problem should be from a skip counting series the students have previously mastered. For example, a problem such as 6 × 7 would not be included until students have mastered counting by 6s. As a general rule, problems with a specific number as the first digit should be included in multiplication tasks after students have practiced saying that count-by series for about 2 weeks. Second, there should be a mix of problems. As a general rule, no more than two or three problems in a row should have the same numeral as the multiplicand or multiplier. Below is an example of an acceptable set of examples:

5 × 2	2 × 2
2 × 4	5 × 4
9 × 3	9 × 1
9 × 5	5 × 3

The mix of problems helps to ensure that students develop the habit of carefully attending to both factors.

Missing Factor Multiplication

Missing factor, or algebra, multiplication is not only a useful skill in its own right, but is also a critical preskill for the simple division strategies, which are discussed in the next chapter. In order to solve an algebra multiplication problem, students must de-

Figure 10.5 Format for Single Digit Multiplication

Day	Part A Pictorial Demonstration Problems	Part B Analyzing Problems	Part C Structured Board Presentation Problems	Part D Structured Worksheet Problems	Part E Less Structured Worksheet Problems	Part F Supervised Practice Problems	Part G Independent Problems
1	2	5					
2	2	5	3				
3		3	5	5			
4			3	5	5		
5-Till accurate						10	
Till fluent							10

PART A: Pictorial Demonstration

TEACHER   **STUDENTS**

Write on board:

    ▭   ▭   ▭
    ▭   ▭   ▭
    ▭   ▭   ▭
    ▭   ▭   ▭
    ▭   ▭   ▭
    5   5   5
    ___

1. "WE'RE GOING TO LEARN A FAST WAY TO WORK
   PROBLEMS THAT TALK ABOUT THE SAME NUMBER
   TIME AND TIME AGAIN." Point to each column and ask,
   "HOW MANY IN THIS GROUP?"   "5"
   "ARE WE TALKING ABOUT THE SAME NUMBER TIME
   AND TIME AGAIN?"   "Yes"

2. "WHEN WE TALK ABOUT THE SAME NUMBER TIME
   AND TIME AGAIN, WE MAKE A TIMES PROBLEM. WHAT
   NUMBER ARE WE TALKING ABOUT TIME AND TIME
   AGAIN?"   "5"
   "SO WE WRITE 5." Write 5. "HOW MANY 5s DO WE HAVE?"   "3"
   TO CORRECT: "COUNT THE GROUPS OF FIVE." Point to
              each group as students count.
   "SO I WRITE TIMES 3." Write × 3.

3. "THE PROBLEM SAYS WHAT?"   "5 × 3"
   "WE FIGURE OUT 5 TIMES 3 A FAST WAY. WE COUNT BY
   5s THREE TIMES: (Point to each group of 5 as you count)
   5, 10, 15. THERE ARE 15 IN ALL."

4. "LET'S COUNT BY 1s AND MAKE SURE 15 IS RIGHT."
   Point to each member as students count. "ARE THERE 15?"   "Yes"
   "SO WE CAN COUNT THE FAST WAY WHEN WE TALK
   ABOUT THE SAME NUMBER TIME AND TIME AGAIN."
   Repeat steps 1-4 with
   ☐   ☐   ☐   ☐
   ☐   ☐   ☐   ☐

PART B: Analyzing Problems

Write on board:
    5 ×
   10 ×
    2 ×
    9 ×

Figure 10.5 cont'd
TEACHER   **STUDENTS**

Reading Partial Problems

1. Point to ×. "THIS SIGN TELLS YOU TO COUNT BY. WHAT
   DOES IT TELL YOU TO DO?"   "Count by"

2. Point to 5 ×. "SO THIS TELLS YOU TO COUNT BY 5. WHAT
   DOES THIS TELL YOU TO DO?"   "Count by 5"

3. Point to 10 ×. "WHAT DOES THIS TELL YOU TO DO?"   "Count by 10"

4. Point to 2 ×. "WHAT DOES THIS TELL YOU DO TO?"   "Count by 2"

5. Point to 9 ×. "WHAT DOES THIS TELL YOU TO DO?"   "Count by 9."
   Repeat step 5 with all examples.

Reading Entire Problems

6. Point to 5 ×. "WHAT DOES THIS TELL YOU TO DO?"   "Count by 5"
   Write 3 after 5 × : 5 × 3. "NOW THIS PROBLEM TELLS YOU
   TO COUNT BY 5 THREE TIMES. WHAT DOES THIS
   PROBLEM TELL YOU TO DO?" Pause, signal.   "Count by 5, three times"

7. Point to 10 ×. "WHAT DOES THIS PROBLEM TELL YOU
   TO DO?"   "Count by 10"
   Write 4 after 10. "WHAT DOES THIS PROBLEM TELL
   YOU TO DO NOW?" Pause, signal.   "Count by 10, four times"

8. Point to 2 ×. "WHAT DOES THIS PROBLEM TELL YOU
   TO DO?"   "Count by 2"
   Write 5 after 2 ×. "WHAT DOES THIS PROBLEM TELL
   YOU TO DO NOW?" Pause, signal.   "Count by 2, five times"

9. Point to 9 ×. "WHAT DOES THIS PROBLEM TELL YOU
   TO DO?"   "Count by 9"
   Write 4 after 9 × : 9 × 4. "WHAT DOES THE PROBLEM
   TELL YOU TO DO NOW?"   "Count by 9, four times"

10. "LET'S START OVER." Point to 5 × 3. "WHAT DOES
    THIS PROBLEM TELL YOU TO DO?"   "Count by 5, three times"
    Repeat step 10 with each problem. Give individual turns to
    several students.

PART C: Structured Board Presentation

Write on board: 2 × 5 = ☐

1. "WHAT DOES THIS PROBLEM TELL US TO DO?" Point
   to problem as students read.   "Count by 2, five times"
   "HOW MANY TIMES ARE WE GOING TO COUNT?"   "5"
   "SO I'LL PUT UP FIVE FINGERS. WATCH ME COUNT BY 2,
   FIVE TIMES: (Count and touch fingers.) 2, 4, 6, 8, 10."

2. "NOW IT'S YOUR TURN TO COUNT BY 2, FIVE TIMES.
   HOW MANY TIMES ARE YOU GOING TO COUNT?"   "5"
   "HOLD UP YOUR FINGERS." Monitor students' responses.
   "YOU'RE COUNTING BY 2, FIVE TIMES. WHAT NUMBER
   ARE YOU GOING TO COUNT BY?"   "2"
   "TOUCH A FINGER EVERY TIME YOU COUNT. COUNT-
   ING BY 2. GET READY, COUNT." Clap at intervals of
   2 seconds.   Students touch an extended finger
                                                               every time they count: 2, 4, 6, 8, 10.
   "WHAT NUMBER DID YOU END WITH?"   "10"
   "SO I'LL WRITE A 10 IN THE BOX." Write 10.

Figure 10.5 cont'd

TEACHER　　　　　　　　　　　　　　　　　　　**STUDENTS**

3. Write on board: $2 \times 3 = \square$
   "WHAT DOES THIS PROBLEM TELL US TO DO?"
   Pause, signal.　　　　　　　　　　　　　　　　"Count by 2, three times"
   "HOW MANY TIMES ARE YOU GOING TO COUNT?"　"3"
   "HOLD UP YOUR FINGERS." Monitor students' responses.
   "WHAT NUMBER ARE YOU GOING TO COUNT BY?"　"2"
   "GET READY TO COUNT." Clap at intervals of 2 seconds.　Students touch an extended finger
   　　　　　　　　　　　　　　　　　　　　　every time they count: 2, 4, 6.
   "HOW MANY DID YOU END WITH?"　　　　　　　"6"
   "SO I'LL WRITE 6 IN THE BOX." Write 6. "WHEN WE
   COUNT BY 2, THREE TIMES WHAT DO WE END WITH?"　"6"

4. Repeat step 3 with $5 \times 4 = \square$, $10 \times 3 = \square$, $2 \times 4 = \square$,
   $9 \times 3 = \square$.

   Give individual turns to several students.

PART D: Structured Worksheet

　a.　$5 \times 3 = \square$

　b.　$10 \times 4 = \square$

　c.　$2 \times 6 = \square$

1. "TOUCH PROBLEM a. WHAT DOES THE PROBLEM TELL
   YOU TO DO?"　　　　　　　　　　　　　　　　"Count by 5, three times"
   "HOW MANY TIMES ARE YOU GOING TO COUNT?"　"3"
   "HOLD UP YOUR FINGERS." Monitor responses.　Students hold up three fingers.
   "WHAT NUMBER ARE YOU COUNTING BY?"　　　"5"

2. "GET READY. COUNT." Clap at intervals of 1 second.　Students count 5, 10, 15, touching
   　　　　　　　　　　　　　　　　　　　　　each extended finger.
   "WHEN YOU COUNT BY 5, THREE TIMES WHAT DO
   YOU END WITH?"　　　　　　　　　　　　　　"15"
   "WRITE 15 IN THE BOX."
   Repeat steps 1 and 2 with remaining problems.

PART E: Less Structured Worksheet

Students have worksheets with variety of
multiplication and addition problems.

　a.　$5 \times 4 = \square$

　b.　$5 + 4 = \square$

　c.　$10 \times 3 = \square$

　d.　$10 \times 5 = \square$

　e.　$10 + 5 = \square$

1. "TOUCH PROBLEM a. PUT YOUR FINGER UNDER THE
   SIGN. WHAT DOES THE PROBLEM TELL YOU TO DO,
   PLUS OR COUNT BY?"　　　　　　　　　　　　"Count by"
   "SAY THE PROBLEM."　　　　　　　　　　　　"Count by 5, four times"
   "WORK IT AND WRITE HOW MANY YOU END WITH IN
   THE BOX."

   Repeat step 1 with remaining problems.

termine the number of times they count by a certain number. For example, in the problem $5 \times \square = 15$, students figure out how many times they have to count by 5 to get to 15. Students extend a finger every time they skip count; they extend one finger when they say 5, a second when they say 10, and a third when they say 15. The three extended fingers represent the answer.

Algebra multiplication problems can be introduced after students have demonstrated mastery in solving regular multiplication problems. A gap of at least 3 to 4 weeks between the introduction of regular multiplication and problems with missing factors is recommended to enable students to develop this mastery.

The format appears in Figure 10.6. In Part A, students learn to translate the problem type; $5 \times \square = 20$ is translated as "count by 5 how many times to end with 20." Next the strategy is modeled. The teacher holds up a closed fist to indicate that the number of times to count is unknown and then extends a finger every time she skip counts. Then the teacher tests the students. In Part B, the structured worksheet, students apply the strategy as the teacher guides them to hold up a fist, to identify the skip counting number and the product, and to extend a finger each time they count. Part C is the less structured worksheet. In that part, students are taught to discriminate between regular problems and algebra problems ($2 \times 8 = \square$, $2 \times \square = 8$).

Example selection guidelines are basically the same as for regular multiplication. The first factor in the problem should represent a count-by series the students have mastered. A mix of numbers should appear as the first factor. Worksheets for parts C, D, and E should include an equal mix of regular multiplication and multiplication problems with missing factors.

Diagnosis and Remediation

Four errors—two component skill and two strategy—account for the majority of missed problems. The first type of error results from students' skip counting incorrectly. Students may either forget a number or switch from one series to another. Although this count-by component skill error is usually obvious on worksheets, it can only be diagnosed for sure by asking students to work problems aloud. A worksheet illustrating this count-by component skill error appears below:

$$5 \times 4 = 20 \qquad 9 \times 3 = 27$$
$$10 \times 3 = 30 \qquad 10 \times 6 = 60$$
$$2 \times 7 = 14 \qquad 9 \times 5 = 47$$
$$9 \times 6 = 50 \qquad 5 \times 2 = 10$$

Figure 10.6 Format for Algebra Multiplication

Day	Part A Structured Board Presentation Problems	Part B Structured Worksheet Problems	Part C Less Structured Worksheet Problems	Part D Supervised Problems	Part E Independent Problems
1	5				
2	3	5			
3		3	6		
4-6			6	4	
Till accurate				10	
Till fluent					8-10

PART A: Structured Board Presentation

TEACHER	STUDENTS

Write on board: $5 \times \square = 20$

Model and Test Translation

1. "HERE'S A NEW KIND OF PROBLEM. HERE'S WHAT IT TELLS US TO DO." Point to each symbol as you read. "COUNT BY 5, HOW MANY TIMES, TO END WITH 20?"

2. Point to $\square$. "DOES THIS PROBLEM TELL HOW MANY TIMES WE COUNT BY 5?"   "No"
"RIGHT, WE HAVE TO FIGURE OUT HOW MANY TIMES WE COUNT BY 5."

Figure 10.6 cont'd

<table>
<tr><td></td><td></td></tr>
</table>

3. "YOUR TURN TO READ THE PROBLEM. I'LL TOUCH AND
   YOU READ." Touch ×, then 5, □ = and 20.
   Repeat step 3 until students respond acceptably.

                                                "Count by 5 how many times to
end with 20"

   Model Strategy

4. "LET'S WORK THIS PROBLEM. WHAT ARE WE GOING
   TO COUNT BY?"

         "5"

   "DO WE KNOW HOW MANY TIMES WE COUNT?"

         "No"

   "I HOLD UP A FIST TO SHOW THAT I DON'T KNOW HOW
   MANY TIMES TO COUNT. HOW MANY ARE WE GOING
   TO END WITH?"

         "20"

5. "MY TURN. I'M GOING TO COUNT BY 5 AND END
   WITH 20." Begin with a closed fist, then hold up a finger
   each time you count. "FIVE, TEN, FIFTEEN, TWENTY. I
   PUT UP A FINGER EACH TIME I COUNTED. HERE'S HOW
   MANY TIMES I COUNTED. HOW MANY?"

         "4"

   "SO HOW MANY 5s IN 20?"

         "4"

   "I WRITE A 4 IN THE SPACE." Write 4 in box.

   Test Strategy

5. "NOW IT'S YOUR TURN." Erase 4 in the space. "SAY
   WHAT THE PROBLEM TELLS US TO DO." Point to 5 × □ = 20.

         "Count by 5 how many times to
end with 20"

   "YOU HAVE TO FIGURE OUT HOW MANY TIMES WE
   COUNT. WHAT DO YOU HAVE TO FIGURE OUT?"

         "How many times we count"

   "WHAT ARE YOU COUNTING BY?"

         "5"

   "DO YOU KNOW HOW MANY TIMES TO COUNT?"

         "No"

   "SO HOLD UP A FIST. WHAT NUMBER ARE YOU GOING
   TO END WITH?"

         "20"

6. "EACH TIME I CLAP YOU COUNT AND PUT UP A FINGER."
   Students are to hold up a finger each time you clap. Clap at
   2 second intervals.

         Students count 5, 10, 15, 20,
putting up a finger each time
they count.

   "NOW COUNT YOUR FINGERS AND SEE HOW MANY
   TIMES YOU COUNTED. (pause) HOW MANY 5s IN 20?"

         "4"

   "YES, SO WHAT DO WE WRITE IN THE SPACE?"

         "4"

   "RIGHT." Write 4.

   Repeat steps 5 and 6 with 2 × □ = 14,
   10 × □ = 30, 9 × □ = 36, 2 × □ = 6.

PART B: Structured Worksheet

   a.   5 × □ = 20
   b.   2 × □ = 10
   c. 10 × □ = 40
   d.   9 × □ = 18
   e.   5 × □ = 30

1. "TOUCH PROBLEM a. WHAT DOES THE PROBLEM TELL
   YOU TO DO?"

         "Count by 5 how many times to
end with 20"

2. "WHAT DO YOU HAVE TO FIGURE OUT?"

         "How many times we count"

   PUT UP YOUR FIST. WHAT ARE YOU COUNTING BY?"

         "5s"

   "WHAT ARE YOU GOING TO END WITH?"

         "20"

Figure 10.6 cont'd

TEACHER **STUDENTS**

3. "COUNT AND PUT UP A FINGER EACH TIME YOU COUNT. GET READY. COUNT." Clap at 2 second intervals.

Students count 5, 10, 15, 20, putting up a finger each time they count.

"HOW MANY TIMES DID YOU COUNT?" "4"
"WRITE 4 IN THE BOX."
Repeat steps 1-3 with remaining problems.

PART C: Less Structured Worksheet

Students have worksheets with an equal mix of regular and missing factor problems

a. $5 \times \square = 10$

b. $9 \times 3 = \square$

c. $2 \times \square = 8$

d. $2 \times 6 = \square$

1. "TOUCH PROBLEM a."

2. "WHAT DOES THE PROBLEM TELL YOU TO DO?" "Count by 5 how many times to end with 10?"

3. "WHAT ARE YOU COUNTING BY?" "5"

4. "DOES THE PROBLEM TELL YOU HOW MANY TIMES TO COUNT?" "No"

5. "SHOW ME WHAT YOU HOLD UP." Students hold up fist.

6. "WORK THE PROBLEM AND WRITE THE ANSWER IN THE BOX."
Repeat steps 1-6 with remaining problems.

Note that of the eight problems on the worksheet, only two were missed. Both these missed problems had 9 as one factor and a number of 5 or more as the other factor. The errors indicate a student difficulty in remembering the upper end of the count-by 9 series. To remedy the count-by skill deficit, the teacher provides oral practice on counting by 9s for several lessons. The student shouldn't be required to solve any multiplication problems involving counting by 9 until he has demonstrated that he can accurately count by 9s (see page 77 for more specifics on remedying count-by errors).

The second error pattern results in answers that are consistently off by one count-by number. For example, in regular multiplication problems a student might answer a set of problems like this: $9 \times 6 = 63$, $7 \times 6 = 49$, $5 \times 6 = 35$. Quite often the cause of this error involves the student's saying the number for the first group and then counting. When students say a count-by number for the first group in multiplication, their answer is too large; in 4×3, a student may count 4, then 8, 12, 16 as he touches the three raised fingers.

To remedy this type of error, the teacher would present Part B, the structured worksheet part of the multiplication format, correcting by modeling and leading.

The exercise would be continued until the students are able to respond correctly to four consecutive problems. Several days of practice on this exercise should be provided before students are given problems to work independently again.

The third type of error occurs when students confuse the multiplication and addition operations. The remediation procedure involves re-presenting the less structured format for regular multiplication, which includes a mix of multiplication and addition problems. For remediation purposes, the teacher would instruct students to circle the sign in the problems before working them.

The fourth type of error common to single digit multiplication occurs when students confuse regular and missing factor multiplication, writing $5 \times \boxed{50} = 10$ or $2 \times \boxed{8} = 4$. The remediation procedure involves re-presenting the less structured part of the algebra multiplication format, which contains a mix of regular and algebra multiplication problems. The teacher should present the less structured worksheet presentation with about 10 problems. She then has students work problems in front of her but with no teacher guidance, except to correct student errors. This remediation is continued daily until students correctly answer 9 of 10 problems without teacher assistance for several days in a row. The diagnosis and remediation information is summarized in Figure 10.7.

Multi-digit Operations

There are two algorithms presented in most commercial programs to solve problems with a multi-digit factor. One algorithm is commonly referred to as the long form or low-stress algorithm. The other algorithm is referred to as the short form. The long form and short form are illustrated in Figure 10.8.

Both algorithms are based on the distributive property of multiplication which states that the product of a multiplier and a multiplicand will be the same as the sum of a series of products from multiplying individual number pairs. For example, 3 × 24 = (3 × 20) + (3 × 4).

The long form algorithm's advantages are that it does not alternate between multiplication and addition and seldom requires renaming, Moreover, it clearly shows the distributive property of multiplication. Its disadvantage, however, is that in problems involving multi-digit factors, many numerals must be written as partial products:

$$\begin{array}{r} 245 \\ \times\ 37 \\ \hline 35 \\ 280 \\ 1400 \\ 150 \\ 1200 \\ \underline{6000} \\ 9065 \end{array}$$

Figure 10.7 Diagnosis and Remediation of Single Digit Multiplication Errors

Error Patterns	Diagnosis	Remediation Procedures	Remediation Examples
a. 9 × 6 = 51 8 × 4 = 32 6 × 5 = 30 9 × 3 = 26	Component skill: Student doesn't know count-by 9 series.	Part B–Count by Preskill Format, Figure 5.10	Practice on counting by 9s.
b. 9 × 6 = 63 8 × 4 = 40 6 × 5 = 36	Component skill: Student not coordinating touching and counting.	Part C–Figure 10.5 for single digit multiplication.	Regular multiplication problems.
c. 9 × 6 = 15 8 + 4 = 12 6 × 5 = 11	Strategy: Student is confusing addition with multiplication; not attending to the sign in the problems.	Less structured worksheet of regular multiplication format, Figure 10.5. Instructions to circle the sign before working the problem.	Mix of addition and multiplication problems.
d. 2 × 16 = 8 6 × 5 = 30 9 × 6 = 54 4 × 32 = 8	Strategy: Student is confusing regular multiplication and missing factor multiplication.	Less structured worksheet of format for problems with missing factors, Figure 10.6.	Mix of regular multiplication problems and problems with missing factor.

Figure 10.8

	Long Form	Short Form
		21
	232	232
	× 7	× 7
	14	1624
	210	
	1400	
	1624	

The advantage of the short form algorithm lies in its relative efficiency in solving problems with multi-digit factors and its widespread usage. Its disadvantage lies with the difficulty a student may have in understanding what is "going on" when he alternates between addition and multiplication and the inclusion of complex addition facts.

In this section we discuss in detail the procedures for teaching the short form algorithm. The main reason we discuss this algorithm in detail is that it is the one used in the majority of classrooms.

The section on the short form algorithm is divided into two parts. The first deals with problems in which one of the factors is a single digit number and the other factor a multi-digit number. The second part deals with problems in which each factor is a multi-digit number.

Single Digit Factor and Multi-Digit Factor

Multiplication problems in which a single digit factor and multi-digit factor are multiplied usually are introduced during mid-third grade. This group of problems includes problems 3b through 4c on the Instructional Sequence and Assessment Chart.

PRESKILLS Three preskills necessary to work these problems are (a) multiplication facts, (b) place value skills including expanded notation and placing a comma in the proper position when writing an answer in the thousands, and (c) advanced addition facts in which a single digit number is added to a two digit number.

Basic multiplication facts include all the possible combinations of single digit factors. Memorizing basic facts is a very demanding and lengthy process. It is not realistic to imagine that most students will have memorized all basic multiplication facts by mid-third grade. Thus, initially problems should be limited so that they include only basic facts the teacher is sure students have memorized. As students learn more basic facts, they should be integrated into multiplication problems.

The place value skill of expanded notation is needed if the student is to understand the renaming procedure in the short form algorithm. Procedures for teaching place value concepts appear in Chapter 6.

The second place value skill, placing a comma, seems trivial but needs to be taught. After completing problems with larger numbers, students are expected to place a comma in the answer. The procedure is simple. The teacher presents a rule, "The comma is written between the hundreds and

thousands." Then the teacher models and tests application of the rule. The teacher writes a series of three, four, and five digit numbers on the board, then demonstrates how to find where to place the comma. Starting at the ones column, the teacher points to each numeral, saying "ones, tens, hundreds, thousands" and then places the comma between the hundreds and thousands columns. After modeling several examples, the teacher tests the students.

Advanced addition facts involve adding a single digit number to a two digit number mentally (e.g., 35 + 7, 27 + 3, 42 + 5). Advanced addition facts were discussed earlier in the addition chapter as a preskill for adding a series of multi-digit numbers. Advanced addition facts are utilized in the short form multiplication algorithm, when the student adds the carried units to the product of a column. For example, in the problem 35 × 9, the student first multiplies 9 × 5 and ends with 45. A 4 is carried to the tens column and a 5 written under the ones column:

$$
\begin{array}{r}
4 \\
35 \\
\times\ 9 \\
\hline
5
\end{array}
$$

The student then multiplies 9 x 3 for a product of 27. Next the student must add the carried 4 to 27:

$$
\begin{array}{r}
4 \\
35 \\
\times\ 9 \\
\hline
315
\end{array}
$$

Adding 27 + 4 is an advanced addition fact.

There are two types of advanced addition facts: an easier type and a more difficult type. In the easier type, the sum has the same number of tens as the original two digit addend: $\underline{6}4 + 3 = \underline{6}7$, $\underline{4}3 + 5 = \underline{4}8$, $\underline{7}5 + 4 = \underline{7}9$. In the more difficult type, the sum has a tens number one higher than the original two digit addend: $\underline{3}6 + 7 = \underline{4}3$, $\underline{5}8 + 8 = \underline{6}6$, $\underline{4}8 + 4 = \underline{5}2$, $\underline{4}9 + 9 = \underline{5}8$. Advanced addition fact teaching would begin in early second grade. First, students are taught to add a single digit number to a teen number: 14 + 3, 16 + 2, then 17 + 6, 15 + 8, etc. After several months' practice with teen numbers, students are introduced to advanced facts with tens numbers—first with easier facts, 24 + 3, 38 + 2, then with more difficult facts, 49 + 6, 45 + 8, etc. Practice would be continued for many months to facilitate development of fluency. Procedures for teaching both the easier and more difficult types appear in Chapter 8, "Addition."

FORMAT Column multiplication is introduced with simple problems involving no renaming. The product of the numbers in the ones column is less than 10:

$$\begin{array}{r}34\\ \times\ 2\\\hline\end{array}\qquad \begin{array}{r}43\\ \times\ 2\\\hline\end{array}\qquad \begin{array}{r}31\\ \times\ 5\\\hline\end{array}\qquad \begin{array}{r}32\\ \times\ 4\\\hline\end{array}$$

When presenting this type of problem, the teacher points out that the student first multiplies the 1s and then the 10s. A format is not included since it would be quite similar to the one that involves renaming (see Figure 10.9).

Problems with carrying are introduced several days after noncarrying problems have been presented. In Part A of the format (Figure 10.9), the structured board presentation, the students break the problem into two parts. The two parts for 5×47 are 5×7 and 5×4 10s. After multiplying in the ones column, the teacher models how to carry, multiply the second part of the problem, add the carried number, and write the answer. Parts B and C provide structured and less structured worksheet practice.

Note in the format the balance between explaining to students the rationale for the procedure and then providing clear guidance about the mechanics of working the problem. Also note the use of a place value grid. The purpose of the grid is to initially prompt the students regarding the importance of placing numerals from the product in the proper column. Proper placement of numerals in the product, though not a critical component of these problem types, is critical in problems with two multi-digit factors. The place value grid would appear on students' worksheets for about a week and then be dropped. The day the grid is dropped, the teacher would lead the students through several problems, pointing out the need to write numerals in the proper position. The teacher would also examine students' worksheets carefully for column alignment errors.

Multi-digit problems written horizontally are introduced after students can correctly work vertically aligned problems. The teacher presents a strategy in which the students rewrite the problem vertically, writing the one digit factor under the multi-digit factor. In later grades, the teacher presents a strategy in which students multiply horizontally, writing the product and carrying:

$$5 \times \overset{1\,2}{324} = 1620$$

This strategy would be taught prior to introducing fraction multiplication:

$$\frac{5}{4} \times 324$$

and division problems with multi-digit divisors:

$$324\overline{)1620}^{\,5}$$

both of which involve horizontal multiplication.

Problems with a one digit factor and a three digit factor (e.g., 243×5 and 342×9) are introduced in late third grade. The format for presenting problems of this type is essentially the same as the format for introducing problems with a two digit factor. The same basic explanation as for carrying from the ones to the tens column would be used in presenting carrying from the tens to the hundreds column. In 543×5 students multiply the four 10s and add the carried 10. Then the teacher explains that they can't have twenty-one 10s in the tens column so they write a 2 over the hundreds column to show twenty 10s and one 10 is written under the tens column. Note that at this point, the teacher need not require the students to say that twenty 10s equal 200 but simply to write the 2 in the hundreds column.

A special problem type includes a zero in the tens column of the three digit factor (e.g., 403×5 and 306×2). Students may have trouble adding the carried 10 to zero. This type of problem is introduced a week after problems with a three digit factor are introduced. Several problems of this subgroup should be presented daily for about 2 weeks. The first several days the teacher models a few problems, then closely supervises students as they work the problems.

EXAMPLE SELECTION Two rules govern example selection. First, the basic facts included in problems should be those which the student has already mastered. Second, less structured, supervised practice and independent worksheets should include a mixture of problems. About 45% of the worksheet should contain problems of the most currently introduced type, and about 45% previously introduced multiplication problems. About 10% of the worksheet should contain addition problems to keep students in the habit of examining the sign in a problem carefully before working it.

SELF-CHECKING In mid-fourth grade, or whenever students become proficient in multiplying by a one digit factor and dividing by a one digit divisor, students should be taught to check their answers. A checking procedure for multiplication is to divide the answer by the one digit factor. If the quotient equals the other factor, the answer is correct. The teacher introduces checking on a worksheet exer-

Figure 10.9 Format for One Digit Factor Times Two Digit Factor—Renaming

Day	Part A	Part B	Part C	Part D	Part E
	Structured Board Presentation Problems	Structured Worksheet Problems	Less Structured Worksheet Problems	Supervised Practice Problems	Independent Practice Problems
1-2	4				
3-4	2	5			
5-6		3	6		
7-accurate			2	8	
Till fluent					8

PART A: Structured Board Presentation

TEACHER **STUDENTS**

Write on board

```
  |4|7|
×| |5|
```

1. "READ THE PROBLEM." — "5 times 47"

2. "FIRST WE MULTIPLY 5 × 7."

3. "WHAT DO WE DO FIRST?" — "Multiply 5 times 7"
   "NEXT WE MULTIPLY 5 × FOUR 10s"

4. "WHAT DO WE DO NEXT?" — "Multiply 5 times 4 10s"
   Repeat steps 1-4 until students respond acceptably.

5. "WHAT IS 5 × 7?" — "35"
   "WE CAN'T WRITE 35 IN THE ONES COLUMN, WE MUST
   CARRY THE 10s. HOW MANY 10s ARE IN 35?" — "3"
   "I PUT 3 ABOVE THE TENS COLUMN AND PUT A PLUS
   SIGN IN FRONT OF IT TO REMIND US TO PLUS THOSE
   10s."

```
 |4|7|
×| |5|
 | |5|
```

6. "THIRTY-FIVE HAS THREE 10s AND HOW MANY 1s?" — "5"
   "I WRITE THE 5 UNDER THE ONES COLUMN. NOW WE
   MULTIPLY 5 × 4 10s. HOW MANY 10s IS 5 × 4 10s?" — "20"
   Pause, signal.

7. "NOW WE ADD THE THREE 10s WE CARRIED. WHAT IS
   20 + 3?" Pause, signal. — "23"
   YES, TWENTY-THREE 10s. I WRITE TWO 100s AND
   THREE 10s IN THE ANSWER."

```
 | |4|7|
×| | |5|
 |2|3|5|
```

8. "WHAT DOES 5 × 47 EQUAL?" — "235"
   Repeat steps 1-8 with

```
  36      42      34
× 2     × 9     × 5
```

PART B: Structured Worksheet

Students have worksheet with these problems:

```
a. |2|5|   b. |1|4|   c. |4|8|   d. |7|6|   e. |3|7|
 × | |9|    × | |7|    × | |2|    × | |5|    × | |2|
```

Figure 10.9 cont'd

TEACHER	**STUDENTS**

1. "READ PROBLEM a."
   "WHAT NUMBERS DO WE MULTIPLY FIRST?"
   "WHAT IS 9 × 5?" Pause, signal.
   "HOW MANY 10s IN 45?"
   "WRITE PLUS 4 OVER THE TENS COLUMN. HOW MANY
   1s IN 45?"
   "WRITE THE 5 UNDER THE ONES COLUMN."

   "9 times 25"
   "9 × 5"
   "45"
   "4"

   "5"

2. "WHAT NUMBERS DO WE TIMES NEXT?"
   "WHAT IS 9 × 2?" Pause, signal.
   "WHAT DO WE DO NOW?"
   "WHAT IS 18 + 4?" Pause, signal.
   "WRITE 22 NEXT TO THE 5 UNDER THE LINE. WHAT
   IS 9 × 25?"
   "READ THE WHOLE PROBLEM."
   Repeat steps 1 and 2 with remaining examples.

   "9 × 2"
   "18"
   "Add 4"
   "22"

   "225"
   "9 × 25 = 225"

PART C: Less Structured Worksheet Presentation

Students have worksheets with these problems:

a.	35	b.	79	c.	35
	× 5		× 2		+ 5

d.	64	e.	83	f.	83
	× 9		× 5		+ 5

1. "READ PROBLEM a."
   "WHAT TYPE OF PROBLEM IS THIS?"[1]
   "WHAT WILL YOU DO FIRST?"
   "WHAT IS 5 × 5?" Pause, signal.
   "CARRY THE 10s IN 25 AND WRITE THE 1s.

   "5 times 35"
   "Times"
   "Multiply 5 × 5"
   "25"

2. "WHAT NUMBERS DO WE TIMES NEXT?"
   "THEN WHAT DO YOU DO?"
   "WORK THE REST OF THE PROBLEM." Pause.

   "5 × 3"
   "Add the 2"

3. "WHAT IS 5 × 35?"
   Repeat steps 1-3 with remaining problems.

   "175"

---

[1]If the problem is addition, tell students to work the problem.

---

cise. After her students complete the first multiplication problem (e.g., 7 × 35), the teacher says, "Here's how to check your work to make sure you have the right answer. We multiplied by 7 so we divide 7 into the answer. If you end with 35, your answer is correct. What's the answer to the multiplication problem? Divide 7 into 245 . . . Write the problem and work it . . . Is the answer the same as the top number in the multiplication problem? . . . So the answer for the multiplication problem must be correct."

Determining whether students check their work in multiplication is easier than in addition because checking requires writing a division problem. An exercise to encourage checking is to give stu-dents already worked problems about half of which have incorrect answers. The teacher instructs the students to check the answer, and the teacher corrects mistakes.

Two Multi-Digit Factors

Problems with two multi-digit factors are usually introduced during mid-fourth grade. There are four problem types within this grouping (types 4d, 4e, 5a, and 5b from the instructional Sequence and Assessment Chart). The simplest problems involve two two-digit factors. Next in difficulty are problems with a two digit factor and a three digit factor. This type is introduced during late fourth grade. The last type, which is presented during fifth grade, includes two three-digit factors.

The preskills for introducing problems with two multi-digit factors include the preskills for problems with a one digit and multi-digit factor (i.e., basic multiplication facts, place value skills, complex addition facts) and a new preskill, column addition with renaming, which is required when the student must add the partial products.

Figure 10.11 includes the format for presenting problem type 4d in which both factors are two digit numbers. We recommend using a place value grid the first several weeks this problem type appears. Examples of problems worked in a grid appear in Figure 10.10. The grids should already be predrawn on students' worksheets. Although drawing the grids provides extra work for the teacher, it saves instructional time that would be used to teach students how to draw them properly. The important part of the task for the student is filling in the numbers in the appropriate columns.

In Part A, the teacher simply presents the numbers in the order in which they are multiplied, for example, in the problem:

$$\begin{array}{r} 52 \\ \times 37 \end{array}$$

"We multiply 7×2, then 7×5, then 3×2, then 3×5." This part simply focuses on mechanics. Part B is a structured board presentation in which the teacher models the steps in solving a problem. Note in steps 3 and 5 that the teacher summarizes what has been done to that point, i.e., "First we multiplied 52×7, now we'll multiply 52 by three 10s." Step 3 also points out that when multiplying by the tens number, a zero must first be placed in the ones column:

$$\begin{array}{r} 25 \\ \times 37 \\ \hline 175 \\ \underline{0} \end{array}$$

This step is critical. Otherwise the digits can end up misaligned.

Part C is a structured worksheet presentation. Step 4 of Part C, during which the teacher leads students in multiplying by the tens number, is the step in which students are most likely to have difficulty. Note the wording is very specific regarding where numerals are placed. Part D is a less structured worksheet presentation. A mix of problems with a two digit factor and problems with a one digit factor as the bottom factor, as well as some addition problems with a one digit factor, appear.

Diagnosis and Remediation

The specific cause of errors will sometimes be obvious, as in problem a, and sometimes not obvious, as in problem b. In problem a, we can readily assume the student made a fact error, multiplying 7×6 and writing 58.

$$\text{a.} \quad \begin{array}{r} 5 \\ 36 \\ \times 7 \\ \hline 268 \end{array} \qquad \text{b.} \quad \begin{array}{r} 4 \\ 36 \\ \times 7 \\ \hline 242 \end{array}$$

In problem b, we cannot be sure of the error. The student may have multiplied wrong or added wrong. If the cause of the error is not clear, the teacher should have the students rework the problem in front of her so that she can ascertain the specific cause of the error.

FACT ERRORS The remediation procedure for basic fact errors depends on the number of fact errors made by the student. If a student makes a few fact errors, the teacher simply records the facts the student missed and incorporates them into fact drill exercises for the next several lessons. If a student makes fact errors on more than 10% of the problems, the teacher should test the student individually to determine what action to take. The teacher would test the student verbally on the facts missed (e.g., What is 8×7? 9×4? 8×6?). If the student responds correctly to the missed facts, the teacher should tentatively consider the cause of errors to be the student's hurrying through the problem and not exercising enough care. The remediation procedure would involve increasing the motivation to perform accurately. If the student's performance indicates he does not know many basic facts, the teacher should devote more time to basic facts and limit problems to include only basic facts the student knows.

COMPONENT SKILL ERRORS Many of the component skill errors have to do with addition. Renaming errors may involve either (a) carrying the wrong number or carrying a number to the wrong column:

$$\begin{array}{r} 2 \\ 58 \\ \times 9 \\ \hline 477 \end{array} \qquad \begin{array}{r} 1 \\ 312 \\ \times 7 \\ \hline 2274 \end{array}$$

or (b) forgetting to add the carried number:

$$\begin{array}{r} 7 \\ 58 \\ \times 9 \\ \hline 452 \end{array} \qquad \begin{array}{r} 1 \\ 82 \\ \times 7 \\ \hline 564 \end{array}$$

Figure 10.10

```
  3 4 2              4 6
×   2 5           × 2 6
1 7 1 0           2 7 6
+6 8 4 0         +9 2 0
8 5 5 0          1 1 9 6
```

Figure 10.11   Format for Two Digit Factor Times Two Digit Factor

Days	Part A Order of Multiplying Problems	Part B Structured Board Presentation Problems	Part C Structured Worksheet Problems	Part D Less Structured Worksheet Problems	Part E Supervised Practice Problems	Part F Independent Practice Problems
1	3	4				
2	3					
3-4	2	3	4			
5-6		2	4	4		
7-Till accurate				4	4	
Till fluent						8

PART A: Order of Multiplying

TEACHER   **STUDENTS**

Write on board:

```
  5 8
×4 3
```

```
  2 7
×9 5
```

```
  4 2
×5 7
```

1. Point to 58 × 43. "READ THE PROBLEM."   "43 times 58"
   "HERE'S HOW WE WORK MULTIPLICATION PROBLEMS
   WITH TWO NUMBERS ON THE BOTTOM. FIRST WE
   MULTIPLY ALL THE NUMBERS ON THE TOP BY THIS
   NUMBER." Point to 3. "THEN WE MULTIPLY ALL THE
   NUMBERS ON THE TOP BY THIS NUMBER." Point to 4.

2. "MY TURN." Point to numbers as you say them. "FIRST WE
   MULTIPLY: 3 × 8, THEN 3 × 5, THEN 4 × 8, THEN 4 × 5."

3. Point to 3. "WHAT NUMBERS DO WE MULTIPLY FIRST?"   "3 × 8"
   Point to 3. "WHAT NUMBERS DO WE MULTIPLY NEXT?"   "3 × 5"
   Point to 4. "WHAT NUMBERS DO WE MULTIPLY NEXT?"   "4 × 8"
   Point to 4. "WHAT NUMBERS DO WE MULTIPLY NEXT?"   "4 × 5"
   Repeat steps 2 and 3 with remaining problems. Give
   individual turns.

Figure 10.11 cont'd

PART B: Structured Board Presentation

TEACHER	**STUDENTS**

Point to

```
   |5|8|
  ×|4|3|
  +-+-+
```

1. "READ THE PROBLEM."   "43 times 58"

2. "WHAT NUMBERS DO WE MULTIPLY FIRST?"   "3 × 8"
   "WHAT IS 3 × 8?" Pause, signal.   "24"
   Point above tens column. "WHAT NUMBER DO I
   WRITE HERE?"   "2"
   Point under ones column. "WHAT NUMBER DO I PUT
   HERE?"   "4"
   "WHAT NUMBERS DO WE MULTIPLY NEXT?"   "3 × 5"
   "WHAT IS 3 × 5?" Pause, signal.   "15"
   "WHAT ELSE DO WE DO?"   "Add 2"
   "WHAT IS 15 + 2?"   "17"
   "THERE ARE NO MORE NUMBERS ON TOP TO MULTIPLY
   SO I WRITE THE 17 UNDER THE LINE NEXT TO THE 4."

3. "WE MULTIPLIED 3 × 58. WHAT IS 3 × 58?"   "174"
   "I CROSS OUT THE 2 WE CARRIED AND THE 3 TO SHOW
   WE'RE FINISHED WITH THOSE NUMBERS.

```
   |2|  |
   |5|8|
  ×|4|3|
  +-+-+
  |1|7|4|
```

   NOW WE MULTIPLY 4 10s × 58. TENS NUMBERS HAVE
   A ZERO SO WE PUT A ZERO IN THE ONES COLUMN TO
   SHOW WE'RE MULTIPLYING 10s. HOW DO WE SHOW
   WE'RE MULTIPLYING BY 10s?"   "Put a zero in the ones column"
   Write 0 under 4.
   "NOW WE MULTIPLY 4 × 8, THEN 4 × 5. WHAT IS 4 × 8?"
   Pause, signal.   "32"
   Point above tens column. "WHAT NUMBER DO I WRITE
   HERE?"   "3"
   Point next to zero. "WHAT NUMBER DO I WRITE HERE?"   "2"
   Write numbers.

```
   |3|  |
   |5|8|
  ×|4|3|
  +-+-+
   |1|7|4|
  |2|3|2|0|
```

4. "NOW WHAT NUMBER DO WE MULTIPLY?"   "4 × 5"
   "WHAT IS 4 × 5?" Pause, signal.   "20"
   "WHAT DO WE DO NOW?"   "Add 3"
   "WHAT IS 20 + 3?" Pause, signal.   "23"
   "WHERE DO I WRITE THE 23?"   "Next to the 2"

5. "FIRST WE MULTIPLIED 3 × 58 AND ENDED WITH 174.
   THEN WE MULTIPLIED 40 × 58 AND ENDED WITH 2320.
   NOW LET'S ADD THOSE NUMBERS AND FIGURE OUT
   WHAT 43 × 58 EQUALS. WHAT IS 4 + 0?"   "4"
   "What is 7 + 2?"   "9"
   "WHAT IS 1 + 3?"   "4"
   "WHAT IS NOTHING AND 2?"   "2"

Figure 10.11 cont'd

6. "WE'RE FINISHED ADDING. I'LL PUT IN THE COMMA.
   WHERE DOES IT GO?"   "Between the 2 and 4"
   "WHAT DOES 43 × 58 EQUAL?"   "2,494"
   Repeat steps 1–6 with remaining problems on board.

PART C: Structured Worksheet

Students have worksheets with problems such as these:

a. $\begin{array}{r} 2\,8 \\ \times\,3\,6 \\ \hline \end{array}$ b. $\begin{array}{r} 6\,4 \\ \times\,2\,8 \\ \hline \end{array}$ c. $\begin{array}{r} 8\,7 \\ \times\,4\,5 \\ \hline \end{array}$

1. "TOUCH PROBLEM a ON YOUR WORKSHEET. READ
   THE PROBLEM."   "36 × 28"
   "WHAT NUMBERS ARE YOU GOING TO MULTIPLY
   FIRST?"   "6 × 8"
   "WHAT IS 6 × 8?" Pause, signal.   "48"
   "WRITE IT; DON'T FORGET TO CARRY THE 10s."
   Monitor responses.

2. "WHAT DO YOU MULTIPLY NEXT?"   "6 × 2"
   "WHAT IS 6 × 2?" Pause, signal.   "12"
   "WHAT DO YOU DO NOW?"   "Add 4"
   "WHAT IS 12 + 4?" Pause, signal.   "16"
   "WRITE 16 NEXT TO THE 8." Monitor responses.

3. "ARE YOU DONE MULTIPLYING BY 6?"   "Yes"
   "CROSS OUT THE 6 TO SHOW YOU'RE FINISHED AND
   CROSS OUT THE CARRIED NUMBER." Monitor
   responses.

4. "WE MULTIPLIED 6 × 28. NOW WE MULTIPLY 30 × 28.
   WHAT DO YOU WRITE TO SHOW THAT YOU ARE MUL-
   TIPLYING BY 10s?"   "Write a zero"
   "WRITE IT." Monitor responses. "WHAT NUMBERS
   DO YOU MULTIPLY NOW?"   "3 × 8"
   "WHAT IS 3 × 8?" Pause, signal.   "24"
   "WRITE THE 4 NEXT TO THE ZERO. WRITE THE 2 OVER
   THE 2." Monitor responses.

4. "NOW WHAT ARE YOU GOING TO MULTIPLY?"   "3 × 2"
   "WHAT IS 3 × 2?" Pause, signal.   "6"
   "WHAT DO YOU DO NOW?"   "Add 2"
   "WHAT IS 6 + 2?" Pause, signal.   "8"
   "WRITE IT." Monitor responses.

5. "WE MULTIPLIED 6 × 28 AND 30 × 28. ADD THE SUMS TO
   SEE WHAT 36 × 28 EQUALS, THEN PUT IN THE COMMA.
   (pause) WHAT IS 36 × 28?" Repeat with several examples.   "1008"

PART D: Less Structured Practice

Give students worksheets with a mix of multiplication
problems with 2 digit and 1 digit factors and some addition
problems.

1. "TOUCH PROBLEM __. READ THE PROBLEM."
   "WHAT KIND OF PROBLEM IS THIS?"

2. "WHAT NUMBERS DO YOU MULTIPLY FIRST?"
   "WHAT NUMBERS DO YOU MULTIPLY NEXT?"
   "WHAT NUMBERS DO YOU MULTIPLY NEXT?"
   "WHAT NUMBERS DO YOU MULTIPLY NEXT?"

3. "WHAT ARE YOU GOING TO DO JUST BEFORE YOU
   START TO MULTIPLY BY FIVE 10s?"
   "RIGHT, DON'T FORGET TO WRITE THE ZERO. WORK
   THE PROBLEM."

If students make frequent errors (more than 10%) in which they carry the ones number to the tens column, the error might be caused by the student's not understanding the place value concept for writing numbers. The teacher would test the students on the tasks in the writing tens number format on pages 95–97 and if necessary, teach these place value skills. When the students consistently respond to place value tasks, such as how many 10s in 57, the teacher would present the multiplication format beginning with the structured worksheet exercise.

If students miss many problems because they fail to add the carried number, the teacher would re-present the structured worksheet part of the format and then progress to the less structured worksheet exercise, emphasizing the need to carry the added 10s.

Addition mistakes account for a sizable proportion of student errors. Below are several examples of addition errors:

```
a.    5        b.   3        c.   5
     88            34            28
   × 7          × 9          × 7
    626           296           186
```

Although, as mentioned earlier, we cannot be absolutely sure that the student's errors resulted from addition mistakes, the probability is high that they did.

In problem a, the student added 5 to 56 and ended incorrectly with a sum of 62. If students make frequent addition errors, the teacher would place extra emphasis on teaching complex addition facts, i.e., facts in which the first addend is a two digit number and the second addend a one digit number. Teachers working with older students who have little knowledge of basic addition facts should permit students to use their fingers in computing complex addition facts; however, they should insist on students' being accurate. Practice should be provided on worksheets which include just complex addition facts. Worksheets of this type would be provided daily until students performed at 95% accuracy for several days.

Students often have difficulty with problems which have a zero in the tens column:

```
   304
 × 7
```

Students may multiply the carried number:

```
   24
  306
 × 7
 2382
```

or treat the zero as if it were a 1:

```
   14
  306
 × 7
 2212
```

The remediation procedure for errors of this type begins with the teacher's testing and, if necessary, teaching times-zero facts. "When you multiply by zero you end up with zero. What is 5×0? 8×0? 3×0?" The teacher would then give students a worksheet containing 10–20 problems. Half the problems would contain a zero in the tens column, a fourth of the problems would include a 1 in the tens column, and another fourth of the problems would have another numeral in the tens column. The teacher would lead the students through several problems using a structured worksheet presentation then present a less structured worksheet exercise with several, and finally have the students work the problems without assistance.

Errors unique to problems with two multi-digit factors include not writing a zero in the ones column when multiplying by 10s:

```
   46
 ×24
  184
   92
```

and inappropriately recording the partial products so that numbers are added in the wrong columns:

```
    425
  ×37
   2975
  12750
  42455
```

Both errors can be identified by closely examining worksheet errors.

To remedy the first error, caused by forgetting the zero, the teacher would lead students through about three multiplication problems using Part D of Figure 10.11, the less structured worksheet of the format for a two digit factor times a two digit factor. In Part D, the teacher prompts students to write a zero when multiplying by 10s but does not guide them on every step. The students would complete the rest of the worksheet independently. The worksheet should contain 4–5 multi-digit problems with a one digit factor mixed in with about 10–15 multiplication problems with two digit factors. The problems with one digit factors require students to remember about putting the zero in the multiplication problems for longer periods of time than if they worked only multiplication problems in which they inserted a zero in every problem. The practice exercise is done daily until students respond correctly to 9 of 10 multiplication problems for several consecutive lessons.

To remedy errors caused by students' inadvertently writing numbers in the wrong columns, the teacher should point out the errors to the students and remind them to carefully align the columns. Often, just providing feedback on why the students missed the problems is enough to encourage students to be more careful. However, if students continue to make column alignment errors, the teacher should reintroduce the use of the place value grid. The teacher should lead students through working the first couple of problems using Part C in Figure 10.11, the structured worksheet, and have the students complete the remaining problems independently. The teacher should probably continue having students use the grid for several days, then have students work problems without the grid.

Students may also answer problems incorrectly because of an error in adding the partial products. In problem a below, the student failed to carry. In problem b, the student made a basic fact error:

```
a.    688        b.    688
     ×94             ×94
     2752            2752
    61920           61920
    63672           64572
```

Carrying errors often result from sloppiness. Teachers should insist that students write neatly. The remediation for carrying errors might involve giving the students a worksheet with about 10 problems. In each problem, the multiplication would be done already. The students' tasks would be to

add the partial products. After the students can perform accurately on this worksheet, the teacher would supervise students as they worked entire problems on their own.

STRATEGY ERRORS Strategy errors indicate that the student simply has not learned the steps in the algorithm. Below are examples of student performance which indicate a strategy deficit:

```
     428            32
    ×   3          ×57
   12616         160224
```

The remediation for such errors involves presenting the entire format for the particular problem type, beginning with the structured board presentation. The diagnosis and remediation information is summarized in Figure 10.12.

Research

Two studies, both of which involve issues of instructional efficiency as well as student achievement in multiplication, are discussed here. First, Carnine (1980) designed a study to determine whether the time at which component skills are taught is a significant instructional variable. The hypothesis of this study was that preteaching the component skills involved in multiplication results in more rapid learning of a complex skill than teaching the components at the same time the more complex skill is introduced. Fifteen below-average (as defined by the Metropolitan Readiness Test) first grade students were assigned to either the preteaching group or the concurrent group. Daily 10-minute instructional sessions were conducted in the afternoon. In the preteaching treatment, students received instruction in three component skills for multiplication—

Figure 10.12 Diagnosis and Remediation of Multi-digit Multiplication Errors

Error Patterns	Diagnosis	Remediation Procedures
Two Digit Factor + One Digit Factor 　　　*34* a.　156 　　× 7 　*1090* 　*8*　　*32* b.　46　156 　× 3　× 7 　*201*　*1074*	*Fact Error*: Student makes an error in problems containing the factor 6 × 7. Component Skill: Student carries the 1s and writes the 10s in the ones column.	Drill on fact 6 × 7. Present place value exercise for writing tens numbers. (Figure 6.12). Then begin with structures worksheet exercise for multiplication format (Figure 10.9).

Figure 10.12 cont'd

Error Patterns	Diagnosis	Remediation Procedures
c. $\begin{array}{r} 46 \\ \times\ 3 \\ \hline 128 \end{array}$ $\begin{array}{r} 156 \\ \times\ 7 \\ \hline 752 \end{array}$	Strategy: Student does not carry the 10s.	Begin with structured worksheet exercise (Figure 10.9).
d. $\begin{array}{r} {}^{1}\ 46 \\ \times\ 3 \\ \hline 148 \end{array}$ $\begin{array}{r} {}^{34}\ 156 \\ \times\ 7 \\ \hline 982 \end{array}$	Component skill: Student does not add the carried number correctly.	Teach complex addition facts. Present worksheets containing complex addition facts.
Problems Containing Zero		
a. $\begin{array}{r} {}^{1}\ 406 \\ \times\ \ 3 \\ \hline 1238 \end{array}$ $\begin{array}{r} {}^{24}\ 106 \\ \times\ \ 7 \\ \hline 982 \end{array}$	Strategy: Student multiplies the carried number.	Test and teach times zero facts. Begin with structured worksheet exercise (Figure 10.9).
b. $\begin{array}{r} {}^{1}\ 406 \\ \times\ \ 3 \\ \hline 1248 \end{array}$ $\begin{array}{r} {}^{4}\ 106 \\ \times\ \ 7 \\ \hline 712 \end{array}$	Fact error: Student multiplies the zero as if it were a 1.	Test and teach times zero facts.
Two Digit Factor × Two Digit Factor		
a. $\begin{array}{r} {}^{1}\ 46 \\ \times 23 \\ \hline 138 \\ 92\ \\ \hline 230 \end{array}$ $\begin{array}{r} {}^{4}\ 56 \\ \times\ 17 \\ \hline 392 \\ 56\ \\ \hline 448 \end{array}$	Strategy: Student does not write zero in ones column when multiplying by 10s.	Begin with less structured exercise (Figure 10.11). Include mix of problems with two digit factor and one digit factor on bottom of problem.
b. $\begin{array}{r} {}^{1}\ 46 \\ \times 23 \\ \hline 138 \\ 920\ \\ \hline 9338 \end{array}$ $\begin{array}{r} {}^{4}\ 56 \\ \times\ 17 \\ \hline 392 \\ 560\ \\ \hline 5992 \end{array}$	Strategy: Addition error; student doesn't align numbers in columns appropriately.	Make worksheets including place value grid. Begin with structured exercise (Figure 10.11) .
c. $\begin{array}{r} 96 \\ \times 78 \\ \hline 768 \\ 6720\ \\ \hline 6488 \end{array}$	Component skill: Addition error; student doesn't carry when adding partial products.	Give worksheet focusing on adding partial products, then supervised practice on multiplication problems.

counting various numbers, decoding facts and applying a count-by strategy—before encountering 16 flash cards containing multiplication facts.

Children in the concurrent group were introduced to 16 facts and the component skills simultaneously, e.g., the experimenters presented a flash card, and modeled decoding the fact, the count-by strategy, and how to apply the strategy. The results indicated that children in the preteaching group reached criterion in significantly less time than children in the concurrent group. More rapid learning in the preteaching group also was accompanied by more correct responses to transfer facts.

Similarly, Cook and Dossey (1982) examined the relative efficacy of two approaches to teaching basic multiplication facts at the third grade level. This study compared the results of teaching a strategy which emphasized thinking patterns based on groups of related facts (2s, 5s, 0s, 1s) to an approach based on the size of the factors (0s, 1s, 2s, 3s). The results of this study support the thinking strategies approach for multiplication fact induction. Although both groups achieved a high level of fact

mastery in the end, students taught the thinking strategies approach made quite a rapid growth and as a result spent less time initially learning facts, allowing more instructional time for review.

Commercial Programs

Multiplication: Multiplying by Two or More Digits

INSTRUCTIONAL STRATEGIES Often when teaching multiplication by two or more digits, examples are given with arrows to display the order in which digits are to be multiplied. However, the actual strategy is not clearly defined in the teacher directions, and often the teacher is told to simply work through repeated examples to model the strategy (see Figure 10.13).

Some basals use various multiplication algorithms to teach multiplication "shortcuts." Because of the vague teacher directions, it is easy to see why the authors warn that "most students will have difficulty at first with this type of multiplication algorithm." (See Figure 10.14 for such an algorithim.)

Practice and Review Many commercial programs do not include a sufficient number of examples in their initial presentations to enable students to develop mastery of complex multiplication. Also, they often fail to provide an adequate mix of problem types.

For example, one program we looked at contained two pages for 2 digit X 2 digit multiplication with renaming in the fourth grade level; one page in the fifth grade level and two pages for practicing complex multiplication in the sixth grade level (Scott Foresman, 1985). Clearly this is not an adequate amount of practice or review on basic strategies for multiplication, especially for many lower-performing students for whom sufficient practice and review are critical.

Figure 10.13

Exercises 13–30 This skill was originally taught on pages 116–117. Direct students' attention to second box and review the idea that when multiplying by a 1-digit number we first multiply the ones, then the tens, then the hundreds. Work through the example, making sure students understand how to make appropriate trades, where to write the digits in the answer, and how to write the necessary zeros in the partial products.

$$\begin{array}{r} {}^{1}{}^{1} \\ 7\,4\,6 \\ \times\ \ 3 \\ \hline 2{,}238 \end{array}$$ Multiply ones. Multiply tens. Multiply hundreds.

$$\begin{array}{r} 574 \\ \times\ \ 28 \\ \hline 4592 \\ 11480 \\ \hline 16{,}072 \end{array}$$

4592 ← 8 × 574
11480 ← 20 × 574
16,072 ← 28 × 574

Source: From *Addison-Wesley Mathematics*, Grade 5 Teacher's Edition, by Robert E. Eicholz, Phares O'Daffer, and Charles R. Fleenor, p. 159. Copyright © 1987 by Addison-Wesley Publishing Company. Reprinted by permission.

Figure 10.14

STUDENT OBJECTIVE
To multiply multiples of 10 by 2-digit and 3-digit numbers.

TEACHING SUGGESTIONS

Multiply by multiples of 10. (Materials: ones, tens, hundreds) Write these examples on the chalkboard or overhead projector:

$$\begin{array}{ccccc} 12 & 12 & 12 & 12 & 12 \\ \times 20 & \times 30 & \times 40 & \times 50 & \times 60 \end{array}$$

Ask the students to lay out a 12 by 20 rectangular array.

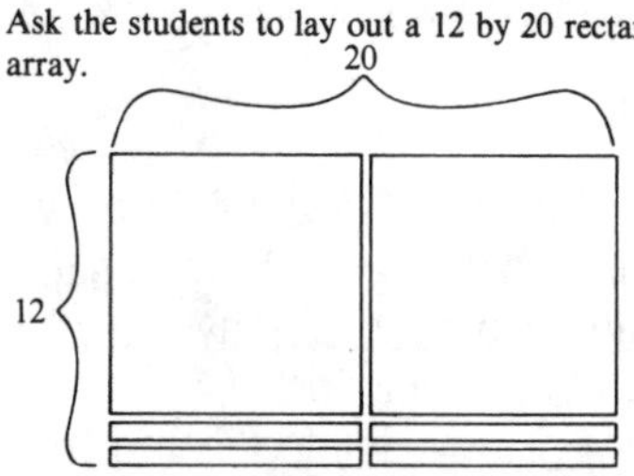

Most students will have difficulty at first with this type of multiplication algorithm, but they will be aware of how easy it is if they follow the steps:

1. Multiply 2 by 12:   24
2. Then multiply 24 by 10:   240

Explain to the students that there is a shortcut for finding such products as 20 × 12.

Source: From *Heath Mathematics*, Grade 4 Teacher's Edition, by Walter E. Rucker, Clyde A. Dilley, and David A. Lowry, p. 256. Copyright © 1987 by D.C. Heath & Company. Reprinted by permission.

Application Items: Multiplication

1. Describe the problem type each example below represents. List the problems in the order they are introduced. Write the grade level when each type is typically introduced.

a.   758
   ×   2

b. $9 \times 4 = \square$

c. 3×26

d.   34
   × 2

e.   37
  × 2

f.   258
  × 37

g.   37
  ×24

h. $5 \times \square = 20$

2. At the beginning of a unit, the teacher tested Jack. His performance on the performance indicators for problem types 3b–4b appears below. Specify the problem type with which instruction should begin. Explain your answer.

Jack

3b.   43   31   32
   × 2 × 5 × 4
   —— —— ——
   86 155 128

        1   2
3c.   35   43   17
   × 5 × 9 × 2
   —— —— ——
  165 377 34

3d. $5 \times 35 = 175$
    $9 \times 34 = 296$
    $7 \times 56 = 392$

4a.   758   364   534
   × 2 × 5 × 9
   ———— ———— ————
  1516 1820 4806

4b.   403   302   105
   × 5 × 5 × 9
   ———— ———— ————
  2105 1600 1305

3. Below are 10 problems which appeared on the worksheet to be done independently by the students in Mrs. Ash's math group. Next to each student's name are the problems missed by the student. For each student, specify the probable cause or causes of the student's error. Describe the remediation procedure.

24   342   61   23   203   60   21   28   432   48
×37 × 7 ×84 ×53 × 5 × 9 ×43 ×73 × 6 ×37

Jill

  203
 × 5
 ——
 1105

Alice

  48   28
 ×37 ×73
 —— ——
 338   84
1440 1980
—— ——
1778 2064

Sam

  203   60
 × 5 × 9
 —— ——
1065 549

Jean

  24
 ×37
 ——
 168
  72
 ——
 240

Sarah

  23   28
 ×53 ×75
 —— ——
  69 140
1150 1960
—— ——
1119 2000

4. A student makes the following errors on the less structured worksheet presentation:

    7
   43
  × 9
  ——
    2

Assume this type of error occurs frequently. What would the teacher do?

5. Write the wording the teacher would use in the structured worksheet part of a format in presenting the problem

   304
 × 7

6. A student's worksheet assignment contains the following worked problems:

$3 \times \boxed{27} = 9$ $2 \times \boxed{12} = 6$

What error is the student making? Describe the remediation procedure.

11 Division

Terms and Concepts

Division   The inverse of multiplication. When a student divides, he is finding a missing factor; 16 ÷ 8 can be expressed as $8 \times \square = 16$.

Measurement Division   Performed when a set of elements is to be separated into equivalent subsets. The answer is the number of subsets; e.g., John has six hats and separates them into groups of two hats. How many groups will he have?

Partitive Division   Performed when a set of elements is to be separated into a given number of subsets. The answer is the size of each subset; e.g., John has six hats and separates them into three groups. How many hats will be in each group?

Dividend   The number being divided. It corresponds to the product in a multiplication problem:

$$6 \text{ in } 2\overline{)6}$$

Divisor   The factor that is given in a division problem. It is written in front of the division sign:

$$2 \text{ in } 2\overline{)6}$$

Quotient   The factor solved for in a division problem. It is written above the division sign:

$$3 \text{ in } 2\overline{)6}^{\,3}$$

Commutativity   The commutative property does not hold:

$$a \div b \neq b \div a$$
$$6 \div 2 \neq 2 \div 6$$
$$3 \neq \frac{1}{3}$$

Associativity   The associative property does not hold:

$$(a \div b) \div c \neq a \div (b \div c)$$
$$(8 \div 4) \div 2 \neq 8 \div (4 \div 2)$$
$$2 \div 2 \neq 8 \div 2$$
$$1 \neq 4$$

Distributivity   The distributive property over addition and subtraction holds:

$$(a + b) \div c = (a \div c) + (b \div c)$$
$$(8 + 4) \div 2 = (8 \div 2) + (4 + 2)$$
$$12 \div 2 = 4 + 2$$
$$6 = 6$$

The distributive property is used extensively in the division algorithm:

$$4\overline{)48} = 4\overline{)40} + 4\overline{)8}$$
$$\begin{array}{cc} 1 & 10 \\ 4\overline{)48} & 4\overline{)40} \end{array} = 4\overline{)8}$$
$$\begin{array}{cc} 4 & 40 \\ \hline 8 \end{array}$$

$$\begin{array}{ccc} 12 & 10 & 2 \\ 4\overline{)48} & 4\overline{)40} & 4\overline{)8} \\ \underline{4} & \underline{40} & \underline{8} \\ 8 \end{array} = 12$$
$$\underline{-8}$$

Note: The distributive property does not hold when the division operation precedes addition:

$$c \div (a + b) \neq c \div a + c \div b$$
$$8 \div (4 + 2) \neq 8 \div 4 + 8 \div 2$$
$$\frac{8}{6} \neq 2 + 4$$

Skill Hierarchy

Figure 11.1 shows the skill hierarchy for division. As with all major operations, division is introduced in two stages: the conceptual stage and the multi-digit operation stage.

During the conceptual stage, exercises providing concrete demonstration of the division concept are presented. Groups of objects are divided into equal-sized small groups, first with problems that have no remainder and later with problems that have a remainder.

During the operation stage, students are taught algorithms to solve division problems that have multi-digit quotients. A significant period of time is needed between the introduction of the conceptual stage and presentation of division algorithms. During that time, the teacher should present exercises to facilitate memorization of basic division facts. Once students know their division facts, division problems with one digit divisors (and multi–digit quotients) can be introduced. Division problems with two digit divisors are substantially more difficult and therefore are introduced later. A list of the specific types and when they are normally intro-

duced appears in the Instructional Sequence and Assessment Chart in Figure 11.2.

Introducing the Concept

There are at least four basic ways to provide concrete demonstrations of division:

1. Removing equivalent disjoint subsets: A picture of 6 fish is shown. The teacher says, "Let's put these fish in little bowls. We'll put 2 in each bowl. Let's see how many bowls we'll need. We put 2 in the first bowl. That leaves 4, then we put 2 in the second bowl. Then we put 2 in the third bowl. We need three bowls if we put 2 fish in each bowl."

2. Arrays: A group of objects aligned in equal piles is an array:

The teacher says, "Let's see how many sets of 6 there are in 30." The teacher counts each set

Figure 11.1 Skill Hierarchy

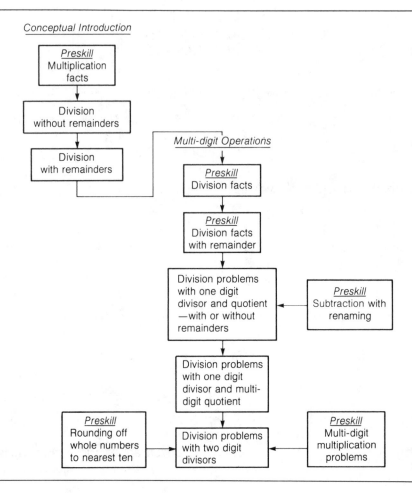

Figure 11.2 Instructional Sequence and Assessment Chart

Grade Level	Problem Type	Performance Indicator		
3a	One digit divisor and one digit quotient; no remainder.	3)15	2)12	5)20
3b	One digit divisor and quotient with remainder.	5)38 R	2)9 R	5)22 R
3c	Division equation with ÷ sign; no remainder; single digit divisor and quotient.	8 ÷ 2 = □ 20 ÷ 5 = □ 36 ÷ 9 = □		
4a	One digit divisor; two or three digit dividend; two digit quotient; no remainder.	5)85	2)172	2)54
4b	One digit divisor; two or three digit dividend; two digit quotient; remainder.	5)87	2)173	2)55
4c	One digit divisor; two or three digit dividend; quotient has two digits, one of which is zero.	5)53	9)274	9)360
4d	One digit divisor; two or three digit dividend; two digit quotient; express remainder as fraction.	Write the remainders as fractions. 5)127	2)91	9)364
4e	One digit divisor; three or four digit dividend; three digit quotient.	5)635	2)1343	2)738

Figure 11.2 cont'd

Grade Level	Problem Type	Performance Indicator		
4f	Same as 4e; zero in quotient.	5)2042̄	2)1214̄	5)520̄
4g	Four digit quotient; one digit divisor, four or five digit dividend.	5)8753̄	2)11325̄	9)36286̄
4h	Rounding to the nearest 10.	76 rounds off to ____ 10s 405 rounds off to ____ 10s 297 rounds off to ____ 10s		
4i	Two digit divisor; one or two digit quotient; all estimation yields correct quotient.	23)94̄	56)857̄	47)1325̄
4j	Same as above except estimation procedures yield quotient which is too large or small.	24)82̄	67)273̄	35)714̄

of 6 as he circles them and then summarizes, "There are 5 sets of 6 in 30."

3. Linear models, usually characterized by use of a number line: in multiplication, students start at zero and jump to the right; e.g., 3 × 4 may be demonstrated as making 3 jumps of 4.
   Division problems are illustrated by saying, "If we start at 12, how many jumps of 4 do we make to get to zero?"

4. Repeated subtraction: This way of introducing division is similar to the removal of equivalent disjoint subsets. The teacher says, "We want to find out how many groups of 4 are in 12. Here's one way to find out. We keep subtracting 4s until we run out. We subtract 4 from 12. That equals 8. Then we subtract 4 from 8. That equals 4, and 4 from 4 equals zero. The teacher then has students count the number of times they subtracted to derive the answer.

Direct instruction procedures introduce the division concept through disjoint sets. Removing equivalent disjoint sets was selected since it can readily demonstrate the relationship between multiplication and division as well as the concept of remainder. Initial direct instruction exercises teach students to remove equivalent sets by circling groups of lines.

Students must have mastered two preskills prior to the introduction of division. The first preskill is knowledge of basic multiplication facts. Students need not have memorized all multiplication facts before division is introduced, but they should at least have memorized multiplication facts with 2 and 5 as factors. A second preskill is column subtraction with renaming, which often is required when students subtract to find a remainder.

Division is usually presented during the midpart of the third grade. Exercises to teach students division facts mentally are introduced about a week or two after the concept of division is introduced. Teachers present facts in related series (e.g., the facts with 5 as a divisor). Ample practice to enable students to develop fluency with a set of facts must be provided before a new set is introduced. Cumulative review of all previously introduced facts must also be provided. The exercise to teach basic division facts is done daily for many months.

The concept of remainder is introduced after students have learned about 20 division facts. More specifically, we recommend that students know the division facts with divisors of 2 and 5 before the remainder concept is introduced. Similar to the initial introduction of division without remainders, the first exercises require the students to circle groups of lines. After several days, exercises to teach students to compute quotients mentally in problems with remainders would be presented. Practice exercises on division facts with remainders would continue for several months.

Problems without Remainders

The format for introducing division appears in Figure 11.3. The format contains four parts. Part A begins with the teacher modeling and testing the translation of a division problem. For example, the problem 5)20̄ is read as "5 goes into 20 how many times" rather than "20 divided by 5." The purpose of this translation is to draw attention to the divisor, since it specifies the size of the equivalent groups—the critical fact in using lines to solve division problems—and to facilitate students using their knowledge of multiplication facts. Note that the students are taught to translate problems so that they are read as a form of missing factor multiplication.

Figure 11.3   Format for Introducing Division

Day	Part A Translating Division Problems	Part B Structured Board Presen- tation Problems	Part C Structured Worksheet Problems	Part D Less Structured Worksheet Problems
1	7	2		
2	4	2	3	
3			3	3
4-5				3

PART A: Translating Division Problems

TEACHER   **STUDENTS**

$$5\overline{)15}^{\,3} \qquad 2\overline{)18}^{\,9} \qquad 6\overline{)30}^{\,5} \qquad 3\overline{)12}^{\,4}$$

$$4\overline{)20}^{\,5} \qquad 7\overline{)28}^{\,4} \qquad 3\overline{)21}^{\,7}$$

1. "THIS IS A DIVISION PROBLEM. WHAT KIND OF
   PROBLEM?"   "A division problem."
   "IT SAYS (point to 5) 5 GOES INTO (point to 15) 15 (point
   to 3) THREE TIMES. WHAT DOES THE PROBLEM SAY?"   "5 goes into 15 three times"
   Point to 5, then 15, then 3 as students answer.
   Repeat step 1 with

$$2\overline{)18}^{\,9} \qquad 6\overline{)30}^{\,5}$$

2. Point to $3\overline{)12}^{\,4}$
   "WHAT DOES THIS PROBLEM SAY?"   "3 goes into 12 four times"
   Point to 3, then 12, then 4 as students answer.
   Repeat step 2 with

$$4\overline{)20}^{\,5} \qquad 7\overline{)28}^{\,4} \qquad 3\overline{)21}^{\,7}$$

Give individual turns to several students.

PART B: Structured Board Presentation
Write on board: $5\overline{)15}$

1. "WHAT KIND OF PROBLEM IS THIS?"   "A division problem"
   "THIS PROBLEM SAYS 5 GOES INTO 15. WHAT DOES
   THIS PROBLEM SAY?" Point to 5, then 15.   "5 goes into 15."
   "WE HAVE TO FIND OUT HOW MANY TIMES 5
   GOES INTO 15. WHEN WE DIVIDE WE START WITH
   A BIG GROUP AND MAKE EQUAL-SIZED SMALLER
   GROUPS." Write 15 lines on board:

   |||||||||||||||

2. "THIS IS A GROUP OF 15 LINES. I WANT TO DIVIDE
   THIS GROUP OF 15 LINES INTO SMALLER GROUPS.
   EACH SMALLER GROUP WILL HAVE 5 LINES IN IT.
   HOW MANY LINES IN EACH SMALLER GROUP?"   "5"

3. "I'LL TOUCH THE LINES. YOU COUNT." Touch   "1, 2, 3, 4, 5"
   five lines. "THIS IS A GROUP OF 5 SO I'LL PUT
   A CIRCLE AROUND IT." Circle five lines.
   Repeat step 3 with remaining groups of five lines.

Figure 11.3 cont'd
TEACHER   **STUDENTS**

4. "WE DIVIDED 15 INTO GROUPS OF 5. LET'S COUNT THE GROUPS." Touch each group.   "1, 2, 3"

5. "HOW MANY TIMES DOES 5 GO INTO 15?"   "3"
"I WRITE THE 3 ABOVE THE LAST DIGIT IN 15." Write

$$\frac{3}{5)\overline{15}}$$

"SAY WHAT THE PROBLEM TELLS US."   "5 goes into 15 three times"
Repeat steps 1-5 with $2)\overline{8}$

PART C: Structured Worksheet

a. $5)\overline{20}$ b. $2)\overline{8}$ c. $2)\overline{12}$

||||||||||||||||||||| ||||||||| ||||||||||||

1. "TOUCH PROBLEM a. THAT PROBLEM SAYS 5 GOES INTO 20. WHAT DOES THE PROBLEM SAY?"   "5 goes into 20"

2. "WE HAVE TO FIND OUT HOW MANY GROUPS OF 5 CAN WE MAKE FROM 20. THERE ARE 20 LINES UNDER THE PROBLEM. MAKE GROUPS OF 5 LINES EACH." Check students' papers.

3. "HOW MANY GROUPS DID YOU MAKE?"   "4"
"WRITE 4 ABOVE THE LAST DIGIT IN 20." Monitor.   Students write 4.

4. "NOW THE PROBLEM SAYS 5 GOES INTO 20 FOUR TIMES. WHAT DOES THE PROBLEM SAY NOW?"   "5 goes into 20 four times"
Repeat steps 1-4 with remaining problems.

PART D: Less Structured Worksheet

1. "TOUCH PROBLEM a."   Students touch $2)\overline{10}$

||||||||||

2. "WHAT DOES THE PROBLEM SAY?"   "2 goes into 10"

3. "HOW MANY IN EACH GROUP?"   "2"

4. "MAKE THE GROUPS AND WRITE HOW MANY GROUPS OVER THE LAST DIGIT IN 10."   Students make circles around each two lines. Students write 5.

5. "READ THE PROBLEM AND ANSWER."   "2 goes into 10 five times."

Part B is a structured board exercise in which the teacher demonstrates with lines the process of taking a big group and making smaller, equal-sized groups. When working the problem, the teacher points out the function of the numbers in a problem. In $5)\overline{20}$ the 20 tells how many lines in all, the 5 tells how many in each group, and the 4 tells how many groups. One minor, but important, aspect of Part B deals with where the quotient is written. If the dividend is a two digit number, the quotient is written over the last digit. For example, in the problem $5)\overline{20}$ the quotient 4 is written over the zero. The purpose of having students write the quotient in the correct place is to prepare them for using the traditional algorithm to solve problems with multi-digit quotients. Improper placement of digits in the quotient leads to various types of errors:

$$
\begin{array}{r}
11.3 \\
5)\overline{607} \\
\underline{5} \\
1\,7
\end{array}
\quad \text{or} \quad
\begin{array}{r}
2.5 \\
5)\overline{1.26} \\
\underline{1\,0} \\
26 \\
\underline{25}
\end{array}
$$

Parts C and D are structured and less structured worksheet exercises. In both exercises, students are given problems for which lines are already drawn. Note that a variety of divisors can be included in these exercises since knowledge of facts is not required. Students just make groups the size of which are defined by the divisor. Note also that students are only assigned two or three problems a day for practice. This exercise is designed to provide a conceptual basis for understanding.

Therefore, teachers need only develop accuracy in such exercises; fluency is not important at this point.

Division Facts

A week or so after students have been introduced to division through the line circling exercises described in Figure 11.3, exercises to facilitate mastery of basic facts can begin.[1] Exercises to demonstrate the relationship between multiplication and division facts would be presented first, e.g., generating two multiplication and two division statements using three numbers:

$$3 \times 4 = 12 \qquad 4 \times 3 = 12$$

$$3\overline{)12}^{\,4} \qquad 4\overline{)12}^{\,3}$$

After relationship exercises are done for several days on a set of facts, those facts would be incorporated into memorization exercises. We recommend that students continue saying the facts in the statement form "5 goes into 20 four times" rather than "20 divided by 5 equals 4" because the former uses the language form presented when division problems with multi-digit quotients are introduced.

Problems with Remainders

The concept of remainders is an important skill in itself and is also a preskill for the short form division algorithm involving multi-digit quotients. Problems with remainders can be introduced when the students have learned division facts with divisors of 2 and 5, which is usually 2 to 4 weeks after division is introduced.

Figure 11.4 contains the format for introducing the remainder concept. In Part A, the teacher writes a problem on the board and has the students read it. After students read the problem, the teacher draws lines. For 13 ÷ 5, the teacher draws 13 lines. The teacher then asks the students for the number in each smaller group and begins drawing circles around groups of 5 lines. After drawing two groups, the teacher points out that he cannot draw a circle around the last lines because there are not 5 lines. The teacher tells the students that only two groups of 5 can be made and that the other lines are called the remainder. The teacher then states the answer to the problem: 5 goes into 13 two times with a remainder of 3.

In Part B and Part C, the students are given a

worksheet with several division problems involving remainders. Next to each problem is a diagram illustrating the problem. For example, next to the problem

$$5\overline{)17}$$

17 lines would be drawn with circles around groups of 5 lines:

The diagram is drawn so that the teacher may concentrate on the mechanics of where to write the number of groups, how to figure out how many parts are used (multiply 5 × 3), where to write the number of parts used (under the 17), and how to compute the remainder (subtract 17 minus 15). Note that practice on this exercise would be continued just for a week or two since the exercise is designed primarily to teach a conceptual understanding.

Remainder Facts

As mentioned earlier, students should have been taught at least 20 division facts before the remainder concept is introduced. About a week after the remainder concept is introduced, exercises to teach students to mentally compute division facts that include remainders should begin:

$$5\overline{)27} \qquad 6\overline{)34}$$

This skill is a critical preskill for division problems with multi-digit quotients since most of these problems involve remainders. For example, in

$$3\overline{)147}$$

students must first determine that 3 goes into 14 four times with a remainder. After multiplying 3 × 4, they then subtract to compute the exact remainder. Figure 11.5 includes the format for teaching students to mentally compute division facts with remainders.

Part A uses a diagram like the one below to introduce remainder facts. When working with students, write numbers in a single row. The circled numbers are all multiples of a particular divisor. In the example below, numbers with a divisor of 5 are circled.

[1] Procedures to teach basic facts are discussed in more depth in Chapter 7.

Figure 11.4 Format for Introducing Division with Remainders

Day	Part A Problems Introduc- ing Remainders with Illustrations	Part B Structured Worksheet Problems	Part C Less Structured Worksheet Problems
1	3		
2-3	2	4	
4-5		4	2
6-7			5

PART A: Introducing Remainders

TEACHER   **STUDENTS**

Write on board: $5\overline{)13}$

1. Point to $5\overline{)13}$. "WHAT DOES THE PROBLEM SAY?"   "5 goes into 13"

2. "FIRST LET'S SOLVE THE PROBLEM BY MAKING
   LINES. THE PROBLEM ASKS HOW MANY GROUPS
   OF 5 IN 13, SO I'LL DRAW 13 LINES." Make 13 lines
   on board. "THE PROBLEM ASKS HOW MANY GROUPS
   OF 5 IN 13. SO I'LL PUT A CIRCLE AROUND EACH
   GROUP OF 5." Count out each group of 5 aloud; after
   circling each group, say, "HERE'S A GROUP OF 5."
   After counting the last 3 lines, say, "WE ONLY HAVE 3
   LEFT SO WE CAN'T MAKE A GROUP OF 5."

3. "NOW LET'S SEE HOW MANY GROUPS OF 5 THERE
   ARE; COUNT THE GROUPS AS I TOUCH THEM."
   Touch groups as students count.   "1, 2"

4. "HOW MANY GROUPS OF 5 IN 13?"   "2"
   "YES, THERE ARE TWO GROUPS." Write
   $\dfrac{2}{5\overline{)13}}$.

5. "ARE THERE LINES LEFT OVER?"   "Yes"
   "WE CALL THOSE LINES THE REMAINDER. HOW
   MANY LINES ARE LEFT OVER?"   "3"

6. "WE SAY THAT 5 GOES INTO 13 TWO TIMES WITH
   A REMAINDER OF 3. HOW MANY TIMES DOES 5
   GOES INTO 13?"   "Two times with a remainder of 3"
   Repeat steps 1-6 with these problems:
   $2\overline{)9}$ $9\overline{)21}$

PART B: Structured Worksheet

Figure 11.4 cont'd

TEACHER	**STUDENTS**
1. "READ PROBLEM a."	"5 goes into 23"
2. "THE PROBLEM ASKS HOW MANY GROUPS OF 5 WE CAN MAKE FROM 23. NEXT TO THE PROBLEM ARE 23 LINES. A CIRCLE HAS BEEN DRAWN AROUND EACH GROUP OF 5 LINES. HOW MANY GROUPS OF 5 ARE THERE?"	"4"
"WRITE 4 ON THE LINE ABOVE THE 3."	
3. "WE WANT TO FIGURE OUT HOW MANY LINES WE USED UP, SO WE MULTIPLY 4 TIMES 5. HOW DO WE FIGURE HOW MANY LINES WE USED UP?"	"Multiply 4 × 5"
4. "WHAT IS 4 × 5?" Pause, signal.	"20"
5. "WRITE 20 UNDER THE 23. WE STARTED WITH 23 AND USED UP 20 SO WRITE A MINUS SIGN IN FRONT OF THE 20. READ THE SUBTRACTION PROBLEM WE JUST WROTE."	"23 - 20"
"SUBTRACT AND WRITE THE REMAINDER. WHAT IS 23 MINUS 20?"	"3"
6. "WE'RE ALL FINISHED; 5 GOES INTO 23 FOUR TIMES WITH A REMAINDER OF 3. HOW MANY TIMES DOES 5 GO INTO 23?"	"Four times with a remainder of 3"
Repeat steps 1–6 with problems b and c.	

PART C: Less Structured Worksheet

1. "READ PROBLEM ___."	"___ goes into ___"
"HOW MANY TIMES DOES ___ GO INTO ___?" Pause, signal.	"___ times"
"WRITE ___ ABOVE THE ___ IN ___. HOW DO WE FIGURE HOW MANY LINES WE USED?"	"Multiply ___ times ___"
2. "WHAT IS ___ TIMES ___?"	"___"
3. "WRITE ___ UNDER THE ___. PUT IN THE MINUS SIGN."	
4. "SUBTRACT." Remind students to borrow when applicable. "WHAT IS THE REMAINDER?"	"___"
5. "HOW MANY TIMES DOES ___ GO INTO ___?"	"___ times with a remainder of ___"

If the teacher is introducing the second part of a series, the teacher writes the higher numbers in the series. For example, if the second half of the five series is being introduced, the teacher writes

$$
\begin{array}{ccccccccc}
\textcircled{25} & 26 & 27 & 28 & 29 & \textcircled{30} & 31 & 32 & 33 \\
34 & \boxed{35} & 36 & 37 & 38 & 39 & \textcircled{40} & 41 & 42 \\
43 & 44 & \textcircled{45} & 46 & 47 & 48 & 49 & \textcircled{50}
\end{array}
$$

in a single row.

After writing the series on the board, the teacher points out that the circled numerals are the numbers that 5 goes into without a remainder. The teacher then models answering the question of how many times 5 goes into various numbers, For example, "5 goes into 23 four times with a remainder"; "5 goes into 10 two times with no remainder"; "5 goes into 9 one time with a remainder." (Note that at this point the quantity of the remainder is not stated.) The teacher then tests the students on a set of examples.

In Part B, the teacher tests the students on various numbers, letting the students refer to the diagram. Part C is a supervised worksheet exercise designed to provide practice that will facilitate fluency in determining division facts. In Part C, the students are given a set of about 30 worksheet problems. The students write the quotient, then multiply and subtract to figure the remainder. The

Figure 11.5 Format for Introducing Remainder Facts

Day	Part A Structured Board Presentation Problems	Part B Less Structured Board Presentation Problems	Part C Supervised Prac- tice Worksheet Problems
1-2	8		
3		8	
4		6	
5-next series			5

This pattern is used when a new set of facts is presented. However, after several sets have been introduced, Parts A and B need no longer be presented.

PART A: Structured Board Presentation

TEACHER   **STUDENTS**

Write on board in a single row:

Ⓞ 1 2 3 4 ⑤ 6 7 8 9
⑩ 11 12 13 14 ⑮ 16 17 18
19 ⑳ 21 22 23 24 ㉕

1. "LISTEN, 5 GOES INTO THE CIRCLED NUMBERS
   WITHOUT A REMAINDER. SAY THE NUMBERS
   THAT 5 GOES INTO WITHOUT A REMAINDER."   "0, 5, 10, 15, 20, 25"

2. "FIVE GOES INTO THE OTHER NUMBER WITH A
   REMAINDER." Point to 1, 2, 3, 4. "THESE ARE NUM-
   BERS 5 GOES INTO ZERO TIMES WITH A REMAIN-
   DER."

3. "MY TURN: HOW MANY TIMES DOES 5 GO INTO 2?
   FIVE GOES INTO 2 ZERO TIMES WITH A REMAIN-
   DER. HOW MANY TIMES DOES 5 GO INTO 2?"   "Zero times with a remainder"
   "HOW MANY TIMES DOES 5 GO INTO 4?"   "Zero times with a remainder"

4. Point to 5. "FIVE GOES INTO 5, ONE TIME." Point to 6,
   7, 8, 9. "THESE ARE NUMBERS 5 GOES INTO ONE
   TIME WITH A REMAINDER." HOW MANY TIMES
   DOES 5 GO INTO 8?"   "One time with a remainder"
   "HOW MANY TIMES DOES 5 GO INTO 6?"   "One time with a remainder"

5. Repeat step 4 using 5 goes into 15 and then 5 goes into 19
   and 5 goes into 17.

6. Repeat step 4 using 5 goes into 20, 5 goes into 24, 5 goes
   into 21.

PART B: Less Structured Board Presentation

Write on board in a single row:

Ⓞ 1 2 3 4 ⑤ 6 7 8 9
⑩ 11 12 13 14 ⑮ 16 17 18
19 ⑳ 21 22 23 24 ㉕

1. "SAY THE NUMBERS 5 GOES INTO WITHOUT A
   REMAINDER."   "5, 10, 15, 20, 25"

2. Point to 13. "THINK, 5 GOES INTO 13 HOW MANY TIMES?"
   Pause, signal.   "Two times with a remainder"
   TO CORRECT: Point to 10. "FIVE GOES INTO 10 TWO
              TIMES." Point to 11, 12, 13, 14. "THESE
              ARE THE NUMBERS 5 GOES INTO TWO
              TIMES WITH A REMAINDER. FIVE GOES
              INTO 13, TWO TIMES WITH A REMAIN-
              DER." Repeat step 2.

3. Repeat step 2 with 20, 24, 0, 3, 9, 16.

Figure 11.5 cont'd

PART C: Structured Worksheet

TEACHER

a. $5\overline{)22}$ b. $5\overline{)16}$ c. $5\overline{)10}$ d. $5\overline{)7}$

1. "READ PROBLEM ____"

2. "HOW MANY TIMES DOES ____ GO INTO ____?"
Pause, signal.

   TO CORRECT: If student says number too low:

$$\begin{array}{r} 3 \\ 5\overline{)22} \end{array}$$

   say, "WE CAN MAKE ANOTHER GROUP OF FIVE—5 TIMES 4 IS 20."
   If student says number too high:

$$\begin{array}{r} 5 \\ 5\overline{)22} \end{array}$$

   say, "5 × 5 IS 25. THAT'S TOO BIG."

3. "WRITE ____ ABOVE THE ____ IN ____."

   "WHAT DO YOU MULTIPLY?"
   "MULTIPLY AND SUBTRACT. (pause) WHAT IS THE REMAINDER? HOW MANY TIMES DOES ____ GO INTO ____?"

Repeat steps 1–3 with several more problems then have students work the rest on their own.

STUDENTS

"____ goes into ____"

Student writes quotient over last number in dividend.
"____ times ____"

"____ times with a remainder of ____"

---

teacher leads the students through several problems and then has them work the rest on their own.

Parts A and B need to be presented only when the first several sets of facts are introduced. Once students have learned to compute division facts mentally with 2s and 5s and 9s, problems with other divisors can be introduced without using the diagram as a prompt.

The sequence in which new division facts with remainders are introduced would parallel the sequence in which basic division facts without remainders are introduced (see Figure 7.9 for suggested sequence for introducing division facts). About 2 weeks after a set of division facts with a particular divisor has been taught, division facts with remainders for the same divisors and quotients would be presented. For example, after students master the division facts for the higher 5s:

e.g., $5\overline{)30}$ $5\overline{)35}$ $5\overline{)40}$ $5\overline{)45}$

problems with the same divisor and quotient but with remainders are introduced:

e.g., $5\overline{)32}$ $5\overline{)41}$ $5\overline{)43}$
$5\overline{)48}$ $5\overline{)36}$ $5\overline{)38}$

The daily worksheet exercise would include about 30 problems. In half the problems, the divisor would be of the set currently being introduced; in the other half of the problems, the divisor would be a number introduced in earlier sets. Although most problems would involve remainders, about a fifth without remainders would be included to buttress against students' developing the potential misrule that all problems must have remainders.

Finally, several problems in which the quotient is zero should be included:

$5\overline{)3}$ $9\overline{)6}$ $2\overline{)1}$

Teaching students to mentally compute the answer to such problems prepares them for long division problems in which zero is in the quotient, such as

$$\begin{array}{r} 104 \ \text{R4} \\ 5\overline{)524} \end{array}$$

Figure 11.6 is a sample worksheet exercise based on the assumption that students have previously mastered problems with divisors of 2, 5, and 9 and are being introduced to the first half of the 7s series.

Worksheet exercises like Figure 11.6 would be presented daily for several months. Students who

Figure 11.6 Sample Worksheet Exercise

7)18	9)46	7)26	7)31	2)7	5)32	7)35	9)27
7)4	7)17	9)58	9)65	7)27	5)3	7)41	9)53
5)30	7)11	7)25	7)32	9)31	5)18	7)3	7)25
9)49	9)26	5)48	2)17	7)36	7)28	7)19	7)36

develop fluency in computing division facts with remainders are less likely to have difficulty when more complex division problems are introduced.

Diagnosis and Remediation

Determining the cause of errors while introducing the concept is fairly easy. The more common causes, besides not knowing basic facts, are component skill errors:

1. Writing quotients that are either too small or too large
2. Subtracting incorrectly
3. Confusing the placement of the quotient and remainder

FACT ERRORS Basic fact errors are illustrated below:

$$
\begin{array}{lll}
\text{a.} & \dfrac{5}{7)33} & \text{b.} & \dfrac{4}{9)42} & \text{c.} & \dfrac{4}{7)32} \\
 & \underline{30} & & \underline{38} & & \underline{26}
\end{array}
$$

As usual, the remediation procedure for basic fact errors depends on the number of fact errors the student makes. If a student makes just an occasional fact error, the teacher simply records the facts the student misses and incorporates those facts into fact drill exercises for the next several lessons. If a student makes fact errors on more than 10% of the problems, he should be tested individually to determine what action to take next. If the teacher finds that the student responds correctly on the individual test to all the missed facts, the teacher should tentatively conclude that the errors resulted

from hurrying through the problems. The remediation procedure would be to increase the student's motivation to perform accurately. If the student's test performance indicates he does not know many previously introduced basic facts, he should be tested on all previously taught multiplication and division facts and provided systematic, intensive instruction on those facts. Also, for several weeks the teacher should carefully control the assignments given to the student so that only facts the student knows appear on worksheet problems. (See Chapter 7 for individualized testing and remediation program.)

COMPONENT SKILL ERRORS This first component skill error involves the student's writing a quotient that is either too large or small. Examples of this error are illustrated below. Problems a and b are examples of computing too small a quotient; problems c and d are examples of computing too large a quotient.

$$
\begin{array}{ll}
\text{a.} & \dfrac{4}{5)28} \\
 & \underline{20}
\end{array}
\qquad
\begin{array}{ll}
\text{b.} & \dfrac{4}{7)35} \\
 & \underline{28}
\end{array}
$$

$$
\begin{array}{ll}
\text{c.} & \dfrac{6}{6)32} \\
 & \underline{36}
\end{array}
\qquad
\begin{array}{ll}
\text{d.} & \dfrac{5}{4)19} \\
 & \underline{20}
\end{array}
$$

If either type of error occurs, in more than 10% of the problems students do independently, the teacher should present an exercise that teaches students to compare the remainder and divisor to determine the correctness of their answer.

The content of the remedial exercise would depend on the type of error made. If the student wrote quotients that were too small:

$$5\overline{)37} \atop \underline{30} \atop 7 \atop 6$$

the teacher would present a format like the one in Figure 11.7. That format contains an exercise in which students are given a worksheet comprised of division problems with the quotients written. In half of the problems the quotient is correct, and in the other half the quotient is too small:

$$9\overline{)38} \atop \underline{27} \atop 11 \atop 3$$

In Part A, the teacher tells students that they must compare the remainder and the divisor to see if they worked the problem correctly. Note that the term *divisor* is not used by the teacher. If students divide by 9, they are taught that the remainder must be smaller than 9; if they divide by 5, the remainder must be smaller than 5; if they divide by 3, the remainder must be smaller than 3, and so on. In Part B, the teacher leads students through determining if the quotient is correct by figuring the remainder and comparing it to the divisor. In problems in which the remainder is not smaller than the divisor, the teacher points out that another group can be made and instructs the student to cross out the answer and in its place write the next higher number. For example, in the problem

$$5\overline{)16} \atop \underline{10} \atop 6 \atop 2$$

the teacher has the students cross out 2 and write 3 as the answer. The student then erases 10, multiplies 3×5, and subtracts 15 from 16. The teacher would guide students through 4–6 problems and then have them work 8-10 problems on their own. The format is presented daily until students are able to successfully solve the problems for several consecutive days.

For errors such as

$$5\overline{)32} \atop 7$$

in which the answer is too large, the teacher should use the format in Figure 11.8. In Part A, the teacher guides the students through a set of problems on the board, pointing out that if they can't subtract, the answer is too big, and the number in the answer must be made smaller. In Part B, the teacher has students work a set of remediation examples in which half the problems have a quotient that is too large and half the problems have a quotient that is correct. As with the previous format, this remediation format should be presented for several lessons.

Column subtraction errors are easy to spot and usually result from a failure to rename. Problems a and b below illustrate subtraction errors.

$$\text{a. } 7\overline{)41} \atop \underline{35} \atop 14 \atop 5 \qquad \text{b. } 9\overline{)71} \atop \underline{63} \atop 12 \atop 7$$

The remediation procedure includes giving students a worksheet with about 10 problems in which borrowing is necessary. The teacher guides students through the first several problems and then has students work the remaining problems on their own. For example, in the problem

---

Figure 11.7 Remediation for Division with Remainders—Quotient Too Small

---

PART A: Recognizing Quotients That Are Too Small

TEACHER	STUDENTS

Write on board: $5\overline{)28}$

1. "THIS PROBLEM SAYS 5 GOES INTO 28. WE'RE FIGURING 5 INTO A NUMBER, SO THE REMAINDER MUST BE SMALLER THAN 5."

2. "WHAT DOES THE PROBLEM SAY?"   "5 goes into 28"

3. "SO WHAT DO YOU KNOW ABOUT THE REMAINDER?"   "It must be smaller than 5"

4. Repeat steps 1-3 with $7\overline{)23}$ $2\overline{)13}$ $6\overline{)14}$ $5\overline{)27}$ $3\overline{)24}$

Figure 11.7 cont'd

PART B: Writing the Correct Answer

TEACHER   **STUDENTS**

a. 4
   5)28   b. 4
           7)31   c. 2
                   9)24

d. 3
   9)43   e. 8
           5)42   f. 5
                   2)13

g. 6
   2)15   h. 5
           5)28

1. "PROBLEM a SAYS 5 GOES INTO 28 FOUR TIMES. WE
   FIGURE THE REMAINDER BY MULTIPLYING 5 × 4
   AND THEN SUBTRACTING. DO THAT ON YOUR
   PAPER."

2. "WHAT'S THE REMAINDER?"   "8"

3. "HERE'S A RULE. IF THE REMAINDER IS TOO BIG,
   WE MAKE THE ANSWER BIGGER. WHAT DO WE
   DO IF THE REMAINDER IS TOO BIG?"   "Make the answer bigger"

4. "IS THE REMAINDER TOO BIG?"   "Yes"
   "SO WHAT MUST WE DO?"   "Make the answer bigger"
   THE REMAINDER IS MORE THAN 5. SO 5 CAN GO
   INTO 28 ANOTHER TIME. CROSS OUT THE 4 AND
   WRITE 5. (check) NOW ERASE 20; MULTIPLY AND
   SUBTRACT TO FIGURE THE NEW REMAINDER.
   WHAT'S THE NEW REMAINDER?"   "3"
   NOTE: If the answer to step 4 is no, tell students, "SO
   THE ANSWER IS CORRECT. LET'S GO TO THE NEXT
   PROBLEM."

5. "IS THE REMAINDER TOO BIG?"   "No"
   "SO THE ANSWER IS CORRECT. READ THE
   PROBLEM."   "5 goes into 28, 5 times with a
                                                                remainder of 3"

6. Repeat steps 1-5 with several problems, then have students
   work remaining problems on their own.

Figure 11.8   Remediation for Division with Remainders—Quotient Too Large

---

PART A: Recognizing Quotients That Are Too Large

TEACHER   **STUDENTS**

Write on board:

   6
5)28
  30

1. "WHAT DOES THIS PROBLEM SAY?"   "5 goes into 28 six times"

2. "THE PROBLEM IS WORKED FOR YOU, BUT THERE
   IS SOMETHING WRONG. CAN YOU SUBTRACT 30
   FROM 28?"   "No"

3. "HERE'S A RULE. IF YOU CAN'T SUBTRACT, MAKE
   THE ANSWER SMALLER. WHAT DO YOU DO IF YOU
   CAN'T SUBTRACT?"   "Make the answer smaller"

4. "WE MAKE THE ANSWER ONE SMALLER. WHAT
   IS ONE SMALLER THAN 6?"   "5"
   Erase 6 write 5. "WHAT IS 5 TIMES 5?"   "25"

Figure 11.8 cont'd

TEACHER   **STUDENTS**

5. Erase 30, write 25. "CAN YOU SUBTRACT 25 FROM 28?"   "Yes"
   "WHAT IS 28 - 25?"   "3"
   "READ THE PROBLEM."   "5 goes into 28 five times with a
                                                               remainder of 3."

6. Repeat steps 1-5 with several examples.

PART B: Writing the Correct Answer

a. $\dfrac{6}{5)\overline{28}}$ b. $\dfrac{4}{7)\overline{31}}$ c. $\dfrac{2}{9)\overline{24}}$

d. $\dfrac{5}{9)\overline{43}}$ e. $\dfrac{8}{5)\overline{42}}$ f. $\dfrac{7}{2)\overline{13}}$

1. "LOOK AT THE PROBLEMS ON YOUR WORKSHEET.
   SOME OF THE ANSWERS ARE TOO BIG. YOU'LL
   HAVE TO FIX THEM."

2. "LOOK AT PROBLEM a. WHAT IS 6 × 5?"   "30"

3. "CAN YOU SUBTRACT 30 FROM 28?"   "No"
   "WHAT MUST YOU DO?"   "Make the answer one smaller"
   Note: Do step 4 only if answer to step 3 is no.

4. "CROSS OUT THE 6. WHAT DO YOU WRITE? WORK
   THE PROBLEM."
   Repeat steps 2-4 with five or six problems, then have
   students complete the worksheet on their own.

Figure 11.9   Diagnosis and Remediation of Beginning Division Errors

Error Patterns	Diagnosis	Remediation Procedures	Remediation Examples
Component Skill Errors			
$\dfrac{4}{7)\overline{35}}$ $\underline{32}$	Fact error: $35 \div 7$	High % fact errors—provide systematic fact instruction. Low % fact errors—increase motivation, include missed facts in fact drills.	See Chapter 7
$\dfrac{3}{6)\overline{24}}$ $\underline{18}$	Component skill: Student computes a quotient that is too small.	Figure 11.7, "Remediation for Division with Remainders—Quotient Too Small."	Partially worked problems, containing quotients. Half of the quotients should be too small, half of them should be accurate: $\dfrac{3}{9)\overline{42}}$ $\dfrac{6}{9)\overline{56}}$
$\dfrac{4}{7)\overline{26}}$ $\underline{28}$	Component skill: Student computes a quotient that is too large.	Figure 11.8, "Remediation for Division with Remainders—Quotient Too Large."	Partially worked problems combining quotients—half of the quotients should be too large, half of them should be accurate.
$\dfrac{7}{8)\overline{62}}$ $\underline{56}$ 14	Component skill: Student incorrectly subtracts.	Lead student through subtraction.	Partially worked problems containing accurate quotients in which students must subtract.
$\dfrac{1 \text{ R4}}{7)\overline{29}}$ $\underline{28}$ 1	Component skill: Student misplaces remainder and quotient.	Part C of Figure 11.5.	

$$7\overline{)41}$$
$$\underline{35}$$
with quotient 5.

the teacher says the following:

TEACHER	STUDENTS
"LET'S SUBTRACT. WHAT DOES THE ONES COLUMN SAY?"	"1 minus 5"
"CAN YOU START WITH 1 AND TAKE AWAY 5?"	"No"
"SO WHAT MUST YOU DO?"	"Borrow a 10 from four 10s"
"DO IT. THEN WRITE THE ANSWER."	

The final error type involves confusion regarding placement of the quotient and remainder. The remediation procedure would be to present Part C of the format in Figure 11.5 with several problems and then supervise the students as they work several more problems.

A summary of the diagnosis and remediation procedures for beginning division appears in Figure 11.9.

Multi-Digit Problems

The second stage of instruction in division focuses on multi-digit problems, which become quite complex. Multi-digit quotients are grouped in this text according to the number of digits in the divisor. Problems with one digit divisors are discussed first, followed by a discussion of problems with two digit divisors.

Two algorithms are taught in most commercial programs. One is commonly referred to as the long form; the other, the short form. The long form and short form division algorithms are illustrated below:

Long Form	Short Form
	54
7)382	7)382
350 50	35
32	32
28 4	28
4___	4
54	

The advantage of the long form algorithm is that it presents a clear interpretation of what is involved in division. The disadvantage is that most upper grade teachers expect students to use the short form algorithm. Another advantage of the short form algorithm is the relatively easy set of

preskills which must be mastered prior to introducing division problems. A disadvantage of the short form algorithm is that students may not understand why it works.

In this section, we discuss in detail the procedures for teaching the short form algorithm. We discuss this algorithm because it is the algorithm most programs eventually encourage students to use. Remember, as mentioned earlier, we believe that lower-performing students will be more successful if just one type of algorithm is presented.

One Digit Divisors

Problems with one digit divisors and multi-digit quotients are usually introduced in late third or early fourth grade. Students should know at least 30 to 40 basic division facts and the corresponding remainder facts prior to the introduction of this type of problem.

Two factors affect the difficulty level of single digit divisor problems: the number of digits in the quotient and the presence of a zero in the quotient, The more digits in the quotient, the more difficult a problem will be. For example, the first problem below is more difficult than the second problem

$$5\overline{)835} \qquad 5\overline{)125}$$

because the former will have a three digit quotient while the later will have a two digit quotient. Each additional numeral in the quotient requires an extra set of computations. Similarly, a problem such as the first one below is more difficult than the second

$$5\overline{)52} \qquad 5\ 85$$

because in the former problem the quotient contains a zero. Students, without careful instruction, are likely to leave out the zero.

$$\begin{array}{r} 1 \\ 5\overline{)52} \\ \underline{5} \end{array}$$

This section discusses procedures for teaching students to work all these problem types.

PROBLEMS WITH A TWO DIGIT QUOTIENT Figure 11.11 includes the format for introducing the division algorithm. The format includes five parts. In Part A, the students are taught an important skill: determining the part of the problem to work first. This preskill is necessary since division problems are worked a part at a time. For example, when working the problem

$$5\overline{)375}$$

the student first works the problem

$$5\overline{)37}$$

then after multiplying and subtracting:

$$\begin{array}{r} 7 \\ 5\overline{)375} \\ \underline{35} \\ 25 \end{array}$$

the student divides 5 into 25. The strategy to determine which part to work first involves comparing the divisor with the first digit of the dividend. If the first digit of the dividend is at least as big as the divisor, only the first digit of the dividend is underlined. For example, in this problem the 9 is underlined:

$$7\overline{)\underline{9}45}$$

because the part of the problem to work first is 7 goes into 9. If the first digit of the dividend is not at least as big as the divisor, students are taught to underline the first two digits of the dividend. For example, in this problem 23 is underlined:

$$7\overline{)\underline{23}6}$$

because the part of the problem to be worked first is 7 goes into 23. Note that in presenting this important preskill, the teacher does not use the words *divisor* or *dividend* but rather refers to the number dividing by and dividing into.

Examples must be carefully selected for Part A. In half of the problems, the first digit of the dividend should be smaller than the divisor. In the other half of the problems, the first digit of the dividend should be the same or larger than the divisor. A variety of divisors can be included since students are not actually working the problems at this point. Below is a sample set.

a. $7\overline{)243}$ b. $5\overline{)85}$ c. $4\overline{)235}$

d. $7\overline{)461}$ e. $9\overline{)362}$ f. $8\overline{)89}$

Part B of this format is a worksheet exercise in which the students practice underlining the part of the problem they work first. The teacher guides the students through several problems, then has the students work the rest on their own. The teacher repeats this part daily until students can perform accurately without teacher assistance. Part C is a structured board exercise in which the teacher demonstrates the entire short form algorithm. Figure 11.10 shows the basic steps in that algorithm illustrated with the problem

$$7\overline{)238}$$

Parts D and E in Figure 11.11 are structured and less structured worksheet exercises.

Note that the teacher specifies where digits from the quotient are to be written. The first digit in the quotient is to be written over the last underlined digit:

$$\begin{array}{r} 3 \\ 7\overline{)\underline{23}8} \end{array} \qquad \begin{array}{r} 1 \\ 7\overline{)\underline{82}} \end{array}$$

Each succeeding numeral is to be written over the succeeding digit in the dividend:

$$\begin{array}{r} 613 \\ 7\overline{)\underline{42}91} \end{array}$$

As mentioned earlier, placing the digits of the quotient in proper position helps students in solving problems with zeroes in the quotient and problems containing decimals.

The example selection guidelines for all worksheet exercises remain the same as for Parts A and B except that since students work the problems, the divisors should be limited to familiar facts. Half of the problems should have two digit dividends, and half should have three digit dividends. All problems should have two digit quotients. Below is a sample set of problems that might appear in an exercise. This worksheet assumes students have learned division facts with 2, 9, 5, and 7 as divisors.

a. $5\overline{)87}$ b. $9\overline{)324}$ c. $5\overline{)135}$

d. $7\overline{)86}$ e. $2\overline{)134}$ f. $7\overline{)94}$

g. $2\overline{)156}$ h. $7\overline{)79}$ i. $2\overline{)29}$

ZERO IN THE QUOTIENT Problems with zero as the last digit of a two digit quotient

$$7\overline{)143} \qquad 2\overline{)81} \qquad 5\overline{)153}$$

require special attention. These problems would be introduced several weeks after division problems with two digit quotients have been presented. Parts D to G of the format in Figure 11.11 can be used.

The critical part of the format occurs after students subtract and bring down the last digit. For example, in

$$\begin{array}{r} 3 \\ 7\overline{)214} \\ \underline{21} \\ 4 \end{array}$$

the teacher asks "7 goes into 4 how many times?" Since the answer is zero, the teacher writes a zero above the 4. The teacher may have to model the answer for the first several problems. The format

Figure 11.10 Basic Steps in the Short Form Algorithm

TEACHER	STUDENTS
"READ THE PROBLEM."	"7 goes into 238"
"UNDERLINE THE PART YOU WORK FIRST."	Students underline 7)$\overline{238}$
"SAY THE UNDERLINED PART."	"7 goes into 23"
"WRITE THE ANSWER ABOVE THE LAST UNDERLINED DIGIT." "MULTIPLY 3 × 7, SUBTRACT, AND THEN BRING DOWN THE NEXT NUMBER."	$\begin{array}{r}3\\7\overline{)238}\end{array}$ $\begin{array}{r}3\\7\overline{)238}\\\underline{21}\\28\end{array}$
"READ THE NEW PROBLEM."	"7 goes into 28"
"WRITE THE ANSWER NUMBER ABOVE THE DIGIT YOU JUST BROUGHT DOWN."	$\begin{array}{r}34\\7\overline{)238}\\\underline{21}\\28\end{array}$
"MULTIPLY AND SUBTRACT TO DETERMINE THE REMAINDER."	$\begin{array}{r}34\\7\overline{)238}\\\underline{21}\\28\\\underline{28}\\0\end{array}$
"SAY THE ANSWER."	"7 goes into 238, 34 times"

Figure 11.11 Format for Division with Two Digit Quotients

Day	Part A Preskill— Problems for Determining Where to Begin	Part B Worksheet on Problems for Determining Where to Begin	Part C Structured Board Presentation Problems	Part D Structured Worksheet Problems	Part E Less Structured Problems	Part F Supervised Practice Problems	Part G Independent Worksheet Problems
1	7						
2-accurate	5	5 (5)					
3-4			4	2			
5-6			2	4			
7-8				2	4	3	
9-accurate						6-8	
Till fluent							8-10

Number in parentheses indicates the number of problems students should work on their own. Do not proceed to day 3 until students can perform accurately on Part B.

Figure 11.11 cont'd

PART A: Determining Where to Begin

TEACHER   **STUDENTS**

1. "WHEN A DIVISION PROBLEM HAS LOTS OF DIGITS
   WE WORK THE PROBLEM A PART AT A TIME. WE
   ALWAYS BEGIN A PROBLEM BY UNDERLINING
   THE FIRST PART WE WORK. SOMETIMES WE
   UNDERLINE JUST THE FIRST DIGIT. SOMETIMES
   WE UNDERLINE THE FIRST TWO DIGITS."

2. Write 6)242̄
   "READ THE PROBLEM."   "6 goes into 242"
   "WE'RE DIVIDING BY 6. IF THE FIRST DIGIT IN THE
   NUMBER WE'RE DIVIDING IS AT LEAST AS BIG AS
   6, WE UNDERLINE THE FIRST DIGIT IN 242. IF 6
   CAN'T GO INTO THE FIRST DIGIT, WE UNDERLINE
   THE FIRST TWO DIGITS. LOOK AT THE NUMBER
   WE'RE DIVIDING INTO. THE FIRST DIGIT WE'RE
   DIVIDING INTO IS 2. IS 2 AT LEAST AS BIG AS 6?"   "No"
   "SO WE UNDERLINE THE FIRST TWO DIGITS."
   Underline 6)2̲4̲2
   "THE UNDERLINED PROBLEM SAYS 6 GOES INTO
   24. WHAT DOES THE UNDERLINED PROBLEM SAY?"   "6 goes into 24"
   Repeat step 2 with these problems:

   a. 5)8̲7̲   b. 9)3̲2̲8   c. 4)3̲8̲

   d. 6)6̲2̲   e. 3)2̲4̲5   f. 7)8̲3̲2

PART B: Worksheet on Determining Where to Begin

a. 7)248   b. 3)527   c. 7)486   d. 5)532

e. 5)234   f. 6)184   g. 6)932

h. 4)128   i. 4)436   j. 8)264

1. "TOUCH PROBLEM a. READ THE PROBLEM."   "7 goes into 248"
   "YOU'RE GOING TO UNDERLINE THE PART OF
   THE PROBLEM YOU WORK FIRST. WHAT ARE YOU
   DIVIDING BY?"   "7"
   "IS THE FIRST DIGIT YOU'RE DIVIDING INTO AT
   LEAST AS BIG AS 7?"   "No"
   SO WHAT DO YOU UNDERLINE?"   "24"
   "UNDERLINE 24. SAY THE UNDERLINED PROBLEM."   "7 goes into 24"

Repeat step 1 with five problems. Then have students underline the part they work first in renaming problems.

PART C: Structured Board Presentation

Write on board: 5)213̄

1. "READ THIS PROBLEM."   "5 goes into 213"
   "TELL ME THE PART TO UNDERLINE." Pause.   "21"
   Underline 21   5)2̲1̲3

   TO CORRECT: "LOOK AT THE FIRST DIGIT.
               IS 2 AT LEAST AS BIG AS 5?
               SO WHAT DO YOU UNDERLINE?"

   "WHAT DOES THE UNDERLINED PROBLEM SAY?"   "5 goes into 21"

2. "HOW MANY TIMES DOES 5 GO INTO 21?" Pause.   "4"

Figure 11.11 cont'd

TEACHER	**STUDENTS**

3. "I'LL WRITE THE 4 OVER THE LAST DIGIT UNDERLINED."

Write $5\overline{)2\underline{1}3}$ with 4 above the 1

4. "NOW MULTIPLY 4 × 5. WHAT IS 4 TIMES 5?" Pause.   "20"
Write 20. "NOW I SUBTRACT 20 FROM 21. WHAT IS
1 - 0?"   "1"
Write 1.

5. Point to 3. "WHAT'S THE NEXT DIGIT AFTER THE
UNDERLINED PART?"   "3"
"I BRING IT DOWN AND WRITE IT AFTER THE 1."
Write

$$\begin{array}{r} 4 \\ 5\overline{)2\underline{1}3} \\ \underline{20} \\ 13 \end{array}$$

"WHAT NUMBER IS UNDER THE LINE NOW?"   "13"

6. "THE NEXT PART OF THE PROBLEM SAYS 5 GOES
INTO 13. WHAT DOES THE PROBLEM SAY NOW?"   "5 goes into 13"
"HOW MANY TIMES DOES 5 GO INTO 13?" Pause.   "2"
"I WRITE THE 2 ABOVE THE DIGIT I BROUGHT
DOWN."
Write

$$\begin{array}{r} 42 \\ 5\overline{)2\underline{1}3} \\ \underline{20} \\ 13 \end{array}$$

7. "NOW I MULTIPLY AND SUBTRACT. WHAT IS 2 × 5?"
Pause.   "10"
"I WRITE 10 UNDER THE 13." Write 10. "WHAT IS 13
MINUS 10?" Pause.   "3"

8. "THE PROBLEM IS FINISHED. EVERY DIGIT AFTER
THE UNDERLINED PART HAS A DIGIT OVER IT. 5
GOES INTO 213, 42 TIMES WITH A REMAINDER OF 3.
HOW MANY TIMES DOES 5 GO INTO 213?"   "42 times with a remainder of 3"
Repeat steps 1-8 with $7\overline{)94}$ $2\overline{)135}$ $3\overline{)65}$

PART D: Structured Worksheet

$$3\overline{)137}$$

1. "TOUCH THE PROBLEM. READ THE PROBLEM."   "3 goes into 137"
"WHAT NUMBERS DO YOU UNDERLINE?" Pause.   "13"

2. "UNDERLINE 13. WHAT DOES THE UNDERLINED
PROBLEM SAY?"   "3 goes into 13"

3. "HOW MANY TIMES DOES 3 GO INTO 13?"   "4"
"WRITE 4 ABOVE THE LAST DIGIT YOU
UNDERLINED."

4. "WHAT NUMBERS DO YOU MULTIPLY?"   "4 × 3"
"WHAT IS 4 × 3?"   "12"

Figure 11.11 cont'd

TEACHER	**STUDENTS**

5. "WRITE 12 UNDER 13, THEN SUBTRACT. WHAT IS 13 - 12?"

"1"

6. "WHAT IS THE NEXT DIGIT IN THE NUMBER YOU'RE DIVIDING INTO?" Pause.

"7"

BRING DOWN THE 7 AND WRITE IT NEXT TO THE 1."

$$\begin{array}{r} 7 \\ 3\overline{)137} \\ \underline{12} \\ 17 \end{array}$$

7. "WHAT NUMBER IS UNDER THE LINE?"
"WHAT DOES THIS PART OF THE PROBLEM SAY?"
"HOW MANY TIMES DOES 3 GO INTO 17?" Pause.

"17"
"3 goes into 17"
"5"

8. "WRITE THE 5 ABOVE THE DIGIT YOU BROUGHT DOWN." Monitor student responses.

9. "WHAT NUMBER DO YOU MULTIPLY?"
"WHAT IS 5 × 3?"
"WRITE 15 UNDER 17 AND SUBTRACT. WHAT IS 17 - 15?"
"IS THERE ANOTHER NUMBER TO BRING DOWN?"

"5 × 3"
"15"

"2"
"No"

10. "EVERY DIGIT AFTER THE UNDERLINED PART HAS A DIGIT OVER IT. SO YOU FINISHED THE PROBLEM. WHAT'S THE REMAINDER?"
"HOW MANY TIMES DOES 3 GO INTO 137?"
Repeat steps 1-10 with remaining problems.

"2"
"45 with a remainder of 2"

PART E: Less Structured Worksheet

$$4\overline{)69}$$

1. "TOUCH THE PROBLEM. READ THE PROBLEM."
"UNDERLINE THE PART YOU WORK FIRST."
"SAY THE UNDERLINED PROBLEM."
"HOW MANY TIMES DOES 4 GO INTO 6?"

"4 goes into 69"
$4\overline{)69}$
"4 goes into 6"
"1"

2. "WRITE THE 1, MULTIPLY, SUBTRACT, AND THEN BRING DOWN THE NEXT DIGIT. (pause) WHAT NUMBER IS UNDER THE LINE NOW?"

"29"

3. "SAY THE NEW PROBLEM."

"4 goes into 29"

"HOW MANY TIMES DOES 4 GO INTO 29?"

"7"

"WRITE 7 IN THE ANSWER. THEN MULTIPLY AND SUBTRACT. (pause) IS THERE ANOTHER NUMBER TO BRING DOWN?"

"No"

"IS THE PROBLEM FINISHED?"

"Yes"

4. "HOW MANY TIMES DOES 4 GO INTO 69?"

"17 with a remainder of 1"

Repeat steps 1-4 with remaining problems.

would be presented for several days. Thereafter, three or four problems with a quotient ending in zero would be included in daily worksheet exercises.

QUOTIENTS OF THREE OR MORE DIGITS Problems with quotients of three or more digits are introduced only when students have mastered problems with two digit quotients. No preskills or board exercises need be presented. The teacher merely presents the less structured part of the division format in Figure 11.11 for several days. The teacher emphasizes the need to keep bringing down digits until an answer has been written above the last digit of the dividend.

Problems with a zero as one of the three digits in the quotient are introduced only after students can solve problems without zeroes in the quotient. Problems with a zero as the last digit could be introduced a week or so after problems with three digit quotients have been introduced. These problems should cause students relatively little difficulty since two digit quotients with a zero would have been taught earlier. On the other hand, problems with a zero as the second digit of a three digit quotient:

$$5)\overline{515}^{103} \qquad 2)\overline{814}^{407}$$

will be difficult for many students. A structured worksheet exercise (Part D of Figure 11.11) should be presented. After bringing down the first number,

$$5)\overline{517}^{1}$$
$$\underline{5}$$
$$1$$

the teacher can say "The next part says 5 goes into 1; 5 goes into 1 zero times, so I write 0 in the answer. What is zero times 5? So I write zero under the 1. Now we subtract and bring down the next number." The teacher presents the structured worksheet exercise for several days with 3–4 problems. Next a supervised worksheet exercise containing about 10 problems, 3 or 4 of which have zero as the middle digit, would be presented. Supervised practice is continued until students develop accuracy.

Problems with quotients of four or more digits are usually presented in late fourth grade or early fifth. For students who have mastered all types of problems with three digit quotients, these longer problems should cause little difficulty.

SELF-CHECKING After students become profi-cient in working division problems with remainders, they should be taught to check their answers. A checking procedure for division is to multiply the divisor and quotient and add the remainder, if there is one. The teacher introduces checking on a worksheet exercise. After the students complete the first problem, he says, "Here's how to check your work to make sure you have the right answer. Multiply the numbers outside the division sign and add the remainder. What are the numbers outside the division sign? . . . Multiply them. What's the remainder? . . . Add and see if that's the number inside the division sign . . . Are the numbers the same? So your answer must be correct."

An exercise to encourage checking is to give students already worked problems, about half of which have incorrect answers. The teacher would instruct the students to check their answers and correct mistakes.

Two Digit Divisors

Solving problems with two digit divisors requires the integration of numerous component skills into a fairly lengthy strategy. The steps in the short form algorithm are outlined in Figure 11.12.

The complexity of problems with two digit divisors is affected mainly by whether or not the estimating, or rounding off, procedure produces a correct quotient. In some cases, the estimate may yield a quotient that is too large. For example, in the problem

$$53)\overline{203}$$

students round off 53 to 5 10s and 203 to 20 10s, and then determine how many 5s in 20. The estimated quotient, 4, when multiplied by 53 equals 212, which is too large to be subtracted from 203. Since the estimate yielded too large a quotient, the actual quotient must be 3, not 4.

In contrast, other estimates may yield a quotient that is too small. For example, in the problem

$$56)\overline{284}$$

when 56 is rounded off to 6 10s and 284 is rounded off to 28 10s, the estimate is a quotient of 4. However, 56×4 is 224, which when subtracted from 284 leaves a difference of 60, from which another group of 56 could be made. Since the estimated quotient yields too small a quotient, the actual quotient must be one larger than 4.

Problems in which the estimated quotient is too large or too small are more difficult and should

Figure 11.12   Short-Form Algorithm—Two Digit Divisors

TEACHER	STUDENTS
1. "READ PROBLEM a."	"37 goes into 1586"
2. "UNDERLINE THE PART TO WORK FIRST."	37)1586
3. "READ THE FIRST PART."	"37 goes into 158"
4. "ESTIMATE THE QUOTIENT AS TENS UNITS."	37 is converted to 4 10s 158 is converted to 16 10s "4 goes into 16 four times"
5. "PLACE ESTIMATED QUOTIENT ABOVE LAST UNDERLINED DIGIT, THEN MULTIPLY AND SUBTRACT."	4 37)1586 148 10
6. "COMPARE THE DIFFERENCE AND DIVISOR TO SEE IF QUOTIENT IS CORRECT. BRING DOWN THE NEXT NUMBER IN DIVIDEND."	37)1586 148 106
7. "READ THE NEW PROBLEM."	"37 goes into 106"
8. "ESTIMATE THE QUOTIENT FOR THE NEXT PROBLEM."	37 is converted to 4 10s 106 is converted to 11 10s "4 goes into 11 two times"
9. "PLACE ESTIMATED QUOTIENT ABOVE THE LAST DIGIT BROUGHT DOWN, THEN MULTIPLY AND SUBTRACT."	42 37)1586 148 106 $\underline{74}$ 32
10. "COMPARE DIFFERENCE AND DIVISOR TO SEE IF QUOTIENT IS CORRECT."	

not be introduced until students can work problems in which the estimated quotients prove to be correct.

PRESKILLS   Students should have mastered all the component skills needed to solve division problems with one digit divisors before problems with two digit divisors are introduced. Additional preskills are rounding off numbers to the nearest tens unit, which is discussed next, and multiplying multi-digit numbers, which was discussed in the previous chapter.

Rounding off numbers to the nearest tens unit is a critical skill for problems with two digit divisors. The first part of the strategy teaches students to estimate how many groups the size of the divisor can be made from the dividend. In

$$54)\overline{186}$$

the question is, "How many times does 54 go into 186?" The estimate is derived by rounding off and expressing both the divisor and dividend as tens units: e.g., 54 is rounded to 5 10s, and 186 is rounded to 19 10s. The students then figure out how many 5s in 19.

Figure 11.13 contains the format for teaching students to round off numbers to the nearest tens unit. In Part A, the teacher models and tests converting a tens number that ends in zero to a unit of tens; 340 = 34 10s, 720 = 72 10s, 40 = 4 10s. The teacher repeats a set of six to eight examples until the students can respond correctly to all of the examples. In Part B, the teacher models and tests rounding numbers that end in any digit to the nearest tens unit. The teacher writes a numeral on the board and asks the students if the number is closer to the tens number preceding it or following it. For example, after writing 236 on the board, the teacher asks the students if 236 is closer to 230 or 240. After the students respond "240" the teacher asks, "So how many 10s is 238 closest to, 23 10s or 24 10s?"

Part C is a worksheet exercise in which the student must write the tens unit closest to the number (e.g., 342 = __ 10s). Students may require several weeks of practice to develop mastery in this skill. Division problems with two digit divisors should not be introduced until mastery of this preskill is achieved.

There are several example selection guidelines for this format: (a) half the numbers to be transformed should have a numeral less than 5 in the ones column while the other half of the numbers should have 5 or a numeral greater than 5; (b) about two-thirds of the examples should be three digit numbers and one-third, two digit numbers, so that practice is provided on the two types of numbers students will have to round off, and (c) numbers which may cause particular difficulty for students should not be included in initial exercises. Two types of numbers may cause difficulty: (a) numbers in which the last two digits are 95 or greater (e.g., 397, 295, 498), which require rounding off to the next hundreds grouping (397 rounds off to 40 10s, and 295 rounds off to 30 10s), and (b) numbers which have a zero in the tens column (e.g., 408, 207, 305). Special emphasis should be given to these two types about a week after the format is initially presented.

sented. About 3–4 examples of these types should also be included in worksheet exercises.

PROBLEMS WITH CORRECT ESTIMATED QUOTIENTS Initially, division problems with two digit divisors should be limited to problems in which the estimated quotients prove to be correct. Also, the first problems should involve a one digit quotient. Problems containing a two digit quotient can usually be introduced several days after problems with a one digit quotient are presented.

The format for teaching the strategy to work problems with two digit divisors appears in Figure 11.14. It includes four parts. Parts A and B teach component skills unique to the short form algorithm: horizontal multiplication and estimating a quotient by rounding off the divisor and dividend.

Part A teaches students to multiply the estimated quotient and divisor, which are written horizontally, and to place the product below the dividend. In the problem

$$57\overline{)391}$$

the estimated quotient 6 and the divisor 57 are multiplied. The student first multiplies 6 x 7, which is

Figure 11.13   Format for Rounding to Nearest Tens Unit

Day	Part A	Part B	Part C
	Express as Tens Unit Problems	Structured Board Problems	Worksheet Problems
1–2	8		
3–4	8	6	
5–accurate		6	6 (14)

Number in parentheses indicates the number of problems students should work on their own.

PART A: Expressing Numbers As Tens Units

TEACHER	STUDENTS
Write on board: 190	
1. "WHAT NUMBER?"	"190"
"ANOTHER WAY OF SAYING 190 IS 19 10s. WHAT'S ANOTHER WAY OF SAYING 190?"	"19 10s"
2. Repeat step 1 with 80, 230.	
3. "WHAT'S ANOTHER WAY OF SAYING 140?"	"14 10s"
4. Repeat step 3 with 280, 30, 580, 420, 60, 500, 280, 40, 700	

Figure 11.13 cont'd

PART B: Structured Board Presentation

TEACHER   **STUDENTS**

Write on board: 186

1. "WHAT NUMBER?"   "186"
2. "IS 186 CLOSER TO 180 or 190?"   "190"

      TO CORRECT: "IF WE HAVE AT LEAST 5 IN THE
                 ONES COLUMN WE ROUND OFF TO
                 THE NEXT HIGHER TENS UNIT.
                 HOW MANY ONES IN 186? SO
                 WE ROUND OFF TO 190."

    "SO IS 186 CLOSER TO 18 10s OR 19 10s?" Pause.   "19 10s"

      TO CORRECT: "186 IS CLOSER TO 190. HOW
                 MANY 10s IN 190?"

3. Repeat step 2 with these examples:

142	14 10s or 15 10s
83	8 10s or 9 10s
47	4 10s or 5 10s
286	28 10s or 29 10s
432	43 10s or 44 10s
27	2 10s or 3 10s
529	52 10s or 53 10s

PART C: Structured Worksheet

Worksheet

Round off these numbers to the nearest 10. Write how many
10s in the rounded off number:

142___10s	87___10s	537___10s	497___10s
287___10s	426___10s	248___10s	321___10s
825___10s	53___10s	632___10s	503___10s
546___10s	182___10s	428___10s	278___10s
932___10s	203___10s	561___10s	426___10s

1. Call on a student to read the directions. "READ THE
   FIRST NUMBER."   "142"

2. "THINK. 142 IS CLOSEST TO HOW MANY 10s?"   "14 10s"

      TO CORRECT: "IS 142 CLOSER TO 140 OR 150? SO IS
                 142 CLOSER TO 14 or 15 10s?" Write
                 the answer.

3. "WRITE 14 IN THE BLANK." Repeat steps 2-3 with
   several more examples.

---

42. The 2 is placed under the 1 in the dividend, and
the 4 is carried over the 5 in the divisor:

$$4 \quad 6$$
$$57\overline{)391}$$
$$\underline{2}$$

The student then multiplies 6 x 5 and adds the
carried 4. The total 34 is written under the 39 in the
dividend:

$$4 \quad 6$$
$$57\overline{)391}$$
$$\underline{342}$$

Part B presents the rounding off strategy to
determine the estimated quotient. The teacher
writes a problem on the board and next to the
problem writes a box with a division sign:

$$37\overline{)1582} \qquad \boxed{)}$$

The rounded off problem is written in the box. The
teacher has students read the problem and determine the part to work first (e.g., 37 goes into 158)
and then underline those numbers in the dividend.
The students then round off 37 to 4 10s and 158 to

Figure 11.14   Format for Correct Estimated Quotients

Day	Part A Multiplying— Board/ Worksheet Problems		Part B Estimating— Board/ Worksheet Problems		Part C Structured Worksheet Problems	Part D Less Structured Worksheet Problems	Part E Supervised Practice Problems	Part F Independent Practice Problems
1	3	3	3	3				
2	2	4 (2)	2	4 (2)				
3	1	2 (4)	1	2 (4)				
4		1 (5)		1 (5)				
5					4			
6					4			
7					2	3		
8					1	4		
9						5		
10-Till accurate							5	
Till fluent								6-8

Numbers in parentheses indicate the number of problems students should work on their own.

PART A: Preskill—Multiplying Quotient Times Divisor

I. Board Presentation

TEACHER	STUDENTS

Write on board:

$$\begin{array}{r} 4 \\ 54\overline{)231} \end{array}$$

1. "THIS PROBLEM SAYS 54 GOES INTO 231, FOUR TIMES. WHAT DOES THE PROBLEM SAY?"   "54 goes into 231 four times"

2. "WE HAVE TO FIGURE OUT THE REMAINDER. WE MULTIPLY 4 TIMES 54. WHAT DO WE MULTIPLY?"   "4 × 54"

3. "WHEN I MULTIPLY 4 × 54, FIRST I MULTIPLY 4 × 4, THEN I MULTIPLY 4 × 5. WHAT IS 4 × 4?"   "16"
   "I WRITE THE 6 UNDER THE LAST UNDERLINED DIGIT AND CARRY THE 1."

Write on board:

$$\begin{array}{r} 1 \quad 4 \\ 54\overline{)231} \\ 6 \end{array}$$

4. "NOW I MULTIPLY 4 × 5 AND ADD THE 1 I CARRIED. WHAT IS 4 × 5?"   "20"
   "AND ONE MORE IS?"   "21"
   "I WRITE THE 21 IN FRONT OF THE 6."

Write on board:

$$\begin{array}{r} 4 \\ 54\overline{)231} \\ \underline{216} \end{array}$$

5. "WHAT IS 4 × 54?"   "216"

Figure 11.14 cont'd

TEACHER	**STUDENTS**

6. "WE SUBTRACT 216 FROM 231 TO FIGURE OUT
   THE REMAINDER. CAN WE START WITH 1 AND
   SUBTRACT 6?"   "No"
   "WE MUST BORROW." Write:

     2 1
   2 3̶ 1.
   "WHAT IS 11 MINUS 6?"   "5"
   "WHAT IS 2 MINUS 1?"   "1"

7. "54 GOES INTO 231 FOUR TIMES WITH A RE-
   MAINDER OF 15. SAY THAT."   "54 goes into 231 four times with
   Repeat steps 1-7 with: a remainder of 15"

$$\overset{3}{48)\overline{156}} \qquad \overset{4}{94)\overline{413}}$$

II. Worksheet

a. $\overset{3}{27)\overline{103}}$ b. $\overset{6}{46)\overline{278}}$ c. $\overset{5}{14)\overline{80}}$

1. "READ PROBLEM a."   "27 goes into 103 three times"

2. "YOU NEED TO MULTIPLY 3 × 27. WHEN YOU
   MULTIPLY 3 × 27, WHAT DO YOU MULTIPLY FIRST?"   "3 × 7"

3. "WHAT IS 3 × 7?"   "21"
   "WRITE THE 1 AND CARRY THE TWO 10s."

   TO CORRECT: "WRITE THE 1 UNDER THE 3. (pause)
              CARRY THE TWO 10s ABOVE THE 2 IN
              27."

4. "NOW WHAT DO YOU MULTIPLY?"   "3 × 2"
   "WHAT IS 3 × 2?"   "6"
   "ADD THE 2 YOU CARRIED. WHAT'S THE ANSWER?"   "8"
   "WRITE THE 8."

5. "FIGURE OUT THE REMAINDER. BE CAREFUL TO
   BORROW IN THE TENS COLUMN."

6. "WHAT IS THE REMAINDER?"   "22"
   "YES, 27 GOES INTO 103 THREE TIMES WITH A
   REMAINDER OF 22. SAY THAT."   "27 goes into 103 three times with
                                                        a remainder of 22"

   Repeat steps 1-6 with several problems; then have students
   work the rest independently (see schedule).

PART B: Preskill—Estimating

I. Board Presentation

Write on board:

$$37)\overline{932} \qquad \boxed{)}$$

1. "WHAT DOES THE PROBLEM SAY?"   "37 goes into 932"

2. "WE HAVE TO UNDERLINE THE PART WE WORK
   FIRST. DOES 37 GOES INTO 9?"   "No"
   "DOES 37 GOES INTO 93?"   "Yes"
   "SO I UNDERLINE THE FIRST TWO DIGITS."

3. "I'LL READ THE PART WE WORK FIRST; 37 GOES
   INTO 93. SAY THE PART WE WORK FIRST."   "37 goes into 93"

4. "TO FIND OUT HOW MANY TIMES 37 GOES INTO
   93 WE MUST ROUND OFF. THE BOX NEXT TO THE
   PROBLEM IS FOR ROUNDING OFF."

Figure 11.14 cont'd

TEACHER | **STUDENTS**

5. "FIRST I ROUND OFF 37; 37 IS ROUNDED OFF TO
HOW MANY 10s?" Pause, write: "4"

$$4\overline{)}$$

"NINETY-THREE IS ROUNDED OFF TO HOW MANY
10s?" Pause, write: "9"

$$4\overline{)9}$$

"READ THE ROUNDED OFF PROBLEM"   "4 goes into 9"

6. "FOUR GOES INTO NINE HOW MANY TIMES?"   "2"
"SO IN THE PROBLEM WE STARTED WITH, I WRITE
2 OVER THE LAST UNDERLINED DIGIT." Write:

$$37\overline{)9\underline{3}2}^{\;2}$$

Repeat steps 1–6 with $24\overline{)136}$ $52\overline{)386}$ $34\overline{)942}$

II. Worksheet

a. $34\overline{)1225}$ $\boxed{\overline{)}}$ b. $79\overline{)246}$ $\boxed{\overline{)}}$

c. $49\overline{)538}$ $\boxed{\overline{)}}$ d. $27\overline{)943}$ $\boxed{\overline{)}}$

e. $36\overline{)193}$ $\boxed{\overline{)}}$

1. "WHAT DOES PROBLEM a SAY?"   "34 goes into 1225"

2. "WHAT DIGITS DO YOU UNDERLINE?" Pause.   "122"
"UNDERLINE THE PART YOU WORK FIRST. SAY
THE UNDERLINED PROBLEM."   "34 goes into 122"

3. "LET'S WRITE THE ROUNDED OFF PROBLEM
FOR 34 INTO 122 IN THE BOX. HOW MANY 10s DOES
34 ROUND OFF TO?" Pause.   "3"
"WRITE 3 IN THE BOX. HOW MANY 10s DOES 122
ROUND OFF TO?" Pause.   "12"
"WRITE 12 IN THE BOX. READ THE ROUNDED
OFF PROBLEM."   "3 goes into 12"
"THREE GOES INTO TWELVE HOW MANY TIMES?"   "4"

4. "WRITE THE ANSWER IN THE PROBLEM YOU
STARTED WITH. WRITE IT ABOVE THE LAST
UNDERLINED DIGIT."
Repeat steps 1–4 with three more problems; then have
students work the next problems on their own (see sched-
ule at beginning of format).

PART C: Structured Worksheet

Sample problem: $38\overline{)1432}$

$$\boxed{\overline{)}}$$

$$\boxed{\overline{)}}$$

1. "READ THE PROBLEM."   "38 goes into 1432"
"UNDERLINE THE PART YOU WORK FIRST.

Figure 11.14 cont'd

TEACHER	**STUDENTS**

WHAT DID YOU UNDERLINE?" — "143"

"READ THE UNDERLINED PROBLEM." — "38 goes into 143"

2. "WRITE THE ROUNDED OFF PROBLEM IN THE
BOX. HOW MANY 10s DOES 38 ROUND OFF TO?" Pause. — "4"

"WRITE 4. HOW MANY 10s DOES 143 ROUND
OFF TO?" Pause. — "14"

"WRITE 14. READ THE ROUNDED OFF PROBLEM." — "4 goes into 14"

3. "FOUR GOES INTO FOURTEEN HOW MANY TIMES?" — "3"

"WRITE 3 ABOVE THE LAST DIGIT YOU
UNDERLINED."

4. "NOW WE MULTIPLY 3 TIMES 38. WHAT IS 3 × 8?" — "24"
Pause. "WRITE 4 BELOW THE LAST UNDERLINED
DIGIT AND CARRY THE 2." Pause. "NOW MULTIPLY
3 × 3 AND ADD 2." Pause. "WHAT'S THE ANSWER?"
Pause. — "11"

"WRITE 11 NEXT TO THE 4."

5. "NOW SUBTRACT 113 FROM 143. (pause)
WHAT IS 143 MINUS 114?" — "29"

6. "LET'S SEE IF THERE'S A SECOND PART TO
WORK. IS THERE A DIGIT AFTER THE UNDER-
LINED PART TO BRING DOWN?" — "Yes"

If the answer to step 6 is no, skip steps 7-10;
go directly to step 11.

7. "BRING DOWN THAT DIGIT. WHAT NUMBER IS
UNDER THE LINE NOW?" — "292"

"SAY THE NEW PROBLEM." — "38 goes into 292"

8. "LET'S WRITE THE ROUNDED OFF PROBLEM IN
THE SECOND BOX. HOW MANY 10s DOES 38
ROUND OFF TO?" — "4"

"WRITE 4. HOW MANY 10s DOES 292 ROUND OFF
TO?" — "29"

"WRITE 29. READ THE ROUNDED OFF PROBLEM." — "4 goes into 29"

9. "HOW MANY TIMES DOES 4 GO INTO 29?" — "7"

"WRITE 7 IN THE PROBLEM YOU STARTED WITH.
WRITE IT ABOVE THE 2 YOU BROUGHT DOWN."

10. "NOW WE MULTIPLY 7 × 38. WHAT DO YOU MULTIPLY?" —

"MULTIPLY AND WRITE THE ANSWER BELOW 292.
(pause) WHAT IS 7 × 38?" — "7 times 38"

"SUBTRACT 292 - 266 TO FIND THE
REMAINDER. (pause) WHAT'S 292 - 266?" — "266"
— "26"

"ARE THERE ANY MORE DIGITS TO BRING DOWN?" — "No"

11. "SO YOU'RE DONE WITH THE PROBLEM. HOW
MANY TIMES DOES 38 GO INTO 1432?" — "37 times with a remainder of 26"

Repeat steps 1-11 with remaining problems.

PART D: Less Structured Worksheet

a. 18)604

Figure 11.14 cont'd

TEACHER	**STUDENTS**
1. "READ PROBLEM a."	"18 goes into 604"
"UNDERLINE THE PART YOU WORK FIRST. WHAT DID YOU UNDERLINE?"	"60"
"READ THE UNDERLINED PROBLEM."	"18 goes into 60"
2. "WRITE THE ROUNDED OFF PROBLEM IN THE UPPER BOX. (pause) SAY THE ROUNDED OFF PROBLEM."	"2 goes into 6"
3. "WRITE THE ANSWER, THEN MULTIPLY." Pause. SAY THE SUBTRACTION PROBLEM."	"60 - 54"
"SUBTRACT 60 - 54." Pause. "WHAT IS 60 - 54?"	"6"
4. "WHAT DO YOU DO NEXT?"	"Bring down the 4"
"DO IT."	
5. "SAY THE NEW PROBLEM."	"18 goes into 64"
6. "WRITE THE ROUNDED OFF PROBLEM IN THE SECOND BOX." Pause. "SAY THE ROUNDED OFF PROBLEM."	"2 goes into 6"
7. "WRITE THE ANSWER, THEN MULTIPLY AND SUBTRACT." Pause. "WHAT IS THE REMAINDER?"	"10"
8. "ARE YOU FINISHED? HOW MANY TIMES DOES 18 GO INTO 604?"	"33 times with a remainder of 10"

16 10s and write the rounded off problem in the box:

$$4\overline{)16}$$

After rounding off, the students figure out the answer to the rounded off problem and write the answer above the last underlined digit in the original problem:

$$\overset{4}{37\overline{)1582}} \qquad 4\overline{)16}$$

Note on the schedule at the beginning of Figure 11.14 that Parts A and B can be introduced at the same time. Also note that both parts contain two sections. In the first section of each part, the teacher presents several problems on the board. In the second section, the teacher guides, that is, leads the students through several worksheet problems and then has them work several problems on their own. Each succeeding day, the students work more problems on their own. On the fourth day, the teacher guides the students through one problem and has them work five on their own. If the students can work at least four of the five problems correctly, they are presented the next day with Part C in which the entire strategy is introduced. If students miss two or more problems, they continue working on Parts A and/or B. Students must be able to perform the multiplication and estimation skills accurately before the entire strategy is presented.

Part C is a structured worksheet exercise in which students are guided through all the steps in the strategy. For the first two weeks, the boxes to do the rounding off should be written on students' worksheets. A sample problem on a worksheet would look like this:

$$37\overline{)1582}$$

The upper box is for writing the rounded off problem for the first part of the problem; the lower box is for writing the rounded off problem for the second part of the problem.

Two example selection guidelines are important to this format. First and foremost, all the problems must yield estimated quotients that are correct. Second, in half of the problems, the first two digits in the dividend must be less than the divisor:

$$37\overline{)2431} \qquad 52\overline{)4681}$$

while in the other problems, the first two digits must be greater than the divisor:

$$37\overline{)441} \qquad 52\overline{)838}$$

Several problems with a one digit quotient should be included in supervised and independent worksheets. The mixture of problems ensures that students will use the steps of determining which part to work first.

PROBLEMS WITH INCORRECT ESTIMATED QUOTIENTS In a minor, but still significant, proportion of problems with two digit divisors, one or more estimated quotients will prove to be incorrect. For example, in the problem

$$39\overline{)155}$$

the estimated quotient would prove too large since 4×39 equals 156. Problems in which the estimated quotient is incorrect should be introduced about a week after students have developed accuracy in working problems in which the estimates are correct. The first problems presented should result in a one digit quotient. The format for presenting these problems appears in Figure 11.15.

The format includes two parts. Part A focuses solely on the component skill of determining if the estimated quotient is correct and what to do if it is not correct. Separate sequences of steps are indicated for problems in which the estimated quotient is too large and for problems in which the estimated quotient is too small. The rules in the formats (If you can't subtract, make the answer smaller; if the remainder is too big, make the answer bigger) are designed to minimize potential student confusion.

In Part A, the students are given a worksheet on which the estimated quotient is written in each problem. The worksheet includes a variety of problems. One-third of the problems have a quotient that is a multiple too large:

$$34\overline{)146} \quad \begin{array}{c}5\end{array}$$

One-third of the problems have a quotient that is a multiple too small:

$$36\overline{)193} \quad \begin{array}{c}4\end{array}$$

The final third of the problems contain the estimated quotients that are correct:

$$28\overline{)153} \quad \begin{array}{c}5\end{array}$$

Students first multiply the quotient and divisor. If the product of these two numbers is greater than the dividend, the teacher points out that the answer

must be less. In

$$\begin{array}{r} 5 \\ 34\overline{)146} \\ \underline{170} \end{array}$$

the teacher says, "We can't subtract. We must make the answer smaller. Cross out the 5 and write 4." In problems in which the estimated quotient is too small, the teacher has the students compare their remainder to the divisor. If the remainder is as big or bigger than the divisor, the quotient is to be made larger. For example, in

$$\begin{array}{r} 4 \\ 36\overline{)193} \\ \underline{144} \\ 49 \end{array}$$

the teacher points out that another group of 36 can be made from 49, so the answer is made bigger. The 4 is erased and replaced with a 5.

A special type of problem yields an estimated quotient of 10 or above. For these problems, the teacher introduces a rule that no matter how high the answer to the rounded off problem, the highest number used in an answer is 9. Then, even though rounding off

$$24\overline{)228} \quad \text{as} \quad 2\overline{)23}$$

yields 11 as an estimated quotient, the student would still use 9 as the quotient. Several problems of this type should be included in the exercises.

Practice on problems yielding an incorrect quotient would be continued daily for several weeks. During this time, problems would be limited to those which have one digit quotients. Problems with multi-digit quotients would not be introduced until students are successful at working problems with single digit quotients. The teacher should prepare worksheets containing a variety of problems. In some problems, the estimate for the first digit of the quotient should prove too large or too small, while the estimate for the second digit proves correct. For example, in the problem

$$64\overline{)1803}$$

only the estimate for the first numeral in the quotient is incorrect (3 is too large). In other problems, the estimate for the first digit of the quotient would be correct while the estimate for the second part would be incorrect. For example, in the problem

$$64\overline{)3317}$$

the estimate for 64 into 331 is correct while the second part of the problem, 64 into 117, yields an

Figure 11.15 Format for Incorrect Estimated Quotients

Day	Part A Structured Worksheet Problems	Part B Less Structured Worksheet Problems	Part C Supervised Practice Problems	Part D Independent Practice Problems
1-3	4 (6)			
4-7		9		
8-accurate			9	
Till fluent				9

Number in parentheses indicates the number of problems students should work on their own.

PART A: Structured Worksheet

TEACHER   **STUDENTS**

a. 4
37)142

b. 5
48)299

c. 5
48)299

d. 4
79)315

e. 3
46)192

f. 3
52)148

g. 4
82)318

h. 5
34)178

i. 2
26)81

1. "THE ANSWERS TO SOME OF THESE PROBLEMS ARE WRONG. TO FIND THE WRONG ANSWERS, YOU FIGURE OUT THE REMAINDER. IF YOU CAN'T SUBTRACT, YOU MUST MAKE THE ANSWER SMALLER. IF YOU FIND A REMAINDER, BUT IT IS TOO BIG, YOU MUST MAKE THE ANSWER BIGGER."

2. "TOUCH PROBLEM a. WHAT DOES THE PROBLEM SAY?"

"37 goes into 142 four times"

3. "WHAT ARE YOU GOING TO MULTIPLY?" "DO THE MULTIPLICATION. WRITE THE MINUS SIGN AND STOP."

"4 times 37"

4. "SAY THE SUBTRACTION PROBLEM."

"142 - 148"

5. "CAN YOU SUBTRACT 142 MINUS 148?" "WE CAN'T SUBTRACT SO WE MUST MAKE THE ANSWER SMALLER."

"No"

6. "SO YOU HAVE TO CROSS OUT THE 4 AND WRITE A 3 ABOVE IT. DO IT, THEN ERASE THE 148."

7. "NOW MULTIPLY 3 × 37."

8. "READ THE SUBTRACTION PROBLEM NOW."

"142 - 111"

9. "SUBTRACT AND FIGURE OUT THE REMAINDER." "THAT'S ALL WE DO FOR NOW."

"31"

Steps 4a-8a are for problems in which the estimated quotient is too small.

The problem is 5
48)299

4a. "SAY THE SUBTRACTION PROBLEM." "CAN YOU SUBTRACT 240 FROM 299?" "SUBTRACT." Pause.

"299 - 240"
"Yes"

Figure 11.15 cont'd

TEACHER	**STUDENTS**
5a. "WHAT IS THE REMAINDER?"	"59"
"IS THE REMAINDER TOO BIG?"	"Yes"

      TO CORRECT: Ask, "WHAT ARE WE DIVIDING BY?
                   IS THE REMAINDER AT LEAST AS BIG
                   AS 48?"

      "YOU CAN MAKE ANOTHER GROUP. SO WE MAKE
THE ANSWER BIGGER. CROSS OUT THE 5 AND
WRITE 6. ERASE 240."

6a. "NOW MULTIPLY 6 × 48."

7a. "READ THE SUBTRACTION PROBLEM NOW."	"299 - 288"
"SUBTRACT."	

8a. "WHAT'S THE ANSWER?"	"11"
"CAN WE MAKE ANOTHER GROUP OF 48?"	"No"
"SO WE'RE ALL FINISHED."	

Repeat steps 1-9 or 4a-8a with three of the remaining problems. Have students work the remaining problems on their own.

PART B: Less Structured Worksheet

a. 42)197   [ )]   b. 36)203   [ )]   c. 58)232   [ )]

1. "TOUCH PROBLEM a. READ THE PROBLEM."   "42 goes into 197"

2. "UNDERLINE THE PART YOU WORK FIRST."

3. "WRITE THE ROUNDED OFF PROBLEM. SAY THE
   ROUNDED OFF PROBLEM."   "4 goes into 20"

4. "WHAT IS THE ANSWER?"   "5"
   "MULTIPLY 5 TIME 42." Pause.
   "CAN YOU SUBTRACT?"   "No"

   Note: Present step 5 or 6.

5. If the answer to step 4 is no say, "SO WHAT MUST YOU DO?
   FIX YOUR ANSWER THEN MULTIPLY AND SUBTRACT."

6. If the answer to step 4 is yes, say, "SUBTRACT ____ FROM
   ____. WHAT IS THE REMAINDER? IS THE REMAINDER
   TOO BIG?" Continue if answer is yes. "SO WHAT MUST
   WE DO? ERASE ____ AND WRITE ____. THEN MULTIPLY
   AND SUBTRACT." Pause. "WHAT IS THE REMAINDER?"
   "IS THAT REMAINDER TOO BIG? SO WE'RE FINISHED.
   SAY THE WHOLE ANSWER."
   Repeat steps 1-6 with remaining problems.

---

estimated quotient that is too large. Finally, in some problems the estimate for both numerals of the quotient would be incorrect. Figure 11.16 includes sets of problems that can be used in these exercises.

Problems in which the estimated quotient is too small are particularly difficult for students. In order to prepare students for this format, the teacher should present an exercise for several days prior to introducing the format in Figure 11.15, focusing on when a remainder is too big. In this exercise the teacher writes about six problems with two digit divisors on the board and models how to determine if the remainder is too big.

Below is a suggested wording:

26)135

TEACHER	STUDENT
1. "READ THE PROBLEM."	"26 goes into 135"
2. "WHAT ARE WE DIVIDING BY?"	"26"
3. "SO, THE REMAINDER IS TOO BIG IF IT IS AT LEAST AS BIG AS 26."	
4. "WOULD A REMAINDER OF 31 BE TOO BIG?"	"Yes"
5. Repeat step 4 with 24, 26, 42, 18, 35.	

Figure 11.16 Examples of Two Digit Divisor Problems with Single Digit Quotients

Estimate Yields Quotient That Is Correct

34)198   82)591   37)1723   72)3924   73)2308   53)230   27)94   52)2731

53)1752   29)2150   48)268   51)78   68)1528   27)941   51)2398   39)94

90)673   80)7485   19)813   86)5000   40)289   48)269   12)384   41)987

25)896   67)242   82)370   89)6703   58)1256   16)415   32)197   11)48

45)968   93)5780   42)534   75)183   28)154   36)2000   84)991   60)2486

Estimate Yields Quotient Too Large

73)289   84)246   91)632   64)3321   53)1524   16)60   23)170   13)68

93)2724   24)900   44)216   72)354   82)2401   52)1020   31)1500   31)180

54)102   71)3520   41)2450   72)2815

Estimate Yields Quotient Too Small

26)185   35)175   38)193   35)1651   25)1852   46)283   86)260   75)300

37)2483   47)1898   57)342   29)114   48)3425   46)1823   85)6913   45)238

58)232   36)1892   16)861   17)698

Problems In Which Estimated Quotient Is Greater Than 9

23)214   21)200   34)312   73)725   74)725   43)412   24)238   14)120

13)104   32)304

Diagnosis and Remediation

Division problems may be worked incorrectly for numerous reasons. Common errors made by students are summarized in the diagnosis and remediation chart in Figure 11.17. The remediation procedures usually involve presenting a structured worksheet exercise focusing on the particular component skill error made by the students. Remember when students miss more than 10-20% of the problems due to a specific type of error, a remediation procedure is needed. When examining student worksheets, the teacher should not only look for the reason why students missed a problem but also should examine problems solved correctly, noting if the students rounded off correctly. Students who round off incorrectly may solve problems correctly but may have done much unnecessary computing. Students who make rounding off errors in 10-15% or more of the problems should receive intensive remediation in rounding off. The teacher would re-present the rounding off formats for several days before reintroducing the less structured presentation.

Research

One of the problems in deciding how to teach relatively complex skills such as division is the degree to which meaning should be stressed as opposed to computational facility. In most skills, these two goals are not in opposition. However, a division strategy has so many steps that a highly meaningful approach that adds steps might hinder computational proficiency. In trying to answer this question, Kratzer and Willoughby (1973) compared meaningful (subtractive or scaffolding) and traditional (distributive) algorithms for division. (The problem 793 ÷ 4 appears on page 251, worked according to both algorithms.) The results of the study indicate that students taught the traditional algorithm solve more transfer problems correctly. While a single study cannot provide definite results (see Underhill, 1981

Figure 11.17 Diagnosis and Remediation of Multi-digit Division Errors

Error Patterns	Diagnosis	Remediation Procedures

One Digit Divisor Problems

a.
```
    64
 7)483
   45
   33
   28
    5
```
Student makes a fact error (6 × 7 = 45).

Depends on frequency of fact error. High % fact errors—provide systematic fact instruction. Low % fact errors—increase motivation, include missed facts in fact drills.

b.
```
    56
 7)413
   35
   43
   42
    1
```
Student makes a subtraction error (41 – 35 = 4)

Less structured worksheet part of Figure 11.11. Remind students to borrow.

c.
```
    81
 6)493
   48
   13
    6
    7
```
Student computes an incorrect quotient. Too small

Remediation formats (Figure 11.7 and 11.8) for incorrect quotients. Problems should have divisor that was in problem missed.

d.
```
    49
 6)288
   24
   48
   54
```
Student computes an incorrect quotient. Too large

e.
```
     335
 7)23458
   21
   24
   21
   38
   35
    3
```
Student computes an incomplete quotient: does not bring down a digit.

Less structured worksheet exercise (Figure 11.11).

f.
```
     514
 4)20568
   20
    5
    4
   16
   16
    0
```
Student computes an incomplete quotient: does not write a quotient for the last digit.

Less structured worksheet exercise focusing on need to keep working problems till each digit after underlined part has a digit over it.

g.
```
    12
 7)714
    7
   14
   14
    7
 5)352
   35
    2
```
Student computes an incomplete quotient in problems with zero in the quotient.

Structured worksheet focusing on problems of this type. See page 232 for directions.

Figure 11.17 cont'd

Error Patterns	**Diagnosis**	**Remediation Procedures**
Two Digit Divisor Problems		
h. $\quad\quad 4$ $39\overline{)155}$ $\quad\;\underline{156}$ $\quad\quad\; 1$ $\quad\quad 2$ $25\overline{)78}$ $\quad\;\underline{50}$ $\quad\; 28$	Student computes quotient that is too large or too small.	Present format for problems in which estimated quotient is incorrect (Figure 11.15).
i. $\quad\quad 9$ $27\overline{)2248}$ $\quad\;\underline{243}$	Student computes an incomplete quotient because of misplacement of products.	Present structured worksheet exercise (Figure 11.14). Focus on where to place digits when multiplying.

for a summary of studies with contradictory results), we suggest that understanding is better stressed with simple problem types (20 ÷ 4) while computational proficiency is stressed, at least initially, with more difficult problem types (207 ÷4).

Meaningful (subtractive)		*Traditional (distributive)*	
198 R1		198 R1	
$4\overline{)793}$		$4\overline{)793}$	
$\underline{400}$	100	$\underline{4}$	
393		39	
$\underline{360}$	90	$\underline{36}$	
33		33	
$\underline{32}$	$\underline{\;\;8}$	$\underline{32}$	
1	198	1	

Regardless of order of introduction, preskills should be taught before the strategy itself. Brownell (1953) found that when strategies were introduced before subskills were mastered, performance on the subskills was erratic, sometimes improving and sometimes deteriorating. A more recent study by Grossnickle and Perry (1985) supports the contention that students are more accurate when they first are taught division preskills and when strategies are presented in a clear concise manner.

In conducting research on common division errors, the Elementary School Mathematics Committee (1975) identified problems with placement of digits in the quotient:

$$8.3$$
$$3\overline{)2.5}$$
$$\underline{2\,4}$$
$$10$$
$$\underline{\;9}$$
$$1$$

with not subtracting:

$$11$$
$$3\overline{)53}$$
$$\underline{3}$$
$$3$$
$$\underline{3}$$

with zero—final zero omitted:

$$3$$
$$3\overline{)30}$$

and medial zero omitted:

$$15$$
$$4\overline{)420}$$
$$\underline{4}$$
$$20$$

with remainder larger than divisor:

$$6\ R7$$
$$5\overline{)37}$$

and with dividing by only the first digit of a two digit divisor:

$$228\ R1$$
$$23\overline{)457}$$
$$\underline{4}$$
$$5$$
$$\underline{4}$$
$$17$$
$$\underline{16}$$

Two digit divisor problems continue to be difficult, even after students learn to attend to both digits. The difficulty stems in part from the fact that in 21% of the problems, the quotient will be either too large or too small because of inevitable rounding errors (Hunnicut & Iverson, 1958).

Figure 11.18

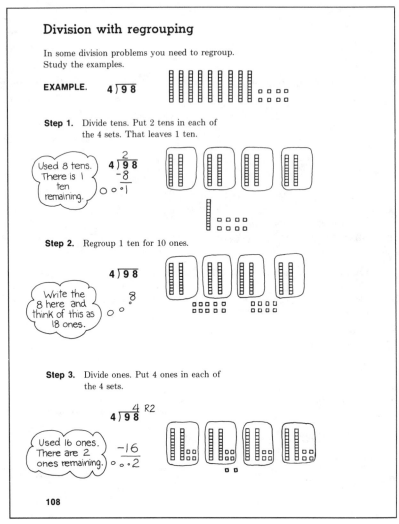

Division with regrouping

In some division problems you need to regroup. Study the examples.

EXAMPLE. 4 ⟌ 9 8

Step 1. Divide tens. Put 2 tens in each of the 4 sets. That leaves 1 ten.

Used 8 tens. There is 1 ten remaining.

Step 2. Regroup 1 ten for 10 ones.

Write the 8 here and think of this as 18 ones.

Step 3. Divide ones. Put 4 ones in each of the 4 sets.

Used 16 ones. There are 2 ones remaining.

108

Source: From *Heath Mathematics*, Grade 5 Teacher's Edition, by Walter E. Rucker, Clyde A. Dilley, and David A. Lowry, p. 108. Copyright © 1987 by D.C. Heath & Company. Reprinted by permission.

To determine the importance of teaching a strategy for simple division, Kameenui, Carnine, Darch and Stein (1986) compared a direct instruction strategy with the procedure suggested in a widely used basal program. All 32 fourth graders from an elementary school were screened to identify students who could not divide. The 24 subjects who could not divide were then randomly assigned to one of the two groups. The direct instruction procedures were similar to those discussed earlier in the chapter. Direct instruction strategy training resulted in rapid student learning of the skill. Direct instruction students correctly answered an average of 74% of the 24 training test items administered following 4 of the 10 training days. Students in the traditional treatment answered an average of 57% of the test items correctly. Differences on tests given at the end of the study-post-test and maintenance test-were not great: 83% versus 74% on the post-test and 83% versus 73% on the maintenance test.

Commercial Programs

Division: Renaming with Single and Double Digit Divisors

INSTRUCTIONAL STRATEGIES The initial strategy presented for division with remainders does not vary significantly in the major programs. The strategy usually includes these steps:

Step 1 – Divide 10s
Step 2 – Regroup
Step 3 – Divide 1s

As with strategies presented for other basic operations, the strategy appears straightforward. However, upon closer inspection we find that critical steps in the strategy are omitted, thereby making use of the strategy more difficult, especially for low–performing students. In some programs students are encouraged to "think through" these critical steps. Also, the use of pictures tends to direct student attention away from necessary steps in the computation process such as how to align numbers in the problem or when and where to subtract (see Figure 11.18). In fact, it is unclear from the teacher's manual whether students are supposed to operate on the pictures or on the numerals first. Naive students would require more explicit instruction on all steps of this computation process to master this skill.

The strategies for division with two digit divisors that appear in the leading basals are again quite similar. Even in initial lessons, students are assumed to have mastered sophisticated prerequisites such as determining where to begin working the problem or estimation. Figure 11.19 is an example of an initial lesson on two digit divisors taken from a program. The problem the teacher writes on the board is $20\overline{)1897}$. The strategy is outlined in four basic steps: regroup thousands, regroup hundreds, regroup tens, and regroup tens again. The process of estimating the answer is already completed for the student. Whether students can estimate on their own is a question. Also, since many errors in division are caused by writing quotients in the wrong columns, the omission in many programs of provisions for teaching students how to align columns in division is noteworthy. In the example provided, the answer is not written for the students so there is not even a model of where to write the answers.

Figure 11.19

USING THE PAGES

Work the example on page 84 on the chalkboard. Go over each step in detail. "There are not enough thousands to put any thousands into each of 20 groups. We regroup the thousand into 10 hundreds. Look at the 18 hundreds. There are not enough hundreds to put any hundreds into each of 20 groups. Regroup the 18 hundreds into 180 tens. Look at the 189 tens. Using the multiplication facts at the top of the page, notice that there are enough tens to put 9 tens into each of 20 groups. That uses 180 tens and leaves 9 tens. Regroup the 9 tens into 90 ones, so we have 97 ones. Again, using the multiplication facts at the top of the page, we can see that there are enough ones to put 4 ones into each of 20 groups (but not enough to put 5 ones in each group). This uses 80 ones and leaves 17 ones."

Assign exercises from pages 84 and 85. Discuss the procedure with individual students as they work. Check to be sure that students are placing digits in the quotient properly.

Source: From *Heath Mathematics*, Grade 6 Teacher's Edition, by Walter E. Rucker, Clyde A. Dilley, David A. Lowry, p. 84. Copyright © 1987 by D.C. Heath & Company. Reprinted by permission.

Application Items: Division

1. Describe the problem type that each example below represents. List the problems in the order they are introduced. Write the grade level when each type is typically introduced.

$$5\overline{)128} \quad 5\overline{)23} \quad 2\overline{)136} \quad 5\overline{)20} \quad 5\overline{)153}$$

$$27\overline{)122} \quad 5\overline{)736} \quad 27\overline{)136} \quad 5\overline{)526}$$

2. Below is an excerpt from the independent worksheet to be given to students who have just demonstrated accuracy in solving problems with a one digit divisor and a three digit quotient (type 4e). The teacher has made some errors in constructing the worksheet.

   a. Indicate any inappropriate examples.

   b. Identify any omitted problem types that should be included on the worksheet.
      (Assume that students know all basic division facts.)

$$7\overline{)932} \quad 5\overline{)1432} \quad 3\overline{)1214} \quad 5\overline{)3752}$$

$$2\overline{)714} \quad 9\overline{)1436} \quad 5\overline{)823} \quad 6\overline{)1443}$$

3. Below are eight problems that appeared on a worksheet to be done independently by the students in Ms. Adams' math group. Below each student's name are the problems missed by the student. For each student, specify the probable cause or causes of the student's errors. Describe the remediation procedure.

$$6\overline{)8324} \quad 4\overline{)12385} \quad 7\overline{)493} \quad 8\overline{)7200} \quad 5\overline{)5214} \quad 7\overline{)9222} \quad 5\overline{)8253} \quad 9\overline{)72990}$$

Barbara

Randy

Fred

4. Below is an error made by Charles on a worksheet assignment. Describe what the teacher says in making the correction.

$$
36\overline{)184}\ \ \begin{array}{r} 4\ R\,40 \\ \hline 184 \\ 144 \\ \hline 40 \end{array}
$$

5. Write the structured worksheet part of a format to present this problem:

$$7\overline{)213}$$

6. Specify the wording the teacher uses to correct the following errors:

a. $27\overline{)482}$ $\boxed{3\!/\!48}$

b. $27\overline{)482}$ $\boxed{2\!/\!4}$

7. Below is an excerpt from the independent worksheet to be given to students who have just demonstrated accuracy in solving problems with two digit divisors and one or two digit quotients, in which estimating produces proper quotient. Indicate the inappropriate examples.

$23\overline{)989}$ $34\overline{)148}$ $76\overline{)793}$

$58\overline{)2938}$ $31\overline{)283}$ $49\overline{)1638}$

12 Math Story Problems

by Mary Gleason with Jerry Silbert and Douglas Carnine

This chapter discusses procedures for teaching students to apply the four operations (addition, subtraction, multiplication, and division) to situations requiring a mathematical solution. Because mathematical terms and properties were introduced in the chapters for each operation, no new terms or properties are presented in this chapter. Nor does this chapter include all the important problem-solving procedures. Problem-solving procedures that cover measurement, percent, decimal, fractions, and time and money applications are dealt with in later chapters. The relationship between problem types discussed in this chapter is shown in the skill hierarchy in Figure 12.1. Specific examples of the various problem types are illustrated in the Instructional Sequence and Assessment Chart in Figure 12.2.

There are two basic groupings of problems. First are those problems involving addition or subtraction. Second are multiplication or division problems. Addition and subtraction are introduced together to allow for discrimination practice. When multiplication and division are introduced together, again for discrimination practice, students also continue to solve addition and subtraction problems.

A new basic problem type is introduced as soon as students have mastered the relevant preskills. For example, multiplication and division story problems are introduced as soon as students have

mastered previously introduced types of story problems and have been introduced to the concept of multiplying or dividing when dealing with groups of equal size. Consequently, not all story problem types are introduced at the same time. A new type is usually introduced soon after a new operation has been mastered.

Besides basic story problem types there are multi-step problems, problems with large numbers, and problems with distractors. Multi-step problems, which usually first appear in third grade, require students to perform two or more different operations. The simplest type of multi-step problem involves adding three numbers. Multi-step problems become more difficult as the number and type of computations to be performed increases. Problems with larger numbers are more difficult because computation is more difficult and the operation called for is less obvious. Problems with irrelevant quantities (distractors) form the third type of more difficult problems. These three problem types as they apply to story problems of all four operations (add, subtract, multiply, divide) will be discussed further near the end of the chapter.

Teachers, especially in the upper grade, must carefully examine student texts for other difficult problem types. Problems become more difficult in later grades not only because of distractors, multi-step operations, and larger numbers, but also because of unfamiliar words and more complex

Figure 12.1 Skill Hierarchy

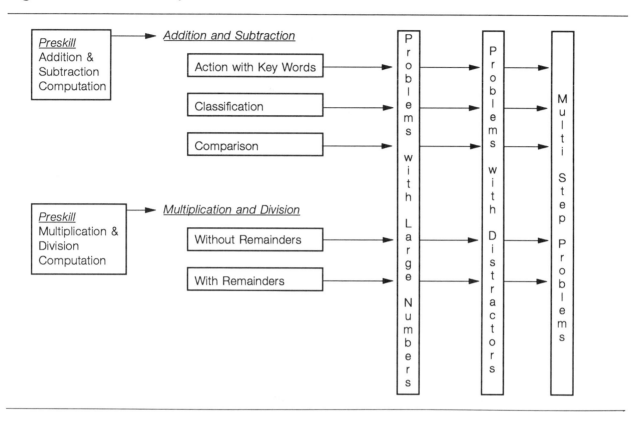

syntax. The two problems below illustrate the importance of number size, distractors, vocabulary, and syntax.

a. Bill wrote 8 sentences. The teacher crossed out 2 of them. How many are left?
b. When the teacher read Bill's paper she deleted 17 sentences and 3 commas. He had initially written 52 sentences. How many sentences did he have at the end?

Both are action problems in which the original amount is stated and the decrease is given. Students must find the difference. Problem b is more difficult for several reasons. First is the presence of the less common vocabulary terms: *deleted* and *initially*. If a student does not know that *delete* means to get rid of, he has no basis for solving the problem. Second, the amount Bill began with is stated first in problem (*a*), but in problem (*b*) it is stated after the amount of the decrease. When the smaller numeral appears first, students are more likely to add. Third is the presence of quantity 3, which must be ignored. Finally, the larger numerals in problem (*b*) require renaming. Teachers must

make sure that students receive ample practice on more difficult problems that include distractors, larger numbers, more complex syntax, and unfamiliar vocabulary.

Addition and subtraction problems are usually introduced in late first grade. An analysis of addition and subtraction problems from commercial programs yielded three main types: (*a*) action problems with key words, (*b*) classification problems, and (*c*) comparison problems. All three types of these one-step addition and subtraction problems are usually introduced by the end of second grade.

Multiplication and division problems are usually introduced during third grade. In most initial problems, the multiplication or division operation is signaled by the presence of the word *each* or *every*. In later years, the words *a* and *per* will also serve as signals for multiplication or division. Multiplication and division problems that do not contain key words are obviously more difficult, but are quite rare in basal mathematics textbooks.

In the remainder of this chapter, detailed procedures are given for teaching students to solve story problems. We have tried to make a balance between keeping the procedures structured enough

Figure 12.2 Instructional Sequence and Assessment Chart

Grade Level	Problem Type	Performance Indicator
1–2a	Addition/subtraction action problems with key words.	Bill had 7 apples. He got 3 more from the store. How many apples does he have in all?
		Lisa had some apples. She bought 3 more. She ended up with 12 apples. How many apples did she start with?
		Carlos had 7 apples. He gave 3 to his sister. How many does he have left?
1–2b	Addition/subtraction classification problems.	Eight men are in the store. Three women are in the store. How many people are in the store?
		Ramona had 4 hats; 3 of the hats are blue. How many hats are not blue?
		Jill sold 5 hats in the morning. She sold 2 hats in the afternoon. How many hats did she sell?
2c	Addition/subtraction comparison problems.	Bill is 7 years old. Alice is 5 years old. How much older is Bill?
		Hole A is 5 feet deep. Hole B is 7 feet deeper than Hole A. How deep is Hole B?
		Hole A is 5 feet deep. Hole B is 7 feet deep. How much deeper is Hole B?
2d	Multi-step problems: add three numbers.	Bill ran 5 miles on Monday, 3 miles on Tuesday, and 4 miles on Wednesday. How many miles did he run altogether?
3a	Multiplication/division problems with the word *each* or *every*.	Bill has 4 boxes. In each box there are 6 pencils. How many pencils does Bill have?
		Tammy jogs 5 miles every day. How far will she jog in 3 days?
		There are 20 students. The teacher wants to divide them into 4 equal groups. How many students will be in each group?
3b	Multiplication/division problems with the word *per* or a phrase using *a*.	The ABC Company makes pens. They put 5 pens in a box. How many pens are in 3 boxes?
		Rosa runs 2 miles per day. How many days will it take her to run 8 miles?
3c	Addition/subtraction problems with larger numbers.	Bill ran 214 miles in January and 158 miles in February. How many more miles did he run in January?
		There are 153 students in the school. If there are 61 girls in the school, how many boys are there?
3d	Multiplication/division problems with larger numbers.	There are 35 students in every class. There are 5 classes in the school. How many students are in the school?
		Jean worked 2 days. If she makes $16 a day, how much did she make?
		Jill has 215 pencils. She wants to make bundles with 5 pencils in each bundle. How many bundles can she make?

Figure 12.2 cont'd

Grade Level	Problems Type	Performance Indicator
3e	Division problems with remainders.	There are 22 students. The teacher wants to divide them into 4 equal groups. How many students will be in each group?
		A mother wants to divide a pie equally among her children. The pie has 19 pieces. There are 9 children. How many pieces should she give to each child?
3f	Addition/subtraction problems with distractors.	There are 20 blue pencils, 5 red pencils, and 16 yellow pens in a bag. How many pencils are in the bag?
		Bill weighed 120 pounds. He ran 5 miles. Now he weighs 117 pounds. How much did he lose?
		Bill had 12 hats; 5 hats were old. He gave away 3 old hats. How many hats does he have left?
4a	Division and multiplication problems with larger numbers (two digit divisor or multi-digit factors).	Sarah wants to save $385. If she puts $35 in the bank each month, how many months will it take her to save the $385?
		A factory produces 325 cars a day. How many cars will it produce in 25 days?
		A pound of apples costs 60¢. How much will 20 pounds of apples cost?
4b	Multi-step problems: three numbers: the sum of two numbers is subtracted from the third number.	Julie sold 12 pencils in the morning. Ann sold 15 in the afternoon. How many more must they sell before they've sold 50 altogether?
		Timmy weighed 84 pounds. He lost 4 pounds in May and 7 pounds in June. How much did he weigh at the end of June?
		Jean sold 10 pens in the morning. She began with 18. If she sells 2 more, how many will she have left?
4c	Three numbers: two quantities are multiplied; the product is added or subtracted from a third number.	Tom has 3 pens in each pocket. He has 5 pockets. Ann has 16 pens. Who has more pens? How many more?
		Ann has $7. If she works 4 hours and earns $3 each hours, how many dollars will she have at the end of the day?
4d	Three numbers: two quantities are added. The sum is divided or multiplied.	There are 10 boys and 20 girls in the class. Each row can sit 5 students. How many rows will there be?
		Jill earns $2 every morning and $4 every afternoon. How much will she earn in 6 days?
5a	Four numbers: two sets of quantities are multiplied; the product of each is added.	Pam ran 5 miles a day for 3 days, and 6 miles a day for 2 days. How many miles did she run altogether?
		Tammy bought 3 cakes and 2 drinks. A cake cost 10¢. A drink cost 15¢. How much did Tammy spend?

Math Story Problems   **259**

Figure 12.2 cont'd

Grade Level	Problems Type	Performance Indicator
5b	Five numbers: two sets of quantities are multiplied; the product of each is added; the sum is subtracted or added to a given quantity.	Bill needs $30. He worked 5 hours on Monday for $2 an hour. He worked 2 hours on Tuesday for $3 an hour. How much more money does he need?
		Bill weighed 135 pounds in May. He gained 3 pounds each month for the next 2 months. Then he gained 5 pounds each month for the next 3 months. How much does he weigh now?

to facilitate success for students, while at the same time providing students with a general understanding of how language and math skills must be integrated to solve problems.

Addition and Subtraction Problems

This section, dealing with procedures for teaching students to solve addition and subtraction problems, is divided into two parts. The first part deals with *introducing the concept* of story problems to first grade students or remedial second graders. The procedures discussed teach students how to solve simple action story problems by drawing pictures, then translating each phrase into a symbol. Teachers working with students performing at second grade level or above who already know some basic facts should not use these procedures but should begin story problem instruction with the exercises described in the second part. The second part teaches a more sophisticated *generalizable problem-solving strategy* that enables students to solve action problems with key words as well as classification and comparison problems. The generalizable strategy is more sophisticated because it must handle the difficulties caused by variations in word usage. The same verb (*lost*) appears in examples (a) and (b), but the usage is such that addition is called for in (a) and subtraction in (b).

a. Jack lost 7 pounds. Sam lost 3 more pounds than Jack. How many pounds did Sam lose?
b. Jack weighed 80 pounds. Then he lost 7 pounds. How much does he weigh now?

Other usage problems occur when the verb gives no information about whether to add or subtract: "Ramon had four pets; three were dogs. How many were not dogs?" The difficulties in usage can only be resolved through the careful teaching of a strategy. Merely illustrating story problems is not enough, because pictures are not available when students encounter story problems in "real life" settings. In addition, as problems become more complex and use larger numbers, drawing pictures would not be a practical or efficient strategy. As noted below, pictures can assist in introducing story problems, but illustrations must later be replaced by a strategy that deals with word usage.

Introducing the Concept

Story problems can be introduced when students can work a page of addition and subtraction problems using a line strategy with 80–90% accuracy. (See Chapters 8 and 9 for addition the fast way and subtraction with the crossing-out strategy.) It is not necessary that students know how to solve missing addend problems or have memorized any basic facts in order to be introduced to story problems.

In addition to solving one-digit addition and subtraction problems by accurately using lines, the format for introducing story problems (see Figure 12.3) is introduced after students (a) know four key phrases, and (b) can translate several key verbs. *About three weeks prior* to the introduction of story problems, the teacher should present a preskill format designed to teach students how to translate four key phrases—*get more*, *get rid of*, *end with*, and *how many*—to symbols. The phrase *get more* translates to a plus sign, *get rid of* to a minus sign, *end with* to an equal sign, and *how many* to an empty box. Teachers should use procedures similar to those specified on pages 58–59 for teaching new vocabulary words through synonyms. The teacher should say the new phrase and tell students what it translates to. For example, the teacher might say "Listen. When you get more, you write a plus sign. What do you write for gets more?" Each second or third day, the teacher would introduce a new phrase and would review the phrases introduced earlier.

After the students know these four terms, the teacher presents another preskill exercise in which the teacher says a common verb and asks if the verb translates to a plus or a minus sign. Several

Figure 12.3 Format for Introducing the Problem-solving Concept

Day	Part A Preskill: Picture Demonstration	Part B Structured Worksheet Problems	Part C Supervised Practice Problems	Part D Independent Problems
1–3	2+, 2–	2		
4–6		4		
7–accurate daily practice			4–6	4–6

PART A: Preskill: Picture Demonstration

Addition Problem

<u>**TEACHER**</u>   <u>**STUDENTS**</u>

1. "LISTEN. ANN HAS SEVEN APPLES. SHE GETS
   THREE MORE APPLES. SHE ENDS WITH HOW
   MANY APPLES?"

2. "LET'S DRAW A PICTURE OF THAT PROBLEM.
   ANN HAS SEVEN APPLES." Draw on board:

   "SHE GETS THREE MORE APPLES, SO I DRAW
   THREE MORE." Draw three more apples:

3. "LET'S WRITE THE EQUATION. HERE'S THE FIRST
   SENTENCE AGAIN. ANN HAS SEVEN APPLES. HOW
   MANY APPLES DOES ANN HAVE?"   "7"
   "I WRITE SEVEN UNDER THE SEVEN APPLES."
   Write 7.
   "HERE'S THE NEXT SENTENCE. SHE GETS THREE
   MORE APPLES. HOW MANY MORE APPLES DID
   SHE GET?"   "3"
   "YES, ANN GETS THREE MORE. WHAT DO I WRITE
   FOR GETS THREE MORE?"   "Plus 3"
   Write + 3.
   "THE PROBLEM SAYS SHE ENDS UP WITH HOW
   MANY APPLES? SO I WRITE EQUALS AND A BOX,
   LIKE THIS:" Write = □ (7 + 3 = □).

4. "READ THE EQUATION."   "7 + 3 equals how many?"
   "LET'S COUNT AND SEE HOW MANY WE END UP
   WITH."
   Touch pictures of apples as students count.   "1, 2, 3, 4, 5, 6, 7, 8, 9, 10"
   "SO ANN ENDS WITH 10 APPLES." Write 10 in the
   box.

Subtraction Problem

1. "LISTEN. ANN HAS SEVEN APPLES. SHE GIVES
   AWAY THREE APPLES. SHE ENDS WITH HOW
   MANY APPLES?"

Figure 12.3 cont'd

TEACHER

2. "LET'S DRAW A PICTURE OF THAT PROBLEM.
   ANN HAS SEVEN APPLES, SO I DRAW SEVEN
   APPLES." Draw on board:

   "SHE GIVES AWAY THREE APPLES, SO I'LL CROSS
   OUT THREE APPLES." Cross out three:

3. "LET'S WRITE THE EQUATION. HERE'S THE FIRST
   SENTENCE AGAIN. ANN HAS SEVEN APPLES. HOW
   MANY APPLES DID ANN HAVE?"   "7"
   "I'LL WRITE A 7."
   Write 7.
   "HERE'S THE NEXT SENTENCE. SHE GIVES AWAY
   THREE APPLES. HOW MANY APPLES DID SHE
   GIVE AWAY?"   "3"
   "WHAT DO I WRITE FOR GIVES AWAY THREE
   APPLES?"   "Minus 3"
   "YES, SHE GIVES AWAY THREE, SO WE WRITE
   MINUS THREE."
   Write − 3.
   THE PROBLEM SAYS SHE ENDS WITH HOW MANY
   APPLES? SO I WRITE EQUALS AND A BOX."
   Write = □ (7 − 3 = □).

4. "READ THE EQUATION."   "7 − 3 equals how many?"
   "LET'S COUNT THE APPLES THAT ARE LEFT AND
   SEE HOW MANY SHE ENDS WITH."
   Touch the remaining apples.   "1, 2, 3, 4"
   "SO, ANN ENDS WITH FOUR APPLES." Write 4 in
   the box.
   Repeat addition or subtraction steps 1–4 with
   several more problems.

PART B: Structured Worksheet

Give students a worksheet that contains a mix of
addition and subtraction problems and includes a box
and the word for the unit answer, like this:

---

a. Jim has six marbles. He finds two more
   marbles. He ends with how many marbles?
                                        □ marbles

b. Jim has six marbles. He gives away two
   marbles. He ends with how many marbles?
                                        □ marbles

---

1. "TOUCH PROBLEM A. LISTEN. JIM HAS SIX
   MARBLES. HE FINDS TWO MORE MARBLES. HE
   ENDS WITH HOW MANY MARBLES?"

Figure 12.3 cont'd

TEACHER	**STUDENTS**

2. "LET'S DRAW A PICTURE OF THAT PROBLEM. JIM HAS SIX MARBLES. DRAW THE MARBLES." Wait while the students draw on their papers, then draw on the board:

Students write:

○ ○ ○ ○ ○ ○   ○ ○ ○ ○ ○

"HE FINDS TWO MORE MARBLES. DRAW THOSE." Wait, then draw on the board:

Students write:

○ ○ ○ ○ ○ ○ ○ ○   ○ ○ ○ ○ ○ ○ ○

3. "LET'S WRITE THE EQUATION.
READ THE FIRST SENTENCE AGAIN.
HOW MANY MARBLES DID JIM HAVE?"
"WRITE 6 UNDER THE 6 MARBLES."
Wait, then write 6 on board.
"READ THE NEXT SENTENCE."
"HOW MANY MORE MARBLES DID HE GET?"
"YES, JIM FINDS TWO MORE. WHAT DO YOU WRITE FOR FINDS TWO MORE?"
"YES, WRITE + 2."
Write +2 on board. "THE PROBLEM SAYS HE ENDS WITH HOW MANY MARBLES? SO, WHAT DO YOU WRITE?"
"WRITE EQUALS HOW MANY."
Write = □ on board (6 + 2 = □).

"Jim has 6 marbles."
"6"

Students write 6.
"He finds 2 more marbles."
"2"

"Plus 2."
Students write + 2.

"Equals box."
Students write = □.

4. "READ THE EQUATION.
LET'S COUNT AND SEE HOW MANY WE END WITH."
Touch pictures of marbles as students count.
"WRITE 8 IN THE BOX AFTER THE EQUAL SIGN."
"NOW, WRITE 8 IN THE ANSWER BOX NEXT TO THE WORD MARBLES. JIM ENDS WITH 8 MARBLES."

"6 + 2 equals how many?"

"1, 2, 3, 4, 5, 6, 7, 8"
Students write 8.

Students write 8 in box next to the word marbles.

Subtraction Problem

1. "TOUCH THE NEXT PROBLEM. LISTEN. JIM HAS SIX MARBLES. HE GIVES AWAY TWO MARBLES. HE ENDS WITH HOW MANY MARBLES?"

2. "LETS DRAW A PICTURE OF THAT PROBLEM. JIM HAS SIX MARBLES. DRAW THE MARBLES." Wait while students draw on their papers, then draw on board:

○ ○ ○ ○ ○ ○

Students write:

○ ○ ○ ○ ○

"HE GIVES AWAY TWO MARBLES. CROSS THEM OUT." Wait, then cross out two:

⌀ ⌀ ○ ○ ○ ○

Students cross out marbles:

⌀ ⌀ ○ ○ ○

Figure 12.3 cont'd

TEACHER	**STUDENTS**
3. "LET'S WRITE THE EQUATION. JIM HAS 6 MARBLES. HOW MANY MARBLES DID JIM HAVE?"	"6"
"WRITE A 6."	Students write 6.
Write 6 on board.	
"HOW MANY DID HE GIVE AWAY?"	"2"
"WHAT DO YOU WRITE FOR *GIVES AWAY TWO MARBLES*?"	"Minus 2"
"YES, HE GIVES AWAY TWO, SO WRITE MINUS TWO."	Students write – 2.
Write – 2 on board.	
"THE PROBLEM SAYS HE ENDS WITH HOW MANY MARBLES, SO WHAT DO YOU WRITE?"	"Equals box"
"WRITE IT."	Students write = □
Write = □ on board (6 – 2 = □).	
4. "READ THE EQUATION."	"6 – 2 equals how many?"
"LET'S COUNT THE MARBLES THAT ARE LEFT AND SEE HOW MANY HE ENDS WITH."	
Touch the remaining marbles.	"1, 2, 3, 4."
"WRITE 4 IN THE BOX AFTER THE EQUAL SIGN."	Students write 4.
Write 4 in the box.	
"NOW WRITE 4 IN THE ANSWER BOX NEXT TO THE WORD *MARBLES*. JIM ENDS WITH 4 MARBLES."	Students write 4 in answer box.
Repeat addition or subtraction steps 1–4 with several more problems.	

common verbs—*buys*, *loses*, *sells*, *eats*, *finds*, *gives away*, *breaks*, and *makes*—should be presented. The teacher equates the verb with getting more or getting rid of before asking the students to translate the verb to a sign. For example, the teacher asks, "When you buy something do you get more or get rid of something? So when you buy something do you plus or minus?"

The format for introducing story problems (see Figure 12.3) is presented when the students have mastered the preskills outlined above. The format includes 2 parts. In Part A, a structured board presentation, the teacher begins story problem instruction by demonstrating on the blackboard how a written or verbal story problem can be solved with semi-concrete objects. In solving problems such as "There were six children. Two children went home. How many were left?" pictures would be used to demonstrate the problem:

onstrates how a verbal or written story problem may be expressed numerically, translating it phrase by phrase into an equation.

There were six children.	6
Two children went home.	–2
How many were left?	= □

In Part B, the structured worksheet exercise, the teacher gives students a worksheet with a set of problems. If the students can decode the words in the story, they read the problems. If the students do not have adequate decoding skills, the teacher should read the problems to them. The teacher has the students read each entire problem and then re-read it phrase by phrase. After reading each phrase, they are directed to draw the appropriate picture. Then, students read the problem again phrase by phrase and write the appropriate symbols. After completing the equation, students are told to figure out the answer by counting the pictures. Practice on story problems should be done daily.

After demonstrating how a verbal or written story problem can be illustrated, the teacher dem-

Example selection for story problems is very important. The verbs in the stories should be fairly common terms such as *buy*, *give away*, *make*, *break*, *find*, *lose*. Moreover, problems should contain words that the students are able to decode, and the problems initially should be relatively short. A random mix of addition and subtraction problems should be used so that students discriminate between the two types of problems.

For the first several weeks, the last sentence in story problems should say "ends with how many?" These words can be literally translated to the symbols = □. After several weeks, final sentences such as "How many does she have now?", "How many does she have left?", and "How many does she have in all?" can be presented. The teacher explains that these sentences mean the same as "ends with how many" and thus can be translated into the symbols = □.

For the first several months of instruction, a box for writing the answers should appear after each story problem. The word the *quantity* refers to would be written next to the box:

Jane had seven stars. She got two more stars. How many stars does she have now?
□ stars

A Generalizable Problem-solving Strategy

Most story problems cannot be translated phrase by phrase into an equation. Consider this problem: "John found five pencils. His brother found two pencils. How many more pencils did John find than his brother?" This problem cannot be translated phrase by phrase; even though the verb *find* usually indicates getting more, students must subtract (5 − 2) to find the answer.

A more sophisticated strategy than phrase-by-phrase translation must be taught for solving story problems. The strategy we recommend integrates the knowledge of the fact family concept with basic language skills involving classification, comparison, and verb knowledge. The fact family concept is that three numbers can be used to form four statements. For example, the numbers 3, 5, and 8 yield 3 + 5 = 8, 5 + 3 = 8, 8 − 5 = 3; 8 − 3 = 5. In the story problem strategy, students are taught to determine whether or not the problem gives the "big number" referred to as the total number of a fact family. In 3, 5, and 8 the number 8 is the "total number."

If a total number of a fact family is given, the problem requires subtraction. For example, "Bill had three cats. Now he has eight cats. How many more cats did he get?" The last sentence asks about how

many more, not about the total. So one of the numbers in the problem, 3 or 8, must be the big number, the total. Obviously, 8 is the total number. Students then subtract 3 from the total number, 8: 8 − 3 = 5. Bill got five more cats.

If the total number of the fact family is not given, the problem requires addition. For example, "There are five cats. There are three dogs. How many pets?" The total number, which tells how many pets, is not given—cats are pets and dogs are pets, so *pets* has to talk about the total number. Students add to determine the total number: 5 + 3 = 8. There are eight pets. Very carefully guided instruction is required to teach students the linguistic elements in a story that tell whether or not the total number is given.

We will discuss procedures for teaching students to solve three types of problems that account for the majority of addition and subtraction problems students will encounter in the elementary grades: action with key words, classification, and comparison problems. We recommend that action with key word problems be introduced first, followed several weeks later by classification problems, then several weeks later by comparison problems. In order to begin solving story problems using these procedures, students must have memorized about twenty addition and twenty subtraction facts.

PRESKILL FOR THE GENERALIZABLE STRATEGY An essential preskill for the generalizable story problem strategy is figuring out the missing number when two of the three numbers in a fact family have been given. Students are taught that if the total number is given, they subtract to find the missing number. For example, if 9 and 4 are given and 9 is the total number, they subtract 4 from 9 to find 5, the missing number. On the other hand, if the total number is not given, they add the two given numbers. For example, if 9 and 4 are given and students are told that neither is the total number, they add 9 + 4 to find 13, the missing number. Students should be able to compute facts mentally rather than using lines. Consequently, problems should be limited to basic facts that students already know.

The preskill format, which appears in Figure 12.4, should be presented approximately 2–3 weeks before action problems with key words are first introduced. This would normally occur sometime during the second grade. Note that this format is similar to those used in fact instruction in Chapter 7. In the fact chapter, the phrases "big number" and "small numbers" were used. Those phrases can be replaced by the phrases "total number" and "parts of the total" when getting ready to solve story problems. These phrases are substituted to prevent students from cueing on every larger number as the big number. When presenting the preskill diagrams, the teacher shows an arrow with two boxes over the arrow and a larger box at the end of the arrow. Below are examples of the diagrams. In problem (a) the total number is given, while in problem (b) the total number is not given. The line below the diagram is for writing the equation to find the missing number.

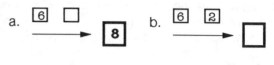

The format has four parts (see Figure 12.4). Part A introduces the rule about what to do when the total number is given: "When the total number is given, you subtract." After telling students the rule, the

Figure 12.4 Fact Family Preskill Format—Finding the Missing Family Member

Day	Part A Subtracting Rule	Part B Adding Rule	Part C Structured Worksheet Problems	Part D Less Structured Worksheet Problems	Part E Supervised Practice Problems
1	4				
2	4	4			
3–4	2	2	6		
5–9			6	6	
10–20 or more					12–16

PART A: Subtracting Rule

TEACHER   **STUDENTS**

Write on the board:

1. "THREE NUMBERS GO TOGETHER TO MAKE A
FACT FAMILY." Point to 8.
"THE TOTAL NUMBER IS ALWAYS AT THE END OF
THE ARROW."
Point to 2. "THIS NUMBER IS PART OF THE
TOTAL."
Point to 6.
"HERE'S THE OTHER PART OF THE TOTAL."
Erase the 8.

"SOMETIMES, WE DON'T KNOW THE TOTAL AND
WE HAVE TO FIGURE IT OUT."
Write the 8 back in; erase the 6.

"SOMETIMES, WE DON'T KNOW PART OF THE
TOTAL AND WE HAVE TO FIGURE IT OUT."

Figure 12.4 cont'd

TEACHER   **STUDENTS**

2. Write on the board:

"IS THE TOTAL NUMBER GIVEN IN THIS   "Yes"
PROBLEM?'
"HERE'S THE RULE: WHEN THE TOTAL NUMBER
IS GIVEN, WE SUBTRACT. THE TOTAL NUMBER
IS 10. SO I START WITH 10 AND SUBTRACT 3."
Write 10 − 3 on the bottom line. "WHAT IS
10 − 3?"   "7"
"SO, I WRITE EQUALS 7." Write = 7 on the line.
"NOW I WRITE 7 IN THE EMPTY BOX."
Write 7 in box.
"THE NUMBERS 3 AND 7 ARE THE PARTS OF THE
TOTAL. THE NUMBER 10 IS THE TOTAL NUMBER."

3. Write on the board:

"IS THE TOTAL NUMBER GIVEN?"   "Yes"
"WHAT DO WE DO WHEN THE TOTAL NUMBER IS
GIVEN?"   "Subtract"
"REMEMBER, WHEN YOU SUBTRACT, YOU START
WITH THE TOTAL NUMBER. WHAT PROBLEM DO I
WRITE ON THE LINE?"   "12 − 5"
Write 12 − 5 on the line. "WHAT IS 12 − 5?"   "7"
Write = 7 on the line. "WHAT NUMBER GOES IN
THE EMPTY BOX?"
Write 7 in the box.   "7"
Repeat Step 3 with:

PART B: Addition Rule

Write on the board:

1. "IN THIS PROBLEM. THE TOTAL NUMBER IS NOT
   GIVEN. WHEN THE TOTAL NUMBER IS NOT GIVEN,
   WE ADD."
   "IS THE TOTAL NUMBER GIVEN IN THIS
   PROBLEM?"   "No"
   "WATCH. THE PARTS ARE 3 AND 5, SO I ADD 3
   AND 5." (Write 3 + 5 on the line.) "WHAT IS
   3 + 5?"   "8"

Figure 12.4 cont'd

TEACHER   **STUDENTS**

"SO, I WRITE EQUALS 8." (Write = 8 on the line.)
"NOW, I WRITE 8 IN THE EMPTY BOX. THE
NUMBERS 3 AND 5 ARE THE PARTS OF THE
TOTAL. THE NUMBER 8 IS THE TOTAL."

2. Write on the board:

"IS THE TOTAL NUMBER GIVEN?"   "No"
"WHAT DO WE DO WHEN THE TOTAL NUMBER IS
NOT GIVEN?"   "Add"
"WHAT PROBLEM DO I WRITE ON THE LINE?"   "7 + 2"
Write 7 + 2 on the line.
"WHAT IS 7 + 2?"   "9"
Write = 9 on the line. "WHAT NUMBER GOES IN
THE EMPTY BOX?"   "9"
Write 9 in the box.
Repeat Step 3 with:

PART C: Structured Worksheet

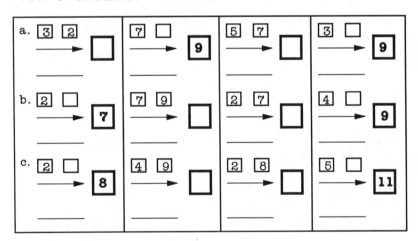

1. "YOU HAVE TO FIGURE OUT THE MISSING
   NUMBER IN ALL THESE PROBLEMS. IT MIGHT BE
   THE TOTAL NUMBER OR IT MIGHT BE PART OF
   THE TOTAL."
   "IF THE TOTAL NUMBER IS GIVEN, WHAT MUST
   YOU DO?"   "Subtract"
   "IF THE TOTAL NUMBER IS NOT GIVEN, WHAT
   MUST YOU DO?"   "Add"
   Repeat Step 1 until students answer correctly.

Figure 12.4 cont'd

TEACHER	**STUDENTS**

2. "TOUCH THE FIRST PROBLEM."
   "TOUCH THE BOX FOR THE TOTAL."

   Students touch the box after the arrow.

   "IS THE TOTAL GIVEN?"   "No"
   "SO WHAT MUST YOU DO?"   "Add"
   "WHAT PROBLEM DO YOU WRITE ON THE LINE?"   "3 + 2"
   "WRITE IT."   Students write 3 + 2.
   "WHAT IS 3 + 2?"   "5"
   "WRITE AN EQUALS SIGN AND THE ANSWER."   Students write = 5.
   "FILL IN THE EMPTY BOX."   Students write 5 in box.
   Repeat Step 2 with remaining problems.

PART D: Less Structured Worksheet

Give students a worksheet like that in Part C.

1. "TOUCH THE FIRST PROBLEM."

2. "IS THE TOTAL NUMBER GIVEN OR NOT GIVEN?"

3. "DO YOU ADD OR SUBTRACT?"

4. "WRITE THE EQUATION ON THE LINE AND WRITE THE ANSWER."

Repeat Steps 1–5 with all problems.

---

teacher demonstrates its application, writing a diagram on the board in which the total number is given:

The teacher points out that because the total number is given the students must subtract to figure out the missing number (8 − 2 = 6). And when they subtract, they must start with the total number.

Part B introduces the rule about what to do when the total number is not given: "When the total number is not given, you add." After telling students the rule, the teacher demonstrates its application, writing a diagram on the board in which the total number is not given:

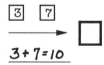

The teacher points out that because the total number is not given, the two given number must be added to figure out the missing numbers (3 + 7 = 10). Note that if students do not understand the terms *add* and *subtract*, the teacher can use *plus* and *minus* instead.

Part C is a structured worksheet with diagrams, half of which give the total number and half of which do not.

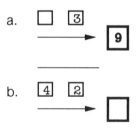

The student's task is to write the appropriate equation on the line under each arrow and to figure out the missing number. In problem (a), the total number is given; therefore, the student would write the subtraction problem 9 − 3 on the line to figure out the missing number. In problem (b), the total number is not given; so the students would write the addition problem 4 + 2 on line to derive the answer.

Part D is a less structured worksheet exercise in which the teacher only asks students whether they add or subtract, then has them work the problem. In parts C and D, the problems should not be written in a predictable order. An addition problem should not always be followed by a subtraction problem.

Table 12.1 Four Types of Action Problems

- Verb indicates ending up with more.

    Addition

    James had 12 apples. He bought 17 more apples. How many apples did he end up with?

    Subtraction

    James had 12 apples. He bought more apples. Now he has 17 apples. How many apples did he buy?

- Verb indicates ending up with less.

    Addition

    James had lots of apples. He sold 17 of the apples. He ended up with 12 apples. How many apples did he start with?

    Subtraction

    James had 17 apples. He sold 12 apples. How many apples did he end up with?

ACTION PROBLEMS WITH KEY WORDS   In action problems a person or thing starts out with a specified quantity, then an action occurs (e.g., *finds*, *loses*, *buys*, *sells*) that results in the person ending up with more or less. There are four basic types of action problems (see Table 12.1). Two are types in which a verb indicates that the person ended up with more (e.g., *gets*, *buys*, *makes*). Two are types in which a verb indicates that the person ends up with less (e.g., *loses*, *eats*, *sells*).

The problems in Table 12.1 indicate that students cannot rely solely on the verb to determine what operation (addition or subtraction) is called for. Even though the presence of verbs such as *buys*, *gets*, and *finds* usually indicates addition, there are a significant number of problems with those verbs that require subtraction. Likewise, students will encounter story problems with verbs that usually indicate subtraction but that are solved by adding (e.g., Tom lost 17 pounds. Now he weighs 132. How much did he weigh before?).

The strategy presented in the format for action problems (see Figure 12.5) teaches the students to look at the overall structure of a story problem. The format utilizes the number family concept. A story problem gives two quantities of the three quantities that make up a number family. If the quantity that represents the total is given in the problem, the students subtract to determine the missing quantity. If the quantity that represents the total is not given in the problem, the students add to determine the missing quantity.

The first step in solving an action problem is to determine whether the total number is how much the person started with or ended with. If the person will end up with more, the total is how much the person ends up with. If the person will end up with

less, the total is how much the person starts with. After determining whether the total will tell how much the person starts with or ends with, the student determines whether the total is given or not given. If the total is given, subtraction is called for. If the total is not given, addition is called for.

Below are the series of steps a student would take to solve problems. Note the use of the number family arrow which is used as a prompt for students. The first problem is a subtraction problem that contains a verb that usually indicates addition. The second problem is an addition problem that contains a verb that usually indicates subtraction.

Subtraction Problem:

Ann had 14 dollars. She worked all day and ended up with 27 dollars. How many dollars did she make during the day?

1.) The problem talks about earning money. Ann will end up with more money. So the total will be how much Ann ends with. The students write *ends* under the box for the total number in the number family diagram.

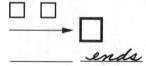

2.) The problem tells how much money Ann ended up with, so the total number is given and students write that number in the box for the total.

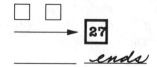

3.) The other number, 14, must be part of the total (a small number) so it's written in a box over the arrow.

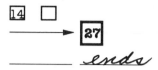

4.) The total number is given, so you subtract to figure out the answer.

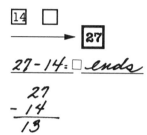

Addition Problem:

Tom lost 14 dollars. Now he has 12 dollars. How many dollars did he have before he lost those dollars?

1.) The problem talks about losing money. That means Tom ended up with less. So the total will be how much Tom started with. The student writes *starts* under the box for the total number in the number family diagram.

2.) The problem doesn't tell how many Tom started with. So the students don't write anything in the box for the total number.

3.) The number specified in the problem must be parts of the total (small numbers), so they're written in the boxes over the arrow.

4.) The total isn't given, so the students add to figure out the answer.

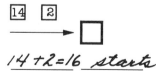

The format for teaching students to work action problems appears in Figure 12.5. The format is

rather lengthy. A good deal of time is spent introducing and reviewing component steps of the strategy.

Part A introduces a rule. "If a problem tells about ending up with more, the total is how much you end up with." The teacher leads students through a set of 8 problems (see example selection guidelines). Under each problem is a fact family arrow with the three boxes and a line under the total box:

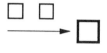

The students are taught to indicate the total is how much the person ends up with by writing *ends* on the line under the box for the total number. The teacher leads the students through three problems on the first day, then has students do the rest on their own. The students write *ends* on the line under the total box for problems in which the person ends up with more. The students do not write anything on the line under the total box for problems in which the person ends up with less. When students can do the exercise without error, then part B can be introduced.

In part B, the teacher introduces the rule. "If the problem tells about ending up with less, the total is how much you start with." The teacher leads the students verbally through a set of problems. If the problem tells about ending up with less, the students write *starts* on the line under the total box. If the problem tells about ending up with *more*, the students write *ends* under the total box. The verbal drill is followed by a written exercise.

Part C, which is introduced when students have mastered the exercises in part B, is a structured worksheet exercise. The teacher leads students through working a set of problems. First, she has the students read a problem and write *ends* or *starts* on the line under the total box (this is the skill students should have mastered in part B). Then, she has the students read the problem again to determine if a number is given for the total. If the problem gives a number for the total, the teacher tells the students to write that number in the total box and the other number stated in the problem in a box that is over the arrow, since that number is a small number in the number family. If the problem does not give a number for the total, the teacher directs the students to write both numbers in the problem in the boxes over the arrow, since these numbers must both be small numbers, part of the total. In the final step, the teacher prompts the students on

Figure 12.5 Format for Action Problems

Day	Part A Preskill	Part B Preskill	Part C Structured Worksheet	Part D Less Structured Structured	Part E Supervised Practice
1–2	6–8				
3–4		6–8			
5–6			6–8		
7–8			4	4	
9				4	
10					6–8
accurate					

Part A: Preskill: Determining if the Problem Tells About Ending Up with More

Teacher gives students a worksheet with a standard mix of addition and subtraction problems. (See example selection guidelines.) Under each problem is a number family; e.g.,

James had 14 apples. He bought some more apples.

Now he has 25 apples.

TEACHER	STUDENTS
1. "HERE ARE RULES ABOUT THE TOTAL NUMBER IN STORY PROBLEMS. IF THE PROBLEM TELLS ABOUT ENDING UP WITH MORE, THE TOTAL IS HOW MUCH YOU END UP WITH." "PROBLEMS THAT TELL ABOUT ENDING UP WITH MORE HAVE WORDS LIKE *GETS, FINDS, BUYS, MAKES*, AND *BUILDS*."	
2. "TOUCH PROBLEM 1. I'LL READ IT. JAMES HAS 14 APPLES. HE BOUGHT SOME MORE APPLES. NOW HE HAS 25 APPLES." "THAT PROBLEM HAS THE WORD *BOUGHT*. WHEN YOU BUY YOU END UP WITH MORE. REMEMBER IN PROBLEMS THAT TELL ABOUT GETTING MORE, HOW MUCH YOU END UP WITH IS THE TOTAL. WRITE *ENDS* ON THE LINE UNDER THE TOTAL BOX."	Students write *ends*.
3. "TOUCH PROBLEM 2. I'LL READ IT. JILL HAD 19 APPLES. SHE LOST SOME APPLES. NOW SHE HAS 15 APPLES. *DOES THAT PROBLEM TELL ABOUT ENDING UP WITH MORE?*" "SO DON'T WRITE ANYTHING UNDER THE LINE UNDER THE TOTAL BOX."	"No"
4. "*READ PROBLEM 3 TO YOURSELF* (Pause.) *DOES THAT PROBLEM TELL ABOUT ENDING UP WITH MORE?*"	"Yes"

Repeat step 4 with remaining problems.

Figure 12.5 cont'd

TEACHER   **STUDENTS**

5. "READ THE REST OF THE PROBLEMS TO YOUR-
   SELF. IF THE PROBLEM TELLS ABOUT ENDING UP
   WITH MORE, WRITE *ENDS* UNDER THE BOX FOR
   THE TOTAL. IF THE PROBLEM DOES NOT TELL
   ABOUT ENDING UP WITH MORE, DON'T WRITE
   ANYTHING ON THE LINE."

PART B: Determining if the Problem Tells About Ending Up with Less

Give students a worksheet like the one constructed in
part A.

1. "REMEMBER THE RULE. IF A PROBLEM TELLS
   ABOUT ENDING UP WITH MORE, THE TOTAL IS
   HOW MUCH YOU END UP WITH."
   "HERE'S A NEW RULE:
   IF A PROBLEM TELLS ABOUT ENDING UP WITH
   LESS, THE TOTAL IS HOW MUCH YOU *START*
   WITH."

2. "LET'S GO OVER THOSE RULES. FINISH THE
   SENTENCE BY SAYING *STARTS WITH* OR *ENDS
   WITH*. THE TOTAL IN PROBLEMS THAT TELL
   ABOUT ENDING UP WITH LESS IS HOW MUCH   "Start with."
   YOU. . . ." (signal)
   "THE TOTAL IN PROBLEMS THAT TELL ABOUT
   ENDING UP WITH *MORE* IS HOW MUCH YOU. . . ." "End with."
   (signal)
   Repeat step 2 until students respond correctly.

3. "READ PROBLEM 1 TO YOURSELF AND SEE IF IT
   TELLS ABOUT ENDING WITH MORE OR ENDING UP
   WITH LESS." (pause)
   "DOES THAT PROBLEM TELL ABOUT ENDING UP
   WITH MORE OR LESS?"

   To correct: "When you (verb), do you end up with
               more or less?"

   "SO DOES THE TOTAL TELL HOW MUCH THE
   PERSON STARTED WITH OR ENDED WITH?"

   To correct: "Remember, if you end up with less,
               the total is how much you started
               with. If you end up with more, the
               total is how much you end up with."

4. Repeat step 3 with remaining problems.

5. "DO THE PROBLEMS ON YOUR OWN. READ EACH
   PROBLEM. WRITE *STARTS* ON THE TOTAL BOX
   LINE IF THE PERSON ENDS UP WITH LESS. WRITE
   ENDS IF THE PERSON ENDS UP WITH MORE."

Figure 12.5 cont'd

PART C: Structured Worksheet

Give students a worksheet like that in part A with 6–8 problems.

TEACHER   **STUDENTS**

1. "WE'RE GOING TO WORK THESE PROBLEMS.
   FIRST WE'LL SEE IF THE TOTAL TELLS ABOUT
   HOW MUCH THE PERSONS STARTED WITH OR
   HOW MUCH THE PERSON ENDED WITH. THEN
   WE'LL PUT THE NUMBERS IN THE BOXES AND
   WORK THE PROBLEM."

2. "TOUCH PROBLEM 1."
   "READ THE PROBLEM TO YOURSELF AND
   FIGURE OUT IF IT TELLS ABOUT ENDING UP
   WITH MORE OR ENDING UP WITH LESS, THEN
   WRITE *STARTS* OR *ENDS* ON THE LINE UNDER
   THE TOTAL BOX." (Pause.)
   "IS THE TOTAL NUMBER HOW MUCH THE PER-
   SON STARTED WITH OR ENDED UP WITH?"

3. "READ THE PROBLEM TO YOURSELF AGAIN AND
   SEE IF A NUMBER IS GIVEN FOR THE TOTAL."
   (Pause)
   "DOES THE PROBLEM GIVE A NUMBER FOR THE
   TOTAL?"

4A. Do these steps if the answer to step 3 was "no."
   "SO THE NUMBERS IN THE PROBLEM ARE NOT
   THE TOTAL. WRITE THEM IN THE BOXES OVER
   THE ARROW."

4B. Do these steps if the answer to step 3 was "yes."
   "WRITE THE NUMBER FOR THE TOTAL IN THE
   TOTAL BOX."
   "THERE ARE TWO BOXES OVER THE ARROW,
   BUT THERE IS ONLY ONE OTHER NUMBER IN
   THE PROBLEM. WRITE THE NUMBER IN A BOX."

5. "IS THE TOTAL GIVEN?"
   "SO DO WE ADD OR SUBTRACT?"
   "WRITE THE EQUATION AND FIGURE OUT THE
   ANSWER."
   "WHAT'S THE ANSWER?"
   Repeat steps 1–5 with the remaining problems.

PART D: Less Structured Worksheet

Give students a worksheet with problems written in this form.

Last year Bill weighed 62 pounds. Now he weighs 89 pounds.

How many pounds did he gain? Answer _____

$$\square \ \square$$
$$\longrightarrow \ \square$$

_____

Figure 12.5 cont'd

TEACHER	**STUDENTS**

1. "READ THE PROBLEM TO YOURSELF AND WRITE *STARTS* OR *ENDS* ON THE LINE UNDER THE TOTAL BOX."

2. "WRITE THE NUMBERS THAT GO IN THE BOXES."

3. "WRITE THE EQUATION AND FIGURE OUT THE ANSWER."

4. "READ THE LAST SENTENCE IN THE PROBLEM AND WRITE THE WHOLE ANSWER, THE NUMBER AND THE WORD ON THE NUMBER LINE."
Repeat steps 1–4 with remaining problems.

applying the preskill rule about what to do if the total is given (subtract) or not given (add). Note that this preskill should have been mastered prior to beginning this format. On the days that parts A and B of this format are presented, the preskill should be practiced in guided worksheet exercises.

The critical step in Part C occurs after the students tell if the total is how much the person starts with or how much the person ends with. The teacher then has the students read the problem again and tell if a number is given for the total.

If students have difficulty with this step, the teacher should do a verbal firm-up with a set of problems. For each problem, the teacher would tell the students if the total is how much the person started or ended with and then have the students tell if the problem gives a number for the total (e.g., "The total in this problem tells how much Julio ended up with. Read the problem and see if it tells how much Julio ended up with").

When selecting examples for this format, the teacher constructs sets of four problems. An exercise might include two sets of four problems for a total of eight problems. Each set should contain two addition and two subtraction problems. One addition problem should have a verb that indicates ending up with more. One addition problem should have a verb that indicates ending up with less. Likewise, one subtraction problem should have a verb that indicates ending up with more and one subtraction problem should have a verb that indicates

ending up with less. The problems should be written in a random order with an addition problem not always followed by a subtraction problem. Problems introduced initially should contain common verbs. Sentences should be relatively simple. All problems should result in equations the students are able to work. For example, if the students have not learned to borrow, subtraction problems should be limited to problems that do not require borrowing. Table 12.2 includes a sample set of action problems.

CLASSIFICATION PROBLEMS Classification problems involve three related objects or actions, one of which is a superordinate class to the other objects or actions; e.g., boys and girls are children; red apples and green apples are apples; running and walking are ways people move; buying hats in the morning and buying hats in the afternoon are part of buying hats all day. Classification problems appear in two forms. In the addition form, two subordinate actions or objects are given, and the student has to figure out the total or superordinate quantity: There are six girls and four boys in our class. How many students are there?

In the subtraction form, the total or superordinate group is given along with the amount of one subordinate group. Students must subtract to figure the number for the other subordinate group: There are ten children in our class. Six are girls. How many are boys?

Table 12.2 Sample Set of Action Problems

Jerry had 98 apples. He gave away 14 apples. How many does he have left?	Alice threw out 14 pencils. She still has 12 pencils. How many pencils did she have to begin with?
Tom had 12 baseball cards. He bought some more. Now he has 15 baseball cards. How many cards did he buy?	Roberto found 12 pennies. He already had 14 pennies. How many pennies does he have now?

Figure 12.6 includes a format for teaching students to work classification problems. Part A is designed to provide practice in the language pre-skill of identifying class names for groups of objects. The teacher says a superordinate class and two related subclasses and asks the students to tell which is the biggest class. This exercise assumes that students already understand the concept of classification. Teachers working with very low-performing students may find that more extensive teaching in this language skill is necessary. Such teachers should refer to a language development program such as *DISTAR II Language*, which includes systematic instruction in classification.

In Part B, a structured worksheet exercise, the teacher introduces classification story problems. Students are given a worksheet with six to eight problems. Part B begins with the teacher reminding the students that when the total number in a fact family is given, they must subtract to find the answer; when the total number is not given, they must add. The teacher then says a problem and tells students the three groups mentioned in the problem: "There are five children. Two of the children are girls. How many are boys? This problem mentions children, girls and boys." After telling students the three groups, the teacher asks which word tells the name of the big class: "Listen: children, girls, boys. Which

Figure 12.6 Format for Classification Story Problems

Day	Part A Language Training Problems	Part B Structured Worksheet Problems	Part C Less Structured Worksheet Problems	Part D Supervised Practice Problems	Part E Independent Worksheet Problems
1–3	6				
4–6		6			
7–10			4	4	
11					
accurate					6–8

PART A: Language Training

<u>**TEACHER**</u>   <u>**STUDENTS**</u>

1. "I'LL SAY SOME CLASS NAMES. YOU TELL ME
   THE BIGGEST CLASS. LISTEN: CATS, ANIMALS,
   DOGS. WHAT IS THE BIGGEST CLASS?"   "Animals"
   Repeat step 1 with: hammer, saw, tool; vehicle,
   car, truck; men, women, people; girls, boys,
   children.

PART B: Structured Worksheet

Give students a worksheet with 6–8 problems written like those below.

a. There are 8 *children*. Three are *boys*. How many are *girls*?

□ □
——→ □

_____ _____

b. Jill has 5 *hammers* and 4 *saws*. How many *tools* does she have?

□ □
——→ □

_____ _____

Figure 12.6 cont'd

TEACHER	**STUDENTS**

1. "LET'S REVIEW SOME RULES YOU ALREADY
   KNOW. IF THE TOTAL NUMBER IS GIVEN, WHAT
   DO YOU DO?"   "Subtract"
   "IF THE TOTAL NUMBER IS NOT GIVEN, WHAT DO
   YOU DO?"   "Add"

2. "IN SOME PROBLEMS WE DON'T SEE WORDS LIKE
   FIND, *LOSE*, *BUY*, OR *GIVE AWAY*. SO WE HAVE
   TO USE A DIFFERENT WAY TO DO THESE
   PROBLEMS."

3. "TOUCH THE FIRST PROBLEM."
   "I'LL READ IT. THERE ARE 8 CHILDREN: 3 ARE
   BOYS. HOW MANY ARE GIRLS?"
   "THE PROBLEM TALKS ABOUT CHILDREN, BOYS,
   AND GIRLS. WHICH IS THE BIG CLASS, CHILDREN,
   BOYS, OR GIRLS?"   "Children"
   "IF CHILDREN IS THE BIG CLASS, THEN THE
   NUMBER OF CHILDREN IS THE TOTAL NUMBER."
   "SO WRITE *CHILDREN* ON THE LINE UNDER THE
   TOTAL BOX.   Students write *children*.

4. "LISTEN." Repeat the problem. "*CHILDREN* IS THE
   TOTAL NUMBER. DOES THE PROBLEM TELL HOW
   MANY CHILDREN?"   "Yes"
   "SO THE TOTAL NUMBER IS GIVEN. WHAT IS THE
   TOTAL NUMBER?"   "8"
   "WRITE 8 IN THE BOX FOR THE TOTAL NUMBER."   Students write 8.

> Note: If the first answer is "no," tell the
> students, "The total is not given, so we
> don't   write anything in the box for the
> total."

5. "NOW WE WRITE THE VALUES FOR BOYS AND
   GIRLS IN THE BOXES OVER THE ARROW.
   "HOW MANY BOYS?"   "3"
   "WRITE 3 IN THE FIRST BOX."   Students write 3.
   "WE DON'T KNOW HOW MANY GIRLS, SO WE
   DON'T WRITE ANYTHING IN THE OTHER BOX."

6. "IS THE TOTAL NUMBER GIVEN?"   "Yes"
   "SO WHAT DO YOU DO TO WORK OUT THE
   PROBLEM?"   "Subtract"
   "I START WITH 8 CHILDREN AND SUBTRACT 3
   BOYS TO FIND OUT HOW MANY GIRLS."
   "WRITE THE EQUATION AND FIGURE OUT THE
   ANSWER."   Students write $8 - 3 = 5$.
   "IF THERE ARE 8 CHILDREN AND 3 ARE BOYS,
   HOW MANY ARE GIRLS?'   "5"

Repeat steps 3–5 with remaining problems.

Figure 12.6 cont'd

PART C: Less Structured Worksheet

Give students worksheet with problems in this form.

Jerry has 7 *pets*. 4 are *dogs*.

How many are *cats*?　　　Answer. _____

☐ ☐

——————➤ ☐

_____

TEACHER

1. "TOUCH PROBLEM ONE."

2. "READ THE PROBLEM. THEN WRITE THE NAME
   FOR THE BIG CLASS UNDER THE TOTAL BOX."

3. "WRITE THE NUMBERS IN THE NUMBER FAMILY
   BOXES."

4. "WRITE THE EQUATION AND FIGURE OUT THE
   ANSWER."

5. "WRITE THE WHOLE ANSWER ON THE NUMBER
   LINE."

   Repeat steps 1–5 with remaining problems.

STUDENTS

Students write name for big
class.

Students write numbers.

Students write equations.

Students write answer.

---

is the big class?" The teacher then repeats the
problem, asking whether or not the total number—
the number of children—is given. Once this question is answered, the students fill in the boxes, tell
what operation is required, and complete the problem. "Children is the big class. We know there are
five children. So we know that the total number is
5." In a problem that says, "There are five boys and
two girls. How many children?" the teacher would
say, "We don't know how many children. The total
number is not given."

Part C is a less structured worksheet exercise.
After reading a problem, the students write the
name of the big class under the box for the total
number, fill in the boxes and write the equation.

EXAMPLE SELECTION　There are several example
selection guidelines. First, there should be an equal
mix of addition and subtraction problems. Second,
problems should initially be written in a relatively
short form with few extraneous words. Third, relatively common classes should be used. A sample
set of four problems appears below:

a. Jill has five roses and four tulips. How many
   flowers does she have?
b. There are nine students. Five are girls. How many
   are boys?
c. Jane has 5 pencils and 3 pens. How many writing
   tools does she have altogether?
d. Eight people are in the store. Three are women.
   How many are men?

During the first week classification problems are
introduced, the key words in the problem can be
underlined to prompt the the students. For example,
in problem (a) above, the words *roses*, *tulips*, and
flowers would be underlined.

There are two special types of classification
problem. The first involves two subordinate groups
that are the same object but are different because
of the presence or absence of a specified characteristic. (For example, tall boys and short boys, dirty
glasses and clean glasses, happy children and
unhappy children, blue pencils and pencils that are
not blue, big cows and cows that are not big.) The
superordinate groups would be the total of both

object types. The second type involves two subordinate groups that represent two parts of a whole action. (For example, hats bought in the morning and hats bought in the afternoon, miles he jogged in January and miles he jogged in February.) Problems of these two types are illustrated below:

a. Bill has 7 apples altogether; 3 apples are green. How many apples are not green?
b. There are 5 heavy boxes and 3 light boxes. How many boxes altogether?
c. Sarah jogged 4 miles in the morning and walked 6 miles in the afternoon. How many miles did she travel in all?
d. Jill sold 5 hats in the morning. She sold 2 hats in the afternoon. How many hats did she sell?

Problems of this nature are introduced when students can work more obvious classification problems. The teacher presents these problems using the same format as in Figure 12.6. Several modifications are required. In Part A, the teacher should model several examples: Tall girls and short girls are girls altogether; green apples and red apples are apples altogether. Note that the word *altogether* functions to prompt the students about the big class. Every problem during the first week should include the term *altogether*. After the first week, problems similar to those presented earlier, except for the deletion of the term *altogether*, would be presented:

with altogether:	Bill bought 9 glasses altogether; 5 were red. How many were not red?
without altogether:	Bill bought 9 glasses; 5 were red. How many were not red?
with altogether:	Jane has 6 red apples and 5 apples that are not red. How many apples does she have altogether?
without altogether:	Jane has 6 red apples and 5 apples that are not red. How many apples does she have?

While students are learning classification problems, they should continue to practice solving action problems with key words separately. After they have demonstrated mastery of classification problems, the teacher would give students worksheets that include a mix of classification and action problems. Worksheets should still include six to eight problems daily, with half classification and half action problems. When the students are first introduced to this mix, the teacher should be particularly careful not to use classification problems that also contain key words commonly used in action problems. For example, the following problem should not be used when students first encounter this mixed worksheet: *Jill sold 5 hats in the morning. She sold 2 hats in the afternoon. How many hats did she sell?* Later, students can be taught that when a problem contains repetitions of a key word, such as *sold*, and a classification structure such as *in the morning* and *in the afternoon*, students should use the classification structure to solve the problem.

Also, when students are first introduced to this mix, follow the instructions described in the "Integrated Review" section that follows the description of comparison problems. When students first encounter a mix of problems, they must again receive teacher direction to be sure that they can discriminate the two kinds of problems they are solving. Even though students have been successful at solving action problems and classification problems independently, do not assume students will be equally successful when two types are mixed on the same worksheet.

COMPARISON PROBLEMS A comparison problem deals with two quantities and the difference between them. There are two basic types of comparison problems. In one type, a quantity is stated describing an attribute of one object (e.g., weight, length, height, age, etc.). Also stated is the difference between that object and another object: "John is 7 years old. Mary is 3 years older. How old is Mary?" The student is asked to find the quantity of the other object. In the second type of problem, the quantities of two objects are stated and the student is asked to find the difference between them: "John is 7 years old. Mary is 10 years old. How much older is Mary?" Both types are introduced concurrently, but only after students are able to complete a worksheet containing action problems with key words and classification problems with 80–90% accuracy.

A two-step strategy for solving comparison problems involves (a) determining which object represents the bigger quantity and (b) determining whether the bigger quantity is given or not given. For example:

Thomas got 10 problems correct. Alex got 2 fewer problems correct than Thomas. How many problems did Alex get correct?

In this problem, the number of problems Alex answered correctly is fewer, so the number of problems Thomas answered correctly represents the bigger number. Because the number of problems Thomas answered correctly is given, the problem requires subtraction.

Figure 12.7 includes the format for presenting comparison problems. The format includes four parts. Part A is a preskill format designed to teach students to determine which object represents the bigger quantity. Note that this part assumes that students understand comparative words such as *deeper, shallower, thicker, thinner, bigger, smaller, heavier, lighter*. If students have difficulty with Part A, it may be because they do not understand the meaning of the comparatives. Teachers should test students' understanding with diagrams or illustrations. For example, the teacher could present illustrations of two holes

and ask, "Show me the hole that is deeper." Procedures for teaching the meaning of these terms can

be found in the *Distar Language I* program (Engelmann & Osborne, 1985).

Part B is a structured worksheet utilizing the prompt of the fact family diagram. The teacher leads the students in determining which object represents the greater quantity. The name of that object is written under the box for the total number in the diagram. The teacher then leads the students in determining if the quantity for that object is given. If it is, the students write that number in the box. The final steps involve determining the type of problem and writing and solving the equation to find the answer.

The critical step in Part B occurs when the teacher asks if the problem gives a number for the total. Students may not read the problem carefully and give a wrong answer. For example, let's say a problem tells that Ann is 12 years older than Sally who is 7 years old. The total will tell how old Ann is. When examining the problem, the students may

Figure 12.7   Format for Comparison Problems

Day	Part A Preskill	Part B Structured Worksheet Problems	Part C Less Structured Worksheet Problems	Part D Supervised Practice Problems	Part E Independent Worksheet Problems
1–2	6				
3–6		6			
7–10		2	6		
11–accurate				8	
Daily practice					6–8

PART A: Preskill: Determining the Total Number

TEACHER

STUDENTS

1. "COMPARISON PROBLEMS TELL YOU ABOUT TWO PERSONS OR THINGS."
   "HERE ARE SOME WORDS YOU'LL SEE IN COMPARISON PROBLEMS: *BIGGER, OLDER, SMALLER, TALLER, WIDER.*
   IF THE PROBLEM TELLS ABOUT TWO PEOPLE AND HAS A WORD THAT ENDS IN *ER* YOU KNOW IT'S A COMPARISON PROBLEM."

2. "LET'S PRACTICE FIGURING OUT WHICH PERSON OR THING IN A COMPARISON PROBLEM TELLS ABOUT THE BIG NUMBER."

3. "LISTEN: A DOG WEIGHS 7 POUNDS.
   A CAT WEIGHS 3 POUNDS MORE THAN THE DOG."
   "WHO DOES THAT PROBLEM TELL ABOUT?"   "A dog and a cat."

4. "LISTEN TO THE PROBLEM AGAIN."
   (Repeat problem)
   "WHO IS HEAVIER?"   "The cat."

Figure 12.7 cont'd

TEACHER	**STUDENTS**

5. "SO THE BIG NUMBER TELLS HOW MANY POUNDS THE CAT WEIGHS."
   Repeat steps 3–5 with these problems:

   Jill is 10 years old. Brian is 8 years younger. Who is older?

   Hole A is 6 feet deep. Hole B is 4 feet deep. Which hole is deeper?

   Jack ran 8 miles. Ann ran 2 miles more. Who ran farther?

   Jane weighs 60 pounds. Ann is 5 pounds lighter. Who is heavier?

   A yellow pencil is 5 inches long. A blue pencil is 3 inches longer. Which pencil is longer?

PART B: Structured Worksheet

Give students worksheets with problems written in this form.

a. Tom's stick is 2 feet long.

   Bill's stick is 5 feet longer.

   How long is Bill's stick?

   Answer: _____

b. Jack is 10 years old.

   Bill is 2 years younger.

   How old is Bill?

   Answer: _____

1. "READ THE FIRST PROBLEM."

2. "WHO DOES THE PROBLEM TELL ABOUT?" — "Tom and Bill."
   "WHICH IS LONGER, BILL'S STICK OR TOM'S STICK?" — "Bill's stick."
   "WRITE *BILL* ON THE LINE UNDER THE TOTAL BOX." — Students write *Bill*.

3. "READ THE PROBLEM AGAIN." (pause)
   "DOES A NUMBER IN THE PROBLEM TELL HOW LONG BILL'S STICK IS?" — "No"

4. "THE PROBLEM DOES NOT GIVE A NUMBER FOR THE TOTAL. THE NUMBERS IN THE PROBLEM TELL ABOUT PARTS OF THE TOTAL. WRITE THOSE NUMBERS IN THE BOXES ON THE ARROWS." — Students write numbers in the boxes.

Figure 12.7 cont'd

TEACHER	**STUDENTS**

5. "WRITE THE EQUATION AND FIGURE OUT THE ANSWER."
Repeat steps 1–5 with the remaining problems.

PART C: Less Structured Worksheet

Give students worksheets written in this form.

1. "READ THE PROBLEM."

2. "WRITE THE WORD THAT TELLS ABOUT THE BIG NUMBER UNDER THE TOTAL BOX."

3. "SEE IF THE BIG NUMBER IS GIVEN IN THE PROBLEM. THEN WRITE THE NUMBERS IN THE BOXES."

4. "WRITE THE EQUATION AND FIGURE OUT THE ANSWER."

5. "WRITE THE WHOLE ANSWER ON THE NUMBER LINE."

Repeat steps 1–5 with the remaining problems.

---

misread the words *Ann is 12 years older* as *Ann is 12 years old*, and write 12 as the total number.

If this type of error occurs frequently, the teacher should do a verbal firm-up exercise that just focuses on this step. For each problem, the teacher would tell the students what the total number tells about and ask if the problem gives a number for the total (e.g., "The total number will tell how old Ann is. Does a number in the problem tell how old Ann is?"). The teacher does the verbal format with a set of six to eight problems.

Part C is a less structured worksheet exercise in which the teacher leads students through applying the strategy.

Examples should be constructed in sets of four. Each set should include the following types.

1. *Two addition problems in which one quantity is stated. The difference indicates the other quantity is greater:*

Bill dug a hole 6 feet deep. Tim dug a hole 2 feet deeper than Bill's hole. How deep is the hole Tim dug?

Bill dug a hole 6 feet deep. Bill's hole is 2 feet shallower than the hole Tom dug. How deep is the hole Tom dug?

2. *One subtraction problem in which one quantity is stated. The difference indicates the other quantity is smaller:*

Bill dug a hole 6 feet deep. Jim dug a hole 2 feet shallower than Bill's hole. How deep is the hole Jim dug?

3. *One subtraction problem in which both quantities are stated. Students must determine the difference:*

Bill dug a hole 6 feet deep. Jim dug a hole 2 feet deep. How much deeper is Bill's hole?

Two addition problems are included in each set so that there will be an equal mix of addition and subtraction problems. After students can work comparison problems accurately, they should be given worksheets including a mix of comparison, action, and classification problems. In the meantime, students should continue daily practice with a mix of action and classification problems as well as daily, but separate, practice of the comparison problems.

Integrated Review

After students have become accurate in solving story problems of a particular type, review worksheet exercises including problems of the new type and previously introduced types should be included as part of the daily lesson. A worksheet would include six to eight problems. For example, after students have mastered separately action problems with key words and classification problems, students will be ready to try a mix of those two types. The following set of problems might be included in a review exercise after the students have mastered classification, comparison, and action problems.

a. There are 19 students in Mr. Jones' class. There are 8 girls in Mr. Jones' class. How many boys are in Mr. Jones' class?
b. Sarah ran 100 miles last week. June ran 10 miles farther than Sarah. How many miles did June run?
c. Bill needs 80 bottle caps. He has collected 30 caps so far. How many more bottle caps does he need?
d. Tom bought 16 apples. Jim bought 8 pears. How many pieces of fruit did they buy altogether?
e. Bill is 10 pounds lighter than his brother. His brother weighs 60 pounds. How much does Bill weigh?
f. Sally bought some cookies. Then, she made 12 more cookies. She ended with 24 cookies. How many cookies did she start with?

Students will most probably need prompting on this worksheet. For the first week or so when a new problem type has been added to the mix, the teacher should present a format in which she has the students read each problem and then prompts the students by asking what the total tells about. If the problem is an action problem, the teachers asks, "Is the total how much the person started with or how much the person ended with?" If the problem is a classification problem, the teacher asks about the classes (e.g., "Does the total tell about cars,

vehicles, or trucks?"). If the problem is a comparison problem, the teacher asks, "Which person or object is the bigger of the two?" The teacher does this verbally with four to six problems and then has the students work all problems on their own. Providing such a review exercise is critical in helping students develop generalizable strategy for working story problems. When students show they can be as successful with a mix of problems as they were with separate types, the integrated review sheets may be completed as independent worksheets. However, the teacher should monitor the accuracy level carefully from day to day.

The number family arrows can be dropped from the worksheets after the students are able to perform at a 80–90% accuracy level. When they are dropped students can be given the option of making their own number family arrow or doing the problems without the number family arrow. If students can work accurately without using the family arrow, they should be allowed to do so.

Multiplication and Division Problems

Multiplication and division operations are used to solve story problems that deal with equal-sized groups. These problems are stated in three basic forms. If a problem tells the number of groups and the number in each group, the problem is a multiplication problem. "Carlos has three piles of toys. There are two toys in each pile. How many toys does Carlos have in all?" The equation is $3 \times 2 = \square$. If the problem tells how many altogether and asks either how many groups or how many in each group, the problem is solved through division. One form asks about the number of objects in each group: "Carlos has six toys. He wants to put the toys in three piles. How many toys will be in each pile?" ($6 \div 3 = \square$). The last form asks for the number of groups: "Carlos has six toys. He'll put two toys in each pile. How many piles will he make?" ($6 \div 2 = \square$).

Multiplication and division problems almost always contain a word or phrase that tells the student that the problem deals with equal-sized groups. Most of the problems contain the word *each* or *every*. Other indications are the word *per* or phrases indicating equal groups like *in a box* or *a dozen*: "John walked 4 miles per day. How many miles did he walk in three days? There were 3 balls in a box. There are 6 boxes. How many balls in all?"

Multiplication and division story problems can be introduced after students have mastered addition and subtraction story problems with 80–90% accuracy and have a viable strategy for figuring out twenty-five or more basic multiplication facts and twenty-five or more basic division facts.

The strategy students will be taught to solve multiplication problems has the students translate the words of the problem into a regular multiplication problem. The strategy that students will be taught to solve division problems has the students translate the words of the problem into a multiplication problem written with a missing factor. For example, here's a division problem: "84 boys will get jobs. The boys will work in 4 equal-sized groups. How many boys will be in each group?" In this problem the students do not know how many are in each group: They write $4 \times \square = 84$. Four groups times how many boys in each group equals 84 boys? To find the answer, the students divide. The problem $4 \times \square = 84$ is rewritten as a division problem: $4\,\overline{)84}$. The division problem can also be thought of as this fraction $\frac{84}{4}$, which reads 84 boys divided into 4 groups.

Preskills

Working multiplication equations with a missing factor and discriminating this type of problem from regular multiplication (e.g., $5 \times 15 = \square$ and $5 \times \square = 15$) are preskills the students should master before being introduced to multiplication and division story problems. The steps in the strategy students learn

in order to translate a story problem into an equation are rather complicated. We use a rote rule to teach the discrimination between regular multiplication equations and multiplication equations with a missing factor.

"If there are two numbers on the same side of the equal sign, you multiply. If there are *not* two numbers on the same side of the equal sign, you divide." Thus when students encounter the problem $2 \times \square = 8$, they write $2\,\overline{)8}$. The division problem is read "2 goes into 8." The format (see Figure 12.8) for teaching this preskill includes only one part, a structured worksheet exercise in which the teacher presents the rules, models their application with several problems, then has the students do the rest of the problems on their own. Daily practice on the preskill should be continued for several weeks. Problems can be done independently after the students demonstrate mastery.

The example selection criteria for this preskill format are (1) limit problems to include only those facts students have learned in earlier exercises; (2) include only single digit numbers in exercises presented during the first week; (3) write multiplication and division problems in a non-predictable order, and (4) when introducing problems with a double-digit number, include minimally different pairs (e.g., $3 \times \square = 15$ and $3 \times 15 = \square$). Note that students will have to be able to translate 3×15 into a column problem. Extra structure should be provided the first day problems of this type appear.

Figure 12.8 Format for Working Simple Multiplication Problems with a Missing Factor

Day	Part A Structured Worksheet Problems
1	8–10 problems
2–15	8–10 problems step 2 & 5 only

Give students a worksheet constructed like the one below.

a) $5 \times 3 = \square$ b) $2 \times \square = 8$ c) $3 \times \square = 6$

5×3 _____ $2\,\overline{)8}$ _____

d) $2 \times 5 = \square$ e) $3 \times 4 = \square$ f) $2 \times \square = 6$

_____ _____ _____

g) $4 \times \square = 8$ h) $3 \times \square = 9$ i) $4 \times 2 = \square$

_____ _____ _____

Figure 12.8 cont'd

TEACHER   **STUDENTS**

1. "ALL THESE PROBLEMS HAVE TIMES SIGNS, BUT
   IN SOME YOU HAVE TO DIVIDE TO FIGURE OUT
   THE ANSWER."
   "HERE'S THE RULES. IF THERE ARE TWO
   NUMBERS ON THE SAME SIDE OF THE EQUAL
   SIGN, YOU MULTIPLY."
   "IF THERE ARE *NOT* TWO NUMBERS ON THE
   SAME SIDE OF THE EQUAL, YOU DIVIDE."
   "LISTEN AGAIN." (repeat rules)

2. "YOUR TURN."
   "IF THERE ARE TWO NUMBERS ON THE SAME
   SIDE WHAT DO WE DO?" (signal)   "Multiply"
   "IF THERE ARE NOT TWO NUMBERS ON THE
   SAME SIDE OF THE EQUAL SIGN, WHAT DO WE
   DO?" (signal)   "Divide"
   Repeat step 2 until firm.

3. "TOUCH PROBLEM (a)."
   "NOW TOUCH THE EQUAL SIGN."   Students touch equal sign.
   "ON ONE SIDE OF THE EQUAL SIGN ARE THE
   NUMBERS 5 & 3. THERE ARE TWO NUMBER ON
   THE SAME SIDE. SO WE MULTIPLY 5 × 3. FILL IN
   THE DOTTED 5 TIMES 3."   Students fill in 5 × 3.
   "FIGURE OUT THE ANSWER AND WRITE IT IN THE
   EMPTY BOX."   Students write 15.

4. "TOUCH PROBLEM (b)."
   "TOUCH THE EQUAL SIGN"   Students touch equal sign.
   "ON ONE SIDE OF THE EQUAL SIGN IS 2 AND AN
   EMPTY BOX. ON THE OTHER SIDE OF THE EQUAL
   SIGN IS THE NUMBER 8. THERE ARE NOT TWO
   NUMBERS ON THE SAME SIDE, SO WE DIVIDE. 2
   GOES INTO 8."
   "FILL IN THE DOTTED 2 GOES INTO 8."   Student fill in $2\overline{)8}$.
   "FIGURE OUT THE ANSWER AND WRITE IT IN THE
   EMPTY BOX."   Students write 4.

5. "WORK PROBLEMS (c) THROUGH (i)."
   "FOR EACH PROBLEM WRITE AN EQUATION AND
   FIGURE OUT THE ANSWER, REMEMBER."
   "IF THERE ARE TWO NUMBERS ON THE SAME SIDE
   MULTIPLY."
   "IF THERE ARE NOT TWO NUMBERS ON THE SAME
   SIDE DIVIDE."

Introducing the Concept

Figure 12.9 introduces students to the concept of multiplication and division story problems by showing students how to draw pictures to solve the problems. This format is designed to assist students in developing an understanding of working with groups of equal size, whether multiplying those groups to arrive a larger number of dividing a larger number into several groups of equal size. Because multiplication and division problems are expressed in three different forms, this format presents three variations of teacher wording for teaching students to draw pictures. Wording is provided for: (a) multiplication problems, (b) division problems in which the number of groups is not given, and (c) division problems in which the number in each group is not given. This particular procedure is time-consuming

Figure 12.9 Format for Introducing the Concept of Solving Multiplication and
Division Story Problems

Day	**Part A** Structured Worksheet Problems
1–3	4

PART A: Structured Worksheet

Give students a worksheet like the one below.

---

1) There are 5 boxes. Bill put 4 apples into each box.

How many apples were there altogether? _____
                                                answer

2) Jill had 4 packages filled with nails. She had 12 nails.

How many nails were in each package? _____
                                                answer

3) There were 18 cookies. Each pan had 6 cookies on it.

How many pans were there? _____
                                    answer

TEACHER

1. "WE'RE GOING TO READ MULTIPLICATION AND
   DIVISION STORY PROBLEMS AND DRAW PICTURES
   TO FIND THE ANSWERS TO THE PROBLEMS.
   LATER WE'LL LEARN HOW TO WRITE EQUATIONS
   TO SOLVE THE PROBLEMS."

A. Steps for multiplication problems

1. "READ PROBLEM 1."

2. "THERE ARE 4 APPLES IN EACH BOX. THERE
   ARE 5 BOXES."
   "DRAW A PICTURE OF 5 SMALL BOXES NEXT TO
   THE PROBLEMS."
3. "HOW MANY APPLES GO IN EACH BOX?"
   "DRAW 4 APPLES IN EACH BOX."

4. "THE PROBLEM ASKS HOW MANY APPLES WERE
   THERE ALTOGETHER? COUNT THE APPLES."
   (pause)
   "HOW MANY ALTOGETHER?"
   "THE ANSWER IS 20 APPLES.
   WRITE THAT ON THE ANSWER LINE."

STUDENTS

"There are 5 boxes. Bill put
4 apples into each box. How
many apples were there
altogether?"

Students draw.
"4"
Students draw 4 apples in
each box.

"20"

Students write *20 apples*.

Figure 12.9 cont'd

TEACHER	STUDENTS
B. Steps for division problem that asks how many in each group.	
1. "READ PROBLEM 2."	"Jill had 4 packages filled with nails. She had 12 nails. How many nails were in each package?"
2. "THE PROBLEM SAYS THERE ARE 4 PACKAGES OF NAILS. DRAW A PICTURE OF 4 PACKAGES."	Students draw.
3. "THERE ARE 12 NAILS. THE PROBLEM ASKS HOW MANY NAILS IN EACH PACKAGE. I'LL COUNT ONE TIME FOR EACH NAIL. EACH TIME I SAY A NUMBER, YOU'LL MAKE A LINE IN A BOX. WHEN I SAY ONE, MAKE A LINE IN THE FIRST BOX. WHEN I SAY TWO, MAKE A LINE IN THE NEXT BOX. AFTER YOU MAKE A LINE IN THE LAST BOX, START OVER." "ONE NAIL, TWO NAILS, THREE NAILS, FOUR NAILS..........TWELVE NAILS."	Students make lines in boxes.
4. "YOU SHOULD HAVE THE SAME NUMBER OF NAILS IN EACH PACKAGE. HOW MANY NAILS IN EACH PACKAGE?" "THE ANSWER IS THREE NAILS. WRITE THAT ON THE ANSWER LINE."	"Three nails" Students write *three nails*.
C. Steps for division problems that ask how many groups.	
1. "READ THE NEXT PROBLEM."	"There were 18 cookies. Each pan had 6 cookies on it. How many pans were there?"
2. "WE WANT TO DRAW 6 COOKIES IN EACH PAN. BUT THE PROBLEM DOESN'T TELL US HOW MANY PANS." "IT DOES TELL US HOW MANY COOKIES." "HOW MANY COOKIES ALTOGETHER?"	"18"
3. "I'LL COUNT. EACH TIME I SAY A NUMBER, YOU DRAW A LITTLE COOKIE. AFTER YOU DRAW 6 COOKIES, YOU'LL MAKE A PAN AROUND THE COOKIES 1, 2, 3, 4, 5, 6. THAT'S 6 COOKIES. DRAW A PAN. 7, 8, 9, 10, 11, 12. THAT'S 6 COOKIES. DRAW A PAN. 13, 14, 15, 16, 17, 18. THAT'S 6 COOKIES. DRAW A PAN."	
4. "HOW MANY PANS DID YOU DRAW?" "RIGHT. IF WE HAVE 18 COOKIES AND PUT 6 COOKIES ON A PAN, WE WOULD USE THREE PANS. THAT'S THE ANSWER. WRITE IT ON THE NUMBER LINE."	"3" Students write *3 pans*.

and inefficient when numbers become larger; therefore, students are introduced to the concept through a structured worksheet only and not required to master the skill independently.

Strategy

The strategy we present teaches students to translate the words and numbers in a story problem into an equation stating the number of groups times the objects in each group equals the total number of objects. The strategy has three steps. First, students find the sentence that signifies that a problem calls for multiplication or division. This sentence will usually have the word *each* or *every*. The students write a fraction which tells how many objects in each group. This fraction serves as a basis for writing the equation. Second, the students create an equation using the numbers given in the problem. Third, the students compute to find the unknown quantity. The steps in this strategy are illustrated below for a division problem and a multiplication problem:

a) division problem

30 students were divided into equal-sized teams. There were 6 teams. How many students on each team?

b) multiplication problem

The students were divided into 30 equal teams. There were 6 students on each team. How many students altogether?

1) Students translate the sentence with the word *each* or *every* into a fraction.

Problem (a)   Problem (b)

$$\frac{\boxed{?} \text{ students}}{\text{team}} \qquad \frac{\boxed{6} \text{ students}}{\text{team}}$$

The sentence with the word *each* or *every* always tells or asks about the number of objects in a group. The word in the problem that follows the word *each* or *every* always gives the name of the group. The name of the group is written on the bottom of the fraction. The name of the objects is written on the top. For the problems above, the word *team* goes on the bottom of both fractions, and the word *students* goes on top of both fractions. In the division problem, we are asked how many students on each team, so a question mark is written in the

box next to students. The problem doesn't tell how many students in each group. In the multiplication problem we are told there are 6 students on each team, so the number 6 is written in front of students.

2) Students create an equation with words and numbers.

Problem (a)

$$\boxed{6} \text{ teams} \times \frac{\boxed{?} \text{ students}}{\text{team}} = \boxed{30} \text{ students}$$

Problem (b)

$$\boxed{30} \text{ teams} \times \frac{\boxed{6} \text{ students}}{\text{team}} = \boxed{?} \text{ students}$$

The students create a multiplication equation to express the idea that the number of groups (teams) times the number of objects (students) in each group equals the total number of objects (students).

3) Students solve the equation by multiplying or dividing.

The students multiply if there are two numbers on the same side of the equal sign (Problem b). The students divide if there are not two numbers on the same side of the equal sign (Problem a).

Problem (a)

$$\boxed{6} \text{ team} \times \frac{\boxed{?} \text{ students}}{\text{team}} = \boxed{30} \text{ students}$$

answer = 5 students in each team

Problem (b)

$$\boxed{30} \text{ teams} \times \frac{\boxed{6} \text{ students}}{\text{team}} = \boxed{?} \text{ students}$$

answer = 180 students

The format for teaching students to solve multiplication and division story problems (see Figure 12.10) is unique in that each part presents a new step in a multi-step strategy. Part A introduces the first step. Part B reviews the first step and presents the second step. Part C reviews the first and second steps and presents the third step and so on.

Throughout the format students are given a worksheet in which a diagram appears under each problem. The diagram serves as a prompt to help the students set up the equation. The diagram appears below:

$$\square \dots\dots\dots \times \square \underline{\hspace{2cm}} = \square \dots\dots\dots$$

The students write a fraction that tells how many objects in each group using the solid line. The name of the group is written on the first dotted line. The name of the object is written on the last line. Numbers given in the problem or a question mark representing the unknown quantity are written in the boxes. The boxes, dotted lines, and solid lines are used as prompts to minimize potentially confusing teacher talk. After the students have mastered working problems using the diagram as a prompt, the diagram is faded and students are taught to create the blank diagram on their own before working a problem.

During the time that the strategy for solving multiplication and division story problems is being presented, the teacher should provide independent review of addition and subtraction story problems on a regular basis. When the students master the strategy for solving multiplication and division problems, an exercise to integrate story problems of all types should be presented.

The format includes seven parts. Part A teaches students to translate a sentence that contains the word *each* or *every* into a fraction expressing a numerical relationship, telling the number of objects in a group. The students are given a worksheet with problems written in this form:

Every apple has 7 seeds

□ _____

There are 7 days in each week

□ _____

A sentence containing the word *each* or *every* is written. Under the sentence is a box and a line. The worksheet contains six to ten sentences. In half the sentences the numbers of objects in a group is given (e.g., There are 6 apples in each box), while the other half of the sentence asks how many objects in the group (e.g., How many apples are in each box?). In half the sentences the word *each* or

every should appear in the subject (Each day has 24 hours) and in half the problems the word *each* or *every* should appear in the predicate (There are 24 hours in each day). Finally, half the sentences should contain the word *each* and half the word *every*.

To create the fraction, students are taught to find the word that comes directly after *each* or *every*. This word, which names the group, always goes on the bottom of the fraction. The word telling the objects in the group always goes on top. If a number is given telling how many objects in the group, the students write that number in the box that is in front of the top word. If the sentence asks how many objects in the group, a question mark is written in the box. The first day this part is presented the teacher models how to create the fraction, then has the students do sentences on their own. On the next day, the teacher reminds the students how to translate the sentence to a fraction, then has the students do the sentences on their own. The part is presented daily until students can work the problems independently without error. Then part B is presented.

Part B teaches the students to locate the sentence with *each* or *every* in the context of a story problem and then to write a fraction for that sentence. The first day the teacher models the steps, then has students do problems on their own. The next day, the teacher just reminds students of the steps and has them translate sentences to fractions on their own. Note that the students are instructed to cross out the sentence with the word *each* or *every* after they write the fraction. The purpose is to make it easier for students in later steps by reducing the number of sentences they have to scan to find other information given in the problem. Again, part C can be presented when students can do the steps in part B.

Part C teaches the student to write all the words that will be in the equation. The teacher first directs the students to find the sentence with the word *each* or *every* and write the word fraction. The teacher then directs the students to write the word that tells the name of the group on the line at the beginning of the equation and the word telling the name of the objects at the end of the question. To keep the language simple, the teacher just refers to the words on the top or bottom of the fraction: "Write the bottom word on the first dotted line. Write the top word on the last dotted line."

In part D, the teacher introduces the final steps in the strategy. After the students write the fraction and fill in the words on the dotted lines, the teacher leads the students first in transferring the numerical values stated in the problem into the equation and then in doing the computation to work the problem.

In part E, the diagram for the equation is no longer written on the students' worksheets. The students write the equation for each problem, fill in the numbers and work the problem with less teacher structure.

In part F, the teacher models how students are to write their answer. If the problem asks how many objects in each group, the answer should contain the name of the objects and the name of the group (e.g., 6 pens in each box). If the problem asks how many groups or how many objects, the answer is just one word (e.g., 6 pens or 6 boxes). On the second day of part F, the teacher demonstrates the "meaningfulness" of the word equation. After the students use a word equation to solve a problem, they draw pictures to represent the word equation and to figure the answer. The steps are the same as in Figure 12.8, which was used to introduce the concept of multiplication and division word problem. For example, for the diagram

$$4 \text{ cartons} \times \frac{6 \text{ bottles}}{\text{cartons}} = 24 \text{ bottles},$$

the students first draw 4 boxes for cartons. They then draw 6 lines (for 6 bottles) in each box. Finally they count all the lines to see if they ended up with the same number as the answer to the equation.

The final part, part G, presents a mix of addition, subtraction, multiplication, and division problems to the students. This part is not introduced until students can work sets of multiplication and division story problems with 80–90 percent accuracy. The part presents these rules: "If a problem has the word *each* or *every*, it tells you to either multiply or divide. If the problem does not have the word *each* or *every*, you add or subtract." The teacher goes through the set of items verbally. For each problem, the teacher has students tell if the word *each* or *every* is present, then asks students what type of problem it is. After doing the verbal exercise, the teacher leads the students in working several problems.

EXAMPLE SELECTION   The problems presented should be carefully controlled. During the period when students are learning to discriminate multiplication problems from division story problems, the following rules should apply:

1) All problems should contain the word *each* or *every*.

2) In half the problems, the word *each* or *every* should appear in the subject of a sentence, and in half the problems in the predicate of the sentence.
3) Sentences should be relatively short.
4) The number facts that students will need to solve the problem should be facts the student have memorized or are able to compute.
5) Problem types should appear in a random order.
6) The presence of two-digit numbers should be carefully controlled. For each division problem that has a two-digit number, there should be a multiplication problem with a two-digit number. This is to prevent students from mistakenly relying on the presence of two-digit number as a clue that a problem calls for division.
7) Several pairs of minimally different problems should be included. Both problems should include the same numbers. In order to make the worksheets unpredictable, the minimally different problems should not be listed one after the other.

Below is a list of four problems which might appear on one of the worksheets:

1. Every day Bill eats 2 eggs. How many days will it take him to eat 8 eggs?
2. There are 30 students in our class. They sit in 5 rows. How many students are in each row?
3. Every day Bill eats 2 eggs. In 8 days how many eggs will he eat?
4. There are 30 students in each class. There are 5 classes. How many students are there?

Multiplication and division problems which do not include the word *each* or *every* can be introduced after students are able to accurately work sets of problems containing addition and subtraction problems and multiplication and division problems that contain the word *each* or *every*.

Division Problems with Remainders

Problems with remainders can be introduced after students have developed accuracy in solving division problems without remainders. Two types of problems with remainders are illustrated below:

1. There are 17 girls in our class. How many teams can we make if we put 5 girls on each team?
2. The teachers had 245 students. The bus drivers said they would take no more than 30 students on each bus. How many buses will they need?

Figure 12.10 Format – Multiplication and Division Story Problems

Day	Part A Translating a Sentence	Part B Translating a Sentence in a Story	Part C Filling Words in a Equation	Part D Structured Worksheet	Part E Diagram faded	Part F Less Structured Worksheet	Part G Four Operation Discrimination
1	6–8						
2-firm		6–8					
3-firm			4–8				
4-firm				4–8			
5-firm					4–8		
6-firm						4–8	
7-firm							4–8

PART A: Translating a Sentence with *Each* to a Word Fraction

Give students a worksheet constructed like the one below.

TEACHER

1. "YOU'RE GOING TO MAKE A FRACTION WITH WORDS.
THAT FRACTION TELLS ABOUT A SENTENCE THAT HAS THE WORD *EACH* OR *EVERY*."
"TOUCH SENTENCE 1."
"READ IT."

"WHAT WORD COMES AFTER THE WORD *EACH*?"
"FILL IN THE DOTTED WORD *BAG* AT THE BOTTOM OF THE FRACTION."
"WHAT IS IN EACH BAG?"
"FILL IN THE DOTTED 5 IN THE BOX AND THE DOTTED WORD *APPLES*."

2. "HERE'S THE RULE ABOUT MAKING THE WORD FRACTION.
THE WORD AFTER *EACH* GOES ON THE BOTTOM OF THE FRACTION."
"WHAT WORD GOES ON THE BOTTOM OF THE FRACTION?"

STUDENTS

"There are 5 apples in each bag."

"Bag"

Students write "5 apples."

Students write.

"The word after *each*."

Figure 12.10 cont'd

TEACHER   **STUDENTS**

3. "TOUCH SENTENCE 2."
   "READ IT."   "How many bottles in each
                                                                crate?"
   "WHAT WORD GOES ON THE BOTTOM OF THE   "Crate"
   FRACTION?"
   To correct: The word that comes after *each* goes
                on the bottom."
   "WRITE CRATE ON THE BOTTOM OF THE LINE."   Students write *crate*.

4. "THE SENTENCE ASKS HOW MANY BOTTLES IN
   EACH CRATE. SO WRITE *BOTTLES* OVER THE
   WORD *CRATE* AND PUT A QUESTION MARK IN
   THE BOX."   Students write *? bottles*.

5. "MAKE THE WORD FRACTION FOR THE REST OF
   THE SENTENCES YOURSELF. REMEMBER THE
   WORD AFTER *EACH* OR *EVERY* GOES ON THE
   BOTTOM OF THE FRACTION."
   "IF THE SENTENCE GIVES A NUMBER, WRITE THE
   NUMBER IN THE BOX AND THE WORD THE
   NUMBER TELLS ABOUT ON THE TOP LINE."
   "IF THE SENTENCE ASKS HOW MANY, WRITE A
   QUESTION MARK IN THE BOX AND THE WORD
   THE SENTENCE ASKS ABOUT ON THE TOP LINE."   Students write fractions.

PART B: Constructing a Word Fraction from a Sentence in a Word Problem

Give the students a worksheet with 6–8 problems written in this form.

Bill has 6 pockets. He has 24 pens. How many pens in each pocket?

[ ] .... × [ ] _____ = [ ] ....

There are 4 boxes of apples. There are 8 apples in each box.
How many apples altogether?

[ ] .... × [ ] _____ = [ ] ....

1. "WHEN YOU WORK PROBLEMS WITH THE WORD
   EACH OR *EVERY*, THE FIRST THINGS YOU DO ARE
   FIND THE SENTENCE WITH *EACH* OR *EVERY* AND
   WRITE THE WORD FRACTION. THEN YOU CROSS
   OUT THE SENTENCE WITH *EACH* AND *EVERY*."

2. "TOUCH PROBLEM 1."
   "TOUCH THE SENTENCE THAT HAS THE WORD
   EACH."   Students touch sentence.

3. "USE THE SOLID LINE TO WRITE THE WORDS FOR
   THE FRACTION. THEN PUT A NUMBER OR
   QUESTION MARK IN THE BOX IN FRONT OF THE
   SOLID LINE."   Students fill in fraction: $\dfrac{\boxed{?} \text{ pens}}{\text{pocket}}$
   "NOW CROSS OUT THE SENTENCE TO SHOW WE'RE
   FINISHED WITH THE PROBLEM."   Students cross out sentence.

Figure 12.10 cont'd

TEACHER

4. "WORK THE REST OF THE PROBLEMS. FOR EACH
   PROBLEM FIND THE SENTENCE THAT HAS *EACH*
   OR *EVERY*. READ THAT SENTENCE. THEN FILL IN
   THE WORDS ON THE SOLID LINE AND FILL IN THE
   EMPTY BOX. THEN CROSS OUT THE SENTENCE
   THAT HAS THE WORD *EACH* OR *EVERY*."

PART C: Filling in All the Words in a Word Equation

Give students a worksheet like that in part B.

1. "YOU'RE GOING TO LEARN TO FILL IN ALL THE
   WORDS AND NUMBERS."
   "TOUCH PROBLEM 1."
   "TOUCH THE SENTENCE THAT HAS THE WORD
   EACH."   Students touch sentence.
   "MAKE THE FRACTION FOR THAT SENTENCE.
   THEN CROSS OUT THE SENTENCE WITH *EACH*."   Students write fraction.
   "TOUCH THE WORD ON THE BOTTOM OF THE
   FRACTION."   Students touch word.
   "WRITE THAT WORD ON THE DOTTED LINE IN
   FRONT OF THE TIMES SIGN."   Students write word.
   "TOUCH THE WORD ON TOP OF THE FRACTION."   Students touch word.
   "WRITE THE WORD ON THE DOTTED LINE AFTER
   THE EQUAL SIGN."   Students write word.

2. "HERE'S THE RULE."
   "THE WORD ON THE BOTTOM GOES ON THE FIRST
   DOTTED LINE."
   "THE WORD ON THE TOP GOES ON THE DOTTED
   LINE AFTER THE EQUAL SIGN."

3. "TOUCH PROBLEM 2."
   "TOUCH THE SENTENCE THAT HAS THE WORD
   EACH."   Students touch sentence.
   "WRITE THE FRACTION. THEN CROSS OUT THAT
   SENTENCE."   Students write fraction.
   "NOW FILL IN THE WORDS THAT GO ON THE DOT-
   TED LINES. REMEMBER THE BOTTOM WORD GOES
   ON THE FIRST DOTTED LINE."   Students write words on
                                                          dotted lines.

4. "FOR THE REST OF THE PROBLEM YOU'RE GOING
   TO WRITE WORDS ON ALL THE LINES."
   "FIND THE SENTENCE WITH *EACH* AND *EVERY*
   AND FILL IN THE WORD FRACTION. THEN CROSS
   OUT THAT SENTENCE."
   "THEN PUT THE BOTTOM WORD ON THE FIRST
   DOTTED LINE AND THE TOP NUMBER ON THE
   LAST DOTTED LINE."

Figure 12.10 cont'd

PART D: Structured Worksheet: Entire Problem

Give students a worksheet with a set of 6–8 multiplication and division problems in this form:

```
There are 20 men:

Each man has 4 hammers.

How many hammers in all?

 [   ] .......... ×  [   ]_____  =  [   ] ..........
```

TEACHER

1. "TOUCH PROBLEM 1."

2. "MAKE THE FRACTION."
   "THEN CROSS OUT THE SENTENCE YOU USED."

3. "NOW FILL IN THE WORDS THAT GO ON THE
   DOTTED LINES."

4. "NOW WE HAVE TO FILL IN THE BOXES THAT GO
   WITH THE WORDS ON THE DOTTED LINES."

5. "TOUCH THE FIRST SENTENCE THAT'S NOT
   CROSSED OUT."
   "DOES THE SENTENCE HAVE A NUMBER?"
   "WHAT DOES THE NUMBER TELL ABOUT?"
   "WRITE THAT NUMBER IN THE BOX IN FRONT OF
   THE CORRECT WORD."

6. "IS THERE ANOTHER NUMBER IN A SENTENCE
   THAT'S NOT CROSSED OUT?"
   "WE ALREADY PUT BOTH NUMBERS INTO BOXES.
   PUT A QUESTION MARK IN THE EMPTY BOX IN
   FRONT OF HAMMERS."

   (If the answer to step 6 is yes, say
   "WHAT DOES THAT NUMBER TELL ABOUT?"
   "WRITE IT IN THE RIGHT BOX.")

7. "NOW YOU CAN FIGURE OUT THE MISSING
   NUMBER. REMEMBER, IF THERE ARE TWO
   NUMBERS ON THE SAME SIDE, WE MULTIPLY. IF
   THERE ARE NOT TWO NUMBERS ON THE SAME
   SIDE, WE DIVIDE."
   "TOUCH THE EQUAL SIGN."
   "ARE THE TWO NUMBERS ON THE SAME SIDE?"
   "WRITE THE EQUATION AND FIGURE OUT THE
   ANSWER."

   Repeat steps 1–7 with the remaining problems.

STUDENTS

Students write $\boxed{4}\dfrac{\text{hammers}}{\text{man}}$

Students write words.

"Yes"
"Men"

Students write 20 in front of
men.

"No"

Students write:

$\boxed{20}\,\text{men} \times \boxed{4}\dfrac{\text{hammers}}{\text{man}} = \boxed{?}\,\text{hammers}$

Students touch equal sign.
"Yes."

Students write 20 × 4 = 80.

294   Skills and Concepts

Figure 12.10 cont'd

PART E: Less Structured Worksheet

Give students a worksheet with no diagrams under the problems. Leave space under each problem for students to write problem.

TEACHER   **STUDENTS**

1. "YOU'VE LEARNED TO WRITE WORDS AND
   NUMBERS ON LINES AND IN BOXES WHEN YOU
   WORK MULTIPLICATION AND DIVISION STORY
   PROBLEMS."
   "NOW YOU'LL WORK PROBLEMS IN WHICH YOU'LL
   HAVE TO PUT IN ALL THE LINES AND BOXES AND
   THE TIMES SIGN AND EQUAL SIGN."

2. (write on board)

   □ _____ × □ _____ = □ _____

   "STUDY THIS DIAGRAM. IN ABOUT 20 SECONDS
   I'LL ERASE IT."
   (Erase diagram)

3. "UNDER PROBLEM 1 WRITE THE DIAGRAM."   Students write diagram.
   "TOUCH PROBLEM 1."
   "READ THE PROBLEM AND FILL IN THE WORDS
   AND NUMBERS IN THE WORD EQUATION."   Students write words and numbers.
   "WRITE THE EQUATION AND FIND THE ANSWER."   Students solve equation.

4. Repeat step 3 with the remaining problems.

PART F: Less Structured Worksheet – Writing Whole Answers

Give students a worksheet with problems written in this form.

Bill has 36 apples. He puts the same number of
apples in each of 4 baskets. How many apples in
each basket?

                                    _____
                                         Answer

---

1. "WHEN YOU WRITE THE ANSWER TO A STORY
   PROBLEM, YOUR ANSWER HAS TWO PARTS: THE
   NUMBER PART AND THE WORD PART. SOME-
   TIMES THE ANSWER HAS ONE WORD, SOMETIMES
   IT HAS MORE THAN ONE WORD. YOU FIND THE
   WORD PART BY READING THE SENTENCE WITH
   THE WORDS *HOW MANY*."

2. "I'LL READ THE *HOW MANY* SENTENCE IN THE
   FIRST PROBLEM AND TELL YOU THE WORDS
   THAT GO IN THE ANSWER."
   "PROBLEM 1. HERE'S THE *HOW MANY* SENTENCE.
   HOW MANY APPLES IN EACH BASKET?"
   "THE WORD PART OF THE ANSWER IS *APPLES IN
   EACH BASKET*."

Figure 12.10 cont'd

TEACHER   **STUDENTS**

"PROBLEM 2. HERE'S THE *HOW MANY* SENTENCE."
"HOW MANY APPLES ALTOGETHER?"
"THE WORD PART OF THE ANSWER IS *APPLES*."

3. "YOU'LL READ THE *HOW MANY* SENTENCE FOR
EACH PROBLEM AND TELL ME WHAT'S THE
WORD PART OF THE ANSWER."
"PROBLEM 1. TOUCH THE *HOW MANY* SENTENCE."
"READ IT."
"WHAT'S THE WORD PART OF THE ANSWER?"
Repeat step 3 with remaining problems.

4. "TOUCH PROBLEM 1 AGAIN."
"READ THE WORD PROBLEM AND FILL IN THE
WORDS AND NUMBERS IN THE WORD EQUATION."
"WRITE THE NUMBER PROBLEM AND FIND THE
ANSWER."
"WRITE THE WHOLE ANSWER ON THE ANSWER
LINE."
Repeat step 4 with the remaining problems.

(Note: On the second day, after the students work
each of the first three problems, have the students
draw pictures to solve the problems using the
same steps as presented in format 12.8.)

PART G: Discriminating Addition, Subtraction, Multiplication and Divide Problems

(Give students worksheet with a mix of the four problem types.)

1. "WHEN YOU WORK STORY PROBLEMS, YOU MUST
FIRST DECIDE IF THE PROBLEM IS
MULTIPLICATION OR DIVISION, OR IF THE
PROBLEM IS ADDITION OR SUBTRACTION."

2. "LISTEN TO THESE RULES:
IF YOU SEE THE WORD *EACH* OR *EVERY*, YOU
MULTIPLY OR DIVIDE."
"IF YOU DON'T SEE THE WORD *EACH* OR *EVERY*,
YOU ADD OR SUBTRACT."
"WHAT DO YOU DO IF YOU SEE THE WORD *EACH*
OR *EVERY*?"   "Multiply or divide."
"WHAT DO YOU DO IF YOU DON'T SEE THE WORD
EACH OR *EVERY*?"   "Add or subtract."
Repeat step 2 until firm.

3. "READ THE PROBLEM 1 TO YOURSELF AND LOOK
FOR WORD *EACH* OR *EVERY*."
"DO YOU SEE THE WORD *EACH* OR *EVERY*?"
"SO WHAT DO YOU DO?"
Repeat step 3 with remaining problems.

4. "READ PROBLEM 1 AGAIN AND LOOK FOR THE
WORD *EACH* OR *EVERY*."
"DO YOU SEE THE WORD *EACH* OR *EVERY*?"
"SO WHAT DO YOU DO?"
"WORK THE PROBLEM. THEN, WRITE THE WHOLE
ANSWER ON THE LINE."
Repeat step 4 with the remaining problems.

The first problem illustrates a type in which a total amount is given, and the problem asks how many groups of a particular size can be made. A format for introducing remainder problems of this type would begin with a diagram illustrating the problem.

For this example, the teacher presents the problem, "There are 17 girls. We want to make teams. Each team will have 5 girls. How many teams will we make?" The teacher draws 17 lines explaining that each line represents a girls in the class. The teacher would draw a ring around each group of five lines, pointing out that only three groups can be made. There are 2 girls left over. This part is quite similar to Part A of the division format in Figure 11.4. Next the teacher gives the students a worksheet with problems that ask two questions: the number of groups that can be made, and the number of units left over—the remainder. Below are such problems:

Tina wants to divide 17 pencils among 5 children. How many pencils should she give to each child?

Answer: _____

How many pencils will she have left over?

Answer: _____

Robert has 32 cents. Candy bars cost 10 cents for each candy bar. How many candy bars can he buy?

Answer: _____

How many cents will he have left over?

Answer: _____

The most likely error is writing the remainder as the number of groups. To reduce the likelihood of this error occurring, the teacher should stress the discrimination between the number of groups and the remainder. After students work division problems, the teacher might have them express the answer as follows: "5 goes into 17 three times with a remainder of 2." The teacher points out that the number of times 5 goes into 15 tells how many groups can be made. The remainder tells how many children are left over.

The second type remainder problem requires the students to add an extra unit to the answer (e.g. Ann wants to put her baseball cards in protective covers. She has 47 card. Each cover can hold five cards. How many covers does she need?) This type can be introduced after students have mastered the type problem discussed above. The teacher models how to work the problem. After the students do the division, the teacher explains "9 covers with 5 in each cover will be 45 cards. We still have two cards, so we need another cover. The answer is 10 covers."

Self-checking

As a final step in solving a problem, students should reread the problem to determine whether the answer they computed makes sense. This step becomes particularly important once students are introduced to worksheets containing a mix of addition, subtraction, multiplication, and division problems.

The self-check procedure can be prompted through an exercise in which the students are given a worksheet containing a mix of problems. The teacher has students read a problem. The teacher then says an answer and asks if it makes sense. For example, with this problem:

Jill ran 5 miles a day. She ran 10 days. How many miles did she run in all?

The teacher would say, "One student said the answer is 2 miles. That doesn't make sense. The problem said that she ran 5 miles a day. The problem asks how many miles she ran in all. We know the answer must be more than 5, since she ran 5 miles each day."

The teacher then goes through a set of problems verbally, reading each problem and saying an answer. For half the problems, the answer should be correct. For half the problems, the answer should be obviously wrong. After reading each problem and saying the answer, the teacher asks if the answer she gave could be correct.

Multi-step Story Problems

Multi-step story problems include three or more quantities, all of which are included in computing the answer. Three factors influence the difficulty or multi-step problems: (1) the number of quantities, (b) the number of different operations involved, and (c) the order in which the information is given. The simplest type of multi-step problem involves adding three quantities. Such problems are usually introduced in second grade. More complex multi-step problems usually do not appear until the mid-intermediate grades. A listing of various types of multi-step problems appears in the Instructional Sequence and Assessment Chart in Figure 12.2.

The teaching procedure involves introducing one new type at a time. The teacher should structure the introduction of each type. The easiest type involves adding three or more amounts, the teacher would model working one of these problems on the board, then have the students work several on their own.

The first complex type involves two operations, addition and subtraction. For problems in which the students have to add before they subtract, or subtract before they add, the teacher presents a set of problems, verbally modelling. Then, the teacher has the students work the problems on their own. An example of the modeling is illustrated below for the following problem.

Tania earned $2 in the morning and $4 in the afternoon. She needs $9 altogether. How many more dollars does she need?

The teacher says "The problem tells us how much she wants to end up with. That's 9 dollars. The problem is about getting more money, so that 9 is the total. To figure out how much more money she needs, we have to figure out how much she has now. How do we do that?....Yes, add 2 and 4. Then we subtract what she earned, $6, from what she needs, $9."

Problems in which students have to add or subtract, then multiply or divide are more difficult. Thus, a more structured approach is needed. Below are four typical problems.

(Add then multiply)
Ann drove 3 hours in the morning and 4 hours in the afternoon. If she drove 55 miles each hour, how many miles did she drive altogether?

(Add then divide)
We want to divide the students in our school into 8 equal sized classes. There are 48 boys and 64 girls in the school. How many students should there be in each class?

(Subtract then multiply)
Jill had 8 packs of gum. She gave 3 packs to her sister. If there are 7 pieces in each pack, how many pieces of gum does Jill still have?

(Subtract then divide)
There are 100 books in the store, 20 of the books were sold. The owner wanted to put the rest away in boxes. Each box can hold 16 books. How many boxes are needed?

A format for introducing this type appears in Figure 12.11. The teacher leads the students through working several problems. First, the teacher has the students locate the sentence that has the word *each* or *every* and write a word equation. Note that during the first several days a blank diagram should appear under each problem. The teacher then points out that two of the numbers in the problem tell about the same thing, but there is only one box in the equation for that thing. So the students have to either add or subtract so they can have just one number to put in the box. The teacher reads the relevant sentences and asks the students what operation is called for. Then, the students either add or subtract, write the answer in the appropriate box, and write an equation and figure out the answer.

Distractors

A distractor is a quantity mentioned in a story problem that has no bearing on the computation for solving the problem. For example, "Jane had 12 hats; 5 of the hats were red; 2 of the hats were old. How many of the hats were new?" The problem asks how many hats were new. The problem is solved by subtracting the number of old hats from the total number of hats: $12 - 2 = 10$. The information about five red hats is irrelevant to solving the problem and must be ignored.

Problems with distractors are introduced in the early intermediate grades. The teaching procedures involve asking students for the name of the thing or event they are going to figure out. In the problem above, students are to determine the number of new hats. The teacher might tell students to cross out numbers that tell about other kinds of hats. The students would then compute the answer by using the remaining numbers.

Diagnosis and Remediation

Teachers should inspect students' worksheets on a daily basis. This checking will tell if the students need reteaching of any previously taught skills. When checking worksheets, teachers should try to

Figure 12.11 Format for Multistep Problems – Add/Subtract then Times/Divide

Day	Part A	Part B
	Structured	Supervised
	Worksheet	Guidance
1–3	4–6	
4–accurate		4–6

PART A: Structured Worksheet

Give students worksheets with problems set up like this.

> A) 75 students tried out for the band. 15 students didn't make it. The band director wants to divide the students who make the band into groups. Each group will have 5 students. How many groups will there be?   Answer _____
>
> ☐ .... × ☐ _____ = ☐ ....
>
> B) There were 45 cats at the pound. 35 more cats were brought in. There were 8 cages. How many cats will be in each cage if the cages have the same number of cats?   Answer _____
>
> ☐ .... × ☐ _____ = ☐ ....

Problems in which a number is stated in the *each* sentence.

TEACHER

1. "READ PROBLEM (A)."

2. "TOUCH THE SENTENCE WITH THE WORD *EACH*."

3. "WRITE THE FRACTION AND THE NUMBERS THAT GO IN FRONT OF THE FRACTION. THEN CROSS OUT THE SENTENCE WITH *EACH*."

   "NOW WRITE THE WORDS THAT GO ON THE DOTTED LINE."

4. "IN THE PROBLEM THERE ARE TWO NUMBERS FOR STUDENTS. THERE'S ONLY ONE BOX FOR STUDENTS IN THE EQUATION."
   "I'LL READ THE SENTENCES.
   75 STUDENTS TRIED OUT FOR THE BAND. 15 STUDENTS DIDN'T MAKE IT. WHAT DO WE HAVE TO DO TO FIND OUT HOW MANY STUDENTS THERE WERE?"
   "WE HAVE TO SUBTRACT."
   "DO THAT. THEN WRITE THE NUMBER OF STUDENTS IN THE BOX FOR STUDENTS."

5. "NOW YOU CAN FIGURE OUT HOW MANY BOXES."
   "WORK THE PROBLEM AND FIGURE OUT THE ANSWER."

STUDENTS

Students write $\dfrac{\boxed{5}\ students}{group}$.

Students write words.

☐ groups × $\dfrac{\boxed{5}\ students}{group}$ = ☐ students

"Subtract"

Students subtract and write 60 in box next to *students*.

Students divide

$5\overline{)60}$ = 12 groups

Figure 12.11 cont'd

Problems in which a number is not stated in the each sentence.

TEACHER	**STUDENTS**

1. "READ PROBLEM (B)."

2. "TOUCH THE SENTENCE WITH *EACH*."

3. "WRITE A FRACTION FOR THAT SENTENCE, AND FILL IN THE BOX. THEN CROSS OUT THE SENTENCE WITH *EACH*."

Students write $\dfrac{\boxed{?}\ \text{cats}}{\text{cage}}$

4. "NOW WRITE THE WORDS THAT GO ON THE DOTTED LINES."

Students write

$\square\ \text{cages} \times \dfrac{\boxed{?}\ \text{cats}}{\text{cage}} = \square\ \text{cats}$

5. "IN THE PROBLEM THERE ARE STILL THREE NUMBERS. TWO NUMBERS TELL ABOUT CATS. ONE NUMBER TELLS ABOUT CAGES. WRITE THE NUMBER ABOUT CAGES IN THE EQUATION."

Students write

$8\ \text{cages} \times \dfrac{\boxed{?}\ \text{cats}}{\text{cage}} = \square\ \text{cats}$

6. "I'LL READ THE SENTENCES ABOUT CATS. THERE WERE 45 CATS AT THE POUND. 35 MORE CATS WERE BROUGHT IN. WHAT DO WE HAVE TO DO TO FIND HOW MANY CATS?"
"WE HAVE TO ADD. DO THAT. THEN WRITE THE NUMBER OF CATS IN THE BOX FOR CATS."

"Add"

Students add and write 80 in box for cats.

7. "NOW YOU CAN FIGURE OUT THE ANSWER."
"WORK THE PROBLEM. WRITE THE ANSWER."

Students divide $8\overline{)80} = 10$ cats in each cage.

---

determine the specific reasons the student missed a problem. Determining the specific reasons for errors is very important, because the selection of the remediation procedure will depend on the cause of the error.

Motivation

In diagnosing skill deficits, teachers should always consider the student's motivation. If the teacher feels that motivation could be the reason for poor performance, the teacher should think about increasing the positive consequences for good performance. The importance of an effective motivational system to encourage students to work carefully cannot be overemphasized. Only with an effective motivation system can the teacher be sure the student's work is a clear reflection of the skills the student has or has not mastered.

Possible Causes of Errors

There are five possible causes for errors on story problems: (a) computation errors, (b) fact errors, (c) decoding errors, (d) vocabulary errors, and (e) translation errors. The specific reason for an error can be determined more readily if students write the equation for the story problem on their worksheets. Thus, teachers should tell students to do all their computation on the worksheet they hand in to the teacher.

COMPUTATION ERRORS A computational error is made when the student translates the problem into the correct equation but makes an error in figuring the answer. If a student misses a problem solely because of a computational error, the remediation procedure does not include presenting any part of the story problem formats. Instead, the teacher checks to see if the student is having consistent difficulty with that type of computation and, if necessary, reteaches the appropriate strategy. Below are problems missed because of computation errors.

a. Jill had 153 apples; 28 were red. How many were not red?

$$153 - 28 = 135$$

b. There were 210 students in one school. We want to divide them into groups of 3. How many groups can we make?

$$210 \div 3 = 7$$

The teacher should analyze the student's computation performance to decide what type of remediation is called for. If the student's error indicates a lack of knowledge of a particular component skill or strategy, the teacher should test students on similar types of problems. For example, problem (a) above was missed because the student failed to rename. The teacher should present several similar problems requiring renaming. If the student missed several of these problems, the teacher should introduce the format that taught renaming. Problem (b) above is a division problem with zero as the final number in the quotient. The teacher should test students on several more problems of this type. If the students missed several of those problems, the teacher should present the format for division problems in which the last digit in the quotient is zero.

FACT ERRORS   The following problem illustrates a fact error:

There were 12 boys; 9 of them were taking chorus. How many boys were not taking chorus?

$$12 - 9 = 4$$

The student has chosen the correct operation and written the equation correctly, but arrives at the wrong answer by making a fact error. The remediation procedure does not require repetition of any part of the story problem format, but rather some additional work on memorizing basic facts (See Chapter 7 for procedures.)

DECODING ERRORS   Decoding causes errors when students incorrectly read one or more critical words in the story. For example, a student reads *bought* for *broke* in this story: "John had 6 glasses. He broke 2. How many does he have now?" Because of the decoding error, the student wrote 6 +

2 = 8, rather than 6 − 2 = 4. Determining if a decoding error caused the error is relatively easy. The teacher merely has the student read the problem out loud.

Teachers working with students who are poor decoders should present difficult-to-decode words in board exercises before students encounter the words in story problems. In the decoding exercise, the teacher writes the words on the board, tells the students the words, then has the students read the list. Teachers working with students who are very poor decoders should not require the students to read written story problems, but rather should read the problems to the students, ask another student to read the problems, or tape record the problems.

VOCABULARY ERRORS   Errors in solving story problems are sometimes caused by students not knowing the meaning of a key word in the problem. For example, in the problem below the student must know that *acquire* means to get more:

Jim had 37 kites. He acquired 11 kites. How many kites does he have now?

The teacher can determine if a vocabulary deficit caused the error by asking the student what a difficult word such as *acquire* means. Teachers working with students who have limited vocabulary knowledge should teach the meaning of less common, crucial vocabulary before students encounter story problems with these terms (see Chapter 4 for suggestions on vocabulary teaching procedures).

TRANSLATION ERRORS   Translation errors occur when a student uses the wrong operation. The student has failed to translate the problem into the correct equation. Some examples of these errors are illustrated below:

a. Jill had 17 apples. She started with 9 apples. How many more apples did she get?

$$17 + 9 = 26$$

b. Joanne runs 7 miles a day. How many miles will she run in 14 days?

$$7 \overline{)14} = 2$$

In problem (a), the student added instead of subtracting. In problem (b), the student divided instead of multiplying. It's also common for students to add instead of multiply or subtract instead of divide. A remediation procedure begins with the

Figure 12.12

Data expressed as number correct over number possible for each problem type

Error code:
C = Computation error
F = Fact error
D = decoding error
V = vocabulary error
T = translation error

Date

Type of Problem	11/21	11/11	11/23	11/24	11/25	11/28	11/29		
simple action	8/10 D	9/10 F	9/10 V	10/10	10/10				
classification	5/10 FTD	4/10 FT	4/10 FT						
multi-step: add 3 numbers	8/10								
mult/div									

teacher determining the type of story problem missed. After determining the type of missed story problem, the teacher examines the student's worksheets to see if other problems of that specific type were missed. If possible, the teacher should also examine worksheets from previous days to see if the student missed more problems of that type. To assist the teacher in looking for error patterns across days, the teacher should record the types of errors that each student makes on a data sheet. Figure 12.12 includes an example of a record keeping sheet.

Specific types of errors made can be coded on the data sheet using letter codes such as D for decoding errors. F for fact errors, and T for translation errors. The teacher uses information collected on the data sheet to determine the necessary remediation. For example, if the student makes translation errors on more than 20% of the story problems of a particular type, a remediation procedure is called for. The intensity of the remediation procedure is dependent on the relative weakness of the student's performance. If a student is missing just 20% of the problems of a particular type, the teacher should present a special worksheet exercise using the less-structured part of the format for that particular type of problem. The worksheet should include six to eight problems, half of which are of that particular type and half of a similar type. The less-structured format should be presented daily until the student is able to perform at a 90% accuracy criterion for several days in a row. In the meantime, students should not be allowed to work on that particular problem type on independent worksheets. If a student misses more than 30% of a particular type of problem, the remediation procedure would begin with Part A of the format for that particular type of problem.

Calculators

We recommend that students use calculators while solving story problems. Using a calculator allows students to find answers quickly, so they can concentrate on reading problems and writing correct equations. By spending less time on computation and using a given amount of time to solve more problems, students will be able to master various types of story problems more quickly. two skills efficiently.

Commercial Programs

The major concerns about the manner in which story problems are presented in basal programs are provisions for practice and review and strategy teaching.

Practice

Three critical aspects of providing adequate practice are providing enough examples of a problem type to develop and maintain mastery, providing distributed practice across the textbook, and providing adequate discrimination practice. When comparing texts published from 1924 to 1984, McGinty, VanBeynen, and Zalewski (1986) found that current texts have 33% fewer story problems and 57% more drill problems. Fewer multi-step problems, more problems in which a key word is given, and more problems similar to prior problems were found when comparing texts from the late 1950s to the textbooks of the 1980s (Nibbelink, Stockdale, & Mangru, 1987).

Although recently published editions show improvement, most basal programs still provide limited discrimination practice. For example, after students have been introduced to multiplication and division problems, textbooks rarely contain pages containing a mix of addition, subtraction, multiplication, and division story problems. Teachers must be prepared to construct worksheets to provide discrimination practice.

The number of story problems appearing in basal series has increased in most recent editions of basal programs. However, the relatively long periods with no review are still a concern. These long gaps result from the unit approach in programming. When units dealing with measurement, geometry, place value, or fractions are presented, story problems are often not mentioned. Many students will require daily practice, which would have to be provided from another program, from supplemental workbook or ditto exercises, or from supplemental worksheets prepared by the teacher.

Although textbooks of the 1980s contain more story problems than textbooks of the 1970s, the number of problems, particularly more difficult problems, is still insufficient to produce good problem-solvers. In examining fourth through sixth grade texts at Scott, Foresman (1980; 1985) and Holt, Rinehart, and Winston (1978; 1987), Kameenui et al. (1988) found that multi-step problems at all levels remained below 1% of the total word problems. While providing additional problems for increased practice, teachers must also give attention to increasing the difficulty level of most problem types.

Strategy

Most commercial programs simply do not provide step-by-step teaching procedures for story problems. The teacher's guide may instruct teachers to explain why the problems call for a certain operation, but it does not provide the teacher with specific wording and strategies, or specific correction procedures.

Research

Although learning to solve story problems is a major objective of mathematics instruction, students from across the U.S. often fail to reach this objective. The first National Assessment of Educational Progress (Carpenter, Coburn, Reys & Wilson, 1976) included five story problems, one focusing on each of the basic four operations and one requiring two operations. Only 25% of the fourth graders and 62% of the eighth graders solved all five problems correctly. Five years later, when the National Assessment was repeated, an 18 percent drop occurred in performance on multiplication verbal problems and a 12 percentage point decline occurred on basic division verbal problems for fourth graders (Carpenter, Corbitt, Kepner, Lindquist, & Reys, 1980). Recent student response to the third National Assessment showed little improvement (Lindquist, Carpenter, Silver, & Matthews, 1983).

Many of the errors made on the three assessments resulted from an inability to correctly translate the word problem into numerical form, which implies that students may have difficulty comprehending what they read. Several researchers have noted a strong correlation between students' reading comprehension and story-problem-solving ability (Aiken, 1971; Balow, 1964), but recent studies disagree about the relative importance of reading and/or computational factors in solving story problems (Ballew & Cunningham, 1982; Knifong & Holtan, 1976, 1977, 1980; Muth, 1984). This disagreement seems to be explained, however, by the results of a careful analysis by Jerman and Mirman (1974) of information by grade level from fourth grade through college. They found that computational variables were more problematic in the early grades and that more errors could be attributed to linguistic variables as students grew older.

Concern over student difficulty with word problems has resulted in two lines of research: documentation of variables that make story problems difficult and interventions for improving student performance on story problems. Numerous variables have been identified as contributing to the difficulty of story problems: the order in which events are presented, placement of the unknown, the presence of extraneous information, the difficulty of syntax and vocabulary, the number of operations required, and whether classification skills are required. Jones, Krouse, Feorene, and Saferstein (1985) found that the order in which word problem types are introduced and how many types are introduced at one time affects the degree of difficulty students will experience in solving them. Rosenthal and Resnick (1974) and Hiebert (1982) found that story problems were more difficult when the unknown came first and the order of events in the story was given in reverse order. Several investigators have noted that extraneous information makes story problems more difficult (Bana & Nelson, 1977, 1978; Blankenship & Lovitt, 1976; Jerman & Rees, 1972; Muth, 1984; Sedlak, 1974; Thibodeau, 1974). Wheeler and McNutt (1983) reported that complex syntax, defined as sentences containing a subordinate clause, made problems more difficult. Other studies (Days, Wheatley, & Kuhn, 1979; Loftus & Suppes, 1972) reported that multi-step problems were more difficult to solve than one-step problems. Finally, Thibodeau (1974) reported that problems based on classification (e.g., John had 3 dogs and 2 cats. How many pets did he have?) were more difficult than those with action verbs (e.g., John had 3 dogs. He lost 1 dog. How many did he end with?).

The research on intervention is difficult to interpret. The specific instructional procedures were usually omitted from the research reports, and the entering skills of the subjects were not specified. What was common to the studies was that some form of explicit instruction enhanced student performance. Blankenship and Lovitt (1976) had students reread, write, and reexamine solutions. Pace's (1961) instructions consisted of having students read a problem, ask themselves how they would solve it, and why they chose that process. Emphasis was placed on justifying the reason for solving the problem with a particular process using rules about the relationships between what was known and what was unknown. Wilson (1967) had students answer questions such as "What are you given?" He taught his students rules such as "Subtraction is used to find the size of one part when we know the total and size of the other part" (p. 492). Bassler, Beers, and Richardson (1975) evaluated Polya's method (1957): the student was instructed to look at the problem as a whole, decide what questions to ask, and identify the unknowns and their relationship to what was given. In the two studies by Wilson and Bassler et al., the experimental intervention proved to be effective, but the two methods used as comparisons for these effective methods also yielded useful information. Results from both studies seemed to indicate that rigid translation of key words and phrases inhibited choosing the correct operation for solving problems and that a more generalizable strategy would be needed. Darch, Carnine, and Gersten (1984) provided an explicit strategy that put major emphasis on choosing the correct operation rather than on translating key words into an equation. Jerman (1973) and Wolters (1983) applied Wilson's method to the solution of multi-step problems. Additional systematic approaches for solving multi-step problems were examined with some success by Fleischner, Nuzum, and Marzola (1987) and Dahmus (1970). Although students performed significantly better than the control groups, more research is needed to establish an intervention that students can use successfully with all multi-step problems. A common feature of the intervention studies was that students were given fairly extensive practice on solving story problems. As Callahan and Glennon (1975) pointed out in their research review, "Results of the study would suggest that children show gains in problem-solving if they are merely presented with many problems to solve, but they show even greater gains if systematic instruction for the purpose of developing understanding of the four processes is provided by the teacher" (p. 147).

Application Items: Story Problems

1. Tell what story problem type each of the following problems represents. Use the types described in the Instructional Sequence and Assessment Chart in Figure 12.2.

   a. Jim has 15 green apples and 17 red apples. He wants to split them equally among his four friends. How many apples should he give to each friend?

   b. Ann has been running for 2 months. She runs 5 miles each day. How many miles will she run in 10 days?

   c. There are 20 balls in the toy closet. Eight of the balls are baseballs. How many of the balls are not baseballs?

   d. Jill has 2 pens in each pocket. She has 8 pens. How many pockets does she have?

   e. Amy had 8 dollars. She spent 3 dollars. How many dollars does she have left?

   f. A girl is 15 years old. Her brother is 2 years younger. How old is her brother?

2. Story problems can be made easier or more difficult by changing one or more aspects. Name several ways in which problems can be made more difficult. For each problem in the item above, change or add to the problem to increase its level of difficulty in some way.

3. Tell the possible cause of the following errors. When there is doubt as to the cause of the error, tell what the teacher does to find out the specific cause. Specify the remediation procedure called for if errors of this type occur frequently.

   a. Jill's team scored 54 points. The other team scored 19 points fewer. How many did the other team score?   36   points

   b. The ABC Company produced 1,534 pool tables last year. This year production decreased by 112 pool tables. How many pool tables did the ABC Company produce this year?   1,646   pool tables

   c. Tim baked 6 cakes every week. He baked for 18 weeks. How many cakes did he bake?   3 cakes

   d. Tara took 20 shots in the basketball game. She made 15 shots. How many shots did she miss?   35 shots

   e. There are 10 boys and 20 girls in the class. Each row can seat 5 students. How many rows will there be?   35   rows

   f. There are 28 students. The teacher wants to divide them into 4 equal groups. How many students will be in each group?   6 students

   g. A factory produces 325 cars a day. How many cars will it produce in 25 days?   8,105   cars

4. Write a structured worksheet format to guide students through solving this problem:
   28 vehicles went past our house. 12 of the vehicles were cars. How many vehicles were not cars?

5. Write a structured worksheet format to guide students through solving this problem:
   Ann runs 5 miles every day. So far she has run 20 miles. How many days has she run?

Fractions

Terms and Concepts

Fractions   A fraction is a numeral of the form y/x where x ≠ 0. Fractions involve division into equal sized segments and a statement regarding the number of segments present, used, or acted upon. For example, "John ate 1/4 of a pie" implies dividing the pie into four equal parts and that John ate one of those parts.

Numerator   The top number in a fraction.

Denominator   The bottom number in a fraction.

Proper Fraction   A fraction whose numerator is less than its denominator.

Improper Fraction   A fraction whose numerator is equal to or greater than the denominator.

Mixed Number   An improper fraction expressed as a whole number and a fraction.

Greatest Common Factor   Largest factor of both the numerator and the denominator; e.g., the greatest common factor for 4/8 is 4.

Lowest Common Denominator   The least common multiple of the denominators; e.g., the lowest common denominator for 1/3 + 1/2 + 1/4 is 12.

Rational Numbers   Rational numbers can be expressed as the quotient of two integers. (Rational numbers can be negative, −3/4 or −7/2, as well as positive, 3/4 or 7/2. The chapters in this text discuss only positive rational numbers.) Fractions, decimals, ratios, proportion, and percent could all be considered different forms of rational numbers. Rational numbers are usually represented in one of the following ways:

1. Portioning off units from a total number of units

$$\left(|\,|\,|\right) |\,|\,|\,|\,|\,|\,| = \frac{3}{10} = .3 = 30\%$$

2. Portioning off subsets of a group of subsets

$$\left(|\,|\,|\,|\right)\left(|\,|\,|\,|\right) \quad \left(|\,|\,|\,|\right) = \frac{2}{3} = .67 = 66\frac{2}{3}\%$$

3. Dividing a whole figure into equal parts

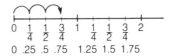 $= \frac{1}{4} = .25 = 25\%$

4. Number line

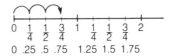

Skill Hierarchy

As can be seen in the skill hierarchy in Figure 13.1, fractions comprise one of the most complex sets of skills covered in elementary mathematics. This complexity is understandable since the entire range of operations discussed in other sections of the book is applicable to fractional numbers. Unfortunately, fractions do not represent a simple extension of familiar skills. While early instruction on whole numbers covers counting by groups of 1 or more than one, that instruction does not help students generalize to dealing with groups less than one. For example, in addition and subtraction of whole numbers, members of a second group relate to the members of the first group based on one-to-one correspondences. For example, in the problem 4 + 3, students increase the first set in units of 1 (5 6 7), producing the answer 7. To solve 4 – 3, students decrease the first set in units of 1, producing the answer 1. In multiplication and division of whole numbers, a second group is related to the first group based on a one-to-many correspondence. For example, in solving for 8 × 2, students count units of 8 for each member of the second group (8, 16), producing the answer 16. In 16 ÷ 2, students determine the answer by counting 1 for each unit of 2 in 16 (1, 2, 3, 4, 5, 6, 7, 8), producing the answer 8.

In operations containing fractions, the correspondences involve fractional numbers. For example, in 2/3 × 4 students count units of 2/3 for each member of the second group. While students can quickly learn to count 2, 4, 6, 8 for 2 × 4, counting 2/3, 4/3, 6/3, 8/3 for 2/3 × 4 is not easy. The problem 2/3 × 4/7 is even less comprehensible because students have no experiential basis for counting 4/7th times. Therefore, fractional correspondences with both whole numbers and other fractions necessitate new strategies.

Another major difficulty with fractions is the incompatibility of different units. Addition and subtraction can only be carried out with equivalent units. Whole numbers represent a simple type of equivalent unit, so they can be added and subtracted in any combination. In contrast, fractional numbers do not represent one type of unit: All thirds represent equivalent units and all fourths represent equivalent units, but thirds are not the same as fourths. Consequently, thirds and fourths cannot be added or subtracted as such. Prior to adding or subtracting fractions, the fractional units must be transformed into a common unit:

$$\frac{1}{4} + \frac{2}{3} = \frac{3}{12} + \frac{8}{12} = \frac{11}{12}$$

The necessity to transform or rewrite fractional numbers is a major source of difficulty in teaching fractions. (This is one reason for the appeal of decimals; they have the uniform base of multiples of 10.)

The skill hierarchy in Figure 13.1 lists three main groupings of fraction topics: fraction analysis, rewriting fractions, and operations (addition, subtraction, multiplication, and division of fractions).

Since application of fraction skills depends on an understanding of fractional numbers, initial instruction on the concepts and conventions characterizing fractions is critical. Therefore, early instruction must deal with fraction analysis skills such as how to construct diagrams to represent fractions, write the fraction represented by diagrams, decode fractions, and determine if a fraction is proper or improper.

The second area, rewriting fractions, includes the following:

1. Rewriting an improper fraction as a mixed number: 13/2 = 6 1/2
2. Rewriting a proper fraction using the smallest possible denominator (reducing fractions): 6/8 = 3/4
3. Rewriting a fraction as an equivalent fraction with a specified denominator: 2/5 = 4/□
4. Rewriting a mixed number as an improper fraction: 2 1/2 = 5/2

Figure 13.1 Skill Hierarchy

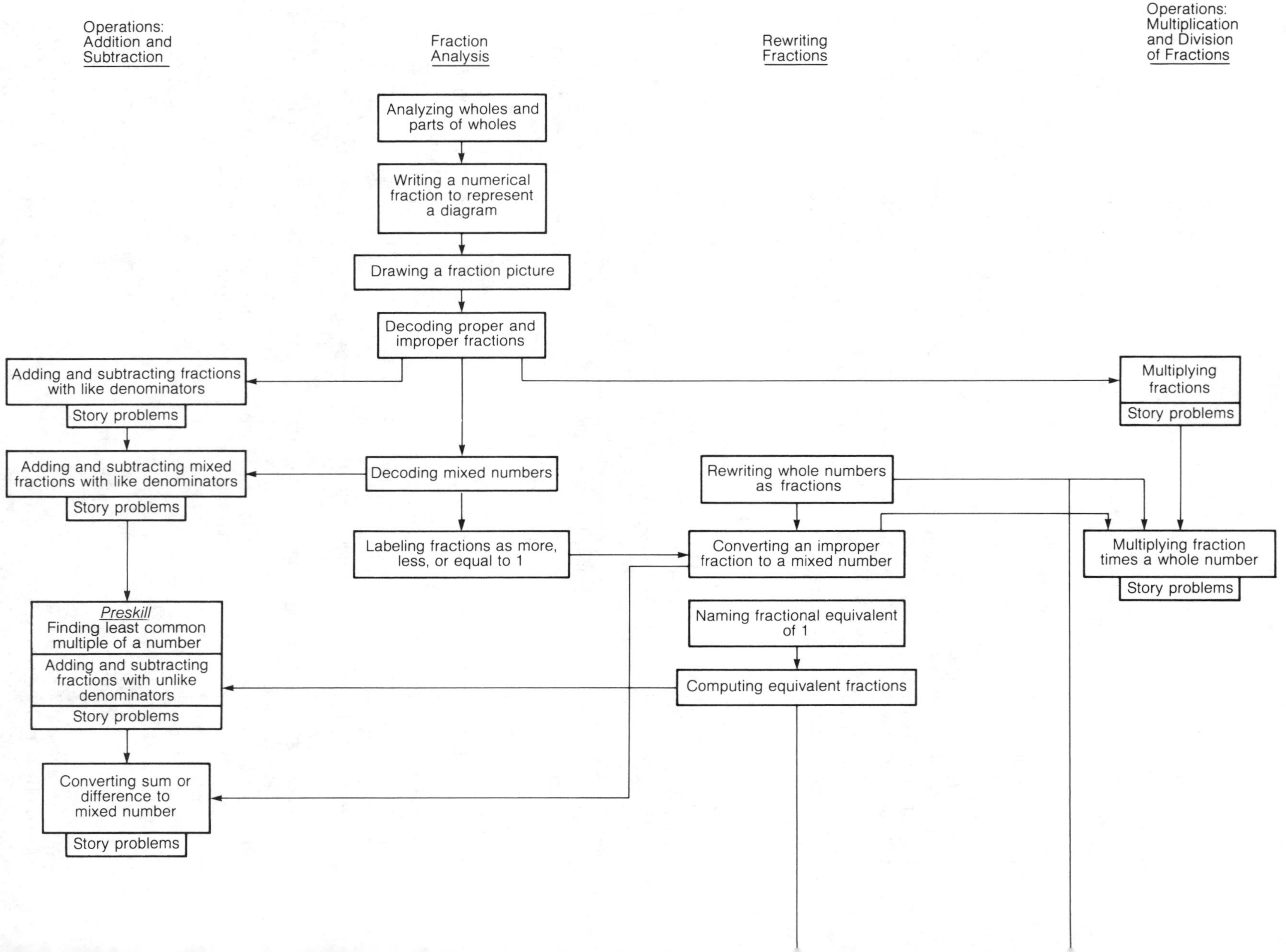

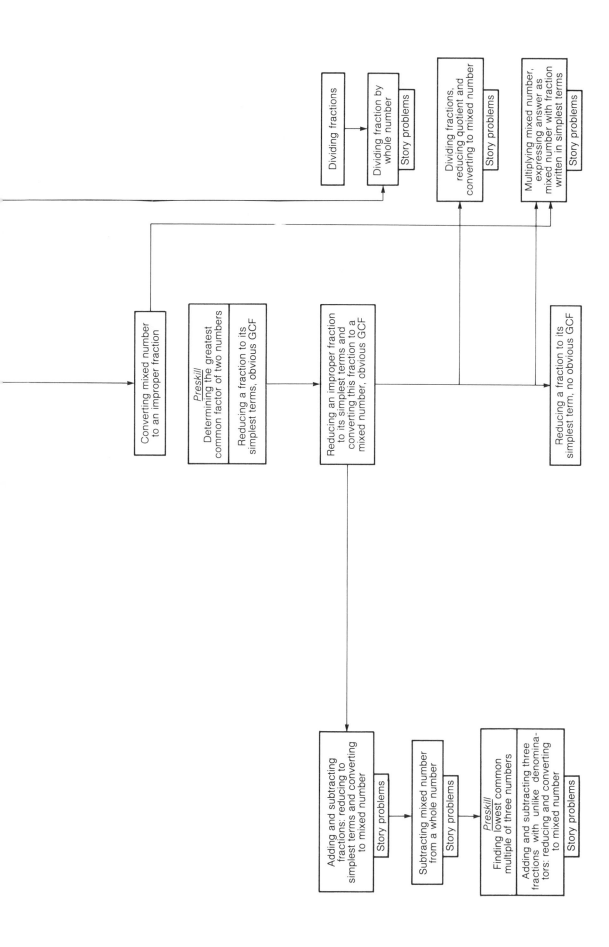

Figure 13.2 Instructional Sequence and Assessment Chart

Grade Level	Problem Type	Performance Indicator
1-2a	Identifying fractions which correspond to diagrams	

a. Circle the picture that shows 2/4.

b. Circle the picture that shows 4/4.

c. Put X on the line below the picture that shows 4/3.

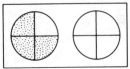 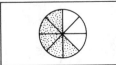

_____   _____

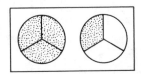

_____

d. Put X on the line below the picture that shows 3/2.

_____   _____   _____

Grade Level	Problem Type	Performance Indicator
1-2b	Drawing diagrams to correspond to fractions	

$\frac{3}{4} =$

$\frac{2}{3} =$

$\frac{3}{2} =$

Figure 13.2 cont'd

Grade Level	Problem Type	Performance Indicator
1–2c	Reading and writing fractions expressed as fractions	Write these fractions: a. two-thirds = □/□ b. five-halves = □/□ c. four-fifths = □/□ (Test students individually. "What does this say: $\frac{2}{3}$ $\frac{4}{5}$ $\frac{5}{2}$?")
2d	Determining whether a fraction is more than, equal to, or less than 1	Write *more than*, *less than*, or *equal to* in each blank. $\frac{4}{3}$ is _____ 1 $\frac{7}{7}$ is _____ 1 $\frac{5}{6}$ is _____ 1
2e	Adding and subtracting fractions with like denominators	$\frac{3}{5} - \frac{2}{5} = $ _____ $\frac{4}{7} - \frac{2}{7} = $ _____ $\frac{3}{5} + \frac{1}{5} = $ _____
2f	Multiplying fractions	$\frac{3}{5} \times \frac{2}{3} = $ _____ $\frac{2}{5} \times \frac{3}{5} = $ _____ $\frac{2}{2} \times \frac{3}{5} = $ _____
3a	Reading and writing mixed numbers	Write two and one-third _____ Write four and two-fifths _____ Write six and one-half _____ (Test students individually. "Read these numbers: $2\frac{1}{4}$ $3\frac{2}{5}$ $7\frac{3}{9}$.)
3b	Adding and subtracting mixed numbers: fractions with like denominators	$5\frac{4}{7} - \frac{2}{7} = $ _____ $3\frac{2}{5} - 1\frac{2}{5} = $ _____
3c	Story problems: Adding and subtracting mixed numbers and fractions with the same denominator	Bill ran 2 2/4 miles on Monday and 3 1/4 miles on Tuesday. How many miles did he run altogether? _____ miles Jack had 4 2/8 pounds of nails. Bill had 2 3/8 pounds of nails. How much more did Jack have? _____ pounds of nails Bob worked 2 1/2 hours on Monday and 3 hours on Tuesday. How many hours did he work altogether? _____ hours

Figure 13.2 cont'd

Grade Level	Problem Type	Performance Indicator
4a	Rewriting fractions as mixed numbers	$\frac{12}{5} = $ _____ $\frac{8}{3} = $ _____ $\frac{21}{9} = $ _____
4b	Rewriting whole numbers as fractions	$9 = \frac{\Box}{\Box}$ $6 = \frac{\Box}{\Box}$ $8 = \frac{\Box}{\Box}$
4c	Multiplying fractions by a whole number; converting answers to whole numbers	$\frac{2}{3} \times 6$ $\frac{1}{3} \times 12$ $\frac{3}{5} \times 20$
4d	Multiplying fractions by whole numbers and converting answers to mixed numbers	$\frac{2}{5} \times 14$ $\frac{3}{7} \times 8$ $\frac{2}{9} \times 15$
4e	Story problems: multiplying fractions by whole numbers	There are 15 children in class. Two-thirds are boys. How many boys in the class? Jack has to study for 30 hours. He has done half of the studying. How many hours did he study? Ann's coach told her to run 3/4 of a mile a day. How many miles will she run in 5 days?
4f	Writing a fraction as an equivalent to one whole group	$1 = \frac{\Box}{4}$ $1 = \frac{\Box}{7}$
4g	Rewriting fractions as equivalent fractions with larger denominators	$\frac{2}{5} = \frac{\Box}{10}$ $\frac{3}{4} = \frac{\Box}{12}$ $\frac{2}{3} = \frac{\Box}{9}$
4h	Finding the lowest common multiple of two small numbers	Find the lowest common multiple of 6 and 4 _____ Find the lowest common multiple of 5 and 10 _____ Find the lowest common multiple of 5 and 2 _____
4i	Adding and subtracting fractions with unlike denominators	$\frac{3}{4} - \frac{2}{3} = \frac{\Box}{\Box}$ $\frac{2}{5} + \frac{3}{10} = \frac{\Box}{\Box}$ $\frac{1}{2} - \frac{1}{3} = \frac{\Box}{\Box}$ $\frac{2}{6} + \frac{1}{2} = \frac{\Box}{\Box}$

Figure 13.2 cont'd

Grade Level	Problem Type	Performance Indicator
4j	Comparing value of fractions	Which is greater: $\frac{2}{3}$ or $\frac{4}{5}$? $\frac{4}{5}$ or $\frac{2}{3}$? $\frac{2}{7}$ or $\frac{1}{2}$?
4k	Story problems: adding and subtracting fractions with unlike denominators	Bill painted 1/2 of the wall. Jane painted 1/4 of the wall. How much of the wall have they painted altogether? Tom ate 1/3 of the pie, and Jack ate 1/2 of the pie. How much of the pie did they eat?
4l	Determining all factors of a given number	Write all the numbers that are factors of 12. Write all the numbers that are factors of 8.
4m	Determining the greatest common factor	What is the greatest common factor of 8 and 12? What is the greatest common factor of 4 and 8? What is the greatest common factor of 12 and 15?
4n	Reducing a fraction to its simplest terms	Reduce these fractions to their simplest terms: $\frac{12}{18} = \frac{\Box}{\Box}$ $\frac{16}{20} = \frac{\Box}{\Box}$ $\frac{6}{18} = \frac{\Box}{\Box}$
4o	Adding fractions, reducing and converting to mixed numbers	Add these fractions; reduce the answers to simplest terms. Write answers as mixed numbers. $\frac{4}{6} + \frac{2}{5} = $ _____ $\frac{2}{4} + \frac{2}{3} = $ _____ $\frac{6}{10} + \frac{4}{5} = $ _____
4p	Converting mixed numbers to improper fractions	$2\frac{1}{4} = \frac{\Box}{4}$ $3\frac{1}{2} = \frac{\Box}{2}$ $1\frac{3}{5} = \frac{\Box}{5}$
5a	Subtracting mixed numbers from whole numbers	$8 - 1\frac{2}{3} = $ _____ $9 - 2\frac{3}{5} = $ _____ $7 - 4\frac{1}{2} = $ _____

Figure 13.2 cont'd

Grade Level	Problem Type	Performance Indicator
5b	Finding the lowest common multiple of three numbers	Find the lowest common multiple of 3, 6, and 4. Find the lowest common multiple of 2, 4, and 5. Find the lowest common multiple of 2, 5, and 10.
5c	Adding and subtracting three fractions with different denominators	Add these fractions and write the answers with fractions written in simplest terms. $\frac{3}{5} + \frac{1}{2} + \frac{3}{6} = $ _____ $\frac{2}{3} + \frac{2}{4} + \frac{1}{6} = $ _____ $\frac{3}{4} + \frac{1}{2} + \frac{2}{5} = $ _____
5d	Multiplying mixed numbers	$7\frac{3}{4} \times 3\frac{1}{2} = $ _____ $2\frac{3}{5} \times 4 = $ _____ $5 \times 2\frac{1}{2} = $ _____
5e	Dividing fractions	$\frac{3}{4} \div \frac{2}{5} = $ _____ $\frac{5}{6} \div \frac{2}{3} = $ _____ $\frac{7}{9} \div \frac{1}{3} = $ _____
5f	Dividing fractions by whole numbers	$\frac{2}{3} \div 4 = $ _____ $\frac{3}{5} \div 2 = $ _____ $\frac{2}{4} \div 7 = $ _____
5g	Dividing mixed numbers by whole numbers	$3\frac{1}{2} \div 3 = $ _____ $2\frac{1}{5} \div 2 = $ _____ $7\frac{1}{2} \div 4 = $ _____
5h	Story problems: division involving fractions	Two girls picked 5 1/2 pounds of cherries. They want to split up the cherries equally. How much will each one get? Bill has 35 inches of ribbon. He wants to make shorter ribbons. If each ribbon is 1/2″ long, how many ribbons can he make?

The third area, operations, includes addition, subtraction, multiplication, and division of fractions. These operations often incorporate several rewriting fraction skills. For example, to work the problem 3/4 + 5/6, the student must rewrite 3/4 and 5/6 as equivalent fractions with the same denominator: 3/4 = 9/12 and 5/6 = 10/12. The equivalent fractions 10/12 and 9/12 are then added to produce a sum of 19/12, which must be converted to the mixed number 1 7/12. When working the problem 4/5 × 1 3/4 the student must first convert the mixed number 1 3/4 to the improper fraction 7/4. The student then multiplies 4/5 × 7/4, ending with a product of 28/20, which can be converted to the mixed number 1 8/20. The fraction part of this mixed number can be reduced so that the final answer reads 1 2/5.

The skill hierarchy is designed to help the reader see the interrelationship among various fraction skills. Note on the chart the numerous fractions skills that are component skills for other skills. A sequence for teaching fractions must be arranged so that all component skills for an advanced problem type have been presented before the advanced problem type is presented. Note also how the focus of instruction circulates. For example, simple addition and subtraction problems involving fractions with like denominators are introduced at a relatively early stage in the sequence of instruction. Problems involving adding and subtracting fractions with unlike denominators are not introduced until significantly later in the sequence since several rewriting skills must be taught first. The Instructional Sequence and Assessment Chart in Figure 13.2 suggests one possible order for introducing the main types of fraction-related problems students will encounter in elementary school.

Teachers working with intermediate grade students will find it productive to test, and teach when necessary, the skills appearing at the beginning of the sequence chart since these skills lay the foundation for a conceptual understanding of fractions.

Fraction Analysis

Fraction analysis instruction, which usually begins in mid-second grade, is the first set of fraction skills to be introduced. Here are the skills included in this area, listed in their order of introduction:

1. Learning part/whole discrimination: Students learn to discriminate between whole units, the number of parts each unit is divided into, and the number of parts used.
2. Writing a numerical representation for a diagram of whole units divided into equal-sized parts and vice versa:

3. Decoding fractions: 3/4 is read as three-fourths.
4. Determining whether a fraction equals, exceeds, or is less than one whole.
5. Decoding mixed fractional numbers: 3 1/2 is three and one-half.

The strategies in the fraction analysis section have been designed to introduce proper and improper fractions concurrently. This feature prevents students from learning the misrule that all fractions are proper fractions. Without adequate instruction, low-performing students often learn a misrule as evidenced by the fact that they can usually decode and draw a picture of 3/4 but are not able to generalize the skills to the example 4/3. By introducing proper and improper fractions at the same time, teachers show students that the analysis applies to all fractions.

A second important feature of the analysis section is that students are taught initially to interpret what the denominator and numerator tell (e.g., in 3/4 the 4 tells four parts in each whole unit, and the 3 tells three parts are used) rather than to read the fraction in the traditional way (e.g., 3/4 read as three-fourths). The interpretive reading of fractions enables students to represent a diagram as a numerical fraction and facilitates conceptual development.

A third important feature of the fraction analysis is initial limitation of fractions to figures that have been divided into parts:

We recommend delaying the introduction of subsets and number lines as representations of fractions until several months after fractions are introduced in order to simplify initial learning.

Part-Whole Discrimination

Figure 13.3 includes a format for introducing fractions to students. The goal of the format is to teach basic fraction (part-whole) concepts through the use of diagrams. The specific objectives are to teach students to discriminate between the number of parts in each whole unit and the number of whole units.

In the format, the teacher writes a row of circles on the board and divides each into an equal number of parts. The teacher tells the students that each circle is called a whole and then leads the students through determining how many parts in each whole.

Each example set should include a different number of circles (wholes). Also the number of parts each whole is divided into should vary from set to set. For example, the first set might include three circles, each of which is divided into two parts. The next set might include five circles each divided into four parts; the next two circles, each divided into three parts; etc. This format would be presented for several days.

Writing Numerical Fractions to Represent Diagrams

Exercises in which the students write a numerical fraction to represent a diagram (e.g., for

Figure 13.3 Format for Part-Whole Discrimination

PART A: Structured Board Presentation

Write on board:

1. Point to first circle. "THIS IS A WHOLE UNIT. WHAT IS THIS?"

   "A whole unit"

   Point to second circle. "THIS IS A WHOLE UNIT. WHAT IS THIS?"

   "A whole unit"

   "HOW MANY WHOLE UNITS?"

   "2"

2. "EACH WHOLE UNIT HAS PARTS. THE PARTS ARE ALL THE SAME SIZE. LET'S SEE HOW MANY PARTS ARE IN EACH WHOLE UNIT."

3. Point to first unit. "COUNT THE PARTS AS I TOUCH THEM." Touch each part in the first circle.

   "1, 2, 3"

   "HOW MANY PARTS IN THIS WHOLE UNIT?"

   "3"

4. Point to the second circle. "NOW LET'S COUNT THE PARTS IN THIS WHOLE UNIT."

   Touch each part as students count.

   "1, 2, 3"

5. "HOW MANY PARTS IN EACH WHOLE UNIT?"

   "3 parts"

6. "YES, THREE PARTS IN EACH WHOLE UNIT. SAY THAT."

   "3 parts in each whole unit"

7. "NOW THINK. HOW MANY WHOLE UNITS?"

   "2"

   "YES, THERE ARE TWO WHOLE UNITS WITH THREE PARTS IN EACH UNIT."

   Repeat steps 1-7 with these examples:

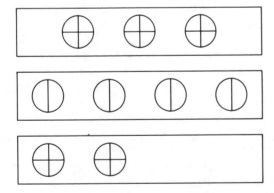

students write 5/4) would be presented after the students have had ample practice, usually several days, to master the part-whole concepts presented in Figure 13.3. The format for writing numerical fractions appears in Figure 13.4. In Part A, the structured board presentation, students learn that the bottom number of a fraction tells how many parts in each whole, while the top number of a fraction represents how many parts are used (i.e., shaded). Parts B and C are structured and less structured worksheet exercises in which the students are to fill in the numerals to represent a diagram. Daily practice would be provided for several weeks followed by intermittent review.

Two guidelines are important for appropriate example selection for this skill. First, the number of parts in each whole unit, the number of whole units, and the number of parts used should vary from example to example. Second, the examples should include a mixture of proper and improper fractions.

Figure 13.4 Format for Writing a Numerical Fraction

Day	Part A Structured Board Problems	Part B Structured Worksheet Problems	Part C Less Structured Worksheet Problems	Part D Supervised Practice Problems	Part E Independent Practice Problems
1	6				
2-3	6	6			
4-5		6	6		
6-accurate				10	10

PART A: Structured Board Presentation

<u>**TEACHER**</u>   <u>**STUDENTS**</u>

Write on board:

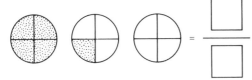

1. "WE'RE GOING TO LEARN TO WRITE FRACTIONS. FRACTIONS TELL US HOW MANY PARTS IN EACH WHOLE UNIT AND HOW MANY PARTS ARE USED."

2. "THE BOTTOM NUMBER OF A FRACTION TELLS HOW MANY PARTS IN EACH WHOLE. WHAT DOES THE BOTTOM NUMBER TELL?"   "How many parts in each whole"

   "LOOK AT THIS PICTURE AND THINK HOW MANY PARTS ARE IN EACH WHOLE." Pause. "HOW MANY PARTS IN EACH WHOLE?"   "4"

   TO CORRECT: "LET'S SEE HOW MANY PARTS ARE IN EACH WHOLE." Point to first circle. "COUNT THE PARTS AS I TOUCH THEM." Touch each part in the first circle. Repeat same procedures with next two circles. "THERE ARE FOUR PARTS IN THIS WHOLE, AND FOUR PARTS IN THIS WHOLE. THERE ARE FOUR PARTS IN EACH WHOLE."

   "SO WHAT IS THE BOTTOM NUMBER OF THE FRACTION?"   "4"

   "I'LL WRITE 4 AS THE BOTTOM NUMBER. THAT TELLS US FOUR PARTS IN EACH WHOLE. WHAT DOES THE 4 TELL US?"   "4 parts in each whole"

3. "THE TOP NUMBER TELLS US HOW MANY PARTS ARE USED. WHAT DOES THE TOP NUMBER TELLS US?"   "How many parts are used"

   "WE FIND HOW MANY PARTS ARE USED BY COUNTING THE SHADED PARTS." Point to each shaded part. "COUNT AS I TOUCH THE PARTS."   "1, 2, 3, 4, 5"
   "HOW MANY PARTS ARE SHADED?"   "5"

   "SO I WRITE 5 AS THE TOP NUMBER OF THE FRACTION." Write 5 on top. "THAT TELLS US FIVE PARTS ARE USED. WHAT DOES THE 5 TELL US?"   "5 parts are used"

4. "I'LL SAY WHAT THE FRACTION TELLS US." Point to 4. "FOUR PARTS IN EACH WHOLE." Point to 5. "FIVE PARTS ARE USED."

Figure 13.4 cont'd

TEACHER

5. "YOU SAY WHAT THE FRACTION TELLS US."
   Point to 4. Signal.
   Point to 5. Signal.
   Repeat step 5 until students respond without hesitation.
   Give individual turns to several students.

6. Repeat steps 1–4 with these problems:

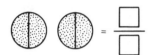 

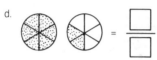

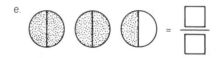

PART B: Structured Worksheet

a. 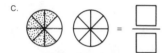   d.

b.   e.

c.    f.

1. "TOUCH PICTURE a. YOU'RE GOING TO WRITE
   THE FRACTION FOR THE PICTURE."

2. "FIRST WE WRITE HOW MANY PARTS IN EACH
   WHOLE. WHERE DO YOU WRITE THE NUMBER OF
   PARTS IN EACH WHOLE?"
   "LOOK AND SEE HOW MANY PARTS IN EACH
   WHOLE. (pause) HOW MANY PARTS IN EACH
   WHOLE?"
   "WHERE DO YOU WRITE 3?"
   "WRITE THE NUMBER."

3. "NOW WE WRITE THE NUMBER OF PARTS USED.
   WHERE DO YOU WRITE THE NUMBER OF PARTS
   USED?"
   "COUNT THE SHADED PARTS. (pause) HOW MANY
   PARTS ARE USED?" Signal.
   "WRITE THE 4."

4. "TOUCH THE BOTTOM NUMBER. (pause) WHAT
   DOES THAT TELL US?"
   "TOUCH THE TOP NUMBER. WHAT DOES THAT
   TELL US?"
   Repeat step 4 until students answer without hesitation.
   Give individual turns to several students on step 4.
   Repeat steps 1–4 with remaining diagrams.

STUDENTS

"4 parts in each whole."
"5 parts are used"

"In the bottom box"

"3"
"In the bottom box"

"On the top"

"4"

"3 parts in each whole"

"4 parts are used"

Figure 13.4 cont'd

PART C: Less Structured Worksheet

TEACHER

Give students worksheet similar to the one in Part B.

1. "TOUCH PROBLEM a."

2. "WHERE DO YOU WRITE HOW MANY PARTS IN EACH WHOLE UNIT?"

3. "WHAT DO YOU WRITE ON THE TOP?"
   "WRITE THE NUMBERS." Pause.

4. "TOUCH THE BOTTOM NUMBER. WHAT DID YOU WRITE?"
   "WHAT DOES IT TELL US?"

5. "TOUCH THE TOP NUMBER. WHAT DID YOU WRITE?"
   "WHAT DOES THE TOP NUMBER TELL US?"
   Repeat steps 1–5 with remaining problems.

STUDENTS

"On the bottom"
"How many parts are used"

"_____ parts in each whole"

"_____ parts are used"

The examples should include some fractions that equal less than a whole unit:

some examples that equal more than one unit:

During the first days, all examples would include circles divided into parts. After several weeks, other shapes (e.g., squares, rectangles, triangles) can be included in exercises.

Special attention should be given to examples containing a series of units that are not divided:

These diagrams will need special explanation. The teacher should point out that if a whole is not divided into parts, students should write a 1 on the bottom. The 1 tells that there is only one part in the whole unit. Examples which yield 1 as a denominator should not be introduced when fractions are initially presented but can be introduced about a week after initial instruction. Thereafter, about 1 in every 10 diagrams should be an example with 1 as a denominator. These examples are important since they present a conceptual base of exercises in which students convert a whole number to a fraction (e,g., 8 = 8/1).

Drawing Diagrams to Represent Fractions

Translating numerical fractions into diagrams is a useful exercise for reinforcing a conceptual understanding of the part-whole fraction relationship. Constructing diagrams can be introduced when students are able to accurately fill in the numerals to represent a diagram. For most students, this should be a week or two after fraction analysis is introduced. The procedure is relatively simple, so we haven't included a format. The teacher should begin instruction by modeling how to divide circles into equal-sized parts, stressing the need to divide the circles so that each part is the same size. Examples can be limited to fractions with 2, 3, or 4 as denominators. This will allow for adequate discrimination without spending an inordinate amount of time teaching younger students to divide circles into more than four parts. After several days of practice dividing wholes into parts, the teacher would present a worksheet exercise, prompting the students as they draw diagrams. The teacher has the student say what each number tells, beginning with the bottom number. For 3/4, the teacher would say "Touch the bottom number. What does it tell you? . . . Draw four parts in each whole . . . . Touch the top number . . . . What does it tell you? . . . Shade in three parts." Figure 13.5 includes a sample worksheet. Note that each example has four circles. The purpose of keeping the number of circles constant is to prevent students from thinking that the number of whole units has something to do with the numerator and/or denominator.

Figure 13.5 Sample Worksheet for Drawing Diagrams from Numerical Fractions

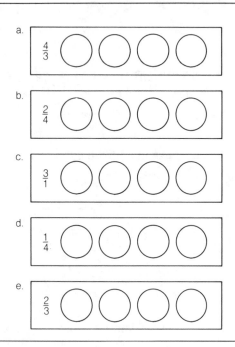

Several weeks after fractions are introduced, reading fractions the traditional way can be taught; 3/4 is read as three-fourths. Figure 13.6 includes a format for teaching students to read fractions the traditional way. The teacher writes several fractions on the board. The teacher first models how to read the fractions, testing after each example. Then the teacher tests students on reading the fractions without first providing the model. The correction is a model and test. After the initial correction, the teacher would use the alternating test pattern to firm the student on the missed example.

This decoding-fractions format should be presented daily for about 2–3 weeks, then once each second or third day for about 3 or 4 weeks until students can accurately read fractions. Thereafter, students receive practice in reading fractions at the same time new fraction skills are introduced. For example, in adding fractions, students receive practice decoding fractions in the step when they are asked to read the problem aloud.

Two example selection guidelines should be followed in teaching students to decode fractions. First, the introduction of fractions with the numbers 2, 3, or 5 as denominators should be delayed several lessons because these denominators are not pronounced by adding the suffix "ths" to the number as is the case for sixths, ninths, and fourths. When a 2 appears as the denominator, students say halves, not "twoths"; when a 3 appears, students say thirds not "threeths"; when a 5 appears, students say fifths, not "fiveths." These denominators need to be introduced one at a time using a model-test procedure. Fractions with 2 as a denominator might be introduced first. When introducing 2 as a

Decoding Fractions

When fractions are initially introduced, students are taught to say what each numeral in the fraction tells. The fraction 3/4 is read as "four parts in each whole; three parts are used up." This translation is recommended since it specifies what to do (make four parts in each whole and then shade three parts), thus facilitating conceptual understanding.

Figure 13.6 Format for Decoding Fractions

PART A: Structured Board Presentation

TEACHER

Write on board: $\frac{4}{9}$ $\frac{1}{9}$ $\frac{3}{4}$ $\frac{1}{4}$ $\frac{6}{7}$ $\frac{1}{7}$ $\frac{2}{4}$ $\frac{1}{4}$

Model and Test

1. "SO FAR WE'VE LEARNED WHAT FRACTIONS TELL US TO DO . TODAY WE'RE GOING TO LEARN TO READ FRACTIONS A NEW WAY. MY TURN TO READ THIS FRACTION." Point to 4. "FOUR" Point to 9. "NINTHS."

2. "YOUR TURN." Point to 4, then 9.

3. Repeat steps 1 and 2 with half the examples on the board.

4. Repeat step 2 only with the remaining examples.

   TO CORRECT: Model correct answer; repeat.

STUDENTS

"Four-ninths"

denominator, about half of the examples in the teaching set should contain 2 in the denominator, while the other half should represent a variety of previously introduced denominators:

$$\frac{1}{2} \quad \frac{1}{4} \quad \frac{3}{2} \quad \frac{3}{8} \quad \frac{5}{2} \quad \frac{5}{7} \quad \frac{1}{6} \quad \frac{4}{2}$$

When students have mastered denominators of 2, they would be introduced in the same way to fractions with 5, then 3, as denominators. A second example selection guideline is concerned with the numerators. In about a fourth of the examples, the number 1 should be written as the numerator. These examples are included so that the students can see the difference between how a fraction is said when the numerator is 1 and when the numerator is more than 1; one-eighth versus four-eighths.

Determining If More, Less, or Equal to One

Determining whether a fraction equals, exceeds, or is less than one whole is an important skill and also serves as a prerequisite for later exercises in which students are expected to convert an improper fraction like 16/7 to a mixed number: 2 2/7. This skill can be introduced when students can accurately decode fractions the traditional way. The format appears in Figure 13.7. Part A is a pictorial demonstration in which the teacher draws diagrams representing fractions of various values (more than 1, less than 1, equal to 1) and asks the students if the picture shows one whole, more than one whole, or less than one whole.

In Part B, the teacher presents rules to be used in determining whether a numerical fraction equals, exceeds, or is less than one whole unit. First, students are taught the rule that when the top and bottom number of a fraction are the same, the fraction equals one whole. After this rule is presented, the teacher tests the students' application of the rule using a series of numerical fractions, about half of which equal one whole:

$$\frac{5}{5} \quad \frac{6}{4} \quad \frac{4}{4} \quad \frac{9}{2} \quad \frac{9}{9} \quad \frac{5}{5} \quad \frac{7}{3} \quad \frac{2}{7} \quad \frac{8}{8}$$

Next the teacher instructs students that when the top number of a fraction is greater than the bottom number, the fraction equals more than one whole; and when the top number is less than the bottom number, the fraction equals less than one whole. Finally, the students are shown fractions and asked to tell whether the fraction is equal to, more than, or

less than 1. A structured worksheet exercise follows in which students must circle either *equal*, *more*, or *less* when given numerical fractions:

$$\frac{3}{4} \begin{array}{l} \text{more} \\ \text{equal} \\ \text{less} \end{array} \qquad \frac{8}{8} \begin{array}{l} \text{more} \\ \text{equal} \\ \text{less} \end{array}$$

Note that in this format, the words *numerator* and *denominator* are not used. The purpose of excluding the terms is to avoid possible confusion for students who may be unclear about which numbers are the numerator and denominator. Similarly, the term *improper fraction* is not included in the format, This term is best introduced in later grades.

Examples for Parts B, C, D, and independent practice should include a variety of problems. In about a third of the examples, the numerator and denominator of the fraction should be the same:

$$\frac{4}{4} \quad \frac{8}{8} \quad \frac{3}{3}$$

in a third, the numerator should be greater than the denominator:

$$\frac{7}{5} \quad \frac{3}{2} \quad \frac{4}{2}$$

and in a third, the numerator should be less than the denominator:

$$\frac{2}{3} \quad \frac{4}{7} \quad \frac{3}{4}$$

Reading and Writing Mixed Numbers

The diagram

may be expressed as the improper fraction 9/4 or as the mixed fractional number 2 1/4. Reading and writing mixed numbers can be introduced relatively early in the fraction sequence, as soon as students can correctly determine when a fraction equals, exceeds, or is less than one whole. However, the teacher must keep in mind that exercises designed to teach students to convert mixed numbers to improper fractions and vice versa would not be introduced until much later in the fraction sequence, since these conversions require students to know basic multiplication facts. Figure 13.8 includes a format designed to teach students to read and write mixed numbers. The format begins with a pictorial demonstration exercise in which students are taught to express the diagram of an improper fraction as a mixed number by counting the number of whole units shaded and writing that number, then deter-

Figure 13.7 Format for Determining Whether a Fraction Equals, Exceeds, or Is Less Than One Whole

Day	Part A Pictorial Demonstrations	Part B Structured Board Problems	Part C Structured Work- sheet Problems	Part D Supervised Prac- tice Problems
1-2	3	8		
3-4		4		
5-6			6	6
7-accurate			4	10

PART A: Pictorial Demonstrations

TEACHER

1. "I'LL DRAW A PICTURE ON THE BOARD. YOU TELL ME IF WE USE UP MORE THAN ONE WHOLE. LESS THAN ONE WHOLE, OR JUST ONE WHOLE."
Draw this diagram:

2. "DID I SHADE MORE THAN ONE WHOLE, LESS THAN ONE WHOLE, OR JUST ONE WHOLE?"
Signal.
"YES, LESS THAN ONE WHOLE UNIT. EACH CIRCLE HAS FOUR PARTS, BUT I ONLY SHADED THREE PARTS."
Repeat step 2 with these examples:

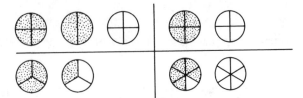

STUDENTS

"Less than one whole unit"

PART B: Structured Board Presentation

1. "WE'RE GOING TO LEARN SOME RULES SO WE CAN TELL IF A FRACTION EQUALS ONE WHOLE OR EQUALS MORE OR LESS THAN ONE WHOLE WITHOUT DRAWING A PICTURE."

2. "FIRST RULE. A FRACTION EQUALS ONE WHOLE WHEN THE TOP NUMBER AND BOTTOM NUMBER ARE THE SAME. WHEN DOES A FRACTION EQUAL ONE WHOLE?"

Write on board: $\frac{4}{4}$

"When the top number and bottom number are the same"

3. Point to the fraction. "DOES THIS FRACTION EQUAL ONE WHOLE?"
"HOW DO YOU KNOW?"

"Yes"
"The top number and bottom number are the same."

Repeat step 3 with
$\frac{7}{4} \quad \frac{2}{3} \quad \frac{5}{5} \quad \frac{1}{4} \quad \frac{8}{8}$

Figure 13.7 cont'd

4. "LISTEN TO THESE NEW RULES. IF THE TOP
   NUMBER IS <u>MORE</u> THAN THE BOTTOM NUMBER,
   THE FRACTION EQUALS <u>MORE</u> THAN ONE
   WHOLE. WHEN DOES A FRACTION EQUAL MORE
   THAN ONE WHOLE?"   "When the top number is more
                                                       than the bottom number"

   "IF THE TOP NUMBER IS <u>LESS</u> THAN THE BOT-
   TOM NUMBER, THE FRACTION EQUALS <u>LESS</u>
   THAN ONE WHOLE. WHEN DOES A FRACTION
   EQUAL LESS THAN ONE WHOLE?"   "When the top number is less
                                                        than the bottom number"

5. Write on board: $\frac{3}{5}$

   "IS THE TOP NUMBER THE SAME AS THE BOTTOM
   NUMBER?"   "No"
   "SO DOES THE FRACTION EQUAL ONE WHOLE?"   "No"
   "IS THE TOP NUMBER MORE OR LESS THAN THE
   BOTTOM NUMBER?"   "Less"
   "SO DOES THE FRACTION EQUAL MORE OR LESS
   THAN ONE WHOLE?"   "Less than one whole"
   "HOW DO YOU KNOW?"   "The top number is less than
   "YES, 5 PARTS IN EACH WHOLE AND   the bottom number"
   ONLY 3 PARTS ARE USED."
   Repeat step 5 with

   $\frac{3}{4}$ $\frac{3}{3}$ $\frac{3}{2}$ $\frac{4}{5}$ $\frac{4}{4}$ $\frac{4}{2}$

PART C: Structured Worksheet

Give students worksheets with problems like these:

a. $\frac{5}{4}$	more	b. $\frac{7}{7}$	more	c. $\frac{3}{7}$	more
	equal		equal		equal
	less		less		less

1. "IN THESE PROBLEMS YOU HAVE TO TELL IF A
   FRACTION IS MORE THAN ONE WHOLE, EQUALS
   ONE WHOLE, OR IS LESS THAN ONE WHOLE."

2. "READ THE FRACTION IN PROBLEM a."   "Five-fourths"

3. "DOES THE FRACTION EQUAL ONE WHOLE?"   "No"

4. "IS THE TOP NUMBER MORE OR LESS THAN THE
   BOTTOM NUMBER?"   "More"
   "SO DOES THE FRACTION EQUAL MORE OR LESS
   THAN ONE WHOLE?"   "More than one whole"
   "PUT A CIRCLE AROUND THE WORD <u>MORE</u>."
   Repeat steps 1-4 with remaining problems.

---

mining the numerator and denominator of the remaining unit. Below is a sample exercise:

 =  =

Part B is designed to teach students to read
mixed numbers. The teacher uses a model/test

procedure, having students first say the whole
number, then the fraction, then the mixed number.
Note that the teacher emphasizes the word *and*
when reading mixed numbers. The purpose of emphasizing *and* is to prevent errors in which the student combines the whole number and the numerator, reading 4 2/3 as "forty two thirds" or leaves out
the numerator, reading 5 1/3 as "five thirds."

Figure 13.8 Format for Reading and Writing Mixed Numbers

Day	Part A Pictorial Demonstrations	Part B Reading Mixed Numbers	Part C Writing Mixed Numbers
1-2	3	6	
3-4		6	
5-6		4	6
7-20		4 (only step 3)	6 (only step 7)

PART A: Pictorial Demonstrations

TEACHER   **STUDENTS**

Write on board:

1. "YOU'RE GOING TO LEARN HOW TO WRITE THE
   FRACTION IN THIS PICTURE A NEW WAY."
2. "FIRST, LET'S WRITE THE FRACTION THE OLD
   WAY. HOW MANY PARTS IN EACH WHOLE?" Pause.   "4"
   "WHERE DO I WRITE IT?"   "On the bottom"
   Do it.
3. "HOW MANY PARTS ARE USED?" Pause.   "14"
   "WHERE DO I WRITE IT?"   "On the top"
   Do it.
4. "NOW WE'RE GOING TO WRITE THE FRACTION
   AS A MIXED NUMBER. A MIXED NUMBER HAS A
   WHOLE NUMBER AND A FRACTION. WHAT DOES
   A MIXED NUMBER HAVE?"   "A whole number and a fraction"
5. "FIRST WE COUNT THE NUMBER OF WHOLES
   USED UP. COUNT AS I POINT. HOW MANY WHOLES
   ARE USED UP?"   "3"
   "SO I WRITE 3 IN THE BOX." Write 3 in the box.
6. "NOW WE WRITE THE FRACTION TO TELL ABOUT
   THE WHOLE NOT USED UP." Point to

   "WHAT DO I WRITE AS THE BOTTOM NUMBER
   IN THE FRACTION?"   "4"
   Write 4.

   TO CORRECT: "THERE ARE FOUR PARTS IN EACH
              WHOLE."

   "WHAT DO I WRITE AS THE TOP NUMBER IN THE
   FRACTION?"   "2"
   Write 2.

   TO CORRECT: "THERE ARE TWO PARTS SHADED."

   "THE FRACTION THAT TELLS ABOUT THE WHOLE
   NOT USED UP SAYS TWO-FOURTHS."

Figure 13.8 cont'd

TEACHER   **STUDENTS**

7. "THE MIXED NUMBER SAYS THREE AND TWO—
   FOURTHS. WHAT DOES THE MIXED NUMBER SAY?"   "3 and 2/4"
   "THERE ARE THREE WHOLE UNITS USED UP
   AND 2/4 OF ANOTHER WHOLE UNIT USED UP."
   Repeat steps 2-7 with these examples:

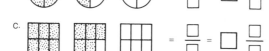

PART B: Structured Board Presentation

Write on board: $2\frac{1}{3}$

1. "A MIXED NUMBER IS A WHOLE NUMBER AND
   A FRACTION. WHAT IS A MIXED NUMBER?"   "A whole number and a fraction"

2. Point to $2\frac{1}{3}$

   "WHAT'S THE WHOLE NUMBER?"   "2"

   "WHAT'S THE FRACTION?"   "$\frac{1}{3}$"

3. "READ THE MIXED NUMBER."   "Two and one third"

   Repeat steps 2 and 3 with

   $5\frac{2}{7}$ $7\frac{1}{2}$ $3\frac{4}{5}$ $6\frac{1}{2}$

PART C: Structured Worksheet

Give students lined paper.

1. "LISTEN, TWO <u>AND</u> THREE-FOURTHS. SAY THAT."   "Two and three-fourths"
   "WHAT IS THE WHOLE NUMBER?"   "2"
   "I WRITE 2 SO THAT IT TAKES UP THE WHOLE
   SPACE:"

   $\underline{2}$

2. "LISTEN, TWO AND THREE-FOURTHS. WHAT'S
   THE FRACTION?"   "Three-fourths"
   "I WRITE THE FRACTION LINE IN THE MIDDLE
   OF THE SPACE NEXT TO THE 2. THEN I WRITE
   THE FRACTION NUMBERS SMALL."
   Write:

   $2\frac{3}{4}$

3. "WHAT IS THE MIXED NUMBER?"   "Two and three-fourths"
   Repeat steps 1-3 with

   $7\frac{1}{2}$ $4\frac{2}{5}$

4. "NOW IT'S YOUR TURN. YOU'RE GOING TO
   WRITE THE MIXED NUMBER FIVE AND TWO-
   THIRDS. WHAT MIXED NUMBER ARE YOU GOING
   TO WRITE?"   "5 2/3"

Fractions   **325**

Figure 13.8 cont'd

TEACHER   **STUDENTS**

5. "LISTEN, 5 2/3. WHAT IS THE WHOLE NUMBER?"   "5"
   "WRITE IT. MAKE IT BIG SO THAT IT TOUCHES
   BOTH LINES." Monitor responses.

6. "LISTEN, 5 2/3. WHAT IS THE FRACTION?"   "2/3"
   "PUT THE FRACTION LINE RIGHT IN THE
   MIDDLE OF THE SPACE NEXT TO THE 5. THEN
   WRITE 2/3. WRITE THE NUMBERS SMALL."
   Repeat step 2 with

   $7\frac{2}{4}$ $9\frac{1}{3}$ $7\frac{1}{2}$ $5\frac{3}{8}$

7. "LISTEN: 3 4/6. SAY IT.   "3 4/6"
   WRITE IT." Monitor responses. Repeat step 7 with

   $7\frac{2}{4}$ $9\frac{1}{3}$ $7\frac{1}{2}$ $5\frac{3}{8}$

Part C is an exercise in which students are taught to write mixed numbers. The teacher gives students lined paper and pencil and points out that when students write mixed numbers, they are to make the whole number big and the numbers in the fraction small: "The big number should be written so that it touches the top and bottom of the line. Then write the fraction line in the middle of the space."

The exercise begins with the teacher saying a mixed number and having students first say and write the whole number, then say and write the fraction part of the mixed number.

Note in the chart at the beginning of the format that practice on reading and writing mixed numbers would be continued for several weeks. In this extended practice, the teacher merely has students read and write mixed numbers without prompting (step 3 of Part B and step 7 of Part C). Thus, the chart specifies presenting only the final steps of the reading and writing exercises.

Rewriting Fractions

The procedures in this section all involve the process of changing a fraction from one form to another without changing its value, i.e., maintaining equivalency. Three main types of conversion skills are discussed:

1. Determining the missing number in a pair of equivalent fractions. Given a problem such as

$$\frac{3}{5} = \frac{\square}{10}$$

the student will determine the missing number. This problem type is a critical component skill for problems involving adding and subtracting fractions with unlike denominators.

2. Reducing fractions to their lowest terms. A fraction is said to be at its lowest term (or simplest form) when both the numerator and denominator have no common factor except 1:

$$\frac{20}{24} \text{ can be reduced to } \frac{5}{6}$$

3. Converting mixed numbers to improper fractions:

$$3\frac{1}{2} = \frac{7}{2}$$

and improper fractions to mixed numbers:

$$\frac{17}{5} = 3\frac{2}{5}$$

A general preskill for all rewriting skills is knowledge of basic multiplication and division facts. To do all three types of conversion problems, students must be able to either multiply or divide. Thus, rewriting fraction skills are usually not introduced until early fourth grade.

The strategies presented here are designed so that students not only learn the necessary computation required to change fractions into parallel forms but also so that they understand the underlying concepts of equivalency that govern each strategy. Without understanding equivalency, students will be able to apply very few of the skills they learn. For example, if students do not understand that when the numerator and denominator are the same, the fraction is equal to 1, they will not understand why 3/4 can be multiplied by 5/5 to create the equivalent fraction 15/20. Although the equivalency concept is relatively sophisticated, the language of the strategies is relatively simple because they are designed for elementary grade students.

Completing Equivalent Fractions

Instruction in equivalent fractions begins with problems in which the student must determine the missing numerator in an equivalent fraction:

$$\frac{3}{4} = \frac{\square}{12} \qquad \frac{1}{2} = \frac{\square}{10}$$

The basic strategy is to multiply the first fraction by a fractional equivalent of one whole. In working the first problem above, the student determines that to end with an equivalent fraction that has 12 as a denominator the fraction 3/4 must be multiplied by 3/3:

$$\frac{3}{4} \times \frac{(3)}{(3)} = \frac{9}{12}$$

Equivalency is maintained since by definition the identity element for multiplication is 1. When multiplying 3/4 by 3/3, we are multiplying 3/4 by a fraction that equals 1, thus we are not changing the value of 3/4.

PRESKILLS Several skills should be mastered prior to introducing equivalency problems: (a) knowledge of the terms *numerator* and *denominator*, (b) how to multiply fractions, and (c) ability to construct a fraction which equals one whole.

The terms *numerator* and *denominator* are usually introduced in second or third grade. The teaching procedure is simple. The teacher tells students the numerator is the top number in a fraction and the denominator is the bottom number in the fraction. The teacher then provides practice by writing several fractions on the board and having students identify the numerator and denominator of each fraction. Daily practice is necessary so students won't forget or confuse the terms.

Multiplication of two fractions is also usually taught in third grade. Procedures for teaching this skill start on page 358 in the "Operations—Multiplying Fractions" section of this chapter.

Constructing fractions equal to one whole is introduced about 2 weeks prior to introducing equivalent fraction problems. Figure 13.9 includes the preskill format for constructing fractions equal to

1. Part A is a board exercise in which the rule for constructing fractions equal to 1 is introduced: "When the top number is the same as the bottom number, the fraction equals 1." After introducing the rule, the teacher presents examples of its application, writing problems such as

$$1 = \frac{\square}{4}$$

in which the student must fill in the missing numerator of a fraction equal to one whole. The board exercise is followed by worksheet exercises of a similar nature.

FORMAT The format for computing equivalent fractions is shown in Figure 13.10. Part A includes a pictorial demonstration introducing the concept of equivalent fractions. The teacher first defines the term *equivalent fractions*, explaining that fractions are equal when they show that equal portions of the wholes are used. The teacher then draws two circles on clear plastic, each divided into a different number of parts, but each with equal portions shaded:

The teacher points out that these fractions are equivalent since the same portion of each whole is shaded. The same demonstration is presented with a diagram in which nonequal proportions of the wholes are shaded:

The teacher points out that the fractions are not equivalent since the shaded portions of the wholes do not take up the same space.

Part B introduces a very critical rule: When you multiply by a fraction that equals 1, the answer equals the number you start with. The teacher tells students this rule, then presents a set of problems demonstrating the rule's application. In some of the problems, the original fraction is multiplied by a fraction which equals 1, and in some the original fraction is multiplied by a fraction not equal to 1. The students are to tell whether or not the answer will equal the original fraction.

Part C is a structured board exercise in which the teacher presents the strategy for working equivalency problems such as

$$\frac{3}{4} = \frac{\square}{20}$$

Figure 13.9 Preskill: Constructing Fractions Equal to 1

Day	Part A Structured Board Presentation Problems	Part B Structured Worksheet Problems	Part C Independent Practice Problems
1	5		
2	3	5	
3		4	4
4-10			6

PART A: Structured Board Presentation

TEACHER

1. "HERE'S A RULE: WHEN THE TOP NUMBER IS THE SAME AS THE BOTTOM, THE FRACTION EQUALS ONE WHOLE. WHEN DOES A FRACTION EQUAL ONE WHOLE?"

2. Write on board:

$$\frac{\square}{5}$$

"WHAT NUMBER IS ON THE BOTTOM OF THIS FRACTION?"
"WHAT FRACTION WITH A 5 AS A DENOMINATOR EQUALS ONE WHOLE?"

TO CORRECT: "A FRACTION EQUALS 1 WHEN THE TOP NUMBER IS THE SAME AS THE BOTTOM NUMBER. WHAT'S THE BOTTOM NUMBER? WHAT MUST THE TOP NUMBER BE?"
Repeat step 2.
"YES, FIVE-FIFTHS EQUALS ONE WHOLE."
Repeat step 2 with

$$\frac{\square}{8} \quad \frac{\square}{3} \quad \frac{\square}{6} \quad \frac{\square}{9}$$

STUDENTS

"When the top number is the same as the bottom number"

"5"

"5/5"

PART B: Structured Worksheet

Give students worksheets with examples like these:

a. $1 = \dfrac{\square}{4}$ b. $1 = \dfrac{\square}{7}$

c. $1 = \dfrac{\square}{4}$ d. $1 = \dfrac{\square}{7}$

1. "WHEN DOES A FRACTION EQUAL ONE WHOLE?"

2. "TOUCH PROBLEM a. IT SAYS 1 EQUALS HOW MANY FOURTHS?"
"READ THE PROBLEM."

3. "TELL ME THE FRACTION WITH 4 AS A DENOMI—NATOR THAT EQUALS ONE WHOLE."
"YES, FOUR-FOURTHS EQUALS ONE WHOLE."

4. "FILL IN THE MISSING NUMBER."

Repeat step 1-4 with remaining problems.

"When the top number is the same as the bottom"

"1 equals how many fourths?"

"4/4"

Students write 4 in box.

Figure 13.10 Format for Completing Equivalent Fractions

Day	Part A Pictorial Demonstrations	Part B Multiplication by 1 Problems	Part C Structured Board Problems	Part D Structured Worksheet Problems	Part E Supervised Practice Problems	Part F Independent Practice Problems
1-2	2	8				
3-4		6	4	6		
5			4	4	6	
6-accurate						5-10

PART A: Pictorial Demonstrations

TEACHER

STUDENTS

1. "FRACTIONS ARE EQUIVALENT WHEN THEY
   SHOW THE SAME AMOUNTS."
   Draw these figures on clear plastic sheets. The circles
   should have the same radius. Use a different color for
   each figure.

2. "THIS IS A PICTURE OF 4/8." Point to first figure.
   "THIS IS A PICTURE OF 1/2." Point to second figure.

3. "WOULD A PERSON WHO HAD 4/8 OF A PIE HAVE
   THE SAME PORTION AS A PERSON WHO HAD 1/2
   A PIE?"   "Yes"
   TO CORRECT: Place one figure on top of the other. Out-
       line the shaded part. "SEE, THE SHADED
       PORTION IS THE SAME SIZE IN
       BOTH PIES."

4. "SO ARE 4/8 AND 1/2 EQUIVALENT FRACTIONS?"   "Yes"

5. "YES, 4/8 AND 1/2 BOTH USE UP THE SAME
   AMOUNT OF A WHOLE."
   Repeat steps 1-3 with these pairs:

a.   b.   c.

PART B: Multiplying or Dividing by 1

1. "WHEN YOU MULTIPLY BY 1, THE ANSWER
   EQUALS THE NUMBER YOU START WITH."

2. Write on board:

   $\frac{3}{8} \times 1$

   "WHAT NUMBER DO WE START WITH?"   "3/8"
   "WILL OUR ANSWER EQUAL 3/8?"   "Yes"
   "HOW DO YOU KNOW?"   "We are multiplying by 1."
   Repeat step 2 with

   $\frac{1}{2} \times 1$ $\frac{1}{4} \times 5$

3. "HERE'S A RULE ABOUT FRACTIONS. WHEN YOU
   MULTIPLY BY A FRACTION THAT EQUALS 1, YOUR
   ANSWER EQUALS THE NUMBER YOU START WITH.
   LISTEN, AGAIN." Repeat rule.

Figure 13.10 cont'd

TEACHER   **STUDENTS**

4. Write on board:

$$\frac{4}{8} \times \frac{2}{2}$$

"WHAT FRACTION DO WE START WITH?"   "4/8"
"WHAT ARE WE MULTIPLYING 4/8 BY?"   "2/2"

5. "DOES 2/2 EQUAL 1?"   "Yes"
   "SO WILL OUR ANSWER EQUAL 4/8?"   "Yes"
   "HOW DO YOU KNOW?"   "We are multiplying by a fraction that equals 1."

   Repeat steps 4 and 5 with

   $$\frac{4}{8} \times \frac{4}{4} \qquad \frac{5}{6} \times \frac{3}{6}$$

   $$\frac{5}{6} \times \frac{2}{3} \qquad \frac{3}{9} \times \frac{8}{8}$$

   $$\frac{7}{2} \times \frac{9}{9} \qquad \frac{2}{4} \times \frac{4}{4}$$

PART C: Structured Board Problems

Write on board:

$$\frac{2}{3}\left(\ \ \right) = \frac{\square}{12}$$

1. "WE DON'T CHANGE THE VALUE OF A FRAC-
   TION WHEN WE MULTIPLY IT BY A FRACTION
   THAT EQUALS 1."

2. "THESE PARENTHESES MEAN TIMES. WE'RE
   GOING TO MULTIPLY 2/3 BY A FRACTION THAT
   EQUALS 1. WE HAVE TO FIGURE OUT THE FRAC-
   TION THAT EQUALS 1."

3. "WE ARE GOING TO END WITH A FRACTION THAT
   HAS THE SAME VALUE AS 2/3." Point to 12.
   "WHAT'S THE BOTTOM NUMBER OF THE FRAC-
   TION WE END WITH?"   "12"
   "THREE TIMES WHAT NUMBER EQUALS 12?"   "4"
   "SO WE MULTIPLY BY A FRACTION THAT
      HAS A DENOMINATOR OF 4."

4. Write 4 inside parentheses:

   $$\frac{2}{3}\left(\frac{\ \ }{4}\right) = \frac{\square}{12}$$

5. "THE FRACTION INSIDE THE PARENTHESES
   MUST EQUAL 1. IF THE BOTTOM NUMBER IS 4
   WHAT MUST THE TOP NUMBER BE?"   "4"
   Write on board:

   $$\frac{2}{3}\left(\frac{4}{4}\right) = \frac{\square}{12}$$

   "YES, WE MULTIPLY 2/3 BY 4/4. WHAT DO WE
   MULTIPLY 2/3 BY?"   "4/4"

330   Skills and Concepts

Figure 13.10 cont'd

TEACHER	**STUDENTS**

6. "WE FIGURED OUT THE FRACTION OF 1 WE'RE MULTIPLYING BY. LET'S MULTIPLY AND FIGURE OUT HOW MANY TWELFTHS, 2/3 EQUAL. TWO TIMES FOUR EQUALS HOW MANY?" Pause.
   Write on board:

   $$\frac{2}{3}\left(\frac{4}{4}\right) = \frac{8}{12}$$

   "8"

7. "WE MULTIPLIED 2/3 BY A FRACTION THAT EQUALS 1 AND ENDED WITH 8/12; 2/3 HAS TO EQUAL 8/12."
   Repeat steps 3–7 with these problems:

   $$\frac{3}{5} = \frac{\square}{10} \qquad \frac{2}{3} = \frac{\square}{15} \qquad \frac{2}{7} = \frac{\square}{21}$$

PART D: Structured Worksheet

Give students worksheet with problems similar to these:

a. $\dfrac{3}{4}(-) = \dfrac{\square}{8}$ b. $\dfrac{5}{9}(-) = \dfrac{\square}{27}$ c. $\dfrac{1}{4}(-) = \dfrac{\square}{20}$

d. $\dfrac{2}{5}(-) = \dfrac{\square}{20}$ e. $\dfrac{3}{5}(-) = \dfrac{\square}{35}$ f. $\dfrac{2}{3}(-) = \dfrac{\square}{12}$

1. "TOUCH PROBLEM a."

2. "IT SAYS 3/4 EQUAL HOW MANY EIGHTHS? WHAT DOES THE PROBLEM SAY?"

   "3/4 equal how many eighths?"

3. "WE HAVE TO MULTIPLY 3/4 BY A FRACTION THAT EQUALS 1. WHAT IS THE BOTTOM NUMBER OF THE FRACTION WE START WITH?"

   "4"

   "WHAT IS THE BOTTOM NUMBER OF THE FRAC-TION WE END WITH?"

   "8"

   "FOUR TIMES WHAT NUMBER EQUALS 8?"

   "2"

   "WRITE 2 AS THE BOTTOM NUMBER IN THE PARENTHESES."

4. "WE'RE MULTIPLYING 3/4 BY A FRACTION THAT EQUALS 1. WHAT FRACTION WITH A DENOMI-NATOR OF 2 EQUALS ONE WHOLE?"

   "Two halves"

   "WRITE 2 AS A NUMERATOR IN THE PAREN-THESES."

5. "WE FIGURED OUT THE FRACTION OF 1. NOW WHAT DO WE MULTIPLY TO FIGURE OUT THE MISSING NUMERATOR?"

   "3 × 2"

   "WHAT IS 3 × 2?" Pause, signal.

   "6"

   "WRITE 6 IN THE BOX."

6. "WHAT FRACTION EQUALS 3/4?"

   "6/8"

7. "HOW DO YOU KNOW THAT 3/4 EQUALS 6/8?"

   "We multiplied by a fraction that equals 1."

Repeat steps 1–7 with remaining problems.

Figure 13.10 cont'd

PART E: Less Structured Worksheet

(Note that parentheses aren't written in.)

a. $\dfrac{5}{6} = \dfrac{\square}{12}$ b. $\dfrac{3}{4} = \dfrac{\square}{20}$ c. $\dfrac{1}{3} = \dfrac{\square}{12}$

d. $\dfrac{1}{5} = \dfrac{\square}{20}$ e. $\dfrac{2}{5} = \dfrac{\square}{15}$ f. $\dfrac{3}{7} = \dfrac{\square}{14}$

1. "TOUCH PROBLEM a. READ THE PROBLEM." $\dfrac{5}{6} = \dfrac{\square}{12}$

2. "WE MUST MULTIPLY 5/6 BY A FRACTION THAT
   EQUALS 1. TO KEEP THE FRACTIONS EQUAL,
   PUT PARENTHESES NEXT TO 5/6."

3. "LOOK AT THE NUMBERS AND GET READY TO
   TELL ME WHAT WE MUST MULTIPLY 5/6 BY."
   Pause.   "Two halves"

   TO CORRECT: "WHAT IS THE BOTTOM NUMBER
               OF THE FRACTION WE START
               WITH? WHAT IS THE BOTTOM NUM-
               BER OF THE FRACTION WE END
               WITH? SIX TIMES WHAT NUMBER
               EQUALS 12? THAT'S THE DENOMI-
               NATOR. THE FRACTION WE'RE
               MULTIPLYING EQUALS 1. WHAT
               FRACTION GOES IN THE PAREN-
               THESES?"

   "WRITE TWO HALVES IN THE PARENTHESES."

4. "MULTIPLY AND WRITE IN THE MISSING NUME-
   RATOR."

5. "WHAT FRACTION DOES 5/6 EQUAL?"   "10/12"
   Repeat steps 1–5 with remaining problems.

The teacher explains that the equal sign tells that the fractions are equal. The student's job is to find the missing numerator in the second fraction.

The teacher writes parentheses after the first fraction

$$\frac{3}{4} \left(\;\;\right) = \frac{\square}{20}$$

explaining that the students must multiply the first fraction by a fraction that equals 1, which will be written inside the parentheses. The parentheses indicate multiplication. The teacher demonstrates how to figure out the denominator to be written inside the parentheses by using a missing factor multiplication strategy. In the problem above, the teacher asks, "4 times what number equals 20?"

The answer, 5, is written as the denominator inside the parentheses:

$$\frac{3}{4} \left(\frac{}{5}\right) = \frac{\square}{20}$$

The teacher then points out that since the fraction inside the parentheses must equal one whole, the numerator must be the same as the denominator. The missing number in the equivalent fraction can be determined by multiplying the numerator in the first fraction and the numerator in the second fraction:

$$\frac{3}{4} \left(\frac{5}{5}\right) = \frac{15}{20}$$

There are three example selection guidelines for this format. The denominator of the first fraction

332   Skills and Concepts

must be a number that can be multiplied by a whole number to end with the denominator of the second fraction. Thus, problems such as

$$\frac{2}{3} = \frac{\square}{5} \qquad \frac{4}{5} = \frac{\square}{8} \qquad \frac{2}{3} = \frac{\square}{7}$$

would not be appropriate to include, while problems such as

$$\frac{2}{3} = \frac{\square}{6} \qquad \frac{4}{5} = \frac{\square}{10} \qquad \frac{2}{3} = \frac{\square}{9}$$

would be appropriate. Second, the numbers to appear in parentheses should vary from problem to problem. For example, in one problem the numerator and denominator in the second fraction could be four times bigger than the original:

$$\frac{3}{5} = \frac{\square}{20}$$

In the next problem, two times bigger:

$$\frac{5}{6} = \frac{\square}{12}$$

In the next, five times bigger:

$$\frac{2}{3} = \frac{\square}{15}$$

and so on. The third guideline is that all problems should require multiplication; i.e., the numbers in the fraction to be completed should be greater than the numbers in the first fraction.

Reducing Fractions

We recommend that reducing fractions be taught in two stages. During the first stage, which would be presented during late fourth grade, the teacher introduces a greatest common factor strategy. In this strategy, students are taught to reduce a fraction to its simplest terms by pulling out the greatest common factor of the numerator and denominator. For example, the fraction 9/15 is reduced by pulling out a 3, which is the greatest common factor of 9 and 15. When the factor 3 is pulled out, 9/15 becomes 3/5.

The greatest common factor strategy is a viable strategy only for problems in which it is relatively easy to find the greatest common factor (e.g., 18/27, 30/35, 8/16). Nearly all reducing problems students encounter in fourth and early fifth grade can be reduced to simplest terms using the GCF (greatest common factor) strategy. During the second stage, students are taught to reduce

fractions in which the greatest common factor is difficult to determine.

PRESKILLS Teaching students to find the greatest common factor of two numbers is the critical preskill for reducing fractions. The greatest common factor of two numbers is the largest number that can be multiplied by whole numbers to end with the two target numbers. For example, the greatest common factor of 12 and 18 is 6. Six can be multiplied by whole numbers to end with 12 and 18.

The first step in teaching students to find the greatest common factor of two numbers is to teach them to determine all possible factors for a given number. For example, the numbers 1, 2, 3, 4, 6, and 12 are all factors of 12, since they can all be multiplied by another whole number to end with 12. Table 13.1 includes a list of the factors for the numbers 1 through 50. Once the students are able to easily determine all factors for a number, finding the greatest common factor is relatively easy.

Table 13.1 Factors for 1 to 50

Number Factors* (other than the number itself and 1)†

4—2, 2	28—14, 2; 7, 4
6—3, 2	30—10, 3; 6, 5
8—4, 2	32—16, 2;
9—3, 3	33—11, 3
10—5, 2	34—17, 2
12—6, 2; 3, 4	35—7, 5
14—7, 2	36—18, 2; 9, 4; 6, 6
15—5, 3	38—19, 2;
16—4, 4; 8, 2	39—13, 3
18—6, 3; 9, 2	40—20, 2; 10, 4; 8, 5
20—10, 2; 5, 4	42—21, 2;
21—3, 7	44—22, 2; 11, 4
22—11, 2	45—9, 5
24—12, 2; 8, 3; 6, 4	46—23, 3
25—5, 5	48—24, 2; 12, 4; 8, 6
26—13, 2	49—7, 7
27—9, 3	50—25, 2; 10, 5

*Factors are listed in pairs.
†Numbers not in list have only the number itself and 1 as factors.

Figure 13.11 includes the format for teaching students to determine factors. In Part A, the teacher introduces the term *factor*, defining factors as any numbers that are multiplied together. In Part B, the teacher presents a strategy for figuring out all factors for a target number. The teacher writes the target number on the board and beside it writes spaces for each factor. For example, if the target

Figure 13.11 Preskill: Format for Determining Factors

Day	Part A Introducing the Concept Problems	Part B Structured Board Presentation Problems	Part C Structured Worksheet Problems	Part D Independent Practice Problems
1	3	2	2	
2		2	2	
3–35		1–2 introduce new target numbers		10–20

PART A: Introducing the Concept

TEACHER

STUDENTS

Write on board:

5 × 3 = 15

9 × 2 = 18

7 × 6 = 42

1. "FACTORS ARE NUMBERS THAT ARE MULTI-PLIED TOGETHER."

2. "READ THE FIRST PROBLEM."   "5 × 3 = 15
"WHAT NUMBERS ARE BEING MULTIPLIED?"   "5 and 3"
"SO 5 AND 3 ARE FACTORS OF 15. WHAT ARE TWO
FACTORS OF 15?"   "5 and 3"

3. "LOOK AT THE BOARD AND TELL ME TWO
FACTORS OF 18."   "9 and 2"

4. "LOOK AT THE BOARD AND TELL ME TWO FAC-TORS OF 42."   "7 and 6"

PART B: Structured Board Presentation

Write on board:

12 (____ ____ ____ ____ ____ ____)

1. "WE WANT TO LIST ALL OF THE FACTORS FOR
12 BEGINNING WITH THE BIGGEST FACTOR.
LISTEN, A NUMBER MULTIPLIED BY 1 ALWAYS
EQUALS ITSELF. SO IS 12 A FACTOR OF 12?"   "Yes"
"YES 12 IS A FACTOR OF 12. WHAT NUMBER TIMES
12 EQUALS 12?"   "1"
"TWELVE AND 1 ARE FACTORS OF 12; 12 IS THE
BIGGEST FACTOR OF 12; 1 IS THE SMALLEST
FACTOR OF 12."
Write 12 and 1.
(12__ ____ ____ ____ ____ 1)

2. LET'S FIND THE NEXT LARGEST NUMBER WE
CAN MULTIPLY AND END WITH 12. I'LL SAY SOME
NUMBERS. YOU SAY STOP WHEN I COME TO A
NUMBER THAT IS A FACTOR OF 12. LISTEN, 10
(pause), 9 (pause), 8 (pause), 7 (pause), 6 (pause), . . ."   "Stop"
"YES, 6 IS THE NEXT BIGGEST FACTOR OF 12."

Figure 13.11 cont'd

TEACHER	**STUDENTS**

TO CORRECT: If students say stop at 10, 9, 8, 7. say, "WE CAN'T MULTIPLY THAT NUMBER AND END WITH 12." If students don't say stop at 6, say, "WE CAN MULTIPLY 6 AND END WITH 12. SO 6 IS A FACTOR OF 12."

"6 TIMES WHAT NUMBER EQUALS 12?"   "2"

"SO 2 IS THE OTHER FACTOR THAT GOES WITH 12." Write 6 and 2. (<u>12</u> <u>6</u> ___ ___ <u>2</u> <u>1</u>)

3. "LET'S FIND THE NEXT LARGEST FACTOR OF 12. I'LL SAY SOME NUMBERS. YOU SAY STOP WHEN I COME TO A FACTOR OF 12.
LISTEN, 5 (pause), 4 (pause) . . ."   "Stop"

"YES 4 IS A FACTOR OF 12. FOUR TIMES WHAT OTHER NUMBER EQUALS 12?"   "3"

"SO 3 IS THE OTHER FACTOR THAT GOES WITH 4." Write 4 and 3. (12 6 4 3 2 1)

"TELL ME ALL THE FACTORS OF 12."   "12, 6, 4, 3, 2, 1"

Repeat Part B with other new example(s) for that day.

PART C: Structured Worksheet

List all the factors for each number.
List the biggest factors first.

a. 10 ___ ___ ___ ___

b. 12 ___ ___ ___ ___

c. 7 ___ ___

1. TOUCH a. THERE ARE FOUR SPACES NEXT TO THE 10. THAT MEANS THERE ARE FOUR NUMBERS THAT ARE FACTORS FOR 10."

2. "WHAT IS THE BIGGEST FACTOR OF 10?"   "10"

"WHAT IS THE OTHER FACTOR THAT GOES WITH 10 TO EQUAL 10?"   "1"

"WRITE 10 IN THE FIRST SPACE. WRITE 1 IN THE LAST SPACE."

3. "WHAT IS THE NEXT BIGGEST FACTOR OF 10?" Pause.   "5"

"WHAT IS THE OTHER FACTOR THAT GOES WITH 5 TO EQUAL 10?" Pause.   "2"

"WRITE 5 AND 2 IN THE NEXT TWO SPACES."

4. "SAY ALL THE FACTORS OF 10."   "10, 5, 2, 1"

Repeat steps 1–4 with new target numbers. Have students do rest of problems on their own.

---

number is 15, the teacher writes 15 on the board and puts four blanks beside it, since four numbers (1, 3, 5, 15) are factors of 15. The teacher then tells the students that they are going to find all the numbers that are factors of 15 by asking if they can multiply a number by another number and end with 15. The teacher always begins with the target number: "Is 15 a factor of 15?" The teacher then points out that they can find another factor by determining what number times that factor equals the target number. For example, after determining that 15 is a factor of 15, the teacher asks, "What number times 15 equals 15?" The answer, 1, is the factor of 15 that goes with 15. The teacher writes 15 in the first space and 1 in the last space: 15 ____ ____1.

The teacher then asks about other numbers, beginning with 10 and proceeding backward (10, 9, 8, 7 . . .): "Can we multiply 10 and end with 15? No, so 10 is not a factor of 15," and so on. The teacher instructs the students to say "stop" when she says a number that is a factor of the target number. When the students identify another factor of the target number, the teacher once again leads them in finding the other factor it goes with to produce the target number. If 15 is the target number, the students say "stop" after the teacher says 5. The teacher asks what number times 5 equals 15. The students answer 3. The teacher points out that 5 and 3 are both factors of 15. When target numbers over 20 are introduced, the teacher models the answer for the larger numbers. That is, the teacher tells the student any two digit number that is a factor of the target number. For example, when introducing 28, the teacher says that 14 and 2 can be multiplied to equal 28.

Part C is a worksheet exercise. Target numbers are written on the worksheet, followed by spaces for each of the factors of that number. For the target number 7, only two spaces would be written since 1 and 7 are the only factors for 7. For the number 12, six spaces would be written since the numbers 12, 1, 6, 2, 4, 3 are factors for 12. Students are to fill in the factors, beginning with the biggest factor.

The objective of this format is to develop student fluency in naming all possible factors of numbers. A systematic plan for introducing new target numbers and reviewing target numbers should be followed. One or two new target numbers can be introduced daily. (Table 13.2 contains a suggested sequence for introducing target numbers.) Part A of the format is used only with the first pair of target numbers. New numbers would be introduced using the board presentation in Part B. The worksheet exercise described in Part C could be done independently after the first several lessons. A target number should appear on practice worksheet exercises daily for several weeks after it is introduced. This practice is very important to developing fluency.

FORMAT FOR GREATEST COMMON FACTORS The format in Figure 13.12 for teaching greatest common factors would be introduced when the students are able to determine the factors of any target number below 20. The format is rela-

tively simple. The teacher defines the phrase *greatest common factor* as the largest number which is a factor of both target numbers. The teacher then leads the students through finding the greatest common factor. First the teacher asks students what the largest factor of the smaller target number is and if that factor is also a factor of the other target number. For example, assuming that 8 and 20 are the target numbers, the teacher asks what the largest factor of 8 is. The students reply, "8 is the largest factor of 8." The teacher then asks, "Is 8 a factor of 20?" Since the answer is no, the teacher asks the students to tell him the next largest factor of 8, "What is the next biggest factor of 8?" After the students answer 4, the teacher asks, "Is 4 a factor of 20? . . . So, 4 is the greatest common factor of 8 and 20."

After about 5 days of presenting the format, the teacher gives students worksheet exercises to work independently. The worksheet includes 8-12 problems daily in which students find the greatest common factor of two target numbers. A common error in independent exercises involves writing a common factor that is not the greatest common factor of the two target numbers; for example, writing 3 as the greatest common factor of 12 and 18. The correction is to point out to students that they can find a larger common factor.

Example selection guidelines are quite important. In about half the problems, the greatest

Table 13.2 Sequence for Introducing Target Numbers and Their Factors

Day	Factors of these numbers are introduced	Day	Factors of these numbers are introduced
1	12, 7	16	27, 29
2	10, 3	17	28
3	16, 5	18	30, 31
4	8, 13	19	32, 33
5	4, 6, 9	20	34, 37
6	2, 17	21	35, 39
7	12, 19	22	36, 41
8	14, 23	23	38, 43
9	15	24	40, 47
10	18	25	42
11	20	26	44
12	21	27	45
13	22	28	46
14	24	29	48
15	25, 26	30	49
		31	50

Figure 13.12 Format for Determining the Greatest Common Factor (GCF)

PART A: Structured Worksheet

TEACHER   **STUDENTS**

Present students with a worksheet similar to this:

a. What is the greatest common factor of 12 and 16? _____

b. What is the greatest common factor of 10 and 5? _____

c. What is the greatest common factor of 4 and 7? _____

d. What is the greatest common factor of 10 and 15? _____

e. What is the greatest common factor of 18 and 9? _____

f. What is the greatest common factor of 12 and 9? _____

1. "FIND PROBLEM a ON YOUR WORKSHEET. READ   "What is the greatest common
   THE DIRECTIONS. LET'S FIND THE GREATEST   factor of 12 and 16?"
   COMMON FACTOR OF 12 AND 16. THE GREATEST
   COMMON FACTOR IS THE LARGEST NUMBER
   THAT IS A FACTOR OF 12 AND 16. WHAT IS THE
   LARGEST NUMBER THAT IS A FACTOR OF 12?"   "12"
   "IS 12 A FACTOR OF 16?"   "No"
   "TWELVE CANNOT BE THE GREATEST COMMON
   FACTOR OF 12 AND 16. WHY?"   "Because 12 is not a factor of 16."

2. "WHAT IS THE NEXT LARGEST FACTOR OF 12?"
   Pause.   "6"
   "IS 6 A FACTOR OF 16?" Pause.   "No"
   "SO 6 IS NOT A FACTOR OF 12 AND 16. WHY?"   "Because 6 is not a factor of 16"

3. "WHAT IS THE NEXT LARGEST FACTOR OF 12?"
   Pause.   "4"
   "IS 4 ALSO A FACTOR OF 16?" Pause.   "Yes"
   "SO WHAT NUMBER IS THE GREATEST COMMON
   FACTOR OF 12 AND 16?"   "4"

4. "WRITE 4."

   Repeat steps 1–4 with remaining examples.

common factor should be the smaller of the two target numbers (e.g., 6, 18; 4, 8; 2, 10; 5, 20). If examples such as these are not included, students might develop the misrule that the smaller number is never the greatest common factor. This would result in errors in which the student might identify 4 rather than 8 as the GCF of 8 and 24. Examples should be limited to numbers for which students have been taught to find factors. Initially, both target numbers should be under 20. As students learn to determine factors for larger numbers, the larger numbers can be included. Several examples should be included in which 1 is the greatest common factor, as in 4 and 7 or 6 and 11. These prepare students for fractions that cannot be reduced (e.g., 4/7, 6/11).

FORMAT FOR REDUCING FRACTIONS The format for reducing fractions (see Figure 13.13) would be introduced when students are able to determine the greatest common factor of any two target numbers below 20. The format includes three parts. Part A is a board exercise in which the teacher presents the strategy for reducing fractions. The teacher writes a fraction on the board with an equal sign next to it. Next to the equal sign are parentheses and a fraction bar for the reduced fraction:

$$\frac{12}{16} = \left(\ \right) -$$

The fraction in which the numerator and denominator are the greatest common factor of the two target numbers will be written inside the parentheses. For

Figure 13.13 Format for Reducing Fractions

Day	Part A Structured Board Problems	Part B Structured Worksheet Problems	Part C Less Structured Worksheet Problems	Part D Supervised Practice Problems	Part E Independent Practice Problems
1-2	4				
3-4	2	6			
5-6		2	6		
7-8			2	6	
9-Until accurate				8	
Until fluent					8-12

PART A: Structured Board Presentation

TEACHER	STUDENTS

TEACHER

Write on board: $\frac{8}{12} = \left(\quad\right)$ —

1. "WE'RE GOING TO REDUCE THIS FRACTION. WE REDUCE BY PULLING OUT THE GREATEST COMMON FACTOR OF THE NUMERATOR AND DENOMINATOR. HOW DO WE REDUCE A FRACTION?"

STUDENTS

"Pull out the greatest common factor of the numerator and denominator."

2. "WE WANT TO REDUCE 8/12. WHAT IS THE GREATEST COMMON FACTOR OF 8 AND 12?" Pause.

"4"

TO CORRECT: Tell correct answer. Explain why student's answer is incorrect.

3. "SO WE PULL OUT THE FRACTION 4/4. WHAT FRACTION DO WE PULL OUT OF 8/12?"

"4/4"

Write on board:

$\frac{8}{12} = \left(\frac{4}{4}\right)$ —

4. "LET'S FIGURE OUT THE TOP NUMBER OF THE REDUCED FRACTION." Point to symbols as you read. "EIGHT EQUALS FOUR TIMES WHAT NUMBER?" Pause.

"2"

Write on board:

$\frac{8}{12} = \left(\frac{4}{4}\right)\frac{2}{}$

5. "LET'S FIGURE OUT THE BOTTOM NUMBER OF THE REDUCED FRACTION." Point to symbols as you read. "TWELVE EQUALS FOUR TIMES WHAT NUMBER?" Pause, signal.

"3"

Write on board:

$\frac{8}{12} = \left(\frac{4}{4}\right)\frac{2}{3}$

6. "THE FRACTION IN PARENTHESES EQUALS 1. WE DON'T CHANGE THE VALUE OF A FRACTION WHEN WE MULTIPLY BY 1. SO WE CAN CROSS OUT 4/4." Cross out. "WHEN WE PULL OUT THE FRACTION OF 1, THE REDUCED FRACTION IS 2/3. WHAT IS THE REDUCED FRACTION?"

"2/3"

Figure 13.13 cont'd

TEACHER   **STUDENTS**

7. "READ THE STATEMENT."   "8/12 = 2/3"
   Repeat steps 1-7 with these problems:

$$\frac{15}{20} = (\quad)—\qquad \frac{9}{36} = (\quad)—\qquad \frac{16}{24} = (\quad)—$$

PART B: Structured Worksheet

a.   b.   c.

$$\frac{10}{15} = (\quad)—\qquad \frac{12}{16} = (\quad)—\qquad \frac{8}{24} = (\quad)—$$

1. "WE'RE GOING TO REDUCE THESE FRACTIONS.   "Pull out the greatest common
   HOW DO YOU REDUCE FRACTIONS?"   factor of the numerator and
                                                          denominator."

2. "TOUCH PROBLEM a. READ THE FRACTION."   "Ten-fifteenths"

3. "WHAT IS THE GREATEST COMMON FACTOR OF
   10 AND 15?" Pause.   "5"

4. "SO WHAT FRACTION DO YOU WRITE IN THE
   PARENTHESES?"   "5/5"
   "WRITE IT."

5. "THE NUMBERS ACROSS THE TOP OF THE FRAC-
   TION SAY 10 EQUALS 5 TIMES WHAT NUMBER?
   WHAT DO THE NUMBERS ACROSS THE TOP SAY?"   "10 equals 5 times what number?"

6. "WHAT DO THE NUMBERS ACROSS THE BOTTOM
   SAY?"   "15 equals 5 times what number?"

7. "FILL IN THE NUMERATOR AND DENOMINATOR
   IN THE REDUCED FRACTION." Pause.   Students write 2 and 3.
   "CROSS OUT THE FRACTION OF 1 IN THE
   PARENTHESES."   Students cross out 5/5.

8. "WHAT IS THE REDUCED FRACTION?"   "2/3"

9. "READ THE STATEMENT."   "10/15 = 2/3"
   Repeat steps 1-9 with remaining problems.

PART C: Less Structured Worksheet

(Note that parentheses are not written.)
Present a worksheet like the following:
Reduce these fractions:

a. $\frac{15}{20}$ b. $\frac{8}{12}$ c. $\frac{6}{18}$

d. $\frac{4}{7}$ e. $\frac{8}{16}$ f. $\frac{5}{8}$

1. "HOW DO YOU REDUCE A FRACTION?"   "Pull out the greatest common
                                                          factor of the numerator and
                                                          denominator."

2. "READ FRACTION a."   "Fifteen-twentieths"

3. "MAKE AN EQUAL SIGN. THEN WRITE PAREN-   Students write
   THESES ON THE OTHER SIDE OF THE EQUAL."
                                                          $\frac{15}{20} = (\quad)$

Figure 13.13 cont'd

TEACHER	**STUDENTS**

4. "WHAT FRACTION ARE YOU GOING TO WRITE IN THE PARENTHESES?" Pause.

     "5/5"

   TO CORRECT: "WHAT IS THE GREATEST COMMON FACTOR OF _____ AND _____?" Repeat step 4.

5. "WRITE FIVE-FIFTHS IN THE PARENTHESES. THEN FIGURE OUT THE REDUCED FRACTION." Pause.

6. "CROSS OUT THE FRACTION OF 1."

7. "WHAT IS THE REDUCED FRACTION?"

     "3/4"

   TO CORRECT: "READ THE TOP NUMBERS OF THE FRACTIONS. WHAT'S THE ANSWER? READ THE BOTTOM NUMBERS OF THE FRACTIONS. WHAT'S THE ANSWER?"

8. "READ THE STATEMENT" Repeat steps 1-8 with remaining problems.

     15/20 = 3/4

---

example, the greatest common factor of 12 and 16 is 4. Thus, the fraction in the parentheses will be 4/4, which equals 1. The teacher then asks, "12 equals 4 times what number?" The answer is 3, which is the numerator of the reduced fraction. The teacher then asks "16 equals 4 times what number?" The answer is 4, which is the denominator of the reduced fraction. Since multiplying by 1 does not change the value of the fraction, 4/4 can be crossed out. Crossing out the fraction equal to 1 leaves the reduced fraction:

$$\frac{12}{16} = \left(\frac{\cancel{4}}{\cancel{4}}\right)\frac{3}{4}$$

Part B is a structured worksheet exercise in which the teacher first asks the greatest common factor of the numerator and denominator of a fraction; in 10/15 the GCF is 5. The teacher then instructs the students to write the corresponding fraction equal to 1 in the parentheses. For example, the fraction written in parentheses for 10/15 is 5/5. The teacher then has the students determine the missing factors in the final fraction, which is the reduced fraction:

$$\frac{10}{15} = \left(\frac{5}{5}\right)\frac{2}{3}$$

There are three example selection guidelines for exercises on reducing fractions. First, the numbers should be ones for which students have been taught to find factors. At first, both the numerator

and denominator should be below 25. As students learn to find factors for larger numbers, fractions with these larger numbers can be included.

Second, a third of the fractions should have the greatest common factor as the numerator. For example, in the fractions 4/12, 8/16, 5/20, the numerator is the greatest common factor.

Third, about a third of the fractions should already be expressed in their simplest terms (e.g., 4/7, 3/5, 6/11). Including several fractions already expressed in their simplest terms provides the students with the knowledge that not all fractions can be reduced. A sample set of items appears below:

a. $\frac{12}{15}$ b. $\frac{4}{8}$ c. $\frac{5}{7}$ d. $\frac{8}{12}$ e. $\frac{3}{5}$

f. $\frac{5}{15}$ g. $\frac{4}{12}$ h. $\frac{6}{9}$ i. $\frac{9}{11}$

Items b, f, and g are fractions in which the smaller number is a factor of the larger number. Items c, e, and i are fractions which are already expressed in their simplest terms and, therefore, cannot be reduced any further.

REDUCING FRACTIONS WITH LARGER NUMBERS After several weeks of practice reducing fractions using the greatest common factor, students can be introduced to the concept of pulling out successive common factors. When the greatest common factor is difficult to find, students can reduce the fraction to its simplest terms by repeatedly pulling out factors. Note the examples below:

a. $\frac{45}{75} = \left(\frac{5}{5}\right)\frac{9}{15} = \left(\frac{3}{3}\right)\frac{3}{5} = \frac{3}{5}$

b. $\frac{24}{72} = \left(\frac{2}{2}\right)\frac{12}{36} = \left(\frac{6}{6}\right)\frac{2}{6} = \left(\frac{2}{2}\right)\frac{1}{3} = \frac{1}{3}$

This strategy is useful for problems with larger numbers. The teacher would guide students through sets of problems, pointing out clues students can use (e.g., If both the numerator and the denominator are even numbers, the fraction can still be reduced. If the numerator and denominator both end in either 5 or zero, the fraction can still be reduced). The teacher would present an exercise in which students check answers to determine if they're reduced to simplest terms. The teacher gives students a worksheet with problems similar to those below, some of which have not been reduced to their simplest terms. The student's task is to find which fractions can be further reduced and to reduce those fractions.

a. $\frac{64}{72} = \left(\frac{4}{4}\right)\frac{16}{18} =$ d. $\frac{65}{85} = \left(\frac{5}{5}\right)\frac{13}{15}$

b. $\frac{45}{75} = \left(\frac{5}{5}\right)\frac{9}{15} =$ e. $\frac{48}{64} = \left(\frac{2}{2}\right)\frac{24}{32} =$

c. $\frac{21}{30} = \left(\frac{3}{3}\right)\frac{7}{10} =$ f. $\frac{56}{84} = \left(\frac{2}{2}\right)\frac{28}{42}$

Converting Mixed Numbers and Improper Fractions

An improper fraction has a numerator that is greater than its denominator, and thus the fraction equals more than one whole. An improper fraction may be converted to a mixed number by dividing its numerator by its denominator. For example, to convert the fraction 13/5 to a mixed number, we divide 13 by 5, which equals 2 with a remainder of 3. The remainder is written as the fraction 3/5; thus, the improper fraction 13/5 is converted to the mixed number 2 3/5.

Converting a mixed number to an improper fraction—requires the reverse operation—multiplication rather than division. Students first change the whole number into a fraction by multiplying the whole number by the number of parts in each whole, indicated by the denominator:

for $6 = \frac{}{4}$, students write $\frac{24}{4}$

To determine the equivalent improper fraction for a mixed number, after students multiply the whole number they add the numerator of the fraction:

$$3\frac{1}{2} = \frac{6+1}{2} = \frac{7}{2}$$

On the Instructional Sequence and Assessment Chart (Figure 13.2), we recommend that converting improper fractions to mixed numbers be introduced in early fourth grade. Students apply this skill when they rewrite their answers after adding or multiplying fractions. Converting a mixed number to an improper fraction should not be introduced until several months later. The time span between the introduction of these two conversion skills is recommended to decrease the probability of students' confusing the two operations. Converting mixed numbers to and from improper fractions requires that students have a firm understanding of the difference between a whole unit and parts of a unit. Thus, students should have mastered all the fraction analysis skills presented earlier.

CONVERTING IMPROPER FRACTIONS TO MIXED NUMBERS The format for converting improper fractions to mixed numbers appears in Figure 13.14. Part A is a pictorial demonstration in which the teacher shows how to construct a diagram to figure out how many whole units an improper fraction equals.

Part B is a structured board presentation in which the teacher presents the strategy of dividing the numerator by the denominator. Note the special emphasis given to explaining how to write the remainder as a fraction. The teacher explains that the denominator of the fraction in the mixed number must be the same denominator as in the original fraction.

Part C is a structured worksheet exercise. The division symbol along with boxes for the whole number and the fraction remainder are written as a prompt on the students' worksheets:

$$\frac{11}{4} = \sqrt{\begin{array}{c}\Box\ \frac{\Box}{\Box}\end{array}}$$

The teacher begins the exercise by instructing the students to look at the fraction and determine whether it is less than one whole, one whole, or more than one whole. If the fraction is less than 1, students are instructed to leave the fraction as it is. If the fraction equals 1, they write = 1. If the fraction equals more than 1, they are instructed to divide and write the answer as a mixed number.

Figure 13.14 Format for Converting Improper Fractions to Mixed Numbers

Day	Part A Pictorial Demonstrations	Part B Structured Board Problems	Part C Structured Worksheet Problems	Part D Less Structured Worksheet Problems	Part E Supervised Practice Problems	Part F Independent Practice Problems
1-2	3	4				
3-4		3	4			
5-6			4	4		
7-8				4	4	
9-Until accurate					6	4-8
Until fluent						6-12

PART A: Pictorial Demonstration

<u>**TEACHER**</u>   <u>**STUDENTS**</u>

Write on board:

$$\frac{13}{5} \quad \bigcirc \bigcirc \bigcirc$$

1. Point to 13/5. "READ THIS FRACTION."   "Thirteen-fifths"

2. "DOES 13/5 EQUAL MORE THAN ONE WHOLE
   UNIT?"   "Yes"

3. "LET'S MAKE A PICTURE AND SEE HOW MANY
   WHOLE UNITS 13/5 MAKES."

4. "HOW MANY PARTS IN EACH WHOLE?"   "5"
   Draw on board:

5. "HOW MANY PARTS DO WE USE UP?"   "13"
   Shade in 13 parts.

6. "LET'S SEE HOW MANY WHOLE UNITS ARE USED."
   Point to first circle. "IS THIS WHOLE UNIT ALL USED
   UP?"   "Yes"
   Point to second circle. "IS THIS WHOLE UNIT ALL
   USED UP?"   "Yes"
   Point to third circle. "IS THIS WHOLE UNIT ALL
   USED UP?"   "No"
   "HOW MANY WHOLE UNITS ARE USED UP?"   "2"
   "TWO WHOLE UNITS ARE USED UP. LET'S LOOK
   AT THE LAST UNIT AND COUNT. HOW MANY
   PARTS ARE USED UP?"   "3"
   "AND HOW MANY PARTS IN EACH WHOLE?"   "5"
   "SO, WE CAN SAY 3/5 OF A UNIT. WE HAVE 2
   WHOLE UNITS AND 3/5 OF ANOTHER UNIT."
   Write 2 3/5.

Figure 13.14 cont'd

PART B: Structured Board Presentation

TEACHER

STUDENTS

1. "WE'RE GOING TO LEARN A FAST WAY TO FIGURE OUT HOW MANY WHOLE UNITS A FRACTION MAKES. WE DIVIDE BY THE NUMBER OF PARTS IN EACH WHOLE UNIT. WHAT DO WE DO TO FIGURE OUT HOW MANY WHOLE UNITS?"

"Divide by the number of parts in each whole unit."

Write on board: $\frac{13}{5}$

"READ THIS FRACTION."

"13/5"

"IS THIS FRACTION EQUAL TO, MORE THAN, OR LESS THAN ONE UNIT?"

"More than one unit"

2. "I WANT TO FIGURE OUT HOW MANY WHOLE UNITS THIS FRACTION MAKES. HOW MANY PARTS IN EACH WHOLE?"
"SO I DIVIDE BY 5."
Write on board:

"5"

3. "LET'S DIVIDE." Point to box. "HOW MANY 5s IN 13?"
Write 2. "WE HAVE TWO WHOLE UNITS." Point under 13. "WHAT NUMBER DO I WRITE HERE?"
Write -10 under 13.

"2"

"10"

4. "WE USE UP 10 PARTS IN TWO WHOLES. NOW LET'S SUBTRACT AND SEE HOW MANY PARTS WE HAVE LEFT. WHAT IS 13 - 10?"

"3"

5. "SINCE WE STARTED WITH A FRACTION, WE WRITE THE REMAINDER AS A FRACTION. REMEMBER, THERE ARE FIVE PARTS IN EACH WHOLE." Point to 5 in 5$\overline{)13}$.
"SO WE WRITE 5 ON THE BOTTOM OF THE FRACTION." Write 5. "HOW MANY PARTS ARE REMAINING?"

"3"

"SO I WRITE 3 ON THE TOP OF THE FRACTION."
Write:

$$2\frac{3}{5}$$
$$5\overline{)13}$$
$$\underline{10}$$
$$3$$

6. "TELL ME THE MIXED NUMBER FOR THE FRACTION 13/5."
"YES, 2 3/5 IS THE SAME AS 13/5."

"2 3/5"

Figure 13.14 cont'd

TEACHER

7. Write $=2\frac{3}{5}$ next to $\frac{13}{5}$.
   "READ THE STATEMENT."
   Repeat steps 1-7 with 12/7 and 9/4.

"13/5 = 2 3/5"

PART C: Structured Worksheet

a. $\frac{11}{4} =$ b. $\frac{8}{5} =$ c. $\frac{7}{3} =$

1. "TOUCH PROBLEM a. READ THE FRACTION."
   "IS 11/4 LESS THAN 1, EQUAL TO 1, OR MORE
   THAN 1?"
   "SO YOU HAVE TO CHANGE 11/4 TO A MIXED
   NUMBER. HOW MANY PARTS IN EACH WHOLE?"
   "SO YOU DIVIDE 4 INTO 11."

   "11/4"

   "More than 1"

   "4"

2. "WRITE THE DIVISION PROBLEM."
   "HOW MANY 4s IN 11?"
   "WE CAN MAKE TWO WHOLE UNITS. WRITE THE
   2 IN THE BIG BOX. MULTIPLY AND SUBTRACT
   TO FIND HOW MANY PARTS ARE LEFT. HOW
   MANY PARTS ARE LEFT?"

   Students write 4)‾11.
   "2"

   "3"

3. "NOW LET'S FIGURE OUT THE FRACTION RE-
   MAINDER. THE BOTTOM NUMBER OF THE FRAC-
   TION TELLS HOW MANY PARTS IN EACH WHOLE.
   HOW MANY PARTS IN EACH WHOLE?"
   "SO WRITE 4 ON THE BOTTOM OF THE
   FRACTION."

   "4"

   Students write 4 in the bottom
   box of the fraction.

   "WHAT DO YOU WRITE FOR THE TOP NUMBER?"
   "WRITE IT."

   "3"

4. "WHAT MIXED NUMBER DOES 11/4 EQUAL?"
   "SAY THE WHOLE STATEMENT."
   Repeat steps 1-4 with remaining problems.

   "2 3/4"
   "11/4 = 2 3/4"

PART D: Less Structured Worksheet

Present a worksheet like the following:

Rewrite the fractions that equal more
than 1 as mixed numbers.

a. $\frac{12}{5}$ b. $\frac{3}{4}$

c. $\frac{15}{4}$ d. $\frac{5}{5}$

1. "SOME OF THESE FRACTIONS EQUAL MORE
   THAN ONE WHOLE UNIT. IF A FRACTION EQUALS
   MORE THAN ONE WHOLE UNIT, CHANGE IT TO
   A MIXED NUMBER. WHAT ARE YOU GOING TO DO
   IF A FRACTION EQUALS MORE THAN ONE UNIT?"
   "IF THE FRACTION DOES NOT EQUAL MORE
   THAN ONE GROUP, DON'T DO ANYTHING."

   "Change it to a mixed number."

Figure 13.14 cont'd

TEACHER	**STUDENTS**
2. "TOUCH PROBLEM a. READ THE FRACTION."	"12/5"
"DOES THE FRACTION EQUAL MORE OR LESS THAN ONE UNIT?"	"More than one unit"
"THE FRACTION EQUALS MORE THAN ONE UNIT, SO WHAT MUST YOU DO?"	"Change it to a mixed number"
"WHAT DO YOU DIVIDE BY?"	"5"
"SAY THE DIVISION PROBLEM."	"5 goes into 12"
"WRITE THE PROBLEM AND WORK IT." Pause. "REMEMBER TO WRITE THE WHOLE NUMBER AS A BIG NUMBER AND THE NUMERATOR AND DENOMINATOR SMALL."	
3. "TWELVE-FIFTHS EQUAL WHAT MIXED NUMBER?"	"2 2/5"
Repeat steps 1–3 with remaining problems.	

Part D is a less structured worksheet exercise in which students convert improper fractions to mixed numbers with minimal teacher prompting. Teachers should insist that students write the whole number part of the answer and the fraction part of the answer neatly. Teachers should watch for students writing answers in which the numerator of the fraction could easily be mistaken for a whole number:

$$3\tfrac{2}{5}$$
$$5\overline{)17}$$

Examples should be selected to provide appropriate discrimination practice. First, there should be a mix of problems. About half the fractions should translate to a mixed number; about a fourth of the fractions should be fractions that translate simply to a whole number (e.g., 6/3, 16/4, 10/5); finally, about a fourth of the fractions should be proper fractions. The inclusion of proper fractions ensures that students do not develop the misrule of inappropriately converting all fractions to mixed numbers (e.g., 3/4 = 1 1/4).

After students have had several weeks of practice converting improper fractions to mixed numbers and reducing fractions to their lowest terms, they can be given exercises in which they must first reduce fractions and then convert them to mixed numbers. No special format is required for such exercises. The teacher gives students a worksheet with directions similar to these: "Change any fraction that equals one or more wholes to a mixed number. Then reduce the fractions." A set of examples would include a mix of proper and improper fractions, some of which can be reduced

and some of which are written in their simplest form. A sample set might include these fractions:

$$\frac{16}{12} \qquad \frac{6}{8} \qquad \frac{9}{7} \qquad \frac{14}{6} \qquad \frac{5}{7}$$

$$\frac{8}{24} \qquad \frac{20}{8} \qquad \frac{9}{12} \qquad \frac{24}{10}$$

Exercises of this type would be continued for several months to develop fluency.

CONVERTING MIXED NUMBERS TO IMPROPER FRACTIONS The format for converting mixed numbers to improper fractions appears in Figure 13.15. The format includes three parts. Part A teaches the component skill of translating any whole number into an improper fraction by multiplying the number of whole units by the number of parts in each whole:

In $6 = \frac{}{4}$, students multiply 6×4.

Since this component skill is very important, both a board and a worksheet exercise are presented.

Part B, a structured board presentation, teaches the strategy to convert a mixed number into an improper fraction. First, the students determine the fraction equivalent for the whole number; then they add the fraction portion of the mixed number. For example, with 6 3/4, students multiply 6×4 and then add 3 to determine the answer:

$$6\frac{3}{4} = \frac{24 + 3}{4} = \frac{27}{4}$$

In order to ensure that students understand the purpose of the computations, the teacher might

Figure 13.15 Format for Converting Mixed Numbers to Improper Fractions

Day	Part A Converting Whole Numbers Board Problems	Part A Worksheet Problems	Part B Structured Board Problems	Part C Structured Worksheet Problems	Part D Less Structured Worksheet Problems	Part E Supervised Practice Problems	Part F Independent Practice Problems
1-2	5	5					
3		10	4				
4-5			4	4			
6-7				4	4		
8-Until accurate						6-8	
12-Until fluent							6-8

PART A: Converting Whole Numbers

<u>**TEACHER**</u>

Board Presentation

Write on board:

$$6 = \dfrac{\Box}{4}$$

1. "THIS PROBLEM SAYS SIX WHOLES EQUAL HOW MANY FOURTHS? WHAT DOES THE PROBLEM SAY?"

2. "WE WANT TO FIGURE OUT HOW MANY PARTS ARE USED WHEN WE HAVE SIX WHOLES. HOW MANY PARTS IN EACH WHOLE?"

3. "WE'RE TALKING ABOUT THE SAME NUMBER AGAIN AND AGAIN, SO WE MULTIPLY 6 × 4. WHAT NUMBERS DO WE MULTIPLY?"

4. "WHAT IS 6 × 4?" Pause, signal.
Write 24 in box.

5. "YES, SIX WHOLE UNITS EQUAL 24 FOURTHS. IF WE USE SIX WHOLE UNITS AND THERE ARE 4 PARTS IN EACH UNIT, WE USE 24 PARTS."
Repeat steps 1-4 with

$$5 = \dfrac{\Box}{3} \qquad 2 = \dfrac{\Box}{6} \qquad 4 = \dfrac{\Box}{5} \qquad 6 = \dfrac{\Box}{3}$$

Worksheet

Give students worksheets with problems such as these:

$$\text{a. } 5 = \dfrac{\Box}{3} \qquad \text{b. } 2 = \dfrac{\Box}{4}$$

$$\text{c. } 7 = \dfrac{\Box}{2} \qquad \text{d. } 5 = \dfrac{\Box}{9}$$

1. "TOUCH PROBLEM a."
2. "READ THE PROBLEM."

<u>**STUDENTS**</u>

"6 wholes equal how many fourths?"

"4"

"6 × 4"

"24"

"5 equals how many thirds?"

Figure 13.15 cont'd

TEACHER	**STUDENTS**

3. "HOW MANY PARTS IN EACH WHOLE UNIT?" — "3"
"HOW MANY WHOLE UNITS?" — "5"

4. "WHAT DO WE DO TO FIGURE OUT HOW MANY
PARTS ARE USED UP?" — "Multiply"
"YES, WE MULTIPLY 5 × 3. MULTIPLY AND WRITE
YOUR ANSWER IN THE BOX."

5. "FIVE EQUALS HOW MANY THIRDS?" — "15 thirds"
"SAY THE WHOLE STATEMENT." — "5 = 15 thirds"
Repeat steps 1–5 with half the problems, then tell students
to do the rest by themselves.

PART B: Structured Board Presentation

Write on board:

$$6\frac{1}{4} = \frac{}{4}$$

1. "THIS PROBLEM SAYS 6 1/4 EQUALS HOW MANY
FOURTHS. WHAT DOES THIS PROBLEM SAY?" — "6 1/4 equals how many fourths?"

2. "FIRST WE FIGURE OUT HOW MANY FOURTHS
IN SIX WHOLE UNITS. THEN WE ADD ON 1/4."
Write + between 6 and 1/4. "WHAT DO WE DO FIRST?" — "Figure out how many fourths in six whole units."

3. "THERE ARE SIX WHOLES WITH FOUR PARTS IN
EACH WHOLE. WHAT DO I DO TO FIGURE HOW
MANY PARTS ARE USED?" — "Multiply 6 × 4."

4. "WHAT IS SIX TIMES FOUR?" Pause. — "24"
Write on board:

$$6\frac{1}{4} = \frac{24}{4}$$

5. "HOW MANY PARTS ARE USED IN THE LAST
WHOLE?" — "1"

6. "I ADD ONE PART." Write on board:

$$6\frac{1}{4} = \frac{24 + 1}{4} =$$

7. "WHAT IS 24 + 1?" — "25"

Write on board:

$$\frac{25}{4}$$

8. "SO 6 1/4 EQUALS 25/4. SAY THAT." — "6 1/4 equals 25/4."
Repeat steps 1–8 with these fractions:

$$3\frac{2}{5} \qquad 7\frac{3}{4} \qquad 2\frac{3}{7} \qquad 5\frac{1}{4}$$

PART C: Structured Worksheet

Present a worksheet like the following:

Convert these mixed numbers to improper fractions.

a. 3 1/2 = _____ = ____   b. 7 3/5 = _____ = ____

c. 4 2/5 = _____ = ____   d. 2 3/4 = _____ = ____

1. "READ THE MIXED NUMBER IN PROBLEM a." — "3 1/2"

Figure 13.15 cont'd

TEACHER

2. "HOW MANY PARTS IN EACH WHOLE UNIT?"
"WRITE 2 AS THE DENOMINATOR IN THE NEW FRACTION."

3. "FIRST WE SEE HOW MANY HALVES IN THREE WHOLE UNITS. THEN WE ADD 1/2. HOW DO WE FIGURE OUT HOW MANY HALVES IN THREE WHOLES?" Pause.
"HOW MANY HALVES IN THREE WHOLES?" Pause.
"WRITE 6."

4. "HOW MANY PARTS IN THE LAST WHOLE?"
"WRITE +1."

5. "WHAT IS 6/2 PLUS 1/2?"
"WRITE EQUALS 7/2."

6. "WHAT FRACTION DOES 3 1/2 EQUAL?"
Repeat steps 1-6 with remaining problems.

STUDENTS

"2"

Students write 2.

"Multiply 3 × 2."
"6"
Students write 6.

"1"
Students write $\frac{6+1}{2}$.

"7/2"
Students write = 7/2

"7/2"

---

have students "check" several problems by drawing the diagram to illustrate the improper fraction or mixed number.

Operations—Adding and Subtracting Fractions

There are three basic groups when adding and subtracting fraction problems. The first group includes addition/subtraction problems which have like denominators:

$$\frac{3}{8} + \frac{1}{8} + \frac{2}{8} = \frac{\square}{\square} \qquad \frac{7}{9} - \frac{3}{9} = \frac{\square}{\square}$$

Problems of this type can be introduced during the primary grades since relatively few preskills are required to work the problems. The students learn that to work such problems they work only across the numerators; the denominator remains constant:

$$\frac{2}{5} + \frac{1}{5} = \frac{3}{5} \qquad \frac{7}{9} - \frac{3}{9} = \frac{4}{9}$$

The second group includes problems with unlike denominators. Problems in this group are limited, however, to those in which the lowest common denominator is relatively easy to figure out. Problems of this type are usually introduced during fourth grade. The strategy for solving these problems involves first figuring out the lowest common denominator, rewriting each fraction as an equivalent fraction with that denominator, then working the problem:

$$\begin{array}{c}\frac{5}{6}\\-\frac{3}{4}\end{array} \quad \text{becomes} \quad \begin{array}{c}\frac{5}{6}\left(\frac{2}{2}\right)=\frac{10}{12}\\-\frac{3}{4}\left(\frac{3}{3}\right)=\frac{9}{12}\end{array} \quad \begin{array}{c}\text{which}\\\text{becomes}\end{array} \quad \begin{array}{c}\frac{10}{12}\\-\frac{9}{12}\\\hline\frac{1}{12}\end{array}$$

The third group includes problems in which the lowest common denominator is difficult to determine. These problems usually have a lowest common denominator that is a relatively large number. For example, in the problem, 5/12 + 3/18, the lowest common denominator is 48. To solve this problem, students must be taught a strategy that involves factoring. Since the discussion of the procedures to teach this strategy would take many pages and since this type of problem is often not introduced until junior high, we have not included it in our scope or sequence.

Fractions with Like Denominators

Adding and subtracting fractions with like denominators is a relatively simple operation that can be introduced after fraction analysis skills have been taught, sometime in second or third grade. A format for teaching students to add and subtract fractions with like denominators appears in Figure 13.16. Part A is a pictorial demonstration in which the teacher demonstrates adding fractions. In Part B, the teacher presents the rule that students can only add and subtract fractions in which each whole has the same number of parts.

Parts C and D are structured and less structured worksheet exercises in which the students are

Figure 13.16 Format for Adding and Subtracting Fractions with Like Denominators

Day	**Part A** Pictorial Demonstration	**Part B** Structured Board Problems	**Part C** Structured Worksheet Problems	**Part D** Less Structured Worksheet Problems	**Part E** Supervised Practice Problems	**Part F** Independent Practice Problems
1-2	2	8				
3-4		4	8			
5-6			4	8		
7-Until accurate					8	
Until fluent						4-8

PART A: Pictorial Demonstration

TEACHER   **STUDENTS**

Draw on board:

——— + ——— = ———

1. "LET'S WRITE A PROBLEM THAT WILL TELL US
   HOW MANY PARTS ARE USED IN THESE WHOLES."

2. "HOW MANY PARTS IN EACH WHOLE?"   "4"
   Write

   $\frac{}{4} + \frac{}{4} = \frac{}{4}$

   "WE'RE TALKING ABOUT WHOLES WITH FOUR
   PARTS IN EACH WHOLE."

3. Point to first circle. "HOW MANY PARTS ARE USED
   IN THIS WHOLE?"   "3"

   Write $\frac{3}{4}$

   Point to second circle. "HOW MANY PARTS ARE
   USED IN THIS WHOLE?"   "2"

   Write $\frac{3}{4} + \frac{2}{4} =$.

4. "HOW MANY PARTS ARE USED ALTOGETHER?"   "5"

   Write $\frac{5}{4}$

5. "WHAT DOES 3/4 + 2/4 EQUAL?"   "5/4"
   Repeat steps 1-5 with

——— + ——— = ———

PART B: Structured Board Presentation

1. "WE CAN ONLY ADD AND SUBTRACT FRACTIONS
   WITH THE SAME NUMBER OF PARTS IN EACH
   WHOLE. LISTEN AGAIN." Repeat rule. Write on board:
   $\frac{3}{4} + \frac{2}{5} =$

2. "READ THIS PROBLEM."

Figure 13.16 cont'd

TEACHER	**STUDENTS**

3. Point to 3/4. "HOW MANY PARTS IN EACH WHOLE?"   "4"
   Point to 2/5. "HOW MANY PARTS IN EACH WHOLE?"   "5"

4. "CAN WE ADD THESE FRACTIONS?"   "No"

5. "RIGHT. WE CAN ONLY ADD FRACTIONS WHICH
   HAVE THE SAME BOTTOM NUMBER."
   Repeat steps 2-5 with

$$\frac{3}{5}+\frac{2}{5} \qquad \frac{5}{7}-\frac{3}{9} \qquad \frac{3}{9}+\frac{3}{5}$$

$$\frac{4}{7}+\frac{2}{7} \qquad \frac{5}{7}-\frac{5}{9} \qquad \frac{4}{9}-\frac{3}{9}$$

   Give individual turns.

PART C: Structured Worksheet

a. $\frac{3}{5}+\frac{1}{5}=$ _____   d. $\frac{5}{9}-\frac{2}{3}=$ _____   g. $\frac{6}{9}-\frac{2}{8}=$ _____

b. $\frac{3}{5}+\frac{2}{7}=$ _____   e. $\frac{7}{9}\times\frac{1}{9}=$ _____   h. $\frac{6}{9}+\frac{2}{9}=$ _____

c. $\frac{4}{7}-\frac{2}{7}=$ _____   f. $\frac{3}{4}-\frac{1}{4}=$ _____   i. $\frac{5}{7}+\frac{3}{5}=$ _____

1. "REMEMBER, YOU CAN ONLY ADD AND SUB-
   TRACT FRACTIONS THAT TELL ABOUT THE
   SAME NUMBER OF PARTS IN EACH WHOLE."

2. "TOUCH PROBLEM a. READ THE PROBLEM."   "3/5 + 1/5"

3. "CAN WE ADD THESE FRACTIONS THE WAY
   THEY ARE NOW?"   "Yes"
   If the answer to step 3 is no, say to students, "YOU CAN'T
   WORK THE PROBLEM, SO CROSS IT OUT." If the
   answer to step 3 is yes, do steps 4-6.

4. "WE'RE TALKING ABOUT FRACTIONS WITH FIVE
   PARTS IN EACH WHOLE SO THE ANSWER WILL
   HAVE FIVE PARTS IN EACH GROUP. WRITE 5 AS
   THE BOTTOM NUMBER IN THE ANSWER."

5. "LOOK AT THE TOP NUMBERS. THEY TELL THE
   NUMBER OF PARTS USED. WHAT IS 3 + 1?"   "4"
   "SO WHAT DO YOU WRITE FOR THE TOP NUM-
   BER IN THE ANSWER?"   "4"
   "WRITE IT."

6. "READ THE WHOLE PROBLEM."   "3/5 + 1/5 = 4/5"
   Repeat steps 1-6 for the remaining problems.

PART D: Less Structured Worksheet

Give students a worksheet with a mix of four addition and
four subtraction problems. About half of the problems
should have like denominators.

1. "READ THE FIRST PROBLEM. IF YOU CAN WORK
   IT, WRITE THE ANSWER. IF YOU CAN'T WORK
   THE PROBLEM, CROSS IT OUT." Monitor student
   performance.

presented with a set of addition and subtraction problems. Half the problems should have like denominators:

$$\frac{3}{4} - \frac{1}{4} \qquad \frac{4}{7} + \frac{2}{7}$$

and half different denominators:

$$\frac{3}{4} - \frac{1}{3} \qquad \frac{5}{7} + \frac{2}{3}$$

Students are instructed to cross out the problems with unlike denominators and work the problems with like denominators. The problems with unlike denominators are included so that students do not learn the misrule of ignoring the denominators.

During the first week or two of instruction, adding and subtracting fraction problems should be written horizontally. When students are able to work problems written horizontally, vertically aligned problems should be introduced:

$$\frac{3}{4} \qquad \frac{4}{8} \qquad \frac{5}{7}$$
$$-\frac{1}{4} \qquad +\frac{3}{8} \qquad +\frac{2}{3}$$

The teacher introduces vertically aligned problems with a board and structured worksheet exercise. Teachers should not assume that because students can work horizontally aligned problems they will all be able to work vertically aligned problems.

Problems with Mixed Numbers

Adding and subtracting mixed numbers in which the fractions have like denominators:

$$3\frac{2}{5} - 1\frac{1}{5}$$

can be introduced when students can read and write mixed numbers and can add and subtract fractions with like denominators. The teaching procedure is relatively simple: The students first work the fraction part of the problem, then the whole number part of the problem. Both horizontally and vertically aligned problems should be presented.

Fractions with Unlike Denominators

Adding and subtracting fractions with unlike denominators is usually introduced during fourth grade. A strategy for solving problems with unlike denominators is outlined in Figure 13.17. Note the integration of several component skills.

PRESKILLS There are two preskills which should be mastered before the format for adding and subtracting fractions with unlike denominators is introduced: (a) finding the least common multiple of two numbers and (b) rewriting a fraction as an equivalent fraction with a given denominator (see Figure 13.10).

The least common multiple of two numbers is the smallest number that has both numbers as factors. For example, the least common multiple (LCM) of the numbers 6 and 8 is 24 since 24 is the smallest number that has both 6 and 8 as factors. Likewise, the LCM of 6 and 9 is 18 since 18 is the smallest number that has 6 and 9 as factors.

Figure 13.18 includes a format for teaching students to figure out the lowest common multiple of two numbers. This format assumes that students are able to say the skip counting series for 2s through 9s.

About 2 months prior to introducing the least common multiple, the teacher should begin review-

Figure 13.17 Outline of Steps for Problems with Unlike Denominators

a. $\frac{3}{4} + \frac{1}{6}$	Students read problem and say, "The problem can't be worked as it is because the denominators are not the same."
b. $\frac{3}{4} + \frac{1}{6}$ $\quad 12 \quad\ 12$	Students determine that the lowest common multiple of 4 and 6 is 12. Thus 12 is the least common denominator. Both fractions must be rewritten with denominators of 12.
c. $\frac{3}{4}\left(\frac{3}{3}\right) + \frac{1}{6}\left(\frac{2}{2}\right)$	Students determine the fraction by which each original fraction must be multiplied to equal 12.
d. $\frac{3}{4}\cancel{\left(\frac{3}{3}\right)}^{9} + \frac{1}{6}\cancel{\left(\frac{2}{2}\right)}^{2}$ $\quad 12 \qquad\quad 12$	Students rewrite each fraction so that it has a denominator of 12.
e. $\frac{3}{4}\cancel{\left(\frac{3}{3}\right)}^{9} + \frac{1}{6}\cancel{\left(\frac{2}{2}\right)}^{2} = \frac{11}{12}$ $\quad 12 \qquad\quad 12$	Students work the problem with equivalent fractions.

Figure 13.18 Preskill: Format for Finding the Least Common Multiple

Day	Part A Structured Board Presentation Problems	Part B Structured Worksheet Problems	Part C Supervised Practice Problems	Part D Independent Practice Problems
1-2	4	4		
3-4		10		
5-6		4	6	
7-accurate			8-10	10

PART A: Structured Board Presentation

TEACHER   **STUDENTS**

Write on the board:

3   6   9   12   15   18

5   10   15   20   25

1. Point to 3. "THESE NUMBERS ARE MULTIPLES OF
   3. SAY THEM."   "3, 6, 9, 12, 15, 18"
   Point to 5. "THESE NUMBERS ARE MULTIPLES OF
   5. SAY THEM."   "5, 10, 15, 20, 25"

2. "WHAT IS THE SMALLEST NUMBER THAT IS A
   MULTIPLE OF 3 AND 5?"   "15"
   "YES, 15 IS THE LEAST COMMON MULTIPLE OF
   3 AND 5." Repeat steps 1 and 2 with these examples:
   2 and 8, 6 and 8, 3 and 9.

PART B: Worksheet Presentation

Write the number which is the least common multiple for each pair of numbers.

a. The L.C.M. of 6 and 9 is _____.   f. The L.C.M. of 4 and 3 is _____.

b. The L.C.M. of 8 and 6 is _____.   g. The L.C.M. of 6 and 2 is _____.

c. The L.C.M of 5 and 2 is _____.   h. The L.C.M. of 4 and 12 is _____.

d. The L.C.M. of 5 and 4 is _____.   i. The L.C.M. of 5 and 3 is _____.

e. The L.C.M. of 6 and 12 is _____.   j. The L.C.M. of 3 and 9 is _____.

1. "THE INSTRUCTIONS TELL US TO FIND THE
   LEAST COMMON MULTIPLE OF THE NUMBERS.
   LCM MEANS LEAST COMMON MULTIPLE. IN
   PROBLEM a YOU MUST FIND THE LEAST COM-
   MON MULTIPLE OF 6 AND 9. THE LEAST COMMON
   MULTIPLE IS THE LOWEST NUMBER THAT IS IN
   BOTH COUNT-BY SERIES."

2. "SAY THE NUMBERS THAT ARE MULTIPLES OF
   6." Stop students at 30.   "6, 12, 18, 24, 30"

3. "SAY THE NUMBERS THAT ARE MULTIPLES OF
   9." Stop students at 45.   "9, 18, 27, 36, 45"

4. "WHAT IS THE LEAST COMMON MULTIPLE OF
   9 AND 6?" Pause, signal.   "18"
   "WRITE IT IN THE SPACE."
   Repeat steps 1-4 with several more problems then have
   students work the rest of the problems on their own.

ing the skip counting series (see pages 74–77 of Chapter 5 for teaching skip counting). Students who know their basic multiplication facts should have little trouble learning the series.

The strategy students are taught requires them to say the skip counting series for each target number and to select the smallest number appearing in both series. This strategy is viable for examples in which the target numbers are small. A more sophisticated strategy would need to be taught to figure the least common multiple of larger numbers for which the students could not say the skip counting series. This more sophisticated strategy, which involves factoring, is not discussed in this text.

The format includes two parts. In Part A, the teacher writes count-by series of two numbers on the board so that students can visually find the lowest common multiple. In that part also, the term *multiple* is introduced. Part B is a worksheet presentation in which the teacher leads students in finding the least common multiple for several pairs of numbers and then monitors as students complete the worksheet on their own. Daily practice on worksheet exercises involving finding the least common multiple of two numbers would be continued for several weeks.

There are two example selection guidelines for the least common multiple format. First, in about half the problems the larger number should be a multiple of the smaller number. For the numbers 3 and 12, 12 is a multiple of 3. The least common multiple of 12 and 3 is 12. Likewise, the lowest common multiple of the numbers 2 and 8 is 8.

The second guideline pertains to the other half of the problems in which the larger number is not a multiple of the lower number. In these problems both target numbers should be below 10.

FORMAT The format for adding and subtracting fractions with unlike denominators appears in Figure 13.19. The format has three parts. Part A is a structured board presentation. This part begins with the teacher writing a problem on the board and asking the students if the fractions can be added (or subtracted) as they are. After the students determine the fractions cannot be added (or subtracted) because the denominators are not the same, the teacher tells the students that they can work the problem by rewriting the fractions so that both have the same denominator. The teacher then demonstrates the problem-solving strategy outlined earlier: writing the lowest common multiple of both denominators; multiplying each fraction by the fraction of 1,

which enables it to be rewritten with the lowest common denominator; and then adding (or subtracting) the rewritten fraction. In Parts B and C, the structured and less structured worksheet exercises, the teacher leads students through working problems. Note that the example in Figure 13.19 includes problems in which both fractions are rewritten. In many problems, only one fraction will need to be rewritten (e.g., in 3/4 + 1/8, only 3/4 needs to be rewritten as 6/8). When initially presenting this type of problem, the teacher has the students write the fraction (1/1) next to the fraction that does not need to be rewritten:

$$\frac{3}{4}\left(\frac{2}{2}\right) + \frac{5}{8}\left(\frac{1}{1}\right)$$
$$\phantom{\frac{3}{4}}8\phantom{\left(\frac{2}{2}\right) +}8$$

After several weeks, the teacher can explain that if the denominator of the rewritten fraction is to be the same, nothing need be done to that fraction.

There are two example selection guidelines. The first regards the manner in which problems are written. During the first two weeks, all problems should be written horizontally. When students can work horizontal problems, they can be introduced to vertically aligned problems.

The second guideline pertains to the mix of problems. One-half of the problems should have denominators in which the larger denominator is a multiple of the smaller denominator. For example, in the problem

$$\frac{3}{5} + \frac{2}{10}$$

the larger denominator, 10, is a multiple of the smaller denominator, 5. In the other half of the problems, the denominators should both be one digit numbers:

$$\frac{3}{5} + \frac{2}{3} \qquad \frac{3}{4} + \frac{2}{5} \qquad \frac{5}{6} - \frac{1}{4}$$

Several problems involving adding and subtracting fractions with like denominators should also be included. A sample set of problems appears below. Note that problems c and f have like denominators. Problems b, e, and g have a lower denominator which is a multiple of the larger denominator. In problems a, d, and h, both fractions must be rewritten.

a. $\frac{3}{4} + \frac{2}{5}$ b. $\frac{7}{9} - \frac{2}{3}$ c. $\frac{5}{6} - \frac{1}{6}$

d. $\frac{5}{6} - \frac{4}{9}$ e. $\frac{1}{5} + \frac{3}{10}$ f. $\frac{4}{9} + \frac{3}{9}$

g. $\frac{7}{10} - \frac{1}{2}$ h. $\frac{3}{4} - \frac{2}{3}$

Figure 13.19 Format for Adding and Subtracting Fractions with Unlike Denominators

Day	Part A Structured Board Problems	Part B Structured Worksheet Problems	Part C Less Structured Worksheet Problems	Part D Supervised Practice Problems	Part E Independent Practice Problems
1-2	4				
3-4	2	4			
5-6	2	4	2		
7-8		2	6		
9-10			2	8	
11-accurate				10	
Till fluent					10

PART A: Structured Board Presentation

TEACHER	**STUDENTS**

Write on board:

$$\frac{2}{3} + \frac{1}{4} = \underline{\qquad}$$

1. "READ THIS PROBLEM."   "2/3 + 1/4"
   "CAN WE ADD THESE FRACTIONS THE WAY
   THEY ARE WRITTEN?"   "No"

2. "TO WORK THIS PROBLEM WE MUST REWRITE
   THE FRACTIONS SO THEY BOTH HAVE THE SAME
   DENOMINATOR. FIRST, WE FIGURE OUT THE
   LEAST COMMON MULTIPLE OF THE DENOMI-
   NATORS. WHAT IS THE DENOMINATOR OF THE
   FIRST FRACTION?"   "3"
   "WHAT IS THE DENOMINATOR OF THE SECOND
   FRACTION?"   "4"

3. "WHAT IS THE LEAST COMMON MULTIPLE OF
   4 AND 3?" Pause, signal.   "12"

   TO CORRECT: "SAY THE NUMBERS THAT ARE
               MULTIPLES OF 3. SAY THE NUM-
               BERS THAT ARE MULTIPLES OF 4.
               WHAT IS THE LEAST COMMON
               MULTIPLE?"

4. "WE MUST REWRITE EACH FRACTION AS EQUI-
   VALENT FRACTIONS WITH DENOMINATORS OF
   12." Write 12 under each denominator.

   $$\frac{2}{3} \quad + \frac{1}{4}$$
   12   12

   "I WANT TO REWRITE 2/3 AS A FRACTION WHICH
   HAS 12 AS A DENOMINATOR. REMEMBER, I DON'T
   WANT TO CHANGE THE VALUE OF 2/3. WHAT
   FRACTION DO I MULITPLY 2/3 BY TO END WITH
   A FRACTION THAT HAS A DENOMINATOR OF
   12?" Pause, signal.   "4/4"

   TO CORRECT: "WHAT IS THE DENOMINATOR
               OF 2/3? WHAT MUST I MULTIPLY 3
               BY TO END WITH 12? SO I MUST
               MULTIPLY 2/3 TIMES 4/4. WHAT DO
               I MULTIPLY 2/3 BY?"

Figure 13.19 cont'd

TEACHERS   **STUDENTS**

Write on board:

$$\frac{2}{3}\left(\frac{4}{4}\right) + \frac{1}{4}$$
$$\ \ 12 \quad\quad 12$$

	STUDENTS
"WHAT IS 2 × 4?" Pause, signal.	"8"
Write 8. "WHAT IS 3 × 4?" Pause, signal.	"12"

Cross out 2/3. Write on board:

$$\overset{8}{\cancel{\frac{2}{3}}}\left(\frac{\cancel{4}}{\cancel{4}}\right) + \frac{1}{4}$$
$$\ 12 \quad\quad 12$$

"WE REWROTE 2/3 AS 8/12. WHAT DID WE RE-WRITE 2/3 AS?"	"8/12"

5. "NOW LET'S REWRITE 1/4 AS A FRACTION THAT HAS 12 AS A DENOMINATOR. REMEMBER, I DON'T WANT TO CHANGE THE VALUE OF 1/4. WHAT FRACTION MUST I MULTIPLY 1/4 BY?" Pause, signal.   "3/3"

TO CORRECT: "WHAT IS THE DENOMINATOR OF 1/4? WHAT DO I MULTIPLY 4 BY TO END WITH 12? SO I MUST MULTIPLY 1/4 by 3/3. WHAT DO I MULTIPLY 1/4 BY?"

Write on board:

$$\overset{8}{\cancel{\frac{2}{3}}}\left(\frac{\cancel{4}}{\cancel{4}}\right) + \frac{1}{4}\left(\frac{3}{3}\right)$$
$$\ 12 \quad\quad 12$$

"WHAT IS 1 × 3?"	"3"
Write 3. "WHAT IS 4 × 3?"	"12"

Cross out 1/4. Write on board:

$$\overset{8}{\cancel{\frac{2}{3}}}\left(\frac{\cancel{4}}{\cancel{4}}\right) + \overset{3}{\cancel{\frac{1}{4}}}\left(\frac{3}{3}\right)$$
$$\ 12 \quad\quad\quad\quad 12$$

"WE REWROTE 1/4 AS 3/12. WHAT DID WE REWRITE 1/4 AS?"	"3/12"

6. "NOW THE DENOMINATORS ARE THE SAME AND WE CAN ADD. THE PROBLEM NOW SAYS 8/12 + 3/12. WHAT DOES THE PROBLEM SAY?"   "8/12 + 3/12"

7. "WHAT IS 8/12 + 3/12?"   "11/12"

Repeat steps 1-7 with

$$\frac{4}{5} - \frac{7}{10} \quad\quad\quad \frac{3}{6} - \frac{1}{4} \quad\quad\quad \frac{1}{9} + \frac{2}{3}$$

PART B: Structured Worksheet

Give students worksheets with a set of problems like this:

a. $\frac{5}{6} - \frac{2}{4} =$ d. $\frac{5}{10} - \frac{2}{5} =$

b. $\frac{2}{9} + \frac{2}{3} =$ e. $\frac{7}{9} - \frac{2}{3} =$

c. $\frac{2}{3} - \frac{3}{5} =$ f. $\frac{2}{5} - \frac{1}{3} =$

Figure 13.19 cont'd

TEACHER	**STUDENTS**
1. "READ PROBLEM a."	"5/6 - 2/4"
"CAN WE WORK THE PROBLEM THE WAY IT IS?"	"No"
If the answer is yes, tell the students to work the problem.	
If the answer is no, continue the format.	
"WHY NOT?"	"The denominators aren't the same."

2. "WHAT ARE THE DENOMINATORS?" — "6 and 4"
   "WHAT IS THE LEAST COMMON MULTIPLE OF
   6 AND 4?" Pause, Signal. — "12"
   "WRITE 12 UNDER EACH FRACTION."

3. "THE FIRST FRACTION SAYS 5/6. WRITE PAREN-
   THESES NEXT TO IT. WHAT FRACTION DO YOU
   MULTIPLY 5/6 BY SO THAT YOU'LL END WITH A
   DENOMINATOR OF 12?" Pause, signal. — "2/2"
   "WRITE TWO HALVES IN THE PARENTHESES."

   TO CORRECT: "THE DENOMINATOR IS 6; 6
   TIMES WHAT NUMBER EQUALS 12?
   SO WE MUST MULTIPLY A FRAC-
   TION THAT HAS 2 AS A DENOMINA-
   TOR. WE DON'T WANT TO CHANGE
   THE VALUE OF 5/6 SO WE MULTIPLY
   IT BY 2/2."

   "LET'S MULTIPLY 5/6 BY TWO HALVES AND
   WRITE THE NEW FRACTION. WHAT IS 5 TIMES
   2?" — "10"
   "WRITE 10 OVER THE FRACTION. FIVE-SIXTHS
   EQUALS HOW MANY TWELFTHS?" — "10 twelfths"
   Cross out 5/6.

4. "THE SECOND FRACTION SAYS 2/4. WRITE PAR-
   ENTHESES NEXT TO IT. WHAT FRACTION DO
   YOU MULTIPLY 2/4 BY SO THAT YOU'LL END
   WITH A DENOMINATOR OF 12?" Pause, signal. — "3/3"

   TO CORRECT: Same as step 3.

   "MULTIPLY 2/4 BY 3/3 AND WRITE THE NEW
   FRACTION." Pause. "TWO-FOURTHS EQUALS
   HOW MANY TWELFTHS?" — "6/12"
   Check students' papers. "CROSS OUT 2/4."

5. "READ THE PROBLEM SAYING THE REWRITTEN
   FRACTIONS." — "10/12 - 6/12"
   "CAN YOU WORK THE PROBLEM NOW?" — "Yes"
   "HOW DO YOU KNOW?" — "The denominators are the same."

6. "WORK THE PROBLEM AND WRITE THE ANSWER."

7. "WHAT IS THE ANSWER?" — "4/12"

PART C: Less Structured Worksheet

Give students a worksheet like that for structured worksheet
exercise.

1. "READ PROBLEM a. CAN WE WORK THE PROBLEM
   THE WAY IT IS?" If the answer is yes, tell students to
   work the problem. If the answer is no, continue the format.
   "WHY NOT?"

Figure 13.19 cont'd

TEACHER **STUDENTS**

2. "WHAT IS THE LEAST COMMON MULTIPLE OF THE DENOMINATORS?" Pause, signal. "WRITE IT UNDER THE FRACTION."

3. "WHAT FRACTION WILL YOU MULTIPLY THE FIRST FRACTION BY SO THAT IT WILL HAVE A DENOMINATOR OF _____?" Pause, signal.

4. "WHAT FRACTION WILL YOU MULTIPLY THE SECOND FRACTION BY SO THAT IT HAS A DENOMINATOR OF _____?" Pause, signal.

5. "REWRITE THE FRACTIONS AND WORK THE PROBLEM." Pause.

6. "WHAT IS YOUR ANSWER?"

Reducing and Rewriting Answers as Mixed Numbers

The skills of reducing fractions to their lowest common terms and converting an improper fraction to a mixed number can be integrated into problems after students have had several weeks of practice working problems with unlike denominators. A sample worksheet students might be given appears in Figure 13.20. Note that the problems are in a multiple choice format. To determine the correct answer, the student must convert the answer to a mixed number (when necessary) and/or reduce.

Teachers should lead students through determining the correct answer for several days. Daily practice with six to eight problems should continue for several weeks.

More Complex Problems with Mixed Numbers

A rather difficult problem type involving mixed numbers is illustrated below:

$$\begin{array}{r} 8 \\ -3\frac{2}{4} \\ \hline \end{array}$$

It is a subtraction problem involving renaming. The student must rewrite the 8 as 7 and 4/4 to work the problem. Prior to introducing such a problem, the teacher would present an exercise like the one below in which the student must rewrite a whole number as a whole number and a fraction equivalent to 1 (e.g., 6 = 5 + 4/4).

$$6 = \boxed{5} + \frac{\square}{4} \qquad 9 = \boxed{8} + \frac{\square}{6}$$

$$6 = \boxed{5} + \frac{\square}{3}$$

In leading students through this preskill exercise, the teacher points out that they have to take one whole away from the original whole number and rewrite that one whole as a fraction. Once this preskill is taught, students should have little difficulty with problems that involve renaming.

Comparing Fractions

Students are often asked to compare the values of fractions. For example, which has the greater value, 1/5 or 1/3? Which has the lesser value, 2/3 or 5/9? During second and third grade, students usually are asked to compare fractions with numerators of 1 but with different denominators. The students can be prepared for early comparison questions by pictorial demonstrations illustrating that the more parts a unit is divided into, the smaller the size of each part. Thus, the rule is "the bigger the denominator, the smaller the value of each part." The demonstrations can then be followed by a rule application exercise in which the teacher presents pairs of fractions asking which fraction has a greater value.

In later grades, students are asked to compare fractions which have numerators other than 1 (e.g., 3/4 and 5/9). The strategy for comparing the two fractions involves rewriting fractions so that they have common denominators (e.g., 3/4 would be rewritten as 27/36 and 5/9 as 20/36).

Once fractions have been rewritten so they have common denominators, their values are readily apparent. Procedures for teaching students to rewrite fractions with common denominators would be the same as those discussed in the early steps of the format to add and subtract fractions with different denominators: determining the lowest common multiple of the denominators and multiplying each fraction by a fraction equal to 1.

Figure 13.20 Sample Worksheet for Adding and Subtracting Fractions

Circle the correct answers.

a. $\frac{3}{4} + \frac{1}{2} =$	$\frac{4}{6}$	$\frac{4}{4}$	$1\frac{1}{4}$	$1\frac{4}{1}$
b. $\frac{7}{9} - \frac{1}{9} =$	$\frac{6}{9}$	$\frac{2}{3}$	$\frac{2}{9}$	$\frac{2}{5}$
c. $\frac{5}{6} + \frac{1}{3} =$	$\frac{6}{9}$	$1\frac{1}{3}$	$1\frac{5}{6}$	$1\frac{1}{6}$
d. $\frac{6}{8} - \frac{1}{4} =$	$\frac{5}{4}$	$\frac{1}{4}$	$\frac{1}{2}$	$\frac{1}{3}$

Story Problems

The basic guideline in introducing fraction story problems is that a new type of problem should be integrated into story problem exercises as soon as the students can accurately compute problems of that type. Story problems involving adding and subtracting fractions with like denominators should be introduced after students work such problems independently. Story problems with unlike denominators should be introduced only after students have mastered the strategy for adding/subtracting that type of problem. All of the various types of addition and subtraction problems described in the problem solving chapter (Chapter 12) would be included in the exercises. Figure 13.21 shows a sample worksheet that might be given to students shortly after they learn how to add/subtract mixed numbers with fractions that have like denominators. Note the variety of story problem types, e.g., classification, action, and comparison.

Operations—Multiplying Fractions

There are three types of multiplication problems. The first type, which involves multiplying two proper fractions, is usually introduced in third grade:

$$\frac{3}{4} \times \frac{2}{5} \qquad \frac{4}{9} \times \frac{1}{3}$$

The second type, which also is usually introduced during third or fourth grade, involves multiplying a fraction and a whole number:

$$\frac{3}{4} \times 8$$

This type of problem is important since it occurs often in story problems. The third type of problem, usually introduced in fifth grade, involves multiplying one or more mixed numbers:

$$5 \times 3\frac{2}{4} \qquad 4\frac{1}{2} \times 2\frac{3}{5} \qquad \frac{3}{4} \times 2\frac{1}{2}$$

Multiplying Proper Fractions

Multiplying proper fractions can be introduced several weeks after students have learned to add and subtract fractions with like denominators. The format for multiplying fractions appears in Figure 13.22. Note that no pictorial demonstration is included since it would be too complex. The main reason why multiplying proper fractions is taught at this point is that it is a prerequisite for equivalent fraction tasks and for the second type of multiplication problem, a fraction times a whole number. The format includes two parts. In Part A, the structured board presentation, the teacher presents the rule about multiplying fractions—"Work top times the top and bottom times the bottom"—and demonstrates its application with several problems.

Part B is a structured worksheet presentation. Note that the examples in this part include an equal mix of multiplication problems and problems which involve addition and subtraction of like denominators. This mix is essential to provide students with practice in learning the difference between the multiplication strategy (multiply across the top and bottom) and the addition/subtraction strategy (work only across the top). Part B begins with a verbal exercise in which the teacher asks students how they work a particular type of problem (i.e., What do you do when you times fractions? What do you do when you add or subtract fractions?).

Tina ran 3 2/5 miles in the morning and 2 1/5 miles in the afternoon. How many miles did she run altogether?

We had 3/4 of an inch of rain on Monday and 1/4 of an inch of rain on Tuesday. How much more rain did we have on Monday?

Ricardo's cat weighed 14 2/6 pounds. If the cat gains 3 1/6 pounds, how much will it weigh?

Joan bought 6 2/4 pounds of meat. After she cooked the meat it weighed 2 1/4 pounds. How much less does it weigh now?

Fractions Times Whole Numbers

Problems that involve multiplying a fraction and a whole number are important because they have many real-life applications. For example, consider the following problem: "A boat engine called for 2/3 quarts of oil for every gallon of gasoline. John had 9 gallons of gas, How much oil did he need?" Fraction times whole number problems can be introduced when students have mastered multiplying proper fractions and converting an improper fraction to a mixed number. The steps in the problem-solving strategy are outlined below:

$$\frac{3}{4} \times 8$$

Students read problem.

$$\frac{3}{4} \times \frac{8}{1}$$

Students make whole number into a fraction.

$$\frac{3}{4} \times \frac{8}{1} = \frac{24}{4}$$

Students multiply numerator and denominator.

$$\frac{3}{3} \times \frac{8}{1} = \frac{24}{4} = 6$$

Students convert product into a whole number or mixed number.

Picture demonstrations of what takes place when multiplying a whole number by a fraction might precede the introduction of the format. In these demonstrations, the teacher explains that the bottom number tells how many groups to form and the top number tells how many groups are used. For example, for the problem 2/3 × 12, the following diagram might be drawn:

The teacher first draws 12 lines and says, "I've made three groups. Now I'm going to circle two of the groups." The teacher circles two groups:

Figure 13.22 Format for Multiplying Two Proper Fractions

Day	Part A Structured Board Problems	Part B Structured Worksheet Problems	Part C Supervised Practice Problems	Part D Independent Practice Problems
1-2	4	4		
3-4		6		
5-Till accurate			10	
Till fluent				10

PART A: Structured Board Presentation

TEACHER

Write on board:

$\frac{3}{4} \times \frac{2}{5} =$

1. "READ THIS PROBLEM."

STUDENTS

"Three-fourths times two-fifths"

Figure 13.22 cont'd

TEACHER   **STUDENTS**

2. "WE WORK TIMES PROBLEMS WITH FRACTIONS BY MULTIPLYING TOP TIMES THE TOP AND BOTTOM TIMES THE BOTTOM. HOW DO WE WORK TIMES PROBLEMS WITH FRACTIONS?"

"Top times the top; bottom times the bottom"

3. "FIRST WE MULTIPLY TOP TIMES THE TOP. WHAT IS 3 × 2?" Pause, signal.
Write on board:

$$\frac{3}{4} \times \frac{2}{5} = \frac{6}{}$$

"6"

4. "NOW WE MULTIPLY BOTTOM TIMES THE BOTTOM. WHAT IS 4 × 5?" Pause, signal.
Write on board:

$$\frac{3}{4} \times \frac{2}{5} = \frac{6}{20}$$

"20"

5. "WHAT DOES 3/4 × 2/5 EQUAL?"
Repeat steps 1-5 with several more problems.

"6/20"

PART B: Structured Worksheet

Give students worksheets with a mix of multiplication, addition, and subtraction problems.

a. $\frac{3}{4} + \frac{2}{4} = \frac{\square}{\square}$ b. $\frac{3}{2} \times \frac{4}{2} = \frac{\square}{\square}$

c. $\frac{6}{3} - \frac{1}{3} = \frac{\square}{\square}$ d. $\frac{6}{3} \times \frac{1}{3} = \frac{\square}{\square}$

1. "WHEN YOU TIMES FRACTIONS YOU WORK TOP TIMES TOP AND BOTTOM TIMES BOTTOM. WHEN YOU TIMES FRACTIONS WHAT DO YOU DO?"

"Top times top and bottom times bottom"

2. "BUT WHEN YOU PLUS OR MINUS FRACTIONS YOU WORK ONLY ACROSS THE TOP. WHEN YOU ADD OR SUBTRACT FRACTIONS, WHAT DO YOU DO?"

"Work only across the top"

3. "WHAT DO YOU DO WHEN YOU ADD OR SUBTRACT FRACTIONS?"

"Work across the top"

"WHAT DO YOU DO WHEN YOU TIMES FRACTIONS?"

"Top times top and bottom times bottom"

Repeat step 3 until firm.

4. "TOUCH PROBLEM a. READ THE PROBLEM."
"WHAT TYPE OF PROBLEM IS THIS?"
"WHAT DO YOU DO WHEN YOU PLUS FRACTIONS?"
"WORK THE PROBLEM. (pause) WHAT'S THE ANSWER?" Repeat step 4 with remaining problems.

"3/4 + 2/4"
"Plus"
"Work across the top"

The teacher counts the lines within the circles: "We end with 8: 2/3 × 12 = 8."

The format for teaching students to work such problems appears in Figure 13.23. Part A introduces an essential component skill—converting a whole number to a fraction. Any whole number may be converted to a fraction by putting it over a denominator of 1.

Part B is a structured board presentation. Part C is a structured worksheet presentation. Note that the worksheet is set up with a prompt for the students. After a fraction bar for the answer is a division box:

$$\frac{3}{4} \times 8 = \underline{\quad} = \overline{)} = \square$$

The division box serves as a prompt for the students to divide. The box serves as a prompt to write the whole number answer. This prompt should be used the first week this problem type is presented.

Examples should be carefully controlled. Some problems should have answers which are whole numbers:

$$\frac{3}{4} \times 8 = 6$$

and some should have answers which are mixed numbers:

$$\frac{2}{3} \times 7 = 4\frac{2}{3}$$

Initially, the whole number should be a relatively small number (e.g., below 20). As students learn to multiply and divide larger numbers, the examples should include hundred and then thousand numbers:

$$\frac{3}{4} \times 2000$$

Multiplying Mixed Numbers

Problems in which a mixed number and a whole number are multiplied are an important component skill for advanced map reading skills. For example, if 1 inch equals 50 miles, how many miles will 3 1/2 inches equal?

$$50 \times 3\frac{1}{2} = 175$$

Initially we recommend a strategy in which the students convert a mixed number into an improper fraction before working the problem. Problems in a and b in Figure 13.24 show the steps in working problems.

Later, a more sophisticated strategy involving the distributive property may be introduced for problems in which a whole number and mixed number are multiplied. The students first multiply the whole number factor by the whole number from the mixed number factor, then multiply the whole number factor by the fraction, and finally add the products. This process is shown below:

$$5 \times 3\frac{1}{2} = (5 \times 3) + (5 \times \frac{1}{2})$$
$$= 15 + 2\frac{1}{2}$$
$$= 17\frac{1}{2}$$

Operations—Dividing Fractions

Dividing fractions is usually introduced in fifth grade. Problems may be divided into three types. First are those in which a proper fraction is divided by a proper fraction:

$$\frac{2}{3} \div \frac{3}{4} \qquad \frac{4}{5} \div \frac{2}{7}$$

This type of problem, while having little practical application, is introduced first since it prepares the students for the second type of problem in which a fraction is divided by a whole number:

$$\frac{3}{4} \div 2$$

Such problems have everyday application. For example, John has 3/4 pound of candy. He wants to split the candy up equally among his two friends. How much candy should he give to each friend? The third type of problem involves dividing a mixed number:

$$3\frac{1}{2} \div 4 \qquad 5\frac{1}{2} \div 2\frac{1}{3}$$

The strategy taught to solve division problems involves inverting the second fraction, changing the sign to a times sign, and then multiplying (e.g., 3/4 = 2/3 is worked by inverting 2/3 so that the problem reads 3/4 × 3/2 = 9/8). Because a lengthy explanation is needed for the rationale for this procedure, we recommend presenting the strategy in the elementary grades without rationale. The teacher simply presents the rules: "We cannot divide by a fraction number; we must change the problem to a times problem. Here's how we do that; we invert the second fraction and change the sign." The teacher illustrates the meaning of *invert* as she demonstrates solving the problem.

Figure 13.23 Format for Multiplying a Fraction and a Whole Number

Day	Part A Preskill— Convert Whole Number to Frac- tion Problems	Part B Structured Board Problems	Part C Structured Worksheet Problems	Part D Supervised Practice Problems	Part E Independent Practice Problems
1	5				
2	5	3			
3-4		3	4	4-6	
5-accurate					4-6

PART A: Converting a Whole Number to a Fraction

TEACHER

STUDENTS

1. "LISTEN TO THIS RULE: WE CAN CHANGE A WHOLE NUMBER INTO A FRACTION BY GIVING IT A DENOMINATOR OF 1. HOW DO WE CHANGE A WHOLE NUMBER INTO A FRACTION?"

"Give it a denominator of 1"

2. Write on board: 3.
"WHAT NUMBER IS THIS?"

"3"

"HOW DO I CHANGE IT INTO A FRACTION?"

"Give it a denominator of 1"

"WATCH ME CHANGE 3 INTO A FRACTION."
Write 1 under 3:
$$\frac{3}{1}$$
"A 3 OVER 1 IS THE SAME AS 3. I'LL DRAW A PIC- TURE TO SHOW YOU THAT 3/1 EQUALS 3."
Draw on board:

"WE HAVE THREE WHOLES USED UP."

3. Write on board: 5. "HOW DO I CHANGE 5 INTO A FRACTION?"

"Give it a denominator of 1"

"YES, 5 OVER 1 EQUALS 5 WHOLES." Write
$$\frac{5}{1}$$
Repeat step 3 with 2, 9, 4, 8.

PART B: Structured Board

Write on board:

$$\frac{3}{4} \times 8 = \underline{\quad} = \overline{)\quad\quad} = \square$$

1. "LISTEN TO THIS RULE ABOUT MULTIPLYING FRACTIONS: A FRACTION CAN ONLY BE MULTI- PLIED BY ANOTHER FRACTION. LISTEN AGAIN."
Repeat the rule.

2. "READ THIS PROBLEM." Point to 3/4.

"3/4 × 8"

"IS THIS FRACTION MULTIPLIED BY ANOTHER FRACTION?"

"No"

"SO BEFORE WE CAN WORK THE PROBLEM WE HAVE TO CHANGE 8 INTO A FRACTION. HOW DO I CHANGE 8 INTO A FRACTION?"

"Give it a denominator of 1"

Write on board:
$$\frac{3}{4} \times \frac{8}{1} =$$

Figure 13.23 cont'd

TEACHER	**STUDENTS**

3. "NOW WE'RE READY TO MULTIPLY ACROSS THE TOP AND BOTTOM. WHAT IS 3 × 8?" — "24"

Write $\underline{24}$

"WHAT IS 4 × 1?" — "4"

Write $\dfrac{24}{4}$

4. "DOES 24/4 EQUAL MORE OR LESS THAN ONE WHOLE?" — "More"

"HOW DO WE FIGURE OUT HOW MANY WHOLE GROUPS 24/4 EQUALS?" — "Divide 4 into 24"

"FOUR GOES INTO 24 HOW MANY TIMES?" — "6"

Write 6 in box.

5. "WHAT DOES 3/4 × 8 EQUAL?" — "6"

Repeat steps 2–5 with

$\dfrac{2}{3} \times 9 \qquad \dfrac{3}{5} \times 10 \qquad \dfrac{1}{4} \times 8$

PART C: Structured Worksheet

Give students worksheets with problems similar to the following problem:

a. $\dfrac{2}{3} \times 7 = \underline{\qquad} = \overline{\smash{)}} = \square$

1. "TOUCH PROBLEM a. READ IT." — "Two-thirds times seven equals how many?"

"IS 2/3 MULTIPLIED BY ANOTHER FRACTION?" — "No"

"SO WHAT DO YOU HAVE TO DO?" — "Change 7 into a fraction."

"DO IT." Monitor responses.

2. "NOW MULTIPLY THE FRACTIONS." Monitor responses. "WHAT FRACTION DID YOU END UP WITH?" — "14/3"

3. "IS 14/3 MORE OR LESS THAN ONE WHOLE GROUP?" — "More"

"HOW DO YOU FIGURE OUT HOW MANY WHOLE GROUPS?" — "Divide 3 into 14"

"DIVIDE—DON'T FORGET TO WRITE THE REMAINDER AS A FRACTION."

4. "WHAT DOES 2/3 × 7 EQUAL?" — "4 and 2/3"

Repeat steps 1–4 with remaining problems.

Figure 13.24

Steps	Problems	
	a. $5\frac{1}{2} \times 3\frac{2}{4} =$	b. $5 \times 2\frac{3}{4}$
1. Convert mixed number to improper fraction.	$\dfrac{11}{2} \times \dfrac{14}{4} =$	$\dfrac{5}{1} \times \dfrac{11}{4} =$
2. Multiply.	$\dfrac{11}{2} \times \dfrac{14}{4} = \dfrac{154}{8}$	$\dfrac{5}{1} \times \dfrac{11}{4} = \dfrac{55}{4}$
3. Convert answer to mixed number.	$\dfrac{154}{8} = \underset{8\overline{)154}}{19\frac{2}{8}} = 19\frac{1}{4}$	$\dfrac{55}{4} = \underset{4\overline{)55}}{13\frac{3}{4}} = 13\frac{3}{4}$

Problems in which students divide by a whole number are solved by first converting the whole number to a fraction and then inverting that fraction:

$$\frac{3}{4} \div 2 = \frac{3}{4} \div \frac{2}{1} = \frac{3}{4} \times \frac{1}{2} = \frac{3}{8}$$

Problems that include a mixed number are solved by converting the mixed number to an improper fraction, inverting, and multiplying.

Story Problems—Multiplication and Division

Multiplication and division story problems can be introduced when students can solve the respective problem types. Multiplication story problems with fractions usually involve figuring out what a fractional part of a specified group equals. Here is a typical problem:

There are 20 children in our class; 3/4 of the children are girls. How many girls are in the class?

This type of problem is introduced shortly after students can solve problems in which a fraction and a whole number are multiplied (e.g., 3/4 × 12). As an intermediate step to prepare students for the story problems, the teacher can present problems like these:

$$\frac{3}{4} \text{ of } 12 = \frac{\square}{\square} = \square \qquad \frac{2}{3} \text{ of } 9 = \frac{\square}{\square} = \square$$

Students would be taught that *of* in this problem can be translated to *times*. The problem 3/4 of 12 would be converted to 3/4 × 12 and worked:

$$\frac{3}{4} \times \frac{12}{1} = \frac{36}{4} = 9$$

As students are able to solve operations with larger numbers, the examples in the story problems should include larger numbers. Instead of 2/3 of 12, a problem might ask 2/3 of 126.

The most common type of division story problem involves dividing a fraction by a whole number. Here is an example of this type of problem:

John has 3/4 pound of candy. He wants to divide the candy equally among 3 friends. How much candy should he give to each friend?

This type of problem can be introduced when students can work problems in which a fraction can be divided by a whole number.

Diagnosis and Remediation

Students may miss fraction problems for one or a combination of the following reasons:

1. A computational error (e.g., dividing 18 by 3 and ending with 5, multiplying 7 × 8 and ending with 54). If a student misses a problem solely because of a computational error, the teacher need not spend time working on the fraction skill but should reteach the specific computational skill.
2. A component skill error. The student makes an error on a previously taught fraction skill, which causes the student to miss the current type of problem. For example, when working the problem 2/3 × 12, the student converts 12 to the fraction 1/12 instead of 12/1, writing 2/3 × 1/12 = 2/36. The remediation procedure involves reteaching the earlier taught component skill. In the example given, the teacher would first reteach the student how to convert a whole number to a fraction. When the student's performance indicates mastery of the component skill, the teacher leads the student through solving the original type of problem, using the structured worksheet part of the appropriate format.
3. A strategy error. A strategy error occurs when the student does not correctly chain the steps together to solve a problem. For example, when attempting to convert 12/4 to a whole number, the student subtracts 4 from 12, ending with 8. The remediation procedure involves reteaching the strategy beginning with the structured board part of the format.

The following sections give examples of common errors made on the various types of fraction problems along with suggestions for remediation.

Reading and Writing Fractions and Mixed Numbers

Students should read a problem as the first step in any part of the format. If the teacher notes the student reading a fraction or mixed number incorrectly, the teacher should reintroduce the reading format, stressing the particular type of fraction missed. For example, if a student reads 5 1/3 as 5/3, the teacher would present the reading mixed number format.

Adding and Subtracting Fractions

When adding fractions with like denominators, students will usually make (a) strategy errors or (b) computational errors. Note the problems below:

a. $\dfrac{7}{9} - \dfrac{2}{9} = \dfrac{5}{0}$ b. $\dfrac{4}{8} + \dfrac{2}{8} = \dfrac{6}{16}$

c. $\dfrac{7}{9} - \dfrac{2}{9} = \dfrac{6}{9}$ d. $\dfrac{4}{8} + \dfrac{2}{8} = \dfrac{7}{8}$

Problems a and b illustrate strategy errors. The student does not know that the denominators are not added or subtracted. The remediation procedure involves reintroducing the format for adding and subtracting fractions, beginning with Part A. Problems c and d, on the other hand, indicate computational errors. The student knows the strategy but missed the problems because of basic fact errors. The remediation procedure depends on the number of problems missed. If a student misses less than 10% of the problems because of computational errors, the teacher merely works on the particular basic fact missed, writing the fact for the student and testing her periodically on it for several days. If the student misses more than 10% of the problems because of computational errors, the teacher must work on improving fact accuracy through instituting a stronger motivational system and/or providing more practice on basic facts. In neither case must the teacher re-present the adding and subtracting fraction format.

Problems involving adding or subtracting fractions with unlike denominators may be missed because of fact, component skill, or strategy defi-cits. Note the problems in Figure 13.25. The cause of the error and the remediation procedure are listed for a few of the many possible mistake patterns.

Research

Research has shown that not only are operations more difficult when applied to fractions than to whole numbers (Scott, 1962), but understanding of whole number concepts and operations interferes with fractions introduction (Behr, Wachsmuth, Post, & Lesh, 1984). While research on teaching fractions operations is difficult to interpret, the evidence does suggest clearly that too many students perform poorly on fraction computation. The National Assessment of Educational Progress reported that nationally "performance of fraction computation is low, and students seem to have done their computation with little understanding" (Lindquist, Carpenter, Silver, & Matthews, 1983). Peck and Jencks (1981) similarly found through interviews with sixth graders that even though students had been working with fractions from 3 to 5 years, 55% lacked a meaningful concept of fractions and fewer than 10% were able to add or compare fractions accurately.

Carnine (1977) compared a direct instruction strategy and a more traditional approach of analyzing fractions. The direct instruction was similar to the formats on pages 315–324. In the traditional treatment, fractions were introduced as part of common objects.

Figure 13.25

Error Patterns	Diagnosis	Remediation Procedures
a. $\dfrac{4}{5} + \dfrac{2}{3} = \dfrac{4}{5}\big(\times 3\big) + \dfrac{2}{3}\big(\times 5\big) = \dfrac{6}{15}$ 15 15	Component error: student failed to multiply numerator.	Present format on page 342 beginning with Part A.
b. $\dfrac{4}{8} + \dfrac{2}{4} = \dfrac{4\times4}{8\times4} + \dfrac{2\times8}{4\times8} = \dfrac{32}{32}$ 16 16 32 32	Component skill error: student did not find lowest common multiple. Note that answer is correct.	Teacher points this out but emphasizes it's important to find the lowest common multiple. Extra practice on finding LCM.
c. $\dfrac{4}{5} + \dfrac{2}{3} = \dfrac{6}{8}$	Strategy error: student adds denominators.	Present entire format for fractions with unlike denominators over, beginning with Part A.
d. $\dfrac{5}{6} + \dfrac{2}{4} = \dfrac{5\times2}{6\times2} + \dfrac{2\times3}{4\times3} = \dfrac{15}{12}$ 10 5 12 12 12 12	Computational errors: student multiplied 2 x 3 incorrectly.	Teacher works on 2 x 3 fact. No reteaching of fraction format necessary.

Students in the direct instruction treatment made more correct post-test and transfer responses in illustrating fractions, writing fractions for illustrations, and determining whether fractions for illustrations were more, equal, or less than 1.

In order to determine whether curriculum design alone would lead to differences in student performance, Kelly, Gersten, and Carnine (in press) examined the effectiveness of a fractions curriculum (called Instructional Design) that incorporates design principles of systematic practice in discriminating among related problem types, separation of confusing elements and terminology, and use of a wide range of examples to illustrate each concept. Instructional Design was compared to a basal curriculum that was implemented with all other instruction kept constant. Although both programs were successful in teaching fractions material to students, the Instructional Design group achieved significantly higher results. Providing a wider range of examples, clearer step-by-step strategies, and discrimination practice can augment the effectiveness of fractions instruction in any mathematics curriculum.

Commercial Programs

Fractions: Adding and Subtracting Fractions with Unlike Denominators

INSTRUCTIONAL STRATEGIES   The main concern regarding the way fractions are taught lies with the lack of specificity generally found in the instruction. Structured teaching presentations become particularly important when more complex strategies are introduced. For example, Figures 13.26 and 13.27 show the initial instruction for subtracting mixed numbers with regrouping in a fifth grade text. These are particularly difficult problems, requiring a thorough understanding of fraction analysis skills. Note the minimal guidance provided in the teacher's guide. The teacher demonstrates one example on the board and there is a model of one problem in the student's text. There is no demonstration for subtracting a mixed number from a whole number, yet nine problems are of this type. Considering that not only must students rename but in many problems they must also first rewrite the fractions with common denominators, it is highly likely that some students will have difficulty. Note that the only reference to a correction procedure suggests that the teacher work with those students having difficulty on an individual basis (see Figure 13.27).

REVIEW   The second focus of concern with instruction in fractions has to do with the amount of review provided in the programs. In grades one through three, only 1 to 3 weeks are typically devoted to fraction skills. Minimal review is presented on fraction skills after the unit is presented. Because of this minimal review, it is highly likely that many students will not retain fraction-related skills taught in these earlier grades. In intermediate grades, the critical fraction analysis skills taught in early grades are briefly reviewed prior to teaching new skills. The amount of practice provided in the programs must be significantly supplemented if the students are to develop mastery. Teachers must not go on to a new skill until students have developed accuracy on its preskills. When the more complex fraction skills are introduced in the intermediate grades, the programs tend to provide enough initial practice (with all of the supplemental worksheets available). However, the practice usually is concentrated in a short amount of time with little systematic review built into the program outside of the fractions units themselves, as in the earlier grades. Low performing students require continual review if they are to maintain acquired skills.

Figure 13.26

TEACHING SUGGESTIONS

Learn about regrouping with subtraction of fractions. Write this problem on the chalkboard:

$$6\frac{1}{3}$$
$$-2\frac{2}{3}$$

We must regroup 1 one to $\frac{3}{3}$ before we can subtract. Work through the steps on the chalkboard:

$$6\frac{1}{3} = 5\frac{4}{3}$$
$$-2\frac{2}{3} = 2\frac{2}{3}$$
$$\overline{\phantom{-2\frac{2}{3}=}3\frac{2}{3}}$$

Of course, this can be done by shorter steps, but at this time focus on the renaming procedure so that the fractions can be subtracted.

READINESS

For students who need help with mixed numbers.

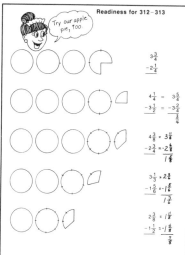

Copymaster S126 or Duplicating Master S126

Draw this example on the chalkboard:

"We can't subtract $\frac{3}{4}$ from $\frac{1}{2}$, so we use a whole circle and the half circle to make $\frac{4}{4}$ and $\frac{2}{4}$, which totals $\frac{6}{4}$." Demonstrate. "Now we can subtract $\frac{3}{4}$." Demonstrate by crossing off three $\frac{1}{4}$ segments. "How many fourths do we have now? (3) Now subtract 2 whole circles."

Guide the students through the exercises. Have them rewrite each problem on the right side of the page after they draw the regrouping.

⚫⚫⚫ **Cooperative Learning Groups**

More about subtracting mixed numbers

Sometimes you have to regroup before you subtract.

EXAMPLE. $8\frac{1}{4}$
$-3\frac{3}{8}$

Step 1.
Change to a common denominator.

Step 2.
Since $\frac{2}{8}$ is less than $\frac{3}{8}$, regroup 1 as $\frac{8}{8}$.

Step 3.
Subtract.

$$8\frac{1}{4} = 8\frac{2}{8}$$
$$-3\frac{3}{8} = 3\frac{3}{8}$$

$$8\frac{1}{4} = 8\frac{2}{8} = 7\frac{10}{8}$$
$$-3\frac{3}{8} = 3\frac{3}{8} = 3\frac{3}{8}$$

$$8\frac{1}{4} = 8\frac{2}{8} = 7\frac{10}{8}$$
$$-3\frac{3}{8} = 3\frac{3}{8} = 3\frac{3}{8}$$
$$\overline{\phantom{-3\frac{3}{8}=3\frac{3}{8}=}4\frac{7}{8}}$$

$$8\frac{1}{4} = \cancel{8}\frac{\overset{7\frac{10}{8}}{2}}{8}$$
$$-3\frac{3}{8} = 3\frac{3}{8}$$
$$\overline{\phantom{-3\frac{3}{8}=}4\frac{7}{8}}$$

Here is how I find the difference.

EXERCISES
Subtract. Write the difference in simplest form.

1. $5\frac{1}{4} = 5\frac{1}{4} = 4\frac{5}{4}$
   $-2\frac{1}{2} = 2\frac{2}{4} = 2\frac{2}{4}$
   $\phantom{-2\frac{1}{2}=2\frac{2}{4}=}2\frac{3}{4}$

2. $6\frac{1}{8} = 6\frac{1}{8} = 5\frac{9}{8}$
   $-3\frac{3}{4} = 3\frac{6}{8} = 3\frac{6}{8}$
   $\phantom{-3\frac{3}{4}=3\frac{6}{8}=}2\frac{3}{8}$

3. $7\frac{2}{3} = 7\frac{8}{12} = 6\frac{20}{12}$
   $-4\frac{3}{4} = 4\frac{9}{12} = 4\frac{9}{12}$
   $\phantom{-4\frac{3}{4}=4\frac{9}{12}=}2\frac{11}{12}$

4. $6 = 5\frac{4}{4}$
   $-2\frac{1}{4} = 2\frac{1}{4}$
   $\phantom{-2\frac{1}{4}=}3\frac{3}{4}$

5. $9 = 8\frac{3}{3}$
   $-5\frac{2}{3} = 5\frac{2}{3}$
   $\phantom{-5\frac{2}{3}=}3\frac{1}{3}$

6. $7 = 6\frac{8}{8}$
   $-3\frac{5}{8} = 3\frac{5}{8}$
   $\phantom{-3\frac{5}{8}=}3\frac{3}{8}$

312

USING THE PAGES

Go through the exposition on page 312. Have the students work exercises 1–6 on scratch paper while you work them on the chalkboard. Keep a close check on the students' work and the way they record it. Assign exercises 7–28.

⋮ **ERROR-ANALYSIS NOTE** ⋯⋯⋯⋯⋯

When a mixed number is subtracted from a whole number, some students may not regroup but just write the fraction as part of the answer—for example,

$$\frac{6}{-4\frac{3}{8}}\quad\text{instead of}\quad\frac{\overset{5}{\cancel{6}}\frac{8}{8}}{-4\frac{3}{8}}$$
$$\overline{2\frac{3}{8}}\qquad\qquad\overline{1\frac{5}{8}}$$

Point out to these students that since they are subtracting more than 4 from 6, their answer must be less than 2. They need to regroup.

○○○○○○ → ○○○○○❀
Subtract $4\frac{3}{8}$ → ∅∅∅∅∅❀

7. $9\frac{5}{9}$
$-4\frac{1}{9}$
$\overline{5\frac{4}{9}}$

8. $8\frac{4}{5}$
$-2\frac{3}{5}$
$\overline{6\frac{1}{5}}$

9. $5\frac{3}{4}$
$-1\frac{1}{2}$
$\overline{4\frac{1}{4}}$

10. $9\frac{5}{6}$
$-4\frac{2}{3}$
$\overline{5\frac{1}{6}}$

11. $7\frac{1}{2}$
$-2\frac{1}{3}$
$\overline{5\frac{1}{6}}$

12. $9\frac{3}{4}$
$-4\frac{2}{3}$
$\overline{5\frac{1}{12}}$

13. 8
$-3\frac{1}{2}$
$\overline{4\frac{1}{2}}$

14. 6
$-4\frac{3}{5}$
$\overline{1\frac{2}{5}}$

15. 12
$-3\frac{7}{10}$
$\overline{8\frac{3}{10}}$

16. 11
$-5\frac{3}{4}$
$\overline{5\frac{1}{4}}$

17. 15
$-6\frac{3}{8}$
$\overline{8\frac{5}{8}}$

18. 16
$-9\frac{4}{5}$
$\overline{6\frac{1}{5}}$

19. $9\frac{1}{4}$
$-3\frac{1}{2}$
$\overline{5\frac{3}{4}}$

20. $8\frac{1}{2}$
$-4\frac{3}{4}$
$\overline{3\frac{3}{4}}$

21. $7\frac{3}{8}$
$-2\frac{3}{4}$
$\overline{4\frac{5}{8}}$

22. $10\frac{2}{3}$
$-8\frac{5}{6}$
$\overline{1\frac{5}{6}}$

23. $11\frac{1}{8}$
$-6\frac{3}{4}$
$\overline{4\frac{3}{8}}$

24. $12\frac{2}{3}$
$-8\frac{5}{6}$
$\overline{3\frac{5}{6}}$

25. Diane is $8\frac{3}{4}$ inches taller than her little brother. If Diane is $58\frac{1}{2}$ inches tall, how tall is her brother? $49\frac{3}{4}$ inches

26. One week, David watched $6\frac{1}{4}$ hours of television. The next week he watched 8 hours of television. How much more did he watch the second week? $1\frac{3}{4}$ hours

27. In basketball, the rim of the basket is 10 feet above the floor. Stan can jump up and reach $7\frac{1}{4}$ feet above the floor. How much higher must he jump to touch the basket rim? $2\frac{3}{4}$ feet

28. A share of certain stock sold for $32\frac{5}{8}$ dollars. Two weeks later it sold for $34\frac{1}{8}$ dollars a share. How much did the value of the stock increase? $1\frac{1}{2}$ dollars

KEEPING SKILLS SHARP

Add or subtract.

1. 8.4
$+3.29$
$\overline{11.69}$

2. 7.34
-2.6
$\overline{4.74}$

3. 13
$+89.2$
$\overline{102.2}$

4. 87
-9.6
$\overline{77.4}$

5. 0.67
$+5.8$
$\overline{6.47}$

6. 9
-2.57
$\overline{6.43}$

7. $37 + 8.6$ — 45.6

8. $37 - 8.6$ — 28.4

9. $2.6 + 0.57$ — 3.17

10. $2.6 - 0.57$ — 2.03

313

PRACTICE

ENRICHMENT

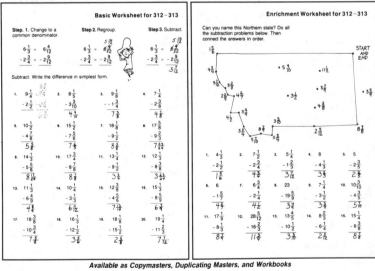

Available as Copymasters, Duplicating Masters, and Workbooks

LESSON FOLLOW-UP

REINFORCEMENT   *ERROR ANALYSIS*

Diagnosis and remediation. Identify the students having difficulty and work with them individually. You may want to select exercises from this lesson for these students to work on the chalkboard while you watch. As necessary, go back to page 312 and emphasize the sequence of steps to follow.

ENRICHMENT

Build a number. (Materials: digit cards) Pair students and give them a deck of digit cards. As they draw in turn, they complete a mixed number. The student building the larger number wins one point. The first student to get 5 points wins the game.

CHALLENGE

An excursion on adding and subtracting decimals.

Copymaster S192 or Duplicating Master S192

After the students have played a few games, set up a tournament to determine the class champion.

Figure 13.27

Application Items: Fractions

1. Below are various fraction-related problems. Describe the type each problem represents. List the types in their order of introduction.

   a. $\frac{2}{3} - \frac{1}{3}$

   b. Circle the picture that shows 2/4.

   c. Read this fraction: $\frac{3}{5}$

   d. $\frac{3}{4} + \frac{2}{5}$

   e. $5\frac{4}{7} - 3\frac{2}{7}$

   f. $\frac{12}{5} =$

   g. $\frac{3}{5} = \frac{\square}{10}$

   h. $5\frac{1}{2} \times 3$

   i. $3\frac{4}{5} = \frac{}{5}$

2. Write a structured worksheet presentation for teaching students how to solve the following type of problem:

   Draw a picture for this fraction: $\frac{3}{4} = \bigcirc\bigcirc$

3. A teacher is presenting the first lesson in which she is teaching students to decode fractions in the traditional manner (e.g., 2/3 is read as two-thirds). Below are four sets of examples. One set is appropriate. Tell which set is appropriate. Tell why the other three sets are not appropriate.

   a. $\frac{2}{3}$ $\frac{1}{2}$ $\frac{4}{5}$ $\frac{7}{3}$ $\frac{1}{4}$ $\frac{2}{9}$ $\frac{3}{2}$ $\frac{1}{5}$

   b. $\frac{1}{8}$ $\frac{1}{4}$ $\frac{1}{9}$ $\frac{1}{6}$ $\frac{1}{5}$ $\frac{1}{7}$

   c. $\frac{1}{8}$ $\frac{3}{4}$ $\frac{7}{6}$ $\frac{1}{6}$ $\frac{2}{8}$ $\frac{9}{4}$ $\frac{1}{4}$

   d. $\frac{3}{4}$ $\frac{7}{9}$ $\frac{8}{4}$ $\frac{2}{9}$ $\frac{4}{6}$ $\frac{8}{6}$ $\frac{5}{7}$

4. A student writes the mixed number five and one-third as 5/3. Specify the wording the teacher uses in making the correction.

5. Specify the wording the teacher uses in making the correction for the following error:

   $$\frac{3}{4} = \frac{\boxed{3}}{8}$$

6. Cross out the examples below that would not be included in an early equivalent fraction exercise.

   a. $\frac{2}{3} = \frac{\square}{9}$

   b. $\frac{5}{7} = \frac{\square}{28}$

   c. $\frac{3}{4} = \frac{\square}{6}$

   d. $\frac{4}{5} = \frac{\square}{20}$

   e. $\frac{3}{5} = \frac{\square}{20}$

   f. $\frac{4}{6} = \frac{\square}{10}$

7. Below are four sets of examples constructed by the teacher for an early reducing fraction exercise. One set is appropriate. Three are not appropriate. Identify the inappropriate sets. Tell why they're inappropriate.

   a. $\dfrac{8}{12}$ $\dfrac{7}{9}$ $\dfrac{6}{18}$ $\dfrac{4}{6}$ $\dfrac{5}{20}$ $\dfrac{2}{3}$

   b. $\dfrac{8}{12}$ $\dfrac{6}{18}$ $\dfrac{4}{6}$ $\dfrac{5}{20}$ $\dfrac{3}{12}$ $\dfrac{6}{8}$

   c. $\dfrac{8}{12}$ $\dfrac{7}{9}$ $\dfrac{10}{15}$ $\dfrac{12}{20}$ $\dfrac{3}{5}$ $\dfrac{6}{8}$

   d. $\dfrac{4}{7}$ $\dfrac{5}{20}$ $\dfrac{22}{36}$ $\dfrac{8}{16}$ $\dfrac{18}{34}$ $\dfrac{5}{9}$

8. Write the structured worksheet presentation used in leading students through reducing the fraction 12/18 to its lowest terms.

9. Below are sets of examples prepared by various teachers for an exercise in which students convert improper fractions to mixed numbers. Tell which sets are inappropriate.

   a. $\dfrac{9}{5}$ $\dfrac{11}{3}$ $\dfrac{9}{3}$ $\dfrac{12}{7}$ $\dfrac{14}{5}$ $\dfrac{12}{4}$

   b. $\dfrac{9}{4}$ $\dfrac{3}{7}$ $\dfrac{8}{2}$ $\dfrac{7}{5}$ $\dfrac{8}{3}$ $\dfrac{5}{9}$ $\dfrac{9}{3}$ $\dfrac{7}{3}$

   c. $\dfrac{9}{5}$ $\dfrac{3}{7}$ $\dfrac{5}{2}$ $\dfrac{4}{9}$ $\dfrac{7}{3}$ $\dfrac{9}{2}$

10. Below are sets of examples prepared by several teachers for an indepdendent worksheet exercise focusing on adding and subtracting fractions with unlike denominators. Tell which sets are inappropriate. Explain why.

   a. $\dfrac{6}{14} - \dfrac{3}{8}$ $\dfrac{5}{8} + \dfrac{1}{5}$ $\dfrac{4}{9} - \dfrac{5}{12}$ $\dfrac{3}{8} + \dfrac{2}{8}$

   b. $\dfrac{3}{8} + \dfrac{1}{5}$ $\dfrac{5}{7} - \dfrac{1}{4}$ $\dfrac{3}{8} + \dfrac{2}{8}$ $\dfrac{3}{5} + \dfrac{2}{3}$ $\dfrac{2}{3} - \dfrac{1}{2}$ $\dfrac{4}{7} - \dfrac{2}{5}$

   c. $\dfrac{3}{4} - \dfrac{2}{3}$ $\dfrac{4}{9} - \dfrac{2}{9}$ $\dfrac{2}{9} + \dfrac{2}{3}$ $\dfrac{5}{7} - \dfrac{1}{2}$ $\dfrac{3}{8} + \dfrac{1}{4}$ $\dfrac{3}{7} + \dfrac{2}{7}$

11. Below are problems missed by students. These examples are typical of the errors made by students. Specify the diagnosis and remediation for each student.

William

$$\frac{7}{8} - \frac{1}{6} = \frac{5}{2}$$

Ann

$$\frac{5}{9} + \frac{2}{5} = \frac{5}{5}\left(\frac{5}{5}\right) + \frac{2}{5}\left(\frac{9}{9}\right) = \overset{25}{\cancel{\frac{5}{9}\cancel{\frac{5}{5}}}} + \frac{2}{5}\left(\frac{9}{9}\right) = \frac{42}{45}$$

Samuel

$$\frac{4}{5} + \frac{1}{2} = \frac{4}{5}\left(\frac{2}{2}\right) + \frac{1}{2}\left(\frac{5}{5}\right) = \frac{4}{5}\overset{8}{\left(\frac{2}{2}\right)} + \frac{1}{2}\overset{5}{\left(\frac{5}{5}\right)} = \frac{13}{10} = \frac{3}{10}$$

Jean

$$\frac{3}{5} + \frac{2}{3} = \frac{3}{5}\left(\frac{5}{3}\right) + \frac{2}{3}\left(\frac{3}{5}\right) = \frac{3}{5}\overset{15}{\left(\frac{5}{3}\right)} + \frac{2}{3}\overset{6}{\left(\frac{3}{5}\right)} = \frac{21}{15}$$

12. Write a structured worksheet exercise to lead students through solving this problem:

$$8 - 3\frac{4}{5}$$

13. Specify the diagnosis and remediation procedures for each student.

Jim $\frac{6}{7}$ of 28 = $\frac{162}{7}$ = $23\frac{1}{7}$

Sarah $\frac{6}{7}$ of 28 = $\frac{6}{196}$ = $\frac{3}{98}$

William $\frac{6}{7}$ of 28 = $\frac{168}{7}$

14 Decimals

Terms and Concepts

Decimal Fractions Fractions with a denominator of 10 or any multiple of 10: 1/10, 1/100, 1/1000, etc.

Decimals Decimals are similar to fractions in that they both deal with something that has been divided into equal parts. Decimals are restricted, however, to situations with 10 parts or any power of 10, that is, 10, 100, 1000, etc. In a decimal, the number of equal parts is not indicated by a denominator but rather through place value. The position of a number in relation to a decimal point expresses the number of equal parts. For example, one digit after the decimal point indicates 10 equal parts, two digits indicates 100 equal parts, etc. The value of the digit represents the number of parts present, used, or acted upon; for example, .5 equals 5/10 and .5 represents a division into 10 equal parts with 5 parts present.

Mixed Decimal An expression consisting of a whole number and a decimal: 3.24, 18.05.

Percent The symbol % reads percent. It represents the ratio of two quantities with the denominator being hundredths. The fraction 2/5 may be converted to an equivalent fraction 40/100 which in turn may be expressed as 40%. When presenting the various forms of rational numbers, the teacher must consider their interrelatedness. Problem solving strategies designed for teaching fractions should be presented in a manner that will prepare students for decimals. Likewise, the strategies presented for decimals should prepare students for percent.

Skill Hierarchy

Instruction in decimals covers seven main areas:

1. Reading and writing decimals and mixed decimal numbers
2. Converting decimals to equivalent decimals
3. Adding and subtracting decimals
4. Rounding off decimals
5. Multiplying decimals
6. Dividing decimals
7. Converting between the decimal notation system and fraction notation system

The skill hierarchy in Figure 14.1 illustrates the relationship of the various skill areas to one another with respect to the sequence of their introduction. Note that analyzing fractions is a preskill for decimals. Students must understand what the numerator and denominator in a fraction represent: the denominator signifying the parts in each whole; the numerator, the parts that are used. They must also understand the concept of whole units versus parts of a whole. An understanding of fraction analysis skills is critical since decimals are explained as an alternative representation of fractions which have 10 or a multiple of 10 (100, 1000, etc.) as a denominator.

Also note that reading and writing decimals are component skills for all the other decimal operations. Too frequently an insufficient amount of instructional time is allotted to teaching students to accurately read and write decimals. Without adequate practice on these basic decimal reading and writing skills, students will encounter unnecessary difficulty when more advanced decimal skills are introduced.

Reading and Writing Decimals and Mixed Decimals

This section includes procedures for teaching students to read and write decimals and mixed decimals expressed as tenths, hundredths, and thousandths. Early direct instruction procedures for teaching students how to read and write decimals focus student attention on the number of digits after the decimal point (i.e., one digit after the decimal point indicates tenths; two digits after the decimal point indicate hundredths; three digits after the decimal point indicate thousandths).

Decimals and mixed decimals representing tenths and hundredths are usually introduced in fourth grade, while decimals and mixed decimals representing thousandths are introduced in fifth grade. The sequence for introducing these skills follows:

1. Reading decimals representing tenths or hundredths
2. Writing decimals representing tenths or hundredths
3. Reading and writing mixed decimals; decimals represent tenths or hundredths
4. Reading decimals representing thousandths
5. Writing decimals representing thousandths
6. Reading and writing mixed decimals; decimals represent thousandths

Note that students are taught to write decimal numbers immediately after they can read them.

Reading Decimals Representing Tenths and Hundredths

The format for reading decimals, which appears in Figure 14.3, introduces students to decimals as an alternative system for writing fractions of tenths and hundredths. The teacher begins by writing two fractions on the board, one with 10 as a denominator and one with 100 as a denominator (e.g., 4/10, 24/100) and has students read the fractions. Next the teacher explains that there is another way to express fractions which have 10 or 100 as a denominator. In this alternative method, a decimal point is used in lieu of the denominator. The teacher explains that if one digit is written after the decimal point, the decimal tells how many tenths; but if two digits are written after the decimal point, the decimal tells how many hundredths. (If students are unfamiliar with the term *digit*, they should be told that a digit is any written numeral from 0 to 9.)

After telling students the rule regarding the number of digits after the decimal, the teacher has the students read a list of numbers comprised of an equal mixture of tenths and hundredths decimals. Several minimally different sets (e.g., .07, .70, .7 and .4, .04, .40) are included among the examples. Included in the minimally different sets would be three decimal numbers: a decimal representing tenths (e.g., .8) and two decimals representing hundredths. In one of these hundredth decimals, a zero would precede the numeral (.08) while in the other hundredth decimal, the zero would follow the numeral (.80). The purpose of these minimally different sets is to focus student attention on the number of digits following the decimal.

The correction for errors in reading decimals is to have students identify the number of places after the decimal and then model and test identifying the decimal. For example, if a student misreads .04 as four-tenths, the teacher says, "How many digits after the decimal? So what does the 4 tell about?"

A critical teacher behavior for this format is monitoring student responses. To avoid student problems in confusing whole number and decimal numbers, teachers should be sure that students are adding the *ths* endings to tens, hundreds, and thousands. For example teachers should be sure .40 is pronounced as "forty hundredths" not "forty hundreds." Individual turns should be given frequently during the first several lessons. Practice on reading decimal numbers would be presented daily for 2–3 weeks. After the first several lessons, the

Figure 14.1 Skill Hierarchy

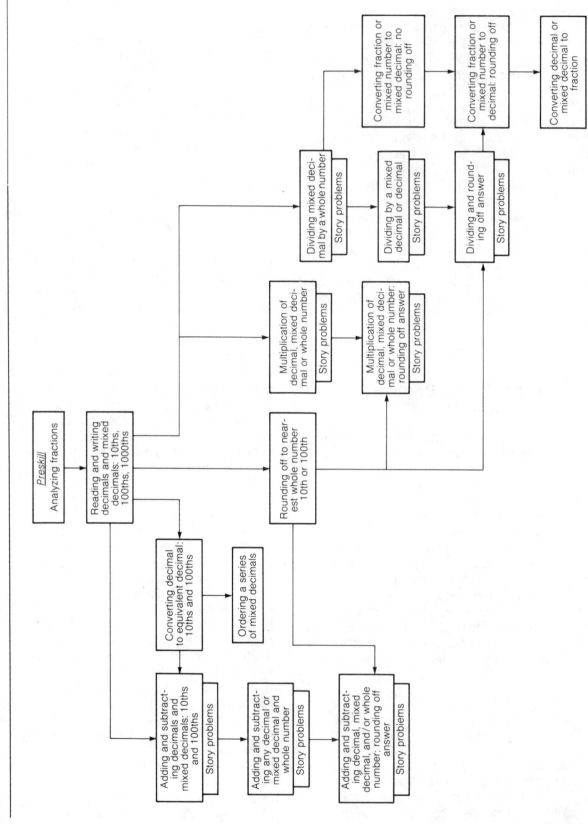

Figure 14.2 Instructional Sequence and Assessment Chart

Grade Level	Problem Type	Performance Indicator
4a	Reading tenths and hundredths	Circle the correct decimal: five-tenths 5 .05 .5 four-hundredths 4 .04 .4 seventy-hundredths 70 .70 .07
4b	Writing tenths and hundredths	Write these fractions as decimal numbers: $\frac{5}{100} =$ $\frac{5}{10} =$ $\frac{19}{100} =$

4c	Reading mixed decimals; tenths and hundredths	Circle the correct mixed decimal:
		five and three-tenths
		   .53 5.03 5.3
		ten and four-hundredths
		   1.04 10.04 10.4
		eighteen and six-hundredths
		   18.6 1.86 18.06

4d	Writing mixed decimals: tenths and hundredths	Write the mixed decimal for each mixed number: $10\frac{14}{100}$ ——— $16\frac{3}{10}$ ——— $40\frac{18}{100}$ ———
4e	Column alignment: adding tenths, hundredths, and whole numbers	Write these problems in columns and work them: 8.23 + 12.1 + 6 = 7 + .3 + 45 = .08 + 4 + .6 =
4f	Subtracting tenths and hundredths from whole numbers	5 – 3.2 = 8 – .34 = 7 – .3 =
4g	Ordering mixed decimals	Rewrite these numbers in order beginning with the smallest: 10.8 10.10 10.3 10.03 ——— ——— ——— ———
5a	Reading thousandths	Circle the correct decimal: five-thousandths .05 .5 .005 .500 ninety thousandths .90 .900 .090 .009
5b	Writing thousandths	Write these fractions as decimals: $\frac{342}{1000} =$ $\frac{60}{1000} =$ $\frac{5}{1000}$
5c	Multiplying decimals: one-digit or two digit factor times three digit factor	$\begin{array}{r} 7.14 \\ \times\ \ .5 \\ \hline \end{array}$ $\begin{array}{r} 214 \\ \times\ \ .7 \\ \hline \end{array}$
5d	Multiplying decimals: zero to be placed after decimal point	$\begin{array}{r} .1 \\ \times .7 \\ \hline \end{array}$ $\begin{array}{r} .02 \\ \times\ .8 \\ \hline \end{array}$

Figure 14.2 cont'd

Grade Level	Problem Type	Performance Indicator
5e	Rounding off decimals	Round off these numbers to the nearest whole number: 8.342 _____ 7.812 _____ Round off these numbers to the nearest tenth: 8.34 _____ 9.782 _____ Round off these numbers to the nearest hundredth: 8.346 _____ 9.782 _____
5f	Dividing: whole number divisor, no remainder	$5\overline{)32.45}$ $7\overline{)215.6}$ $2\overline{).856}$
5g	Dividing by whole number: quotient begins with zero	$9\overline{).036}$ $9\overline{).36}$ $9\overline{).0036}$
5h	Rounding off where there is a 9 or 99 after the decimal	Round off these numbers to the nearest tenth: 9.961 _____ 19.942 _____ 29.981 _____ Round off these numbers to the nearest hundredth: 14.993 _____ 14.996 _____ 29.9982 _____
5i	Dividing: whole number divisor, zeroes must be added to dividend after decimal point	Divide and write answer as mixed decimal: $2\overline{)3}$ $5\overline{)3.1}$ $4\overline{)21}$
5j	Dividing: whole number divisor, rounding off	Divide; write answer to mixed decimal; round off to the nearest hundredth: $7\overline{)3.1}$ $9\overline{)7}$ $3\overline{)2}$
5k	Converting proper fraction to decimal: no rounding off required	Rewrite these fractions as decimals: $\frac{2}{5} =$ $\frac{3}{4} =$ $\frac{3}{10} =$
5l	Converting proper fraction to decimal: rounding off required.	Rewrite these fractions as decimals; round off to nearest hundredth: $\frac{3}{7} =$ $\frac{4}{6} =$ $\frac{2}{9} =$
5m	Multiplying mixed decimal by 10 or 100: no zeroes added	$10 \times 34.2 =$ $100 \times 34.52 =$ $10 \times 34.52 =$
5n	Multiplying mixed decimal by 10 or 100: zeroes added	$100 \times 34.2 =$ $100 \times 3.42 =$ $100 \times 342 =$ $10 \times 342 =$
5o	Dividing: divisor is decimal, no adding zeroes in dividend necessary	$.2\overline{)23.74}$ $.2\overline{)14.26}$ $.05\overline{).345}$

Figure 14.2 cont'd

Grade Level	Problem Type	Performance Indicator
5p	Same as above: adding zero in dividend required	$.5\overline{)13}$ $\quad$ $.50\overline{)275}$ $\quad$ $.02\overline{)3.1}$ $\quad$ $.05\overline{)2}$
5q	Converting decimal to fractions	Circle the correct answer: .75 equals $\quad\frac{1}{4}\quad\frac{5}{7}\quad\frac{2}{3}\quad\frac{3}{4}$ .8 $\quad$ equals $\quad\frac{4}{5}\quad\frac{8}{8}\quad\frac{1}{8}\quad\frac{2}{5}$ .67 equals $\quad\frac{1}{4}\quad\frac{2}{3}\quad\frac{6}{7}\quad\frac{1}{6}$
5r	Converting mixed numbers to mixed decimals	Rewrite these mixed fractions as mixed decimals: $2\frac{3}{5} =$ $7\frac{1}{4} =$

teacher need not present all the steps in Part A but would just write decimals on the board and have students read them (step 4).

Part B includes a worksheet exercise designed both to provide practice in reading decimals and to reinforce the relationship between decimal fractions and decimals. Students are given worksheets with two types of items. In the first type, a decimal number is written to the left of three fractions:

$$.8 \;=\; \frac{8}{10} \qquad \frac{8}{100} \qquad \frac{1}{8}$$

The students read the decimal and then circle the fraction equivalent of the decimal number. In the second type of item, a fraction is written, and students must find the corresponding decimal among several similar-looking decimals:

$$\frac{4}{100} \;=\; .4 \qquad\quad .40 \qquad\quad .04$$

About five of each type of item would appear daily on worksheets for several weeks.

Writing Decimals Representing Tenths and Hundredths

Writing decimals representing tenths and hundredths is introduced after students can read those decimals accurately. A format for teaching students to write these decimals appears in Figure 14.4. The format includes three parts.

Part A is a structured board format in which the teacher demonstrates how to write a decimal fraction as a decimal. The teacher writes a fraction on the board and has the students read it. The teacher then asks how many digits must be after the decimal point and models writing it as a decimal number. Special attention must be given to frac-

tions with a hundred as the denominator and with a numerator less than 10 (e.g., 7/100, 4/100, 1/100).

When presenting these examples, the teacher demonstrates that in order to make two digits after the decimal, a zero must be written immediately after the decimal point. For example, "In writing 7/100, we write zero seven after the decimal point; in writing 4/100 we write zero four after the decimal point" (i.e., .07 and .04).

Practice on writing decimal numbers should be provided daily for several weeks. This practice can be provided in the form of written worksheets. On the worksheet would be fractions with 10 or 100 as the denominator. The student would write the decimal equivalents.

The example selection guideline is basically the same as that for the reading decimals format. Several minimally different sets (e.g., 8/10, 8/100, 80/100) would be included to provide students with the practice to determine when a zero is needed immediately after the decimal point. Several extra examples of hundredths fractions with a numerator below 10 would be included to provide extra practice on this difficult type of decimal.

Reading and Writing Mixed Decimals: Tenths and Hundredths

When the students are able to read and write tenths and hundredths decimals without prompting from the teacher, mixed decimals, numbers formed by a whole number and a decimal (e.g., 9.3, 16.4, 27.02), can be introduced. Students are first taught to read mixed decimals, then write them. The format for these skills appears in Figure 14.5. In Part A, the board presentation, the teacher introduces reading mixed decimals, explaining that the numerals before

Figure 14.3 Format for Reading Decimals

Day	Part A Structured Board Presentation Problems	Part B Structured Worksheet Problems	Part C Independent Practice Work- sheet Problems
1-4	8		
5-7	6 (step 4 only)	10	
8-Until accurate and fluent			10

PART A: Structured Board Presentation

TEACHER

Write on board:

$\frac{3}{10}$ and $\frac{3}{100}$

1. "READ THESE FRACTIONS."

2. "WE'RE GOING TO LEARN ANOTHER WAY TO WRITE TENTHS AND HUNDREDTHS." Write a decimal point on the board. "THIS IS A DECIMAL POINT. WHAT IS THIS?"
"ONE DIGIT AFTER THE DECIMAL POINT TELLS ABOUT TENTHS. WHAT DOES ONE DIGIT AFTER THE DECIMAL TELL ABOUT?"
"TWO DIGITS AFTER THE DECIMAL POINT TELL ABOUT HUNDREDTHS. WHAT DO TWO DIGITS AFTER THE DECIMAL POINT TELL ABOUT?"
"REMEMBER IF THERE IS ONE DIGIT AFTER THE DECIMAL POINT, THE NUMBER TELLS ABOUT TENTHS. IF THERE ARE TWO DIGITS AFTER THE DECIMAL POINT, THE NUMBER TELLS ABOUT HUNDREDTHS."

3. Write .9 on board.
"LISTEN. THERE'S ONE DIGIT AFTER THE DECIMAL POINT. THE 9 TELLS ABOUT TENTHS. THIS SAYS 'NINE TENTHS'." Write .09 on board. "LISTEN. THERE ARE TWO DIGITS AFTER THE DECIMAL POINT. THE 9 TELLS ABOUT HUNDREDTHS. THIS SAYS 'NINE HUNDREDTHS'. YOUR TURN."

4. Write .3 on the board.
"HOW MANY DIGITS AFTER THE DECIMAL POINT?"
"WHAT DOES THE 3 TELL ABOUT?"
"SAY THE DECIMAL NUMBER."

TO CORRECT: "HOW MANY DIGITS AFTER THE DECIMAL POINT? THERE IS/ARE _____ DIGIT(S) AFTER THE DECIMAL SO THE _____ TELLS ABOUT _____. THE DECIMAL SAYS _____."

Repeat step 3 with .03, .30, .6, .60, .06, .58.

5. Write on board: .7
"SAY THIS DECIMAL NUMBER."
Repeat step 4 with .70, .07, .9, .09, .90, .05, .4, .32.

STUDENTS

"Three-tenths, three-hundredths"

"A decimal point"

"Tenths"

"Hundredths"

"One"
"Tenths"
"Three-tenths"

Figure 14.3 cont'd

PART B: Structured Worksheet

TEACHER   **STUDENTS**

a. $\underline{.4} = \dfrac{4}{100} \quad \dfrac{4}{10} \quad \dfrac{40}{1000}$ g. $\dfrac{38}{100} = .3 \quad .38 \quad 38.$

b. $\underline{.40} = \dfrac{40}{100} \quad \dfrac{40}{10} \quad \dfrac{4}{10}$ h. $\dfrac{4}{100} = .40 \quad .04 \quad .4$

c. $\underline{.04} = \dfrac{40}{100} \quad \dfrac{40}{10} \quad \dfrac{4}{100}$ i. $\dfrac{40}{100} = .40 \quad .4 \quad .04$

d. $\underline{.61} = \dfrac{61}{100} \quad \dfrac{61}{10} \quad \dfrac{61}{1000}$ j. $\dfrac{8}{100} = .80 \quad .08 \quad .080$

e. $\underline{.06} = \dfrac{60}{100} \quad \dfrac{6}{100} \quad \dfrac{6}{10}$ k. $\dfrac{80}{100} = .80 \quad .08 \quad .8$

f. $\underline{.6} = \dfrac{6}{100} \quad \dfrac{6}{1000} \quad \dfrac{60}{100}$ l. $\dfrac{7}{10} = .70 \quad .07 \quad .7$

1. "READ THE DECIMAL NUMBER NEXT TO a."   "4 tenths"
   "WE HAVE TO FIND THE FRACTION THAT SAYS .4."

2. "READ THE FIRST FRACTION." Pause, signal.   "4 hundredths"
   "READ THE NEXT FRACTION." Pause, signal.   "4 tenths"
   "READ THE NEXT FRACTION." Pause, signal.   "40 thousandths"

3. "THE DECIMAL SAYS FOUR-TENTHS. DRAW A
   CIRCLE AROUND THE FRACTION THAT SAYS
   FOUR-TENTHS." Monitor student responses.

4. "WORK PROBLEMS b-f ON YOUR OWN. REMEM-
   BER TO CIRCLE THE FRACTION THAT SAYS THE
   SAME THING AS THE DECIMAL."

5. "READ THE FRACTION NEXT TO LETTER g."   "38 hundredths"
   "WE HAVE TO FIND THE DECIMAL THAT SAYS
   38 HUNDREDTHS."

6. "READ THE FIRST DECIMAL."   "3 tenths"
   "READ THE NEXT DECIMAL."   "38 hundredths"

7. "IT SAYS THE SAME THING AS THE FRACTION,
   SO DRAW A CIRCLE AROUND IT." Monitor student
   responses.

8. "WORK THE REST OF THE PROBLEMS ON YOUR
   OWN."

Figure 14.4 Format for Writing Decimal Numbers

Day	Part A Structured Board Presentation Problems	Part B Less Structured Worksheet Problems	Part C Independent Practice Problems
1-2	5	5	
3-5		5	5
6-Until accurate and fluent			10-15

PART A: Structured Board Presentation

TEACHER   **STUDENTS**

Write on board: $\dfrac{73}{100}$

Figure 14.4 cont'd

TEACHER	**STUDENTS**
1. "READ THIS FRACTION."	"73 hundredths"
2. "I WANT TO WRITE 73 HUNDREDTHS AS A DECIMAL."	
3. "HOW MANY DIGITS AFTER THE DECIMAL POINT WHEN A DECIMAL TELLS ABOUT HUNDREDTHS?"	"Two"
4. "SO I WRITE A DECIMAL POINT THEN 73. WHAT DO I WRITE AFTER THE DECIMAL POINT TO WRITE 73 HUNDREDTHS?"	"73"
5. Write .73. "READ THE DECIMAL."	"73 hundredths"

Repeat steps 1-5 with: 7/10, 7/100, 70/100, 4/100, 48/100, 6/10, 6/100, 60/100, 3/100.

Note: When presenting fractions like 7/100, the teacher says in step 4, "SO I WRITE A DECIMAL POINT THEN ZERO SEVEN."

PART B: Less Structured Worksheet

a. $\frac{4}{100}$ = _____   g. $\frac{32}{100}$ = _____

b. $\frac{4}{10}$ = _____   h. $\frac{28}{100}$ = _____

c. $\frac{40}{100}$ = _____   i. $\frac{9}{10}$ = _____

d. $\frac{7}{100}$ = _____   j. $\frac{92}{100}$ = _____

e. $\frac{7}{10}$ = _____   k. $\frac{9}{100}$ = _____

f. $\frac{70}{100}$ = _____   l. $\frac{5}{10}$ = _____

1. "READ THE DIRECTIONS."	"Write these fractions as decimals."
2. "READ THE FRACTION NEXT TO a."	"4 hundredths"
3. "HOW MANY DIGITS MUST THERE BE AFTER THE DECIMAL POINT FOR HUNDREDTHS?"	"Two"
4. "WHAT DO YOU WRITE AFTER THE DECIMAL POINT TO SAY FOUR HUNDREDTHS?"	"Zero four"
5. "NOW WRITE THE DECIMAL POINT AND THE NUMERAL(S) TO SAY SEVEN HUNDREDTHS."	

Repeat steps 2-5 with remaining examples.

Figure 14.5 Format for Reading and Writing Mixed Decimals

Day	Part A Structured Board Presentation Problems	Part B Structured Worksheet Problems	Part C Independent Practice Problems
1-2	6		
3-4	6 (step 3 only)	6	
6-Until accurate and fluent	6 (step 3 only)		10

Figure 14.5 cont'd

PART A: Structured Board Presentation

TEACHER   **STUDENTS**

1. Write a decimal point on the board. "THE NUMERALS
   ON THIS SIDE OF THE DECIMAL POINT (motion
   to the left) TELL ABOUT WHOLE NUMBERS. WHAT
   DO THE NUMERALS ON THIS SIDE OF THE DECI-
   MAL POINT (motion to the left) TELL ABOUT?"   "Whole numbers"
   "THE NUMERALS AFTER THE DECIMAL POINT
   (motion to the right) TELL ABOUT THE DECIMAL
   NUMBER."

2. Write on board: 2.4
   "THIS IS A MIXED DECIMAL. IT HAS A WHOLE
   NUMBER AND A DECIMAL NUMBER. IT SAYS TWO
   AND FOUR-TENTHS. WHAT IS THIS MIXED
   DECIMAL?"   "2 and 4 tenths"
   "WHAT'S THE WHOLE NUMBER IN THE MIXED
   DECIMAL?"   "2"
   "WHAT'S THE DECIMAL?"   "4 tenths"
   "SAY THE MIXED DECIMAL"   "2 and 4 tenths"

   Repeat step 2 with 9.03, 14.2, 16.23, 7.4, 9.03.

3. Write on board: 8.4
   "SAY THE MIXED DECIMAL." Repeat step 3
   with 8.04, 7.41, 19.2, 8.50, 19.02.

PART B: Structured Worksheet

Write the mixed decimal

a. eight and four tenths =   _____
b. sixteen and two hundredths =   _____
c. five and sixteen hundredths =   _____
d. eleven and four tenths =   _____
e. eleven and four hundredths =   _____
f. eleven and forty hundredths =   _____

g. $17\frac{9}{10}$ =   _____

h. $8\frac{45}{100}$ =   _____

i. $16\frac{1}{100}$ =   _____

j. $16\frac{5}{100}$ =   _____

k. $16\frac{10}{100}$ =   _____

1. "READ THE WORDS IN a."   "Eight and four tenths"

2. "WHAT'S THE WHOLE NUMBER?"   "Eight"
   "WRITE IT."

3. "WHAT'S THE DECIMAL NUMBER?"   "Four-tenths"
   "WRITE IT—DON'T FORGET THE DECIMAL
   POINT." Monitor responses.

4. "WHAT MIXED DECIMAL DID YOU WRITE?"   "Eight and four-tenths"

   Repeat steps 1–4 with problems b–f.

5. "READ THE MIXED NUMBER IN PROBLEM g."   "Seventeen and nine-tenths"

   Repeat steps 2–5 with remaining problems.

the decimal point represent whole numbers while the numerals after the decimal point tell about the decimal number. The teacher then models and tests reading several numbers, having the students say the whole number, the decimal, then the mixed decimal. Note that in saying mixed decimals, the teacher should heavily emphasize the word *and* (e.g., 15.03 should be read "fifteen and three hundredths"). This voice emphasis is designed to help students discriminate between the whole number and the decimal parts of the mixed decimal in preparation for writing mixed decimals. Reading mixed decimals is practiced daily for several weeks. No prompting is required after the first several days.

Part B, a structured worksheet exercise, includes two types of items. In the first type, a mixed fraction is written, and the student rewrites it as a mixed decimal:

12 3/100 is written as 12.03

In the second type, the words representing a mixed decimal are written and the student must write the mixed decimal; e.g., twenty eight and four hundredths is written as 28.04. This type of item is appropriate, of course, only for students able to decode well.

Reading and Writing Decimals Representing Thousandths

Decimals representing thousandths are introduced after students have mastered reading and writing decimals and mixed decimals representing tenths and hundredths. Thousandths decimals are taught with the same basic formulas as used for reading and writing tenth and hundredth decimals (see Figures 14.3 and 14.4) with the added explanation that if there are three digits after the decimal point the decimal tells about thousandths.

During the first several lessons, examples should concentrate entirely on thousandth numbers. Minimally different groupings such as

.809	.080	.008
.004	.040	.400
.070	.007	.753

should be presented. In these sets, two of the three digits in each decimal are zeroes and one digit is a numeral other than zero. In each decimal, the nonzero digit is placed in another position:

.003 .030 .300

After several lessons comprised of just thousandth decimals, the teacher would present ex-

amples including tenths, hundredths and thousandths Again, minimally different groupings should be included:

.4	.04	.004
.70	.070	.700

to focus student attention on the number of digits after the decimal point.

Writing decimals representing thousandths is particularly difficult because students must discriminate when to write two zeroes after the decimal point (e.g., .001, .009) from when to write one zero after the decimal point (e.g., .010, .090). Therefore, the teacher should be prepared to provide extensive practice on examples of this type.

Equivalent Decimals

Equivalent decimals are decimals that have the same value. The mixed decimals 8.30 and 8.3 are equivalent since they both represent the same quantity.

Converting a decimal, mixed decimal, or whole number to an equivalent mixed decimal is an important preskill for addition, subtraction, and division operations with decimal numbers. For example, when subtracting .39 from 5, students must convert 5 into 5.00. Students should be introduced to equivalent decimal conversions shortly after they can read and write decimals and mixed decimal numbers.

Figure 14.6 includes the format for teaching students how to convert decimals into equivalent decimals. Although the rewriting skill is simple since the students simply add or take away zeroes, students should understand why adding or taking away zeroes is permissible. Part A illustrates the rationale behind adding zeroes·by using equivalent fractions. The teacher demonstrates that changing a fraction like 3/10 to 30/100 involves multiplying by a fraction equal to 1(10/10) and, therefore, does not change the value of the original fraction. Since 3/10 = 30/100, then .3 = .30.

Part B is a structured board exercise demonstrating how to rewrite decimals. Part C is a worksheet exercise in which the students are given a chart containing columns for whole numbers, tenths, hundredths, and thousandths. The student's task is to write equivalent mixed decimals in other spaces across the row. For example, 9.1 is written in the tenths column. The student would add a zero, writing 9.10 in the hundredths column; and add two zeroes, writing 9.100 in the thousandths column. For whole numbers, the teacher explains that a

Figure 14.6 Format for Rewriting Decimals

Day	Part A Demonstration Problems	Part B Structured Board Problems	Part C Less Structured Worksheet Problems
1	4		
2		6	
3-4		4	6-8
5-Until accurate and fluent			8-10

PART A: Demonstration

TEACHER

1. "LISTEN TO THIS RULE. WHEN WE WRITE ZEROES AFTER A DECIMAL NUMBER, WE DON'T CHANGE THE VALUE OF THE NUMBER. SAY THAT."

2. Write on board: .3
   "READ THIS DECIMAL."
   "I'LL WRITE A ZERO AFTER THE DECIMAL." Add a zero .30. "NOW READ THE DECIMAL."
   "I CHANGED 3 TENTHS TO 30 HUNDREDTHS BY ADDING A ZERO AFTER A DECIMAL NUMBER."

3. "I'M GOING TO USE FRACTIONS TO SHOW THAT 3 TENTHS EQUALS 30 HUNDREDTHS."
   Write on board: $\dfrac{3}{10}$
   "READ THIS."
   "WE START WITH 3 TENTHS AND WE END WITH 30 HUNDREDTHS."
   Write on board: $\dfrac{30}{100}$
   "WHAT DO I MULTIPLY 10 BY TO MAKE IT 100?"
   "WHAT DO I MULTIPLY 3 BY TO MAKE IT 30?"
   Write on board: $\dfrac{3}{10} \cdot \left(\dfrac{10}{10}\right) = \dfrac{30}{100}$
   I MULTIPLIED 3 TENTHS BY 10 TENTHS: 10 TENTHS EQUAL 1. REMEMBER WHEN WE MULTIPLY BY 1 WE DON'T CHANGE THE VALUE OF A NUMBER. SO 3 TENTHS EQUALS 30 HUNDREDTHS." Write .3 = .30.

4. Repeat steps 2 and 3 changing .5 to .500.

5. "HERE'S ANOTHER RULE ABOUT ZEROES. IF WE CROSS OUT ZEROES AT THE END OF A DECIMAL NUMBER, WE DON'T CHANGE THE VALUE OF THE DECIMAL." Write .50. "READ THIS DECIMAL NUMBER."
   "I'LL CROSS OUT THE ZEROES AT THE END OF THE DECIMAL." Cross out zero: .50. "NOW WHAT DOES THIS DECIMAL SAY?"

STUDENTS

"When we write zeroes after a decimal number, we don't change the value of the number."

"Three-tenths"

"Thirty-hundredths"

"Three-tenths"

"10"
"10"

"Fifty hundredths"

"Five tenths"

Figure 14.6 cont'd

TEACHER	**STUDENTS**

6. "LET'S USE FRACTIONS TO SHOW THAT 50 HUN-
DREDTHS EQUAL 5 TENTHS."

Write on board: $\dfrac{50}{100} = \dfrac{5}{10}$

"FIFTY EQUALS 5 TIMES WHAT
NUMBER?" — "10"

"ONE HUNDRED EQUALS 10 TIMES WHAT
NUMBER?" — "10"

Write on board: $\dfrac{50}{100} = \dfrac{5}{10} \left(\dfrac{10}{10}\right)$

"TO MAKE 5 TENTHS INTO 50 HUNDREDTHS WE
MULTIPLIED IT BY 10 TENTHS. TEN-TENTHS
EQUAL 1. WHEN WE MULTIPLY BY 1 WE DON'T
CHANGE THE VALUE OF A NUMBER SO .50 = .5."

Repeat steps 5 and 6 with 300/1000 = 3/10.

PART B: Structured Board Presentation

1. Write on board: 8.4
"READ THIS NUMBER." — "8.4"
"I WANT TO REWRITE THIS MIXED DECIMAL SO
THAT THE DECIMAL TELLS ABOUT THOU-
SANDTHS."

2. "WHEN WE WRITE A DECIMAL THAT TELLS
ABOUT THOUSANDTHS HOW MANY DIGITS MUST
THERE BE AFTER THE DECIMAL POINT?" — "3"

3. "I ALREADY HAVE ONE DIGIT AFTER THE DECI-
MAL POINT, SO HOW MANY ZEROES MUST I ADD?" — "2"
Write 8.400.

4. "READ THE DECIMAL NUMBER NOW." — "8.400"
"DID WE CHANGE THE VALUE OF 8.4?" — "No"
"NO, 8.400 IS THE SAME AS 8.4. WHEN WE ADD
ZEROES AT THE END OF THE DECIMAL WE DON'T
CHANGE ITS VALUE."

Repeat steps 1–4 changing 5.1 to 5.10; 9.300 to 9.3,
7 to 7.00, 9 to 9.0.

PART C: Less Structured Worksheet

Give students a worksheet like this one:

Mixed Decimals

Tenths	Hundredths	Thousandths
3.7	———	———
———	———	———
9.2	———	———
———	———	———
———	6.20	———

1. Point across row a. "YOU HAVE TO FILL IN THE
MISSING MIXED DECIMAL NUMBERS. EVERY
MIXED DECIMAL IN A ROW MUST HAVE THE
SAME VALUE. READ THE NUMBER CLOSEST
TO a." — "3.7"

Figure 14.6 cont'd

TEACHER   **STUDENTS**

2. "TOUCH THE SPACE IN THE NEXT COLUMN.
   THE HEADING SAYS HUNDREDTHS. WE MUST
   REWRITE 3.7 SO THAT THE DECIMAL EXPRESSES
   HUNDREDTHS. HOW MANY DIGITS MUST BE
   AFTER THE DECIMAL POINT FOR HUNDREDTHS?"   "2"
   "THE MIXED DECIMAL 3.7 HAS ONE DIGIT AFTER
   THE DECIMAL. WHAT MUST YOU DO?"   "Add one zero"
   "WRITE THE MIXED DECIMAL IN THE HUN-
   DREDTHS COLUMN. WHAT MIXED NUMBER DID
   YOU WRITE IN THE HUNDREDTHS COLUMN?"   "3.70"

3. Repeat step 2 with the thousandths column.

   Repeat steps 2 and 3 with remaining examples.

   Note: When converting whole numbers to mixed decimals, the teacher explains that a decimal point
   is written after the whole number. After the decimal
   point, zero(es) are added: one zero if the decimal
   expresses tenths, two zeroes if it expresses hundredths, and three zeroes if it expresses thousandths.

whole number is converted into a mixed decimal by writing a decimal point after the number and writing zero(es) after the decimal point.

Adding and Subtracting Decimals and Mixed Decimals

Addition and subtraction problems with decimals and/or mixed decimals can be divided into two groups for instructional purposes. The first group contains those problems in which each number in the problem has the same number of decimal places; e.g., in the problems below all numbers have decimals representing hundredths:

$$
\begin{array}{r} 435.42 \\ +\ 17.82 \end{array}
\qquad
\begin{array}{r} 24.35 \\ -\ 1.48 \end{array}
$$

The second group is comprised of those problems in which the addends (in an addition problem) or the minuend and subtrahend (in a subtraction problem) have different numbers of digits after the decimal point:

$$
\begin{array}{r} 9.1 \\ -3.87 \end{array}
\qquad
\begin{array}{r} 4 \\ +3.64 \end{array}
\qquad
\begin{array}{r} 4 \\ -3.64 \end{array}
$$

Decimals Having the Same Number of Places

Problems in which each number has the same number of digits after the decimal point can be introduced when students can read and write decimals and mixed decimals. Problems of this type are relatively easy. The only new step involves placing the decimal point in the answer. Because the teaching procedure is simple, no format has been included.

The first problems should be vertically aligned so students can be taught to bring the decimal point straight down without first having to determine if the columns are properly aligned. For these problems, the teacher just instructs students to write the decimal in the answer below the other decimal points.

Problems written horizontally (e.g., 7.24 + 19.36) can be introduced shortly after the introduction of vertically aligned problems. For horizontal problems, we recommend teaching students to rewrite the problem so that the decimal points are in a column. When horizontal problems are introduced, teachers should initially monitor students' worksheets daily to see that students align the numbers correctly.

Decimals with Different Number of Places

Problems in which each mixed decimal has a different number of digits after the decimal point are introduced after students are able to rewrite decimal numbers as equivalent decimal numbers by adding zeroes after the decimal. This normally would be only a week or two after the easier addition and subtraction problems are presented. The strategy for solving these more complex problems involves rewriting one or more of the mixed decimal numbers so that each mixed decimal in the problem has the same number of digits after the decimal point. Once the problem has been rewritten, students are instructed to bring the decimal point straight down, then solve the problem. For example:

$$8.1 \quad \text{becomes} \quad 8.10$$
$$\underline{-3.42} \qquad\qquad \underline{-3.42}$$

Horizontally written problems should be introduced once students can solve the vertical problems. The key to accurately solving horizontal problems is correctly aligning the numbers vertically. Without direct instruction, students are likely to misalign the numbers as illustrated below:

$$3.72 + 18.4 \quad \text{becomes} \quad 3.72$$
$$\underline{+18.4}$$

The strategy for rewriting the decimal numbers so that each has the same number of digits after the decimal will prevent this alignment error from occurring. Figure 14.7 includes a format for presenting this type of problem.

Problems in which a decimal or mixed decimal is added to or subtracted from a whole number should receive special emphasis (e.g., $7 - 3.8$, $8 - .43$, $4.23 + 7 + 2.1$, $9.2 - 3$). Problems of this type would be introduced several days after problems with mixed decimals expressing various decimal fractions are introduced. The teacher reminds students that a whole number is converted to a mixed decimal by placing a decimal point after it and adding zeroes. The teacher models solving several problems. About half the problems on students' worksheets should include problems with a whole number.

Rounding Off Decimals

Rounding off is not only a useful skill in and of itself but is also a necessary component skill for decimal division and percent. An example of the use of rounding off in percentage problems occurs when converting $3/7$ to a percent: the 3 is divided by 7, which yields a decimal:

$$7 \overline{)3.000} \;\; {}^{.428}$$

The decimal then is rounded off to hundredths to determine the approximate percent, 43%. Although rounding off decimals involves steps similar to those used in rounding off whole numbers, these two skills should not be introduced at the same time

because of potential confusion. Rounding off whole numbers should have been presented many months before rounding off decimals is introduced.

Figure 14.8 includes a format for rounding off decimal numbers to the nearest whole number, tenth, hundredth, or thousandth. The rounding off strategy taught in this format is comprised of three steps:

1. The students determine how many digits will appear after the decimal point when the number is rounded off; e.g., when rounding off to the nearest tenth, one digit will be left after the decimal.
2. The students count that number of digits and then draw a line. If 3.4625 is to be rounded to the nearest tenth, the students place a line after the digit in the tenth place, the 4: 3.4/825. The line serves as a prompt.
3. The students look at the numeral after the line. If it is a 5 or more they add another unit to the digit before the line. For example .54/7 rounded to the nearest hundredth is .55 since 7 appears after the line, If a number less than 5 appears after the line, no extra unit is added. For example, 54/2 is rounded to .54 since a number less than 5 follows the line.

There are three important example selection guidelines for this format:

1. Half of the decimals should require the addition of another unit; i.e., the numeral after the place to be rounded off should be 5 through 9. In the other half of the decimals, the numeral after the place to be rounded off should be less than 5.
2. The numbers should have two or three places after the place to be rounded off. These extra places reinforce the concept that only the digit immediately after the line determines if another unit is added.
3. Examples should include a mix of problems that require students to round off to the nearest tenth or to the nearest hundredth. The sample worksheet in Part B of the format shows an application of these guidelines.

A particularly difficult type of rounding off problem arises when a unit is added to a 9, because the sum is 10. For example, rounding off .498 to the nearest hundredth requires students to add a whole unit to the nine-hundredths, which changes .498 to .50. Likewise, when rounding off 39.98 to the nearest tenth, the answer is 40. Problems of this type should be introduced after students have mastered

Figure 14.7 Format for Addition/Subtraction of Unlike Decimals

Day	Part A Structured Board Presentation Problems	Part B Structured Worksheet Problems	Part C Supervised Practice Problems	Part D Independent Practice Problems
1-2	3	4		
3		4	2	
4-Until accurate and fluent			4	6-10

PART A: Structured Board Presentation

TEACHER

1. "WHEN WE ADD OR SUBTRACT NUMBERS CON-
TAINING DECIMALS, WE FIRST REWRITE THEM
SO THEY ALL HAVE THE SAME NUMBER OF
PLACES AFTER THE DECIMAL POINT."
Write on board: 13.7 - 2.14

2. "READ THIS PROBLEM."

3. "WHICH NUMBER HAS MORE PLACES AFTER THE
DECIMAL POINT?"
"SO WE HAVE TO REWRITE THE PROBLEM SO
THAT EACH NUMBER IS TALKING ABOUT
HUNDREDTHS."

4. Point to 13.7. "WHAT CAN I DO TO 7 TENTHS TO
MAKE IT INTO A NUMBER WITH TWO PLACES
BEHIND THE DECIMAL?"
"YES, I ADD A ZERO AFTER THE 7." Write 0 after
7: 13.70. "NOW WE HAVE 70 HUNDREDTHS. READ
THE PROBLEM NOW."

5. "TO WORK THE PROBLEM, I'LL WRITE THE
PROBLEM IN A COLUMN MAKING SURE THE
DECIMAL POINTS ARE LINED UP."
Write and solve:
```
  13.70
-  2.14
  11.56
```

6. "I'LL WRITE THE DECIMAL POINT IN THE AN-
SWER. REMEMBER, WHEN WE ADD NUMBERS
WITH DECIMALS, WE BRING THE DECIMAL
POINT STRAIGHT DOWN." Write:
```
  13.70
-  2.14
  11.56
```
"READ THE ANSWER."

Repeat steps 1-6 with this problem: 18.9 - 3.425.

STUDENTS

"Thirteen and seven tenths minus
two and fourteen hundredths."

"2.14"

"Add a zero after the 7"

"13.70 - 2.14"

"11.56"

PART B: Structured Worksheet

a. 7.1 - 3.45   b. 16.345 + 8.3

c. 51.43 + 6.85   d. 13.6 – 2.346

e. 19.1 - 8.34   f. 96.4 + 86.4

g. 4.5 + 6.35   h. 271. - 71.42

Figure 14.7 cont'd

TEACHER	**STUDENTS**
1. "READ PROBLEM a ON YOUR WORKSHEET."	"7.1 - 3.45"
2. "DO THE NUMBERS HAVE THE SAME NUMBER OF PLACES AFTER THE DECIMAL POINT?"	"No"
3. "RIGHT. ONE NUMBER HAS TENTHS, AND THE OTHER HAS HUNDREDTHS. WHICH NUMBER HAS MORE PLACES AFTER THE DECIMAL?"	"3.45"
"SO WHICH NUMBER DO YOU HAVE TO CHANGE?"	"7.1"
"WHAT DO YOU DO TO 7.1?"	"Add a zero after the 1"
"ADD THE ZERO." Monitor responses. "NOW RE-WRITE THE PROBLEM IN A COLUMN AND WORK IT." Pause. "WHAT IS THE ANSWER?" Pause, signal.	"1.65"

Repeat steps 1-3 with several more problems.

easier rounding-off problems. When introducing the more difficult type, the teacher should model working several problems.

Most errors in rounding off occur because students do not attend to the relevant digit. A student is likely to round off .328 to .4 if she focuses on the 8 rather than the 2. The basic correction is to emphasize the steps in the strategy by asking the student:

1. "How many digits will there be after the decimal when we round off to the nearest whole (or tenth or hundredth)?"
2. "Where do you draw the line?"
3. "What number comes immediately after the line?"
4. "So do you add another whole (or tenth or hundredth)?"

Multiplying Decimals

Although the concept of multiplying decimals is difficult to illustrate, teaching students to solve a multiplication problem with decimal numbers is relatively simple. A possible demonstration to illustrate the rationale of the multiplying decimal strategy can be done with decimal fractions like these:

$$\frac{32}{100} \times \frac{4}{10}$$

The answer, 128/1000, would then be written as the decimal .128. The original problem would then be written in a decimal form:

$$\begin{array}{r} .32 \\ \times\ .4 \\ \hline \end{array}$$

and the teacher would point out the three decimal places in the two fractions and make three decimal places in the answer. "The factors always have the same number of decimal places as the answer; .32 has two places; .4 has one place. That's three decimal places. The answer has three decimal places too."

Figure 14.9 contains a format for multiplying decimals or mixed decimal numbers. In the board presentation, the teacher introduces the strategy for figuring out where the decimal point goes in the answer. In the worksheet presentation, the teacher gives the student a worksheet with 10 to 15 multiplication problems that have already been worked and leads students in determining where to place the decimal point. Note that in the problems on the worksheet, the decimal point in the factors appears in several different positions.

The less structured worksheet exercise includes a mix of multiplication and addition problems. The purpose of combining multiplication with addition is to ensure that students do not overgeneralize the procedure of counting the places to determine where to put the decimal. A worksheet might include these examples:

9.4 × .5	9.4 + .5	3.2 ×.57
.32 +.57	40 × 3	18 ×.32
.18 +.32	31.4 × .05	3.14 + .05

Before the students work the problems, the teacher should remind them about placing the

Figure 14.8 Format for Rounding Off Decimals

Day	Part A Structured Board Presentation Problems	Part B Structured Worksheet Problems	Part C Less Structured Worksheet Problems	Part D Supervised Practice Problems	Part E Independent Practice Problems
1-2	6				
3-4	2	6			
5-6		2	2	8	
7-accurate till fluent				8-10	8-10

PART A: Structured Board Presentation

TEACHER   **STUDENTS**

Write on board: .376

1. "I WANT TO ROUND OFF THIS DECIMAL TO THE
   NEAREST HUNDREDTH. WHEN WE TALK ABOUT
   HUNDREDTHS, HOW MANY DIGITS WILL WE
   HAVE AFTER THE DECIMAL?"   "Two"
   "I WILL COUNT OFF TWO DIGITS AFTER THE
   DECIMAL POINT THEN DRAW A LINE AFTER
   THAT DIGIT." Write .37/6.

2. "WHEN WE ROUND OFF A DECIMAL, WE MUST
   LOOK AT THE NUMBER THAT COMES AFTER
   THE LINE. IF THE NUMBER IS 5 OR MORE WE
   MUST ADD ANOTHER UNIT. WHAT NUMBER
   COMES AFTER THE LINE?"   "6"
   "SO MUST WE ADD ANOTHER HUNDREDTH?"   "Yes"
   "IF WE HAD 37 HUNDREDTHS AND WE ADD
   ANOTHER HUNDREDTH, HOW MANY HUN-
   DREDTHS DO WE HAVE?"   "38"
   "SO .376 ROUNDED TO THE NEAREST HUN-
   DREDTH IS . . . ."   ".38"
   Write .38.

3. Repeat steps 1 and 2 with
   .372 rounded to the nearest tenth
   .1482 rounded to the nearest hundredth
   .382 rounded to the nearest whole
   .924 rounded to the nearest hundredth

PART B: Structured Worksheet

a. Round .462 to the nearest tenth   _____

b. Round .428 to the nearest tenth   _____

c. Round .8562 to the nearest hundredth   _____

d. Round .8548 to the nearest hundredth   _____

e. Round .3467 to the nearest hundredth   _____

f. Round .3437 to the nearest hundredth   _____

g. Round .417 to the nearest tenth   _____

h. Round .482 to the nearest tenth   _____

i. Round .3819 to the nearest hundredth   _____

j. Round .3814 to the nearest hundredth   _____

Figure 14.8 cont'd

TEACHER

1. "TOUCH PROBLEM a. WHAT DO WE ROUND OFF THAT DECIMAL TO?"

"To the nearest tenth"

2. "HOW MANY DIGITS WILL BE AFTER THE DECIMAL POINT WHEN YOU ROUND OFF TO THE NEAREST TENTH?"
"COUNT ONE DIGIT AFTER THE DECIMAL POINT AND DRAW A LINE."

"One"

3. "LET'S SEE IF YOU ADD ANOTHER TENTH. WHAT NUMBER COMES JUST AFTER THE LINE?"
"SO DO YOU ADD ANOTHER TENTH?"
"YOU HAD FOUR TENTHS. IF YOU ADD A TENTH HOW MANY TENTHS DO YOU HAVE?"
"IF YOU ROUND OFF .462 TO THE NEAREST TENTH, WHAT DO YOU HAVE?"
"WRITE THE ANSWER ON THE LINE."

"6"
"Yes"

"5"

"5 tenths"
Students write .5.

Repeat steps 1–3 with remaining problems.

PART C: Less Structured Worksheet

1. "READ ITEM a."

2. "DRAW A LINE TO SHOW WHERE YOU ROUND OFF."

3. ROUND OFF AND WRITE YOUR ANSWER ON THE LINE."

4. "READ YOUR ANSWER."

Repeat steps 1–4 with remaining problems.

---

decimal point in different types of problems. "In addition problems, bring the decimal point straight down. In multiplication problems, count the digits after the decimal points in the numbers you multiply." The teacher then carefully monitors the students as they work the first several problems.

A potentially confusing type of multiplication problem is one in which the students must place a zero in front of the digits in the answer. For example, when multiplying $.4 \times .2$, the student must add a zero before the 8; $.4 \times .2 = .08$. Likewise, in $.5 \times .01$, the student must place two zeros after the decimal; $.5 \times .01 = .005$. This type of problem would be introduced after the easier types of problems. The teacher models solving several problems of this type, then includes about three such problems in daily worksheet assignments.

A common error found on independent seatwork is students' simply not putting the decimal point in the answer. The correction is to inform the students that they forgot to put in the decimal point. If the error occurs frequently, the teacher should prepare worksheets with about 10 to 15 problems, two-thirds of which contain decimals.

In presenting the worksheet, the teacher tells students that the worksheet was designed to try and fool them—that some of the problems require decimal points in the answer and some don't. The teacher then monitors closely as students complete the worksheet so that immediate corrections can be made.

Dividing Decimals

Dividing decimal numbers is the most difficult decimal operation. Division with decimal numbers can be introduced when students can read and write decimals and perform long division. When long division with whole numbers was taught, the teacher should have stressed placing the digits in the quotient over the proper places in the dividend. For example, when working the problem $186 \div 2$, the quotient should be written as in example a rather than in example b:

$$\text{a. } 2\overline{)186} = 93 \qquad \text{b. } 2\overline{)186} = 93$$

Figure 14.9 Format for Multiplying Decimals

Day	Part A Structured Board Presentation Problems	Part B Structured Worksheet Problems	Part C Less Structured Worksheet Problems	Part D Supervised Practice Problems	Part E Independent Practice Problems
1-3	4	12			
4-5		1	12		
6-accurate				12	
till fluent					12

PART A: Structured Board Presentation

TEACHER   **STUDENTS**

1. Write on board:

$$\begin{array}{r} 34.2 \\ \times\ .59 \\ \hline 3078 \\ 1710 \\ \hline 20178 \end{array}$$

1. "WE'RE MULTIPLYING MIXED DECIMALS SO WE HAVE TO PUT A DECIMAL POINT IN OUR AN-SWER. HERE'S A FAST WAY TO FIGURE OUT WHERE TO WRITE THE DECIMAL POINT IN THE ANSWER. WE COUNT THE PLACES AFTER THE DECIMAL POINTS IN BOTH NUMBERS WE'RE MULTIPLYING."

2. "I'LL TOUCH THE NUMBERS AFTER THE DECI-MAL POINTS AND COUNT THEM (touch 2) ONE (touch 9) TWO (touch 5) THREE. HOW MANY DECI-MAL PLACES IN BOTH NUMBERS?"   "3"

3. "SO I WRITE THE DECIMAL POINT IN THE AN-SWER SO THAT THERE ARE THREE PLACES AFTER IT." Point between 7 and 8. "ONE PLACE." Point between 1 and 7. "TWO PLACES." Point between 0 and 1. "THREE PLACES. I PUT THE DECIMAL POINT HERE." Point between 0 and 1.

4. "HOW MANY PLACES AFTER THE DECIMAL POINT?"   "3"
"READ THE ANSWER."   "20.178"

Repeat steps 1-4 with these problems:

$$\begin{array}{r} 34.2 \\ \times\ \ \ \ 5 \\ \hline \end{array} \qquad \begin{array}{r} 34.2 \\ \times\ \ .7 \\ \hline \end{array} \qquad \begin{array}{r} 351 \\ \times\ .05 \\ \hline \end{array}$$

PART B: Structured Worksheet

a. $\begin{array}{r} 32.1 \\ \times\ \ .9 \\ \hline 2789 \end{array}$	b. $\begin{array}{r} .321 \\ \times\ \ .9 \\ \hline 2789 \end{array}$	c. $\begin{array}{r} 3.21 \\ \times\ \ \ 9 \\ \hline 2789 \end{array}$	d. $\begin{array}{r} 321 \\ \times\ .9 \\ \hline 2889 \end{array}$	e. $\begin{array}{r} 3.421 \\ \times\ \ \ .7 \\ \hline 23947 \end{array}$

f. $\begin{array}{r} 492 \\ \times\ .53 \\ \hline 1476 \\ 24600 \\ \hline 26076 \end{array}$	g. $\begin{array}{r} 4.92 \\ \times\ \ .53 \\ \hline 1476 \\ 24600 \\ \hline 26076 \end{array}$	h. $\begin{array}{r} .492 \\ \times\ 5.3 \\ \hline 1476 \\ 24600 \\ \hline 26076 \end{array}$	i. $\begin{array}{r} 49.2 \\ \times\ \ 53 \\ \hline 1476 \\ 24600 \\ \hline 26076 \end{array}$

Figure 14.9 cont'd

TEACHER **STUDENTS**

j. 429   k. .32   l. 3.2   m. 3.2
  × 53   × .05   × 5   ×.05
  1476   160   160   160
 24600   000   000
 26076   160   160   160

1. "THESE PROBLEMS ARE WORKED ALREADY. ALL YOU HAVE TO DO IS PUT IN THE DECIMAL POINTS."

2. "TOUCH PROBLEM a."

3. "HOW MANY PLACES ARE AFTER THE DECIMAL POINTS IN BOTH NUMBERS BEING MULTIPLIED?" Pause, signal. "2"

4. "WHERE DOES THE DECIMAL POINT GO IN THE ANSWER?" "Between the 7 and the 8"

5. "WRITE IT."

6. "READ THE ANSWER." "27.89"

Repeat steps 2-6 with remaining problems.

PART C: Less Structured Worksheet

1. Give students worksheet with a mix of multiplication and addition problems containing decimals and mixed decimals. "REMEMBER WHEN YOU MULTIPLY YOU COUNT THE PLACES AFTER THE DECIMAL POINT. WHEN YOU ADD YOU BRING THE DECIMAL POINT STRAIGHT DOWN."

2. "WORK PROBLEM a." Pause.

3. "WHERE DOES THE DECIMAL POINT GO?"

Repeat steps 1-3 with remaining problems.

If students have not learned to write numerals in the quotient in the proper position, errors of misplacing the decimal in the quotient are likely to occur:

$$\frac{9.3}{2\overline{)1.86}} \quad \text{rather than} \quad \frac{.93}{2\overline{)1.86}}$$

Procedures for teaching proper placement of the digits in the quotient of long division problems are discussed in Chapter 11.

Division problems with decimals can be categorized into four types according to their relative difficulty. The first three types have divisors that are whole numbers.

1. Problems in which the quotient does not have a remainder and requires no conversion of the dividend:

$$\frac{.69}{5\overline{)3.45}} \quad \text{or} \quad \frac{.03}{7\overline{)21}}$$

2. Problems in which the dividend must be converted to an equivalent decimal so that no remainder will be present:

$$\frac{.7}{5\overline{)3.7}} \quad \text{becomes} \quad \frac{.74}{5\overline{)3.70}}$$
$$\frac{3\ 5}{2}$$

3. Problems with a remainder that requires rounding off:

$$\frac{.342}{7\overline{)2.400}} = .34$$
$$\frac{2\ 1}{30}$$
$$\frac{28}{20}$$
$$\frac{14}{6}$$

4. Problems in which the divisor is a decimal or mixed decimal number and must be converted to a whole number:

$$.4\overline{)61.32} \quad \text{becomes} \quad .4\overline{)61.32}$$

Decimal or Mixed Decimal Divided by a Whole Number

Division problems in which the dividend is a mixed decimal or decimal number and the divisor a whole number are usually introduced in late fourth or early to mid-fifth grade. An elaborate format is not required to introduce the problem type in which the divisor goes into the dividend without leaving any remainder:

$$5\overline{)2.35} \qquad 7\overline{)84.7}$$

The teacher presents the rule that the decimal point must be written on the line directly above where it appears in the number being divided into. For example, when dividing 69.26 by 6, the student writes the problem:

$$6\overline{)69.26}$$

then places the decimal point on the line on which the quotient will be written directly above the decimal in the dividend:

$$6\overline{)69.26}$$

The teacher then leads students through working several sets of problems, emphasizing the need to place the digits in the quotient in their proper place.

There are two example selection guidelines for problems without remainders. First, the decimal point should appear in different positions in various problems:

a. $5\overline{)3.725}$ b. $2\overline{)184.6}$ c. $9\overline{)1.836}$

d. $7\overline{).364}$ e. $5\overline{)23.5}$ f. $5\overline{).215}$

Second, one or two problems in which a zero must be placed immediately after the decimal point should be included. In problems d and f above, the quotients are .052 and .043. The teacher may have to provide extra prompting on these problems by explaining that a digit must be written in every place after the decimal point. Therefore, in problem d, the teacher might say, "7 doesn't go into 3 so write a zero above the 3." Daily practice would include 6–10 problems.

The second type of decimal division problem requires the student to eliminate a remainder by rewriting the dividend as an equivalent decimal. For example, zeroes need to be added to the dividend in each of the following problems:

a. $5\overline{)3.1} = 5\overline{)3.10}$ with quotient $.62$

c. $4\overline{)3} = 4\overline{)3.00}$ with quotient $.75$

b. $2\overline{)3.45} = 2\overline{)3.450}$ with quotient 1.725

d. $5\overline{)2} = 5\overline{)2.0}$ with quotient $.4$

This type of problem is introduced about 2 weeks after decimal division problems without remainders.

The preskill of converting a decimal to an equivalent decimal should be taught prior to the introduction of this problem type. These problems are not very difficult and like the previous type do not require a lengthy format. In introducing the problems, the teacher would explain that students should work them until there are no remainders. He then models working problems that require the addition of zeroes. For example, after bringing down the final digit, 9, of the dividend in this problem:

```
      5.6
6)33.9
  30
  ──
   3.9
   3 6
   ──
   3
```

the teacher would explain that he must keep dividing since he doesn't want a remainder, "I add a zero after the last digit in the decimal and divide again. Remember adding zeroes after a decimal does not change the value of the number."

```
      5.65
6)33.90
  30
  ──
   3 9
   3 6
   ──
    30
    30
```

Examples in these exercises should be designed so that the addition of one or two zeroes to the dividend eliminates a remainder. Several examples such as

$$4\overline{)3} \quad \text{or} \quad 5\overline{)8}$$

in which a whole number is the dividend should be included. These problems may require the teacher to remind students to write the decimal point first and then add zeroes after the whole number:

$$4\overline{)3} \quad \text{becomes} \quad 4\overline{)3.0}$$

Daily practice exercises would include 6-10 problems.

The third type of decimal division problem requires rounding off. Students are usually instructed to work these problems to the nearest tenth, hundredth, or thousandth. Obviously the preskill is rounding off decimal numbers. The format for presenting this problem type appears in Figure 14.10. In Part A, the teacher demonstrates how to work the problem. The student first reads the directions specifying to what decimal place (tenths, hundredths, thousandths) the answer is to be rounded. The teacher asks how many digits must be written after the decimal point in the answer, then instructs the students to work the problem until they have written that many digits. The teacher instructs the students to draw a line after that last digit in the answer and divide once more so they can decide how to round off the answer. The answer is then rounded off. If the numeral after the line is 5 or greater, another unit is added; if the numeral after the line is less than 5, no additional unit is added.

Special consideration should again be given to those problems in which a whole number is being divided by a larger whole number. These problems are very important since they prepare students to compute percentages; e.g., "John made 4 out of 7 basketball shots. What is his percentage for making shots?" We recommend that students round off answers in this type of problem to the nearest hundredth since percents are based on hundredths.

Dividing by a Decimal or Mixed Decimal

The fourth type of division problem has a decimal or mixed decimal divisor. Problems of this type are relatively difficult because students must multiply the divisor and dividend by 10 or a multiple of 10 to convert the divisor into a whole number. Both the dividend and divisor must be multiplied by the same number, so the numerical value represented by the problem is not altered. For example, to work the problem 8.7 ÷ .35, students must multiply the dividend and divisor by 100, converting .35 to 35 and 8.7 to 870.

The preskill of moving the decimal to the right when multiplying by a multiple of 10 should be taught and practiced for several weeks before introducing division problems with decimal divisors. The format in Figure 14.11 teaches this preskill. Students are taught that when a decimal number is multiplied by 10, the decimal point moves one place to the right; when it is multiplied by 100, the decimal moves two places to the right; and when it is multiplied by 1000, the decimal point moves three places to the right.

Particularly difficult problems are those in which a zero must be added. For example, to multiply 8.7 × 100, the students must add a zero to the 8.7 so they can move the decimal point two places to the right; 8.7 × 100 = 870. The teacher will need to model several of these problems, explaining the need to add zeroes. "You have to move the decimal point two places to the right, but you've

only got one decimal place to the right. Add a zero so you can move the decimal point two places."

The examples included in this preskill exercise should include a mix of problem types. The decimal point should not be placed in the same position from problem to problem. In half the problems, 10 should be a factor, and in the other half, 100 should be a factor. Several problems should require that students add zeroes to a mixed decimal (e.g., 100 × 34.2, 100 × 14.2). Also, several problems should include a whole number that must be multiplied by a multiple of 10 (e.g., 10 × 34, 25 × 100). As the decimal point is moved over, zeroes are added. For example, with 15 × 100, the student writes 15 then adds two zeroes: 1500. The teacher models working several of these problems, pointing out that a whole number can be converted to a mixed decimal by adding a decimal point after the last digit in the whole number (e.g., 15 is written as 15.).

Teachers can demonstrate that moving the decimal and adding a zero when multiplying by a multiple of 10 is valid by beginning with a problem like this:

$$\begin{array}{r} 3.4 \\ \times 10 \\ \hline 00 \\ 340 \\ \hline 34.0 \end{array}$$

The teacher would point out that when he multiplies by 10, the answer is 34 with the decimal point moved one place to the right and a zero added. Next the teacher would write this problem:

$$\begin{array}{r} 3.4 \\ \times 100 \\ \hline 00 \\ 000 \\ 3400 \\ \hline 340.0 \end{array}$$

and point out that when he multiplies by 100, the answer is 34 with the decimal point moved two places to the right.

Division problems with decimal or mixed decimal divisors are introduced when students have mastered the multiplying by multiples of 10 preskill and can work all types of problems in which the divisor is a whole number and the dividend a decimal or mixed decimal number. Figure 14.12 shows a format for teaching students to work problems with a decimal or mixed decimal divisor.

In Part A, the teacher presents a rule: "We cannot divide by a decimal number" and demonstrates how the divisor and dividend must be

Figure 14.10 Format for Division with Decimals—Rounding Off

Day	Part A Structured Board Presentation Problems	Part B Structured Worksheet Problems	Part C Less Structured Worksheet Problems	Part D Supervised Practice Problems	Part E Independent Worksheet Problems
1	4				
2-3	3	4			
4-5		4	2	2	
6-accurate till fluent				6-8	6-8

PART A: Structured Board Presentation

TEACHER

Write these instructions on the board:

Work the problem, express your answer to the nearest hundredth: 7)3.24

1. "READ THE PROBLEM."
   "THE INSTRUCTIONS TELL US TO WORK THE PROBLEM TO THE NEAREST HUNDREDTH. HOW MANY DIGITS AFTER THE DECIMAL POINT WHEN WE HAVE HUNDREDTHS?"
   "SO WE WORK THE PROBLEM UNTIL WE HAVE TWO DIGITS AFTER THE DECIMAL POINT."
   Write on board:

   ```
       .46
   7)3.24
     2 8
       44
       42
        2
   ```

2. "WE HAVE HUNDREDTHS IN THE ANSWER, BUT WE'RE NOT DONE BECAUSE WE HAVE A REMAINDER. WE HAVE TO WORK THE PROBLEM TO THOUSANDTHS AND THEN ROUND TO HUNDREDTHS. SO I DRAW A LINE AFTER THE 6."

3. "WE HAVE TO DIVIDE ONE MORE TIME SO WE KNOW HOW TO ROUND OFF. HERE'S WHAT WE DO. WE ADD A ZERO AFTER THE 4 IN THE NUMBER WE'RE DIVIDING. REMEMBER, WHEN YOU ADD A ZERO AFTER THE LAST DIGIT IN A DECIMAL NUMBER, YOU DON'T CHANGE THE VALUE OF THE NUMBER."
   Write on board:

   ```
       .46
   7)3.240
     2 8
       44
       42
        2
   ```

STUDENTS

"7 goes into 3 and 24 hundredths"

"2"

Figure 14.10 cont'd

TEACHER	**STUDENTS**

"NOW WE CAN DIVIDE AGAIN. WE BRING DOWN
THE ZERO." Write 0 next to 2. "HOW MANY 7s IN
20?" Pause, signal.   "2"
Write 14 and 2.

```
     .462
  7)3.240
    28
    44
    42
     20
     14
      6
```

4. "DO I ROUND OFF TO 46 HUNDREDTHS OR 47
   HUNDREDTHS?"   "46 hundredths"

   TO CORRECT: "WHAT NUMBER IS AFTER THE
                ROUNDING OFF LINE? THAT IS LESS
                THAN 5 SO WE DON'T ADD ANOTHER
                UNIT."

   Repeat steps 1–4 with these problems:

   9)$\overline{4}$ round off to nearest tenth

   7)$\overline{26.3}$ round off to nearest hundredth

   3)$\overline{2}$ round off to nearest hundredth

PART B: Structured Worksheet

a. Work these problems and round off to the nearest
   hundredth.

   1. 3)$\overline{7.4}$ =   2. 6)$\overline{5}$ =

b. Work these problems and round off to the nearest tenth.

   3. 4)$\overline{2.31}$ =   4. 7)$\overline{3}$ =

1. "READ THE INSTRUCTIONS FOR a."   "Work these problems and round
                                             off to the nearest hundredth."
   "READ PROBLEM ONE."   "3 into 7.4"

2. "YOU HAVE TO ROUND THE PROBLEM TO THE
   NEAREST HUNDREDTH. HOW MANY DIGITS
   WILL THERE BE AFTER THE DECIMAL POINT
   IN YOUR ANSWER?"   "2"
   "WORK THE PROBLEM. STOP AFTER THERE ARE
   TWO DIGITS AFTER THE DECIMAL POINT."
   Monitor students' work

```
        2.46
     3)7.40
       6
       1.4
       1 2
        20
        18
```

3. "YOU'RE NOT FINISHED BECAUSE YOU STILL
   HAVE A REMAINDER. DRAW A LINE AFTER THE
   LAST DIGIT IN YOUR ANSWER. NOW ADD A ZERO
   TO 7.40 AND DIVIDE AGAIN." Pause.

Figure 14.10 cont'd

TEACHER	**STUDENTS**

4. "WHAT NUMERAL DID YOU WRITE AFTER THE
   LINE IN THE ANSWER?"   "6"
   "SO DO YOU ADD ANOTHER HUNDREDTH?"   "Yes"
   "WRITE YOUR ROUNDED OFF ANSWER. WHAT'S
   YOUR ANSWER?"   "2.47"

PART C: Less Structured Worksheet

1. "READ THE INSTRUCTIONS FOR a."

2. "READ PROBLEM ONE."

3. "WHERE ARE YOU GOING TO DRAW THE LINE
   FOR ROUNDING OFF: AFTER THE FIRST,
   SECOND, OR THIRD DIGIT BEHIND THE DECI-
   MAL POINT?"

4. "WORK THE PROBLEM AND WRITE YOUR
   ROUNDED OFF ANSWER."

Figure 14.11 Preskill: Multiplying Decimals by Multiples of 10

Day	Part A Structured Board Presentation Problems	Part B Structured Worksheet Problems	Part C Supervised Practice Problems	Part D Independent Practice Problems
1-2	6	6		
3-4		6	6	
5-accurate			15-20	
6-fluent				15-20

PART A: Structured Board Presentation

TEACHER	**STUDENTS**

1. "HERE ARE SOME RULES ABOUT MULTIPLYING
   DECIMALS BY 10 OR 100. WHEN YOU MULTIPLY
   BY 10 YOU MOVE THE DECIMAL ONE PLACE TO
   THE RIGHT. WHAT DO YOU DO TO THE DECIMAL
   POINT WHEN YOU MULTIPLY BY 10?"   "Move it one place to the right."
   "WHEN YOU MULTIPLY BY 100 YOU MOVE THE
   DECIMAL POINT TWO PLACES TO THE RIGHT.
   WHAT DO YOU DO WITH THE DECIMAL POINT
   WHEN YOU MULTIPLY BY 100?"   "Move it two places to the right"

2. Write on board: 37.48×10
   "READ THE PROBLEM."   "37.48×10"
   "WE'RE MULTIPLYING BY 10. WHAT DO YOU DO
   TO THE DECIMAL POINT WHEN YOU MULTIPLY
   BY 10?"   "Move it one place to the right"

3. Write on the board: $37.48 \times 10 = 3748$
   "THE DECIMAL POINT WAS BETWEEN THE 7
   AND THE 4. IF I MOVE IT ONE PLACE TO THE
   RIGHT, WHERE WILL THE DECIMAL BE?"   "Between the 4 and 8"
   Write on board: $37.48 \times 10 = 374.8$
   "READ THE ANSWER."   "374.8"

Figure 14.11 cont'd

TEACHER   **STUDENTS**

4. Repeat steps 2 and 3 with these problems:
   37 × 100
   8.532 × 10
   7.2 × 100
   25 × 100
   2.5 × 10

PART B: Structured Worksheet

a. 3.74 × 10 =   e.   16 × 100 =

b. .894 × 100 =   f.   15 × 10 =

c. 42.8 × 100 =   g. .0382 × 10 =

d. 3.517 × 10 =   h. 49.2 × 100 =

1. "WHEN YOU MULTIPLY BY 10 WHAT MUST YOU DO?"

                                                              "Move the decimal one place to the right."

   "WHEN YOU MULTIPLY BY 100 WHAT MUST YOU DO?"

                                                              "Move the decimal two places to the right."

2. "READ PROBLEM a."   "3.74 × 10"

3. "YOU'RE MULTIPLYING BY 10, SO WHAT MUST YOU DO TO THE DECIMAL POINT?"

                                                              "Move it one place to the right."

4. "WHERE WILL THE DECIMAL POINT BE IN THE ANSWER?"

                                                              "Between the 7 and the 4"

5. "WRITE THE ANSWER."   Students write 37.4.

6. "READ YOUR ANSWER."   "37.4"

   Repeat steps 1-6 with remaining problems.

---

revalued. Both the divisor and dividend are multiplied by whatever multiple of 10 is needed to change the divisor into a whole number. The teacher revalues the divisor first by moving the decimal point to the right. The dividend is revalued by moving the decimal point the same number of spaces to the right. Note in the format the demonstration of how to revalue a problem is kept relatively simple to avoid confusing students by lengthy explanations.

There are two example selection guidelines. First, the number of places in the divisor and dividend should vary from problem to problem. For example, a worksheet might include the following problems:

a. $.5\overline{)3.75}$ b. $.05\overline{)37.5}$ c. $2.5\overline{)75}$

d. $.2\overline{)1368}$ e. $.03\overline{)24}$ f. $.5\overline{)21.85}$

Changing the type of decimal divisor forces students to attend carefully to moving the decimal. A second guideline involves including some examples

in which zeroes must be added to the dividend (e.g., problems b, c, and e above). After a week or so, some problems in which a decimal or mixed decimal is divided by a whole number should be included so that students will receive adequate practice applying the strategies for the various types of problems.

If the teacher wishes to demonstrate the validity of moving the decimal point, she begins with a division problem:

$$.5\overline{)2.4} = \frac{2.4}{.5}$$

"Dividing by a decimal is too hard, so I have to change .5 into a whole number. I do that by multiplying by 10. If I multiply the denominator by 10, what do I have to do to the numerator? . . . Right, ten-tenths equal 1, and when we multiply by 1 we don't change the value of the fraction." The teacher writes this:

$$\frac{2.4}{.5} \times \frac{10}{10} = \frac{24}{5}$$

Figure 14.12 Format for Dividing by Decimals

Day	Part A Structured Board Presentation Problems	Part B Structured Worksheet Problems	Part C Supervised Practice Problems	Part D Independent Practice Problems
1	5			
2-3	3	5		
4-5	1	4	4	
6—When students reach 90% accuracy			6	
				6-8

PART A: Structured Board Presentation

TEACHER	**STUDENTS**

Write on board: .5)⎺5̅1̅.̅7̅5̅

1. "HERE'S A RULE ABOUT DECIMAL DIVISION. WE DON'T DIVIDE BY A DECIMAL NUMBER. (Point to .5.) WE MUST CHANGE THE DIVISOR TO A WHOLE NUMBER."

2. Point to .5)⎺5̅1̅.̅7̅5̅
   "WHAT IS THE DIVISOR IN THIS PROBLEM?"   ".5"
   CAN WE WORK THE PROBLEM THE WAY IT IS?"   "No"
   "WHAT MUST WE DO?"   "Change the divisor to a whole number"

3. "WE MAKE FIVE-TENTHS A WHOLE NUMBER BY MOVING THE DECIMAL POINT. A NUMBER IS A WHOLE NUMBER WHEN THERE ARE NO DIGITS AFTER THE DECIMAL POINT. HOW MANY PLACES MUST I MOVE THE DECIMAL POINT OVER TO THE RIGHT TO MAKE .5 INTO A WHOLE NUMBER?"   "One"
   Draw arrow: .5␣)⎺5̅1̅.̅7̅5̅

   "I MOVED THE DECIMAL ONE PLACE TO THE RIGHT. WE HAVE TO MOVE THE DECIMAL POINT THE SAME NUMBER OF PLACES IN THE DIVIDEND. HOW MANY PLACES TO THE RIGHT MUST WE MOVE THE DECIMAL POINT IN THE DIVIDEND?"   "One"
   Write on board: .5␣)⎺5̅1̅.̅7̅5̅

   "NOW WE CAN WORK THE PROBLEM. I WRITE THE DECIMAL POINT ON THE ANSWER LINE, THEN DIVIDE."
   Write on board: ⨯5.)⎺5̅1̅⨯7̅.̅5̅

4. "I'LL DIVIDE."

```
        10 3.5
  ⨯5.)⎺5̅1̅⨯7̅.̅5̅
        5
        01 7
         1 5
           2 5
           2 5
```

Figure 14.12 cont'd

5. "WHAT'S THE ANSWER?"   "103.5"
   Repeat steps 1 – 5 with these problems:

   $.05)\overline{5.125}$ $.7)\overline{28}$

   $.0)\overline{21.9}$ $.07)\overline{28}$

PART B: Structured Worksheet

TEACHER   **STUDENTS**

$.05)\overline{3.25}$ $.5)\overline{32}$ $.04)\overline{92}$

$.3)\overline{9.6}$ $.03)\overline{9.6}$

1. "READ THE FIRST PROBLEM."   ".05 into 3.25"

2. "WHAT IS THIS DIVISOR?"   ".05"

3. "CROSS OUT THE DECIMAL POINT AND MOVE IT TO
   THE RIGHT TO MAKE A WHOLE NUMBER."   Students write: $\cancel{.}05)\overline{3.25}$

4. "HOW MANY PLACES DID YOU MOVE THE DECIMAL
   POINT TO THE RIGHT?"   "2"
   "THAT'S WHAT YOU MUST DO IN THE DIVIDEND.
   CROSS OUT THE DECIMAL POINT AND WRITE IT
   WHERE IT BELONGS." Monitor students' work.   Students write:
                                                   $\cancel{.}05)\overline{3\cancel{.}25}.$

5. "NOW WRITE THE DECIMAL POINT WHERE IT WILL
   BE IN THE ANSWER." $\cancel{.}05)\overline{3\cancel{.}25}\overset{.}{}$

6. "WORK THE PROBLEM."

7. "WHAT'S THE ANSWER?"   "65"
   Repeat steps 1 – 7 with remaining problems.

"Now we can divide by a whole number." The teacher then writes this problem:

$$5)\overline{24}$$

Converting Fractions and Decimals

Decimals and fractions are both numerical systems for representing part(s) of a whole. Converting a fraction to a decimal is an important skill in itself as well as a component skill of percent problems. Converting a decimal to a fraction is less important, since it has less practical application.

Converting a Fraction to a Decimal

The strategy for converting a fraction to a decimal involves dividing the numerator by the denominator. For example, 3/8 is converted to a decimal by dividing 8 into 3:

$$\begin{array}{r} .375 \\ 8)\overline{3.000} \end{array}$$

The preskills for this conversion strategy, which we discussed earlier in this chapter, are (a) decimal di-

vision problems in which a whole number is divided by a larger whole number (e.g., 3 ÷ 7, 3 ÷ 5) and (b) rounding off decimals.

Because students who have mastered these preskills should have no difficulty converting a fraction to a decimal, an elaborate format is not required. The teacher merely presents the rule, "To change a fraction into a decimal, divide the numerator by the denominator." The teacher then models application of the rule with several problems and supervises students as they complete a worksheet. Proper and improper fractions should be included in the exercise.

Initial examples used to illustrate this strategy should be limited to fractions that can be divided evenly to the nearest tenth, hundredth, or thousandth:

$$\frac{4}{8} = \begin{array}{r} .5 \\ 8)\overline{4.0.} \\ 4\,0 \end{array}$$

Fractions that result in repeating decimals should not be introduced until several days later since they require rounding off:

$$\frac{2}{3} \quad \begin{array}{r} .6666 \\ 3)\overline{2.0000} \end{array}$$

When these problems are presented, instructions should specify to what place the decimal should be rounded off.

Mixed numbers can be converted to a mixed decimal by first converting the mixed fraction to an improper fraction:

$$3\frac{2}{5} = \frac{17}{5} = 5\overline{)17.0}^{\;3.4}$$

$$5\frac{3}{4} = \frac{23}{4} = 4\overline{)23.00}^{\;5.75}$$

Conversion of a mixed number would be introduced about a week after the introduction of repeating decimal problems.

In a final type of problem, the denominator is a two digit number (e.g., 8/12, 15/18). Students should be taught to first reduce the fraction to its lowest common terms before converting the fraction to a decimal:

$$\frac{8}{12} = \frac{3}{4} = 4\overline{)3.00}^{\;.75}$$

$$\frac{15}{18} = \frac{5}{6} = 6\overline{)5.000}^{\;.833}$$

Reducing is helpful in that dividing by a one digit divisor is easier than dividing by a two digit divisor. If the fraction cannot be reduced, students must be able to work problems with a two digit divisor. Daily practice including four to eight problems should be provided over a period of several weeks.

Converting a Decimal to a Fraction

Converting a decimal to a fraction can be presented when students have learned to read and write fractions and can reduce fractions to their lowest terms. The strategy for converting a decimal to a fraction involves the students' first rewriting the decimal as a decimal fraction, then reducing this decimal fraction to its lowest terms. For example, the decimal .75 would first be converted to the fraction 75/100, which in turn would be reduced to 3/4.

Initially, students should be given a worksheet like the one below, and the teacher should lead students through completing several items.

Decimal	Decimal Fraction	Common Fraction
.8	$\frac{8}{10}$	$\frac{4}{5}$
.80		
.35		

After several lessons, the teacher could introduce a worksheet exercise like the one below. The teacher guides students in converting the decimal to a decimal fraction, then reducing this fraction to its lowest terms.

Circle the fraction that is equivalent to the decimal number.

.60	$\frac{6}{9}$	$\frac{3}{6}$	$\frac{3}{5}$	$\frac{6}{6}$
.75	$\frac{2}{3}$	$\frac{3}{4}$	$\frac{5}{7}$	$\frac{7}{5}$
.8	$\frac{8}{5}$	$\frac{1}{8}$	$\frac{4}{5}$	$\frac{3}{5}$

Diagnosis and Remediation

Students may miss decimal problems for one or a combination of the following reasons:

1. A computational error. For example, when working the problem 9.63 ÷ 9, the student writes 1.08 as the answer, The student's only mistake was dividing 9 into 63 incorrectly.

   If a student misses a problem solely because of a computational error, the teacher need not spend time working on the fraction skill but should reteach the specific computational skill.

2. A component skill error. The student makes an error on a previously taught decimal skill, which causes the student to miss the current type of problem. For example, when converting 3/7 to a decimal, the student divides 3 by 7 correctly to 428, but then rounds off the answer to .42.

   The remediation involves reteaching the earlier taught component skill. In the example given, the teacher would first reteach students how to round off. When the students indicate mastery of the component skill, the teacher leads the students through solving the original type of problem, using the structured worksheet part of the appropriate format.

3. A strategy error. A strategy error occurs when the student does not correctly chain the steps together to solve a problem. For example, when attempting to convert 3/4 to a decimal, the student divides 4 by 3. The remediation procedure involves reteaching the strategy beginning with the structured board part of the format.

Figure 14.13 includes examples of common errors made on the various types of decimal problems along with suggestions for remediation.

Figure 14.13 Diagnosis and Remediation of Decimal Errors

Error Patterns	Diagnosis	Remediation Procedures
Adding or Subtracting 3.5 + 2 = **3.7** 5 - .3 = **2**	Student does not convert whole number to mixed decimal.	Teach students to rewrite whole number as mixed decimal, see Figure 14.6. Present structured worksheet working addition and subtraction problems, see Figure 14.7.
Multiplying 3.45 × .5 17.25	Strategy error: placing decimal point in wrong position in answer.	Present format in Figure 14.9. Be sure to include mix of addition and multiplication problems in less structured worksheet exercise.
Dividing 461 7)32.27	Component skill error: misalignment of digits in quotient	Present format for teaching long division in figure. Stress proper alignment of digits.
.63 .05)3.15	Strategy error: failure to rewrite divisor and dividend	Present format in Figure 14.12.
Rounding off: 3.729 **3.8** 8.473 **8.4**	Strategy error	Present format in Figure 14.8.

Application Items: Decimals

1. Describe the problem type that each example below represents. List the problems in the order they are introduced.

   a. 14.3 + 8.5

   b. 7 × 34.8

   c. 9 – 3.28

   d. Convert 4/7 to a decimal.

   e. Convert 2/5 to a decimal.

   f. Read this number   8.04.

   g. $.9\overline{)28}$

   h. $9\overline{)2.7}$

   i. $9\overline{)2.8}$

   j. Round off 3.4785 to the nearest hundredth.

2. Construct a structured board presentation to teach students to read decimals expressed as thousandths.

3. Below are the examples various teachers used in presenting reading decimals (tenths and hundredths). Tell which teacher used an appropriate set of examples. Tell why the other sets are inappropriate.

Teacher A	.04	.09	.08	.05	.01	.07
Teacher B	.7	.37	.48	.5	.28	
Teacher C	.7	.70	.07	.4	.40	.04

4. Specify the wording the teacher uses to present the following problem:
   8 – .34 =

5. Below is a set constructed by a teacher for a rounding-off exercise. It is inappropriate. Tell why.
   Round off 3.482 to the nearest tenth
   Round off 7.469 to the nearest hundredth
   Round off 4.892 to the nearest tenth
   Round off 6.942 to the nearest whole number

6. A student rounds off 3.738 to the nearest hundredth writing 3.73. Specify the wording the teacher uses in making the correction.

7. Which problems below would not be included in the initial exercises teaching students to divide a whole number into a decimal or mixed decimal number. Tell why.

   a. $7\overline{)37.8}$

   b. $4\overline{)23.5}$

   c. $9\overline{)84.86}$

   d. $.7\overline{)34.3}$

   e. $9\overline{)3.87}$

   f. $2\overline{)1.46}$

8. Tell the probable cause of the student's error. Specify the remediation procedure for the type of error.

   Write this fraction as a decimal rounded off to the nearest hundredth: $\frac{5}{7}$.

   Rebecca

   $$\frac{5}{7} = 7\overline{)5.00} = 7\overline{)5.00}^{.614} = .61$$

   Jill

   $$\frac{5}{7} = 5\overline{)7.0}^{1.4}$$

   Tamara

   $$\frac{5}{7} = 7\overline{)5.0}^{.714} = .72$$

15 Percent and Ratio

Terms and Concepts

Percent A notation for hundredths.

Percentage The number obtained by finding the percent of another number.

Ratio The ratio of two comparable quantities is the numerical expression of the relationship. Usually the ratio is the result of dividing the first quantity by the second.

The concepts of percentage and percent are applied frequently in real-life situations.

Percentage
"Prices went up 15%."
"The store is having a 20% reduction sale."
"The loan charges are 8%."
Percent (Ratio)
"Alice made 3 of 7 shots."
"Mary worked 8 of 10 problems."
"Carlos saw 2 of the 3 movies."

The introduction of percentage and ratio usually follows instruction on most of the basic fraction and decimal skills discussed in the earlier chapters.

Ratio problems require students to convert a numerical relationship (ratio) between two quantities into a percent. The fraction 3/4 is converted to 75%. An example of a ratio application problem is Ann made 3 of 7 shots. What percent of her shots did she make?

Percentage problems require the student to figure out the quantity that represents a given percent of another quantity. For example, *(a)* What is 30% of 60? *(b)* You need to get 70% of the questions on the test correct to pass. If there are 20 problems on the test, how many must you get correct to pass?

Note on the Skill Hierarchy in Figure 15.1 how various decimal skills are preskills for percent and ratio problems. For example, to solve a percentage problem, the student must be able to multiply mixed decimals; to solve a ratio problem, the student must be able to convert a fraction to a decimal or mixed decimal and round off the decimal or mixed decimal number.

A specific sequence for introducing the major types of problems students encounter in the elementary grades appears in the Instructional Sequence and Assessment Chart (see Figure 15.2). Note on the chart that we recommend introducing percentage-related skills before ratio-related skills.

Figure 15.1 Skill Hierarchy

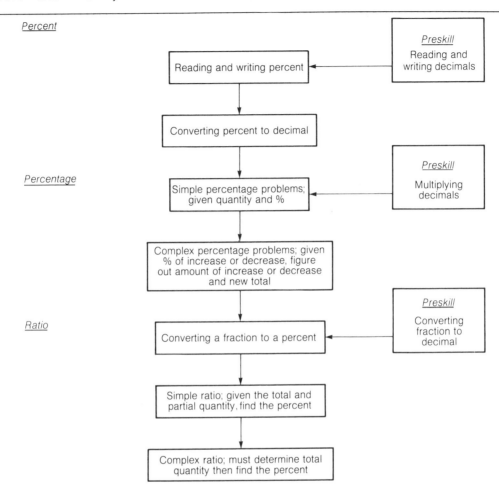

Percent

Reading and writing percent ← *Preskill* Reading and writing decimals

Converting percent to decimal

Percentage

Simple percentage problems; given quantity and % ← *Preskill* Multiplying decimals

Complex percentage problems; given % of increase or decrease, figure out amount of increase or decrease and new total

Ratio

Converting a fraction to a percent ← *Preskill* Converting fraction to decimal

Simple ratio; given the total and partial quantity, find the percent

Complex ratio; must determine total quantity then find the percent

This recommendation is made since the former skills require mastery of fewer preskills.

Percentage Problems

Two types of percentage problems are common to elementary mathematics instruction. The easier type of problem states a percent and quantity and asks students to find the percentage:

> The teacher said that 70% was passing. There are 50 problems on the test. How many problems must I get to pass? (70% of 50 is .70 × 50 = 35)

The more difficult problem type requires the student to figure the percentage of an original quantity, then either to add or subtract that amount from the original quantity:

> Bill borrowed $80 from the bank. He must pay 8% interest on the loan. How much must he pay back

to the bank? (.08 × 80 = 6.40; $80.00 + $6.40 = $86.40)

This problem type would not be introduced until students had a great deal of practice with the easier type.

Converting Percent to Decimal

Prior to introducing percentage problems, students should have mastered *(a)* multiplying decimal and mixed decimal numbers and *(b)* converting a percent figure to a decimal.

A format that introduces the percent concept and teaches students to convert a percent to a decimal appears in Figure 15.3. The format contains four parts. In Part A, the teacher simply presents the percent sign and teaches students to read percent numbers. In Part B, a structured board exercise, the teacher demonstrates how a percent number can be written as a decimal number by rewriting the numerals, deleting the percent sign, and placing a

Figure 15.2 Instructional Sequence and Assessment Chart

Grade Level	Problem Type	Performance Indicator
5a	Converting percentages to decimal figures	Write these percents as decimals: 45% = 15% = 6% = 1% =
5b	Determining a percent of a given number	What is 8% of 20? What is 25% of 12? What is 130% of 50?
5c	Simple percentage story problems	Jane took 20 basketball shots. She made 60% of her shots. How many shots did she make? Tara scored 5% of her team's points. Her team scored 60 points. How many points did Tara score? In May a store sold 300 shirts. In June the store sold 130% of what it sold in May. How many shirts did it sell in June?
5d	Converting a decimal to a percent	.32 = % .6 = % 3.4 = %
5e	Converting a fraction to a percent: percentage comes out even	Convert these fractions to percentages: $\frac{3}{5}$ = % $\frac{7}{10}$ = % $\frac{5}{4}$ = %
5f	Converting a fraction to a percent: rounding off required	$\frac{3}{7}$ = % $\frac{4}{9}$ = % $\frac{5}{3}$ = %
5g	Simple ratio story problems; total is given	Bill took 20 basketball shots. He made 12. What is his shooting percentage? Ann has 15 friends; 9 of her friends are from Texas. What percentage of her friends are from Texas?
6a	Complex percentage problems	Jill earned $80 in May. In June she earned 30% more than she did in May. How much did Jill earn in June? Tim borrowed $200. He must pay 9% interest. How much must he pay back altogether?
6b	Complex ratio problems; total not given	I got A's on 5 tests and B's on 4 tests. What percent of the tests did I get A's on? There are 4 boys and 6 girls. What percent of the class is boys? Bill has 5 blue pens and 15 red pens. What percent of the pens are blue?

Figure 15.3 Format for Converting Percent to Decimal

Day	Part A Reading and Writing the Percent Sign Problems	Part B Structured Board Presentation Problems	Part C Structured Worksheet Problems	Part D Supervised Practice Problems	Part E Independent Practice Problems
1	6				
2	4	6			
3-5		3	6		
6-till accurate				9	9
Till fluent					9

PART A: Reading and Writing the Percent Sign

TEACHER

1. Write on board: %
   "THIS IS A PERCENT SIGN. WHAT IS THIS?"

2. Write on board: 42%
   "THIS SAYS 42%. WHAT DOES THIS SAY?"

3. Repeat step 2 with 20%.

4. Write on board: 30%
   "WHAT DOES THIS SAY?"

   Repeat step 4 with 8%, 142%, 96%, 300%.

STUDENTS

"A percent sign"

"42%"

"30%"

PART B: Structured Board Presentation

1. "PERCENT MEANS HUNDREDTHS. WHAT DOES PERCENT MEAN?"

2. "87% MEANS 87 HUNDREDTHS. WHAT DOES 87% MEAN?"
   Repeat step 2 with 50%, 214%.

3. "WHAT DOES 30% MEAN?"
   Repeat step 3 with 248%, 8%.

4. "HOW MANY DECIMAL PLACES IN A HUN-DREDTHS NUMBER?"

5. "HERE'S A RULE FOR CHANGING A PERCENT NUMBER TO A DECIMAL NUMBER. GET RID OF THE PERCENT SIGN AND PUT IN A DECIMAL POINT SO THAT THERE ARE TWO DECIMAL PLACES. HOW MANY DECIMAL PLACES MUST WE HAVE WHEN WE CHANGE A PERCENT NUMBER TO A DECIMAL NUMBER?"

6. Write on board: 236%
   "READ THIS."
   "I WANT TO CHANGE THIS NUMBER TO A DECI-MAL. WHAT DOES 236% MEAN?"
   "HOW MANY DECIMAL PLACES IN A HUN-DREDTHS NUMBER?"
   "SO I GET RID OF THE PERCENT SIGN AND PUT IN TWO DECIMAL PLACES." Write 2.36.
   "READ THIS."
   "YES, 236% = 2.36."

"Hundredths"

"87 hundredths"

"30 hundredths"

"Two"

"Two"

"236%"

"236 hundredths"

"Two"

"2 and 36 hundredths"

Figure 15.3 cont'd

TEACHER

7. Write on board: 8%
   "READ THIS."

   "I WANT TO CHANGE THIS NUMBER TO A DECI-
   MAL. WHAT DOES 8% MEAN?"

   "HOW MANY DECIMAL PLACES IN A HUN-
   DREDTH NUMBER?"

   "SO I GET RID OF THE PERCENT SIGN AND PUT
   IN TWO DECIMAL PLACES." Write .08.

   "READ THIS"

   "YES, 8% = .08."

   Repeat steps 6 and 7 with 34%, 126%, 5%, 82%.

"8%"

"8 hundredths"

"Two"

"8 hundredths"

PART C: Structured Worksheet

Change these percents to decimals:

a. 35% =_____   d. 72% =_____   g. 374% =_____
b. 200% =_____   e.   1% =_____   h. 2% =_____
c.   6% =_____   f. 192% =_____

1. "READ THE DIRECTIONS."

2. "READ THE PERCENT NUMBER IN PROBLEM a."

3. "WHAT DOES 35% MEAN?"

4. "HOW MANY DECIMAL PLACES IN A HUN-
   DREDTHS NUMBER?"

5. "WHERE WILL WE WRITE THE DECIMAL POINT?"

6. "WRITE THE DECIMAL NUMBER."

7. "WHAT DECIMAL DID YOU WRITE?"
   "YES, 35% EQUALS 35 HUNDREDTHS."

   Repeat steps 1-7 with remaining problems.

"Change these percents to
decimals."

"35%"

"35 hundredths"

"Two"

"In front of the 3"

Students write .35.

"35 hundredths"

---

decimal point so that there are two decimal places. Part C is a structured worksheet exercise. Daily worksheet practice should continue for several weeks.

Example selection is quite important in this format. One-third of the percent figures should be below 10%, one-third between 10 and 100% and one-third over 100%. For example, a conversion exercise might include the following percents: 5%, 28%, 1%, 235%, 30%, 300%. Exposure to these problem types provides students with the practice needed to generalize the strategy to a wide range of examples. Percents below 10 are included to teach students that when converting a percent below 10 they must write a zero in front of the decimal number (e.g., 6% = .06, 1% = .01). Percents of 100 and above are included to show that a whole number can be produced (e.g., 354% = 3.54, 200% = 2).

Problems in which a percent, such as 87.5%, is converted to a decimal would not be included

initially. Problems of this type require the students to add two more decimal places (e.g., 87.5% = .875). An adaptation of the format in Figure 15.3 would be used. The teacher would explain that two more decimal places must be added.

Percentage Problems

Simple percentage problems are comprised of a quantity multiplied by a given percent; students must determine the percentage (e.g., 30% × 40 = 12). This problem type can be introduced after the students can translate percent to decimals and can accurately multiply decimal numbers.

Figure 15.4 includes a format for teaching students to solve simple percentage problems. Part A is designed to teach students a rule that will help them determine if their answers to subsequent problems are correct. The students are taught that if the problem asks for 100%, then the answer is the same as the number being multiplied (e.g., 100% × 20 is 20). Likewise, if the percent is more than 100%, the answer is more than the number being multiplied; if less than 100%, the answer is less than the number being multiplied. Students then use the rules to predict the answers to some numerical problems. Although these rules appear to be extremely simple, by examining the errors of students who have not been explicitly taught this information, it is clear that many students never figure out these relationships on their own.

Part B is a structured board presentation in which the strategy for solving percentage problems is presented: Convert the percent to a decimal, then multiply that decimal and the amount given. The rules learned in Part A are utilized to check the answer.

Part C is a structured worksheet exercise in which the students solve problems. Note that when multiplying a two digit and three digit number, the student should be instructed to write the two digit number on the bottom. For example, in solving 125% × 60, the student writes:

$$\begin{array}{r} .125 \\ \times\ \ 60 \\ \hline \end{array}$$

Examples should include sets of three problems in which the same number is being multiplied. In one problem, the percent would be below 10%; in one problem, between 10 and 99%; and in another problem, more than 100%. For example, a sample set for an exercise might include these problems:

30% × 60	25% × 36
3% × 60	2% × 36
130% × 60	125% × 36

The inclusion of these three types in a set provides practice in the wide range of problems students will encounter.

Simple Percentage Story Problems

Simple percentage story problems state an amount and ask the student to determine a percentage. A distinguishing characteristic of these problems is the inclusion of the word *of*. Below are several typical simple percentage problems:

> There are 60 children in our school. 75% of the children are girls. How many girls are there in our school?

> Sarah made 60% of her shots. She took 20 shots. How many shots did she make?

Story problems of this type are introduced when students can solve problems such as 40% × 20 accurately. As preparation, teachers first give students simple equations in which the word *of* is substituted for the times sign (e.g., 75% of 48). After several lessons, the teacher introduces story problems, modeling and testing how to solve them. After solving them, the teacher repeats the problem, asking whether they multiplied by more or less than 100%, and if the answer made sense (e.g., The problem said she got 60% of her shots in. She took 25 shots. We know the answer must be less than 25 because she made less than 100% of her shots). A worksheet should include problems with a percent below 10, problems with a percent between 10 and 99, and problems with a percent above 100.

Complex Percentage Problems

Complex percentage problems usually state the percent an original amount has either increased or decreased and asks the students to figure out the amount of the increase (or decrease) and the new total. These complex percentage problems should not be introduced until students have practiced simple percent problems for at least several weeks. This type of problem is illustrated below:

> The hat store sold 50 hats in May. In June the sales went up 20%. How many more hats did the store sell in June than May? How many hats did the store sell in June?

The teaching procedure involves the teacher's modeling how to solve the problem: first computing the percentage increased or decreased by converting the percent to a decimal and then multiplying. This amount is then added to or subtracted from the original amount to determine the new total. For example, in the problem above, the student converts 20% to .20 and multiplies .20 × 50 to end with 10. The store sold 10 more hats in June than in May. This 10 is added to the 50 hats sold in May to determine that 60 hats were sold in June.

A special type of problem involves computing interest.[1] The teacher can explain the term *interest* to students by using an explanation similar to the one below: "When you borrow money from a bank, you must pay back the bank extra money. The extra money is interest. If the bank charges 10% interest, you must pay back the money you borrowed plus 10% of the amount you borrowed."

---

[1] The term *interest* used here refers to simple interest. Compound interest would be presented in junior or senior high.

Figure 15.4 Format for Solving Simple Percentage Problems

Day	Part A More/Less Than 100% Problems	Part B Structured Board Presentation Problems	Part C Structured Worksheet Problems	Part D Supervised Practice Problems	Part E Independent Practice Problems
1-2	6				
3-4	4	6	3		
5-6	4		6	3	
7-till accurate				6	
Till fluent					6

PART A: More/Less Than 100%

<table>
<tr><td>TEACHER</td><td>STUDENTS</td></tr>
<tr><td>

1. Write on board: 100%
"I WANT TO CHANGE 100% TO A DECIMAL, SO I GET RID OF THE PERCENT SIGN AND PUT IN TWO DECIMAL PLACES."
Write on board: 1.00
"100% EQUALS WHAT WHOLE NUMBER?"
"YES, 100% EQUALS ONE WHOLE. SO WHEN WE MULTIPLY BY 100%, WE DON'T CHANGE THE VALUE OF THE NUMBER WE'RE MULTIPLYING. THE ANSWER IS THE SAME AS THE NUMBER WE'RE MULTIPLYING."

</td><td>

"1"

</td></tr>
</table>

2. "HERE ARE SOME RULES ABOUT OTHER PERCENTS. IF WE MULTIPLY BY MORE THAN 100%, OUR ANSWER IS BIGGER THAN THE NUMBER WE'RE MULTIPLYING. IF WE MULTIPLY BY LESS THAN 100%, OUR ANSWER IS LESS THAN THE NUMBER WE'RE MULTIPLYING."

3. "IF YOU MULTIPLY BY 100%, WHAT DO YOU KNOW ABOUT THE ANSWER?"

"The answer is the same as the number we're multiplying."

4. "IF YOU MULTIPLY BY LESS THAN 100%, WHAT DO YOU KNOW ABOUT THE ANSWER?"

"The answer is less than the number we're multiplying."

"RIGHT, WHEN THE PERCENT IS LESS THAN 100, YOU MULTIPLY BY A NUMBER LESS THAN 1. SO THE ANSWER MUST BE LESS THAN THE NUMBER WE'RE MULTIPLYING."

5. "IF YOU MULTIPLY BY MORE THAN 100%, WHAT DO YOU KNOW ABOUT THE ANSWER?"

"The answer is more than the number we're multiplying."

Repeat steps 2-5 until students respond correctly.

6. "HERE'S A PROBLEM—60% × 20. SAY THE PROBLEM."

"60% × 20"

"WHAT'S THE PERCENT?"

"60"

"IS THE ANSWER MORE THAN 20, LESS THAN 20, OR EQUAL TO 20?" Pause, signal.

"Less than 20"

Figure 15.4 cont'd

TEACHER	**STUDENTS**

TO CORRECT: "REMEMBER IF THE PERCENT IS
LESS THAN 100, THE ANSWER IS
LESS THAN THE AMOUNT WE'RE
MULTIPLYING. IS THE PERCENT
LESS THAN 100? SO, TELL ME ABOUT
THE ANSWER." Repeat step 6.

"HOW DO YOU KNOW?"
                                                  "The percent is less than 100."

7. Repeat step 6 with 140% of 20, 100% of 20, 24% of 150,
100% of 150, and 60% of 150.

PART B: Structured Board Presentation

1. Write on board: 75% × 20
"READ THIS PROBLEM."   "75% times 20"
"WHAT IS THE PERCENT?"   "75"
"WHAT IS THE AMOUNT?"   "20"
"WILL THE ANSWER BE MORE OR LESS THAN 20?"   "Less than 20"

2. "HERE'S HOW WE FIND THE EXACT ANSWER. WE
CHANGE THE PERCENT TO A DECIMAL, THEN MULTI-
PLY. HOW DO WE FIND THE EXACT ANSWER?"
                                        "Change the percent to a
decimal and multiply."

3. "FIRST WE WRITE 75% AS A DECIMAL; 75% EQUALS
HOW MANY HUNDREDTHS?"
                                        "75"
"YES, 75% CAN BE WRITTEN AS 75 HUNDREDTHS."
Write .75.

4. "NOW WE MULTIPLY." Write on board:

$$\begin{array}{r} 20 \\ \times.75 \\ \hline 100 \\ \underline{1400} \\ 1500 \end{array}$$

"WE MULTIPLIED BY A DECIMAL NUMBER SO I MUST
PUT A DECIMAL POINT IN THE ANSWER. WHERE DO I
PUT THE DECIMAL POINT?"   "After the 5"
"SO WHAT WHOLE NUMBER DO WE END WITH?"   "15"

5. "WHAT IS 75% TIMES 20?"   "15"
"WRITE 75% × 20 = 15. SAY THE STATEMENT."   "75% times 20 equals 15."

6. "LET'S SEE IF THAT FOLLOWS THE RULES. THE AMOUNT
WE BEGAN WITH WAS 20. WE WERE FINDING
LESS THAN 100%. OUR ANSWER MUST BE LESS THAN
20. IS 15 LESS THAN 20?"   "Yes"
"SO OUR ANSWER MAKES SENSE."
Repeat steps 1–6 with these problems: 125% × 20, 5% × 20,
120% × 65, 12% × 65, 20% × 65.

PART C: Structured Worksheet

a.   30% × 50 equals   □

b. 130% × 50 equals   □

c.   3% × 50 equals   □

d. 25% × 72 equals   □

Figure 15.4 cont'd

e.　5% × 72 equals　☐

f.　125% × 72 equals　☐

1. "TOUCH PROBLEM a. READ THE PROBLEM."　　　　　"30% times 50 equals how many?"

2. "WHAT MUST WE DO TO 30% BEFORE WE WORK
   THE PROBLEM?"　　　　　　　　　　　　　　　"Change it to a decimal"

3. "WHAT DECIMAL NUMBER DOES 30% EQUAL?"　　　"30 hundredths"

4. "MULTIPLY 30 HUNDREDTHS TIMES 50. (pause)
   DON'T FORGET TO PUT THE DECIMAL POINT IN
   THE ANSWER. WHAT IS 30% of 50?"　　　　　　　"15"

5. "LET'S SEE IF THAT MAKES SENSE. WE'RE MULTI-
   PLYING 50 BY 30%; 30% IS LESS THAN 100%, SO OUR
   ANSWER MUST BE LESS THAN 50. WAS OUR AN-
   SWER LESS THAN 50?"　　　　　　　　　　　　"Yes"
   "SO THAT ANSWER MAKES SENSE."
   Repeat steps 1-5 with remaining problems.

Figure 15.5

Amount of Loan	Interest Rate for 1 Year	Amount of Interest for 1 Year	Amount of be Paid Back at End of 1 Year
a. $500	5%	_____	_____
b. $500	8%	_____	_____
c. $1000	4%	_____	_____
d. $1000	7%	_____	_____

Figure 15.5 is a sample interest exercise. Students fill in missing amounts in a table that provides practice in determining interest for various loans. More complex interest problems would be introduced in later grades.

Ratio Problems

In ratio problems, students must convert a fraction to a percent figure. Here are three basic types of problems:

1. Numerical problems for converting a fraction to percent:

$$\frac{2}{5} = 40\% \qquad \frac{5}{4} = 125\%$$

2. Simple ratio story problems. In these problems, the total and one partial quantity are given. The student calculates the percent. Sarah made 10 out of 20 shots. What percent of her shots did she make?

$$\frac{10}{20} = 50\%$$

3. Complex story problems. In these problems, the student is required to add the amounts given prior to determining a percent. Ann got 10 shots in and missed 10 shots. What percent of her shots did she make?

$$10 + 10 = 20 \qquad \frac{10}{20} = 50\%$$

Converting a Fraction to a Percent

Converting a fraction to a percent can be introduced several weeks after students have mastered simple percentage problems. Figure 15.6 includes a format to teach this conversion skill. The format assumes that students have previously mastered converting fractions to decimals by dividing the numerator by the denominator (see pages 400–402) which in turn requires students to divide and round off decimal numbers.

The format includes six parts. In Part A, the teacher presents a strategy for converting decimal numbers to percent numbers: "Write a percent sign and move the decimal point two places toward the percent sign." The wording for this procedure has been designed as an aid to students in determining the direction to move the decimal point. After presenting the rule, the teacher presents examples of its application in converting decimals to percents. Examples should include mixed decimals and decimal numbers with tenth, hundredth, and thousandth decimals.

Part B is a worksheet exercise in which students practice converting decimals to a percent. The teacher guides the students through several conversions, then the students work the rest of the problems themselves. Several days of practice on this skill should be provided before introducing Part C. The examples selected for Parts A and B should include a mix of decimals, whole numbers, and mixed decimals. Decimals expressed as tenths, hundredths, and thousandths should be included as well as one or two whole numbers and several mixed decimals. A sample set for a worksheet exercise might include these numbers: 3.2, .475, 6, .08, .4, .37, 2, 6.1, 35, .875, and .1. When converting a tenths decimal or whole number, the teacher tells the students the number of zeroes to add:

$$.1 = .10 = .10\% = 10\%$$

In Part C, a structured board exercise, the teacher presents the two-step strategy for converting fractions to a percent: "First convert the fraction to a decimal, then convert that decimal to a percent." The teacher then demonstrates its application with several fractions.

Part D is a structured worksheet exercise in which students are given a worksheet with prompts to help make the conversion. A prompted problem looks like this:

$$\frac{3}{4} = .\underline{\hspace{1cm}} = \underline{\hspace{1cm}}\%$$

Part E is a less structured worksheet exercise in which no prompts are written on the students' worksheets. There are two example selection guidelines for Part C, D, and E:

1. There should be a mix of proper and improper fractions so that students can see that the strategy also applies to percents greater than 100 percent (e.g., 5/4 = 125%, 7/5 = 140%).

2. Problems should initially be limited to fractions that do not require rounding off to compute the percent. Problems requiring rounding off require an extra step and thus should not be introduced for several weeks. The fractions 3/4, 1/2, 7/5, 7/10, 6/8, and 6/4 are examples of fractions that do not require rounding off. The fractions 5/7, 2/9, 4/3, 3/11, and 6/5 are examples of fractions that do require rounding off.

When problems requiring rounding off are introduced, the teacher tells the students to divide until the answer has three digits after the decimal and then instructs them to round off to the nearest hundredth. For example, when converting 5/7 to a percent, the student divides to hundredths, then writes a line after the 1 (the hundredths number) and divides once again, then rounds off the answer to 71:

$$
\begin{array}{r}
.71|4 \\
7\overline{)5.00|0} \\
\underline{49} \\
10 \\
\underline{7} \\
30 \\
\underline{28} \\
2
\end{array}
$$

For examples such as 3/8 in which there is no remainder after dividing in the thousandth column, the teacher can demonstrate how to express the answer as 87.5 or 87 1/2 percent. This type of problem is potentially confusing and should not be introduced until students have mastered the rounding-off strategy.

After students have had several weeks of practice in converting fractions to decimals, the teacher can introduce the new steps of reducing the fraction before dividing, when possible. For example, 9/12 can be reduced to 3/4, so students would divide 3 by 4 instead of 9 by 12. Reducing fractions prior to dividing is especially helpful when dealing with two digit denominators. If the denominator can be reduced to one digit, the division problem will be much easier.

A final consideration in converting fractions to decimals concerns providing students with adequate practice so that they memorize the percents that more common fractions represent. The percents for these fractions should be taught: 1/4, 3/4, 1/2, 1/3, 2/3, 1/5, 2/5, 3/5, 4/5 as well as 1/10, 2/10, 9/10. Students should receive adequate practice so that they can tell the percents these fractions represent instantaneously. To facilitate this memori-

Figure 15.6 Format for Converting Decimals to Percents

Day	Part A Converting Decimals to Percent Problems	Part B Converting Decimal to Percent Worksheet Problems	Part C Structured Board Presentation Problems	Part D Structured Worksheet Problems	Part E Less Structured Worksheet Problems	Part F Supervised Practice Problems	Independent Practice Problems
1-2	6	6					
3-5		4 (8)					
6-8		(6)	3	4-6			
7-10		(6)		2	5		
11-till accurate		(6)				6	
Till fluent		(6)					6

(Numbers in parentheses indicate problems to be worked without assistance.)

PART A: Converting Decimals to Percent

TEACHER

STUDENTS

1. "WE CHANGE A DECIMAL TO A PERCENT BY ADD-ING A PERCENT SIGN AFTER THE NUMBER AND MOVING THE DECIMAL POINT TWO PLACES TO-WARD THE PERCENT SIGN. LISTEN AGAIN."
Repeat rule.
Write on board: .486

2. "READ THIS DECIMAL."   "486 thousandths"
"I WANT TO CHANGE THIS DECIMAL TO A PER-CENT NUMBER. FIRST I WRITE THE PERCENT SIGN AFTER THE NUMBER.
Write on board: .486%

3. "NOW I MOVE THE DECIMAL POINT TWO PLACES TOWARD THE PERCENT SIGN. WHAT DO I DO?"   "Move the decimal point two places toward the percent sign.

Erase decimal point. Move two places to right: 48.6%.

4. "WHAT PERCENT DO WE END WITH?"   "48.6%"

Repeat steps 1-4 with 1.4, 2, .73, .04.

PART B: Converting Decimal to Percent Worksheet

Convert these decimals and mixed decimals to percent:

a. .38 = _____   e. 3 = _____   i. 7.3 = _____

b. 4.1 = _____   f. .542 = _____   j. .485 = _____

c. .7 = _____   g. .04 = _____   k. 8 = _____

d. .07 = _____   h. .4 = _____   l. .02 = _____

1. "READ THE INSTRUCTIONS."   "Convert these decimals and mixed decimals to percent."

2. "WHERE DO WE WRITE THE PERCENT SIGN?"   "After the number"
3. "WHAT DO WE DO TO THE DECIMAL POINT?"   "Move it two places toward the percent sign."

4. "TOUCH a. READ THE NUMBER."   ".38"
5. "WRITE THE DIGITS 3 AND 8 IN THE SPACE NEXT TO THE DECIMAL. WRITE IN THE PERCENT SIGN."

Figure 15.6 cont'd

TEACHER	**STUDENTS**
6. "WHAT MUST YOU DO TO THE DECIMAL POINT?"	"Move it two places toward the percent sign."
"PUT IN THE DECIMAL. WHAT PERCENT DOES 38 HUNDREDTHS EQUAL?"	"38%"
Repeat steps 4-6 with several more problems; then have students work the rest on their own.	

PART C: Structured Board Presentation

1. Write on board: $\frac{5}{4}$	
"I WANT TO WRITE THIS FRACTION AS A PERCENT. HERE'S HOW WE CHANGE A FRACTION TO A PERCENT. FIRST WE CHANGE THE FRACTION TO A DECIMAL AND THEN CHANGE THAT DECIMAL TO A PERCENT. LISTEN AGAIN." Repeat procedure. "READ THIS FRACTION."	"Five-fourths"
"I WANT TO CHANGE THIS FRACTION TO A PERCENT. FIRST I CHANGE THE FRACTION TO A DECIMAL. WHAT DO I DO FIRST?"	"Change the fraction to a decimal."
"HOW DO I CHANGE 5/4 TO A DECIMAL?"	"Divide 4 into 5."
"I'LL WORK THE PROBLEM. I DIVIDE UNTIL THERE IS NO REMAINDER."	

Write on board:

$$\frac{5}{4} = 4\overline{)5.00}^{1.25} = 1.25$$
$$\underline{4}$$
$$1\,00$$
$$\underline{80}$$
$$20$$

"WHAT MIXED DECIMAL DOES 5/4 EQUAL?"	"1 and 25 hundredths"
3. "FIRST I CHANGED THE FRACTION TO A DECIMAL. NOW I CHANGE THE DECIMAL TO A PERCENT. WHAT DO I DO NEXT?"	"Change the decimal to a percent."
"I WRITE THE PERCENT SIGN AND MOVE THE DECIMAL TWO PLACES TOWARD THE PERCENT SIGN."	
Write on board: 125%	
"HOW MANY PERCENT DOES 5/4 EQUAL?"	"125 percent"
Repeat steps 1-3 with 3/5, 1/2, and 7/5.	

PART D: Structured Worksheet

Change these fractions to percents:

a. $\frac{3}{4} = \overline{)}$ = _____ = _____%

b. $\frac{2}{5} = \overline{)}$ = _____ = _____%

c. $\frac{8}{4} = \overline{)}$ = _____ = _____%

1. "IN THESE PROBLEMS, YOU MUST FIGURE OUT THE PERCENT A FRACTION EQUALS. FIRST YOU CHANGE THE FRACTION TO A DECIMAL. WHAT DO YOU DO FIRST?"	"Change the fraction to a decimal."
"HOW DO YOU CHANGE 3/4 TO A DECIMAL?"	"Divide 4 into 3."

Figure 15.6 cont'd

TEACHER	**STUDENTS**

"DIVIDE 4 INTO 3. DON'T FORGET TO PUT THE DECIMAL POINT IN THE ANSWER. (pause) WHAT DECIMAL DOES 3/4 EQUAL?"

    ".75 hundredths"

"WRITE 75 HUNDREDTHS IN THE SPACE NEXT TO THE DIVISION PROBLEM. NOW YOU CHANGE THE DECIMAL TO A PERCENT."

2. "WHAT DO YOU DO?"

    "Change the decimal to a percent."

"DO IT AND WRITE YOUR ANSWER IN THE LAST SPACE." Pause.

3. "WHAT PERCENT DOES 3/4 EQUAL?"

    "75%"

Repeat steps 1–3 with remaining problems.

PART E: Less Structured Worksheet

Change each fraction to a percent:

a. $\frac{3}{4}=$ b. $\frac{5}{2}=$

c. $\frac{3}{5}=$ d. $\frac{5}{4}=$

1. "READ THE DIRECTIONS."

    "Change each fraction to a percent."

2. "TOUCH a."

3. "WHAT IS THE FIRST FRACTION?"

    "3/4"

"WHAT DO YOU DO FIRST TO 3/4?"

    "Make it a decimal."

"DO IT. MAKE 3/4 INTO A DECIMAL." Pause.

"WHAT DECIMAL DOES 3/4 EQUAL?"

    "75 hundredths"

4. "NOW WRITE 75 HUNDREDTHS AS A PERCENT." Pause. "WHAT PERCENT DOES 75 HUNDREDTHS EQUAL?"

    "75%"

Repeat steps 1–4 with remaining problems.

---

zation, the teacher can do flash card drills or another type of memorization exercise. However, this memorization drill would not begin until after several weeks of instruction on conversions to percents.

Simple Ratio Story Problems

In simple ratio story problems two related quantities are given, and students are asked to express the relationship between these two quantities as a percent figure. Most simple ratio problems deal with a subset of a total set. For example, shots made (subset) out of shots attempted (total set); girls (subset) out of children (total set); red apples (subset) out of apples (total set). Problems a and b are examples of this type of problem:

a. There were 20 problems on the test. Jack got 14 right. What percent of the problems did Jack get correct?

b. There are 12 children in our class; 8 are girls. What percent of our class are girls?

Simple percentage problems can be introduced when students have mastered converting fractions to a percent figure. The format for simple ratio problems contains two parts (see Figure 15.7). In Part A, the board presentation, students are taught the component skill of converting the relationship expressed in the story to a fraction. The teacher presents the rule that the number that tells how many altogether is written as the denominator of the fraction, then models and tests with several examples. For example, "Sheila took 12 shots; she made 10" translates to the fraction 10/12.

Part B provides worksheet practice on converting ratio story problems to fractions. Part C is a less structured worksheet in which the teacher guides students in rewriting a fraction as a percent figure. The teacher first asks students to write the

Figure 15.7 Format for Simple Ratio Story Problems

Day	Part A Structured Board Presentation: Translating to Fractions Problems	Part B Story Problem Worksheet Problems	Part C Less Structured Worksheet Problems	Part D Supervised Practice Problems	Part E Independent Practice Problems
1	5				
2-3	4	2 (4)			
4-5		2	3 (3)		
6-till accurate					
Till fluent				4-6	4-6

(Numbers in parentheses indicate problems to be worked without assistance.)

PART A: Structured Board Presentation: Translating to Fractions

TEACHER

STUDENTS

1. "LISTEN TO THIS PROBLEM: JILL TOOK 8 BAS-
KETBALL SHOTS; SHE MADE 4 OF THE SHOTS.
WHAT FRACTION OF THE SHOTS DID SHE MAKE?
LISTEN AGAIN. JILL TOOK 8 SHOTS. SHE MADE
4 OF THE SHOTS. WHAT FRACTION OF THE
SHOTS DID SHE MAKE?"

2. "THE PROBLEM ASKS WHAT FRACTION OF HER
SHOTS SHE MADE. THE FRACTION WILL BE HOW
MANY SHE ACTUALLY MADE, OVER HOW MANY
SHE TOOK ALTOGETHER. THE BOTTOM NUM-
BER TELLS HOW MANY ALTOGETHER. WHAT
DOES THE BOTTOM NUMBER TELL?"　　　　　　　"How many altogether"
"HOW MANY SHOTS DID SHE TAKE AL-
TOGETHER?"　　　　　　　"8"
"SO I WRITE 8 ON THE BOTTOM."
Write on board: $\frac{}{8}$

3. "THE TOP NUMBER TELLS HOW MANY SHOTS
SHE MADE. HOW MANY SHOTS DID SHE MAKE?"　　　　　　　"4"
"I WRITE 4 ON THE TOP."
Write on board:
$\frac{4}{8}$

4. "ANN TOOK 8 SHOTS. SHE MADE 4 SHOTS. WHAT
FRACTION OF HER SHOTS DID SHE MAKE?"　　　　　　　"4/8"

Repeat steps 1–4 with these examples:

a. Jill has 8 pencils; 5 are blue. What fraction of her pencils
are blue?

b. The class has 8 students; 5 are girls. What fraction of the
students are girls?

c. There are 10 apples in a bag; 6 of the apples are red. What
fraction of the apples are red?

d. Bill saved $5 so far. He needs $8 altogether. What fraction
of the money he needs does he have?

Figure 15.7 cont'd

PART B: Worksheet

TEACHER   **STUDENTS**

Write the fractions for these problems:

a. Jane made 12 out of the 16 shots
   she took during the game.

   ☐
   ☐

b. Alex has 15 friends; 10 of his friends
   live in California.

   ☐
   ☐

c. Sarah won 8 out of the 12 races she
   ran in last year.

   ☐
   ☐

d. Tim picked 30 flowers; 18 are
   roses.

   ☐
   ☐

1. "READ THE DIRECTIONS."   "Write the fractions for
                                                    these problems."

2. "READ PROBLEM a. WHAT SHOULD THE BOTTOM
   NUMBER OF THE FRACTION TELL?"   "How many altogether"
   "WHAT NUMBER TELLS ALTOGETHER?"   "16"
   "SAY THE FRACTION."   "12/16"
   "WRITE IT."

   Repeat step 2 with several problems then have students
   do rest on their own.

PART C: Less Structured Worksheet

a. Jean ran in 8 races. She won 2 of the races. What percent of
   the races did she win?
b. Ann's team won 6 out of 8 games. What percent of the
   games did Ann's team win?
c. Dina got 12 out of 15 problems correct on her test. What
   percent of the problems did she get correct?
d. Jill has 8 pencils; 4 of her pencils are red. What percent of
   her pencils are red?

1. "READ PROBLEM a. THE PROBLEM ASKS FOR A
   PERCENT. TO FIND THE PERCENT, FIRST YOU
   WRITE A FRACTION." Repeat the problem. "WHAT
   FRACTION DO YOU WRITE?" Pause, signal.   "2/8"
   "WRITE IT."

2. "NOW YOU CHANGE THE FRACTION TO A
   PERCENT."

3. "WHAT PERCENT OF THE RACES DID SHE WIN?"   "25%"

fraction indicated by the problem, then to translate that fraction to a percent.

Practice problems should include as many real-life problems pertaining to the classroom as possible (e.g., What percent of the children are girls? What percent of the days has it rained?).

Complex Ratio Story Problems

In complex ratio story problems, the students must add the two quantities to derive a sum that will be the denominator of the fraction used to compute percent. For example, a problem may state there are four boys and six girls and ask for the percent of the children that are girls. For that problem, the quantities four and six must be added to determine the denominator, since the fraction is

$$\frac{\text{girls}}{\text{boys and girls}}$$

Complex ratio story problems are not introduced until students have had several weeks of practice with simple ratio problems.

In Part A of Figure 15.8, the teacher models how the total is derived for complex problems: "The problem asks what fraction of the children are girls, so the fraction will be girls over the children. How many children? So what do I write for the denominator?"

The examples used to teach complex ratio problems should include both simple and complex ratio problems, including sets of related problems such as a and b below:

a. There are 6 children in the club, 4 are girls. What percent of the children are girls?
b. There are 4 boys and 6 girls in the club. What percent of the children in the club are girls?

Problem a is a simple ratio problem. Problem b is a complex ratio problem. Note that the total in both problems is the number of children. In problem a, the number of children is given. However, problem b does not tell the total, and the quantities 4 boys and 6 girls must be added. Presenting related simple and complex problems is necessary to provide students with practice in determining when the quantities should be added to figure the denominator of the fraction.

Figure 15.8 Format for Complex Ratio Problems

Day	Part A Determining the Fraction Problems	Part B Less Structured Worksheet Problems	Part C Supervised Practice Problems	Part D Independent Practice Problems
1-3	6			
4-6	3	4		
7-9		4	2	
10-till accurate			4-6	
Till fluent				4-6

PART A: Determining the Fraction

TEACHER

1. "LISTEN TO THIS PROBLEM. I'M GOING TO TELL YOU ABOUT THE CARS THAT A SALESMAN SOLD IN SEPTEMBER. HE SOLD 10 BLUE CARS (Write 10 blue cars on board.) AND 14 RED CARS (Write 14 red cars on board.) IN SEPTEMBER. WHAT FRACTION OF THE CARS HE SOLD WERE RED?"

2. "THE PROBLEM ASKS FOR THE FRACTION OF THE CARS THAT WERE RED, SO THE FRACTION WILL BE THE NUMBER OF RED CARS SOLD, OVER THE TOTAL NUMBER OF CARS SOLD. WHAT SHOULD THE BOTTOM NUMBER TELL?"

"HOW MANY CARS WERE SOLD ALTOGETHER?" Pause.

Write on board: $\frac{}{24}$

STUDENTS

"The total number of cars sold"

"24"

Figure 15.8 cont'd

TEACHER   **STUDENTS**

    TO CORRECT: "REMEMBER, THE DEALER SOLD
                10 BLUE CARS AND 14 RED CARS.
                TO FIND THE TOTAL NUMBER OF
                CARS SOLD WHAT MUST YOU DO?
                WHAT ARE 10 AND 14?"

3. "WHAT DOES THE TOP NUMBER TELL?"   "The number of red cars sold"
   "HOW MANY RED CARS WERE SOLD?"   "14"

   Write on board: $\frac{14}{24}$

4. "WHAT FRACTION OF THE CARS SOLD IN SEP-
   TEMBER WERE RED?"   "14/24"

   Repeat steps 1–4 with several examples of both simple and
   complex ratio problems.

PART B: Less Structured Worksheet

Use Part C from the simple ratio problem format in Figure 15.7.

Application Items: Percent and Ratio

1. Below are errors made by students. Specify the probable cause of each error and
describe a remediation procedure.

   a. What is 38% of 90?

     Jill

$$\begin{array}{r} 90 \\ \times .38 \\ \hline 720 \\ 2700 \\ \hline 3420 \end{array} = 3420$$

     Tim

$$\begin{array}{r} 90.00 \\ .38 \\ \hline 90.38 \end{array} = 90.38$$

     Sarah

$$\begin{array}{r} 90 \\ .38 \\ \hline 720 \\ 270 \\ \hline 9.90 \end{array} = 9.9$$

   b. What is 5% of 60?

     Jack

$$\begin{array}{r} 60 \\ \times .5 \\ \hline 30.0 \end{array} = 30$$

c. Bill took 15 shots; he made 12 of his shots. What percent of his shots did he make?

Tom

$$\frac{15}{12} = 12\overline{)15.0} \quad \frac{1.25}{} = 125\%$$
$$\frac{12}{}$$
$$\frac{30}{}$$
$$\frac{24}{}$$
$$60$$

Zelda

$$\frac{12}{15} = 15\overline{)12.0} \quad \frac{.69}{} = 69\%$$
$$\frac{90}{}$$
$$\frac{300}{}$$
$$135$$

Elwin

$$\frac{12}{15} = 15\overline{)12.0} \quad \frac{.8}{} = 8\%$$
$$12.0$$

2. Specify the wording the teacher uses in correcting Tom's mistake.

3. Specify the wording the teacher uses in a structured worksheet presentation for converting 3/7 to a percent.

4. Below are sets of examples teachers constructed for an exercise to teach students to convert percent figures to decimals. Tell which sets are inadequate and why.

Set A: 85% 94% 30% 62% 53% 6%

Set B: 40% 5% 135% 240% 7% 82%

Set C: 130% 20% 72% 145% 80% 360%

16 Telling Time

Telling time is not as easy for all students to learn as teachers sometimes assume. Its difficulty is due to the number of discriminations students must make when telling time. In the following list are discriminations that, if not properly taught, tend to cause errors, especially for low-performing students:

1. Direction the clock hands move
2. Discrimination of the minute hand from the hour hand
3. Discrimination of minutes (which are not represented by the numerals on the clock) from hours (which are represented by the numerals on the clock)
4. Vocabulary discrimination; for example, when to use *after* and when to use *before*

Because of these potentially troublesome discriminations, we have divided instruction on telling time into three stages. First, students are taught a strategy for figuring out the time and expressing it as minutes after the hour. Second, after students have mastered minutes after the hour, alternate ways of expressing time as after the hour are taught: using a colon (8:40), quarter past, half past. Third, students are taught a strategy for expressing time as minutes before the hour. The Instructional Sequence and Assessment Chart appears in Figure 16.1 and the Skill Hierarchy Chart in Figure 16.2.

Minutes After the Hour

Preskills

Four preskills for telling time are (1) knowledge of the direction in which the hands of the clock move, (2) discrimination of the hour hand from the minute hand, (3) counting by 5s, and (4) switching from counting by five to counting by ones, which is needed to determine the number of minutes (e.g., 5, 10, 15, 16, 17, 18, 19).

The preskill of knowing which direction the hands on a clock move is critical if students are to figure out the correct hour. A convenient way to teach students about direction on a clock is to have them fill in the missing numerals on several clocks containing boxes instead of numerals:

By doing this exercise, students can develop the pattern of moving in a clockwise direction around the clock face. In the first exercises, some of the numerals should be included as prompts on the clock (e.g., 3, 6, 9, 12). After several lessons, however, these prompts should be removed, and

Figure 16.1 Instructional Sequence and Assessment Chart

Grade Level	Problem Type	Performance Indicator

2a   Expressing time as minutes after the hour—minute hand pointing to a number

a.   b.

_____ minutes after_____   _____minutes after_____

c.

_____ minutes after_____

2b   Expressing time as minutes after the hour—minute hand not pointing to numbers

a.   b.

_____ minutes after_____   _____minutes after_____

c.

_____ minutes after_____

2c   Time expressed with hour stated first

a. Put an X on the line under the clock that says 7:25.

_____   _____

_____   _____

Figure 16.1 cont'd

Grade Level	**Problem Type**	**Performance Indicator**

b. Put an X on the line under the clock that says 4:03.

c. Put an X on the line under the clock that says 2:53.

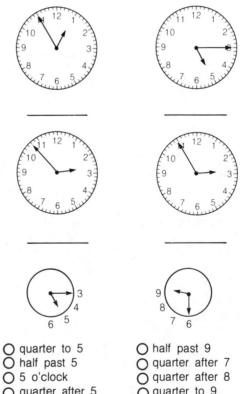

2d	Expressing time as half past or quarter after or to the hour	○ quarter to 5 ○ half past 9
		○ half past 5 ○ quarter after 7
		○ 5 o'clock ○ quarter after 8
		○ quarter after 5 ○ quarter to 9

Figure 16.1 cont'd

Grade Level	Problem Type	Performance Indicator

3a   Expressing time as minutes before the hour—minute hand pointing to number

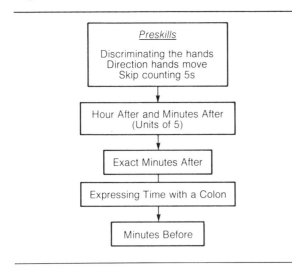

a. _____ minutes before _____   b. _____ minutes before _____

c. _____ minutes before _____

Figure 16.2 Skill Hierarchy

```
┌─────────────────────────────────┐
│           Preskills             │
│  Discriminating the hands       │
│  Direction hands move           │
│  Skip counting 5s               │
└─────────────────────────────────┘
              │
              ▼
┌─────────────────────────────────┐
│  Hour After and Minutes After   │
│         (Units of 5)            │
└─────────────────────────────────┘
              │
              ▼
┌─────────────────────────────────┐
│       Exact Minutes After       │
└─────────────────────────────────┘
              │
              ▼
┌─────────────────────────────────┐
│   Expressing Time with a Colon  │
└─────────────────────────────────┘
              │
              ▼
┌─────────────────────────────────┐
│          Minutes Before         │
└─────────────────────────────────┘
```

the students should fill in all the numbers themselves. Teachers need to monitor students carefully while they work to make sure they fill in numerals in the proper direction.

Teachers can also use a clock with movable hands and ask students to move the clock hands in the appropriate direction.

Counting by 5s is the initial way students are taught to determine the number of minutes. Students are taught to start at the top of the clock and say zero, then count the numbers by 5s until reaching the minute hand. In subsequent strategies, the procedure is modified to teach students to determine the number of minutes when the minute hand

is not pointing to a multiple of 5. In all procedures, however, the skill of counting by 5s or knowledge of the relevant multiplication facts is important. Procedures for teaching counting by 5s can be found in Chapter 5.

Discrimination of the hour hand from the minute hand is taught by describing each hand (the short hand is the hour hand, and the long hand is the minute hand) and then providing discrimination practice in which students identify the hands. The teacher should present pictures of clocks and ask about each hand: "Which hand is this?" "How do you know it's the minute hand?" "Yes, the long hand is the minute hand." Commercial instructional clocks are well suited for this exercise since teachers can manipulate the hands of the clock. The hands on the clock used for initial instruction should be easy to tell apart.

Units of 5 Minutes

The format for teaching students to tell time by determining the number of minutes (in units of 5) after the hour (see Figure 16.3) is divided into three parts. Part A teaches students to determine the hour. The teacher reminds students that the hour hand is the short hand and demonstrates how to figure out the hour by starting at the top of the clock and saying the numbers on the clock until reaching the hour hand.

Part B teaches students to determine the number of minutes after the hour. The teacher instructs students that the long hand is the minute hand and that the minute hand says to count by 5s.

The teacher then models and tests figuring out the minutes. The students are taught to start at the 12 and say zero, then to count by 5 for each number, stopping at the number to which the minute hand is pointing. Examples in this format would all have the minute hand pointing directly to a number.

Part C includes a board demonstration of how the strategies for determining minutes and hours are combined into a total strategy for figuring out the time. Parts D and E are structured and less structured worksheet exercises in which the students are shown a clock and asked to write the time. Daily practice is continued for several weeks for fluency.

As a prompt to help students discriminate the hour and minute hands, we recommend that for the first several days teachers use illustrations like the one below in which the minute hand is drawn longer than usual. Note that in the illustration, the minute hand extends outside the clock and is written as a thin line so that it does not block students' view of the numerals on the clock.

Also when constructing a set of examples, the teacher must be quite careful to include a wide range of problems. In half of the clocks, the hour hand should be pointing toward the right side of the clock; while on the other clocks, the hour hand should be pointing toward the left side of the clock. The same recommendation holds true for the minute hand. This helps prevent students from developing misrules that the strategies only apply to certain positions on the clock.

Examples should also be arranged so that in only half of the examples is the minute hand pointing to a number smaller than the hour hand. If the minute hand were pointing to a number smaller than the hour hand in all the examples, students might inappropriately learn that the hand pointing to the smallest number is the minute hand.

For the first week or two, examples in which the minute hand is pointing to the 12 would be expressed as zero minutes after the hour. When students have demonstrated the ability to use the minutes-after time-telling strategy, the teacher can present the convention for saying o'clock. "When it's zero minutes after 4, the hour we say is 4 o'clock."

As students learn multiplication facts, they should be encouraged to use their knowledge of facts in determining the minutes rather than always starting at the top and counting by 5s. The teacher would explain that in figuring out minutes, each number stands for a group of five. Therefore, when the minute hand points to 4, it is the same as four groups of five. Instead of counting, the minutes can be determined by solving 4×5.

Units of Single Minutes

After several weeks of practice expressing time with examples in which the minute hand points directly to a numeral, students can learn to express time when the minute hand is not pointing directly to a number. Note the example illustrated below:

No elaborate teaching format is required to introduce this type of exercise. Students would be told that to count the space in between the numbers, they count by 1s. The teacher would then model the process of counting by 5s and switching to 1s: "5, 10, 15, 20, 21, 22, 23; the time is 23 minutes after 7."

Alternate Ways of Expressing Time

Quarter After and Half Past

The terms *quarter after* and *half past* are introduced when students master expressing time as minutes after the hour: A quarter after means 15 minutes after; half past means 30 minutes after. Teachers working with lower performers would not introduce both terms at the same time. *Quarter after* might be introduced first. The instructional procedure consists of the teacher's modeling and testing on several examples:

1. "Another way of saying 15 minutes after 2 is a quarter after 2."
2. "What's another way of saying 15 minutes after 2?"
3. "What's another way of saying 15 minutes after 8?"

Figure 16.3 Format for Expressing Time as Minutes After the Hour (Units of 5 Minutes)

Day	Part A Determining the Hour Problems	Part B Minutes After Problems	Part C Structured Board Presentation Problems	Part D Structured Worksheet Problems	Part E Less Structured Worksheet Problems	Part F Supervised Practice	Part G Independent Practice
1-2	6						
3-5	4	4					
6-7			5				
8-9			2	5			
10-11				2	5		
12-till accurate						6	
Till fluent							6-10

PART A: Determining the Hour

TEACHER	STUDENTS
1. "ONE OF THE HANDS IS MISSING ON THIS CLOCK." Point to the hour hand. "THIS SHORT HAND IS THE HOUR HAND. WHAT IS THE SHORT HAND?"	"The hour hand"
2. "LET'S FIGURE OUT WHAT HOUR THE HAND IS AFTER. WE START AT THE TOP OF THE CLOCK AND SAY THE NUMBERS UNTIL WE COME TO THE HOUR HAND. I'LL TOUCH; YOU SAY THE NUMBERS. SAY STOP WHEN I COME TO THE HOUR HAND." Starting with 12, touch each numeral and then the hour hand as the children say:	"12, 1, 2, 3, 4, 5, stop"
3. "WHAT WAS THE LAST NUMERAL I TOUCHED?"	"5"
4. "THE HOUR HAND IS AFTER 5. SO, THE HOUR IS AFTER 5. TELL ME ABOUT THE HOUR." Repeat steps 1-4 with after 8.	"After 5"
5. Point hour hand to after 5. "NOW LET'S FIGURE OUT THE HOUR A FAST WAY, WITHOUT COUNTING. LOOK AT THE CLOCK. WHAT NUMERAL IS THE HOUR HAND AFTER?" "SO TELL ME ABOUT THE HOUR." Repeat step 5 with several more examples: after 9, after 2, after 6, after 3, after 10.	"5" "After 5"

PART B: Minutes After

Figure 16.3 cont'd

TEACHER	**STUDENTS**

1. "THIS LONG HAND IS THE MINUTE HAND. WHAT IS THE LONG HAND CALLED?"

   "The minute hand"

   "THE MINUTE HAND IS VERY FUNNY. IT TELLS YOU TO COUNT BY 5. WHAT DOES THE MINUTE HAND TELL YOU TO DO?"

   "Count by 5"

2. "WATCH ME FIGURE OUT THE MINUTES." Point to the minute hand. "I TOUCH THE TOP OF THE CLOCK AND SAY ZERO. THEN I COUNT BY 5 UNTIL I COME TO THE MINUTE HAND." Touch the clock above 12. "ZERO." Starting with 1, touch each numeral as you count: 5, 10, 15, 20, 25.

3. "TELL ME ABOUT THE MINUTES."

   "25 minutes"

4. "YOUR TURN. I'LL TOUCH THE NUMERALS; YOU COUNT BY 5. REMEMBER TO SAY ZERO WHEN I TOUCH THE TOP OF THE CLOCK." Touch the clock above 12 then touch each numeral as the children count:

   "0, 5, 10, 15, 20, 25"

5. "TELL ME ABOUT THE MINUTES."

   "25 minutes"

   "YES, 25 MINUTES."

Repeat steps 4-5 with five more examples: hand points to 3, hand points to 7, hand points to 2, hand points to 10, hand points to 4.

PART C: Structured Board Presentation

1. "WE'RE GOING TO FIGURE OUT WHAT TIME THIS CLOCK SHOWS. FIRST WE'LL FIGURE OUT THE MINUTES. THEN WE'LL FIGURE OUT THE HOUR."

2. "FIRST THE MINUTES. WHICH HAND IS THE MINUTE HAND, THE SHORT HAND OR THE LONG HAND?"

   "The long hand"

3. "WHAT DOES THE MINUTE HAND TELL YOU TO COUNT BY?"

   "Count by 5"

   "WHERE DO YOU START COUNTING?"

   "At the top of the clock"

   "WHAT DO YOU SAY?"

   "Zero"

   Repeat step 3 until all questions are answered correctly.

4. "COUNTING BY 5 TO THE MINUTE HAND." Touch the top of the clock and then the numerals as the children count:

   "0, 5, 10, 15"

   "HOW MANY MINUTES?"

   "15"

   "I'LL WRITE THE ANSWER." Write 15 minutes under the clock.

5. "WE KNOW IT'S 15 MINUTES, BUT WE DON'T KNOW ABOUT THE HOUR. LOOK AT THE HOUR HAND. TELL ME ABOUT THE HOUR." Pause, signal.

   "After 6"

Figure 16.3 cont'd

TEACHER　　　　　　　　　　　　　　　　　**STUDENTS**

6. "YES, AFTER 6. I'LL WRITE THE ANSWER." Write
after 6. "THAT'S THE TIME THE CLOCK SHOWS,
15 MINUTES AFTER 6. WHAT TIME DOES THE
CLOCK SHOW? SAY THE TIME."　　　　　　　　　　"15 minutes after 6"

Repeat steps 1-6 with 5 minutes after 7, 45 minutes after
4, 20 minutes after 2, 25 minutes after 10.

PART D: Structured Worksheet

Give students worksheet including about six to eight clocks
like these:

___ minutes after___　　　　___ minutes after___

1. "EVERYONE TOUCH THE FIRST CLOCK ON YOUR
WORKSHEET. FIRST YOU'LL FIGURE OUT THE
MINUTES, THEN YOU'LL FIGURE OUT THE
HOUR."

2. "WHICH IS THE MINUTE HAND?"　　　　　　　　　"The long hand"
"WHAT DOES THE MINUTE HAND TELL YOU TO
COUNT BY?"　　　　　　　　　　　　　　　　　　"Count by 5"
"WHERE DO YOU START COUNTING?"　　　　　　　"At the top of the clock"
"WHAT DO YOU SAY AT THE TOP OF THE CLOCK?"　"Zero"
"LET'S FIGURE THE MINUTES."

3. "TOUCH THE 12. COUNT AND TOUCH AS I CLAP."
Clap once each second.　　　　　　　　　　　　　"0, 5, 10, 15, 20, 25, 30, 35"
"HOW MANY MINUTES?"　　　　　　　　　　　　　"35 minutes"
"WRITE 35 IN FRONT OF THE WORD MINUTES."

4. "TOUCH THE HOUR HAND. TELL ME ABOUT THE
HOUR." Pause, signal.　　　　　　　　　　　　　"After 4"
"YES, IT SAYS AFTER 4. WRITE 4 IN THE NEXT
SPACE."

5. "NOW TELL ME WHAT TIME THAT CLOCK SAYS."　"35 minutes after 4"
Repeat steps 1-5 with each remaining clock.

PART E: Less Structured Worksheet

a.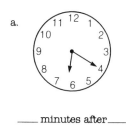

___ minutes after___

Figure 16.3 cont'd

TEACHER

STUDENTS

1. "TOUCH CLOCK a. YOU'RE GOING TO FIGURE OUT THE TIME AND WRITE IT UNDER THE CLOCK."

2. "FIGURE OUT THE MINUTES AND WRITE THE MINUTES IN THE FIRST BLANK." Monitor response. "HOW MANY MINUTES?"

"20"

3. "NOW FIGURE THE HOUR AND WRITE IT IN THE LAST BLANK."

4. "READ WHAT TIME THE CLOCK SAYS."

"20 minutes after 6"

Next, an exercise in which the teacher says the time as a quarter after and the students say it as minutes after would be presented: "If it's a quarter after 2, how many minutes after 2 is it?" The same procedure would be used to teach half past the hour. A final task would be a discrimination exercise including both quarter after and half past the hour time:

1. "What's another way of saying 15 minutes after 6?"
2. "What's another way of saying 30 minutes after 6?"
3. "If it's half past 4, how many minutes after 4 is it?"
4. "If it's a quarter after 4, how many minutes after 4 is it?"

Worksheet exercises like those on the Skill Hierarchy Chart would be presented daily for several weeks.

Using a Colon

When students are able to express time as minutes after the hour, the colon system in which the hour is written first can be introduced: "3:14 is read as three fourteen which means 14 minutes after 3." The procedures for teaching students to express time shown by a colon involves the teacher's modeling and testing how to translate the time expressed as minutes after the hour to time expressed as the hour and then the minutes after: "Here's another way of saying 28 minutes after 5: five twenty-eight. What's another way of saying 28 minutes after 5?" Pause and signal. Student says "5:28." The teacher models and tests several more examples, then tests students on a series of four to six examples by saying the time as minutes after the hour and asking students to express it as hours then

minutes after (e.g, "Tell me another way of saying 35 minutes after 4"). The teacher repeats the set of examples until students can respond correctly to all of them.

After several lessons, students translate the new way they've learned for expressing time into the familiar "minutes after" terminology:

1. "I'll say the time one way, you say it the other way. Listen, 8:24. I'll say the time the other way: 24 minutes after 8."
2. "Your turn: 8:24. Say the time the other way." Repeat step 2 with 4:15, 7:32, 9:28.

After learning to orally express the time as the hour then minutes after, students also can be taught how to read and write the time using a colon. A written task like the one below should be introduced in which students are required to express the time as both minutes after the hour and as the hour and then minutes.

_____ minutes after_____

_____ : _____

Times of less than 10 minutes after the hour are particularly difficult since a zero must be added when the time is expressed both verbally and in written form. For example, 8 minutes after 6 is written as 6:08 and stated as "six oh eight." This type of example should not be introduced until students have mastered easier ones. Several of these more difficult types should appear thereafter on worksheet exercises.

Figure 16.4 Format for Expressing Time as Minutes Before the Hour

Day	**Part A** Determining the Hour Problems	**Part B** Minutes Before Problems	**Part C** Structured Board Presentation Problems	**Part D** Structured Worksheet Problems	**Part E** Supervised Practice Problems	**Part F** Independent Practice Problems
1-2	5	3	4			
3-5		2	6			
6-till accurate				2	6	
Till fluent						6

PART A: Determining the Hour

Write on board:

1. "IN TELLING TIME, YOU'VE LEARNED TO SAY HOW MANY MINUTES AFTER THE HOUR. ANOTHER WAY OF TELLING TIME IS TO SAY THE NUMBER OF MINUTES BEFORE THE HOUR."

2. "LOOK AT THIS CLOCK, WHAT HOUR IS IT AFTER?" ⟶ "4"

3. "THE NEXT BIGGER NUMBER TELLS YOU THE HOUR IT'S BEFORE. TELL ME THE HOUR IT'S BEFORE." ⟶ "5"
   "YES, IT'S BEFORE 5. WHAT IS THE HOUR?" ⟶ "Before 5"

4. Move the hour hand between 7 and 8. "TELL ME THE HOUR BY SAYING WHAT HOUR IT IS BEFORE."
   Pause, signal. ⟶ "Before 8"
   Repeat step 4 moving the hand to five more positions: between 2 and 3, between 10 and 11, between 6 and 7, between 11 and 12, between 12 and 1.

PART B: Minutes before the Hour

Write on board:

1. "NOW WE'LL FIGURE OUT THE MINUTES BEFORE THE NEXT HOUR. WHEN WE FIGURE THE MINUTES BEFORE THE HOUR, WE START AT THE 12 BUT WE COUNT THIS WAY (point ⤺) UNTIL WE GET TO THE MINUTE HAND. MY TURN. 0, 5, 10, 15, 20. IT'S 20 MINUTES BEFORE. HOW MANY MINUTES BEFORE?" ⟶ "20 minutes before"

Figure 16.4 cont'd

TEACHER	**STUDENTS**

2. "SHOW ME WHICH WAY YOU COUNT TO FIGURE
THE MINUTES BEFORE THE HOUR. WHERE DO
WE START COUNTING?"   "At the 12"
   "WHAT DO WE SAY FIRST?"   "Zero"
   Move minute hand to 10. "TELL ME HOW MANY
   MINUTES BEFORE." Pause, signal.   "10 minutes before"

   TO CORRECT: "WE'RE FIGURING OUT MINUTES
               BEFORE SO WE COUNT THIS WAY
               (↶). I'LL TOUCH, YOU COUNT."

   Repeat step 2 with four more examples: hand pointing
   to 10, 8, 11, 7.

PART C: Structured Board Presentation

Write on board:

_____ minutes before_____

1. "LET'S TELL WHAT TIME THIS CLOCK SAYS BY
   TELLING HOW MANY MINUTES BEFORE THE
   HOUR."

2. Point to the hour hand. "WHICH HAND IS THIS?"   "The hour hand"
   "WHAT HOUR IS IT BEFORE?" Pause   "4"
   Write 4.

3. Point to minute hand. "WHICH HAND IS THIS?"   "The minute hand"
   "HOW MANY MINUTES BEFORE 4 IS IT?" Pause.   "20 minutes"
   Write 20.

   TO CORRECT: "SHOW ME WHICH WAY WE
               COUNT WHEN WE FIGURE OUT
               MINUTES BEFORE. COUNT AS I
               POINT."

4. "WHAT TIME DOES THE CLOCK SAY?"   "20 minutes before 4"

   Repeat steps 1–4 with additional times: 5 before 2, 25
   before 8, 15 before 11, 10 before 12, 20 before 5.

PART D: Structured Worksheet

Give students worksheet with six to eight clocks. Under each
clock is written _____ minutes before _____.

1. "LET'S FIND OUT WHAT TIME THESE CLOCKS
   SAY BY FINDING OUT HOW MANY MINUTES BE-
   FORE THE HOUR."

2. "FIND THE HOUR HAND ON CLOCK a. WHAT
   HOUR IS IT BEFORE?" Pause, signal.   "Before 8"

Figure 16.4 cont'd

TEACHER	**STUDENTS**
3. "NOW LET'S FIND OUT HOW MANY MINUTES BEFORE 8. START AT THE TOP OF THE CLOCK— REMEMBER WHICH WAY TO COUNT. HOW MANY MINUTES BEFORE 8?" Pause, signal.	"20 minutes"
4. "WHAT TIME DOES THIS CLOCK SAY?" "FILL IN THE BLANKS."	"20 minutes before 8"
Repeat with remaining examples.	

Minutes Before the Hour

Teachers should not introduce telling time as minutes before the hour until students can express time as minutes after the hour with accuracy and fluency. Students should demonstrate mastery by completing a worksheet of clocks with at least 90% accuracy at a rate of no more than 6 to 7 seconds per clock.

The procedure for teaching students to express time as minutes before the hour is somewhat similar to the one used in teaching students to express time as minutes after the hour. First, the teacher presents a strategy to figure out the hour, then a strategy to figure out the minutes, then an exercise in which both strategies are applied to express the time (see Figure 16.4).

The teacher first presents an exercise in which she places the hour hand between two numbers, then models and tests saying what hour it is after and the hour it is before. For example, if the hour hand were pointing between 5 and 6, the teacher would say the hour is after 5 and before 6. Next the teacher shows students how to figure out the number of minutes before the hour. She points in a counterclockwise direction and tells the students that in figuring minutes before the hour they start at the 12 but count in this direction (pointing counterclockwise). The teacher models and tests several

examples. The next exercise is a structured one in which the teacher leads students through expressing the time as minutes before the hour.

During the first week that expressing time as minutes before the hour is presented, the minute hand should point directly to the numerals so that all minute times involve multiples of five. Examples in which the minute hand points to a line between the numerals are introduced later. Examples should be limited to times that are 30 minutes or less before the hour (i.e., the minute hand is pointing toward the center or the left part of the clock).

Diagnosis and Remediation

Errors in telling time usually are caused by component skill errors. The remediation procedure is to reteach the component skill, then present several structured worksheet examples, then several less structured worksheet examples, and finally to provide supervised practice. Figure 16.5 shows some errors that might indicate a particular component skill error.

In examples a and b, the student's answer is 5 minutes more than the proper time. Probably the student is starting to count by 5s when touching 12 instead of saying 0 when touching 12. The remediation would begin with the part of the format that teaches figuring out minutes after the hour.

Figure 16.5

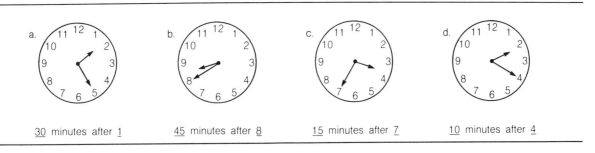

30 minutes after 1   45 minutes after 8   15 minutes after 7   10 minutes after 4

The errors in examples c and d may be caused by the student's confusing the minute and hour hands. If this type of error occurs frequently, the teacher presents exercises focusing on discriminating the hour hand from the minute hand (see page 426). If the confusion is severe, the teacher might use examples in which the minute hand is elongated to serve as a prompt.

Application Items: Telling Time

1. Below are sets of examples prepared by teachers to use in early exercises to teach telling time as minutes after the hour. Which sets are inappropriate and why?

   Set A: 15 minutes after 8,   10 minutes after 7
   　　　　10 minutes after 9,   5 minutes after 7

   Set B: 13 minutes after 2,   25 minutes after 4
   　　　　37 minutes after 10, 10 minutes after 9

   Set C: 20 minutes after 7,   35 minutes after 4
   　　　　15 minutes after 2,   30 minutes after 8

2. Tell the probable cause of each student's errors.

   a. *Homer*

   <u>30</u> minutes after <u>3</u>　　<u>50</u> minutes after <u>8</u>　　<u>10</u> minutes after <u>11</u>

   b. *Elmer*

   <u>50</u> minutes after <u>12</u>　　<u>20</u> minutes after <u>9</u>　　<u>35</u> minutes after <u>5</u>

   c. *Peter*

   <u>30</u> minutes after <u>2</u>　　<u>15</u> minutes after <u>8</u>　　<u>50</u> minutes after <u>6</u>

3. Specify the wording the teacher uses in correcting the first error made by each student in problem 2. The wording will be different for each student.

17 | Money

The need for instruction in money-related skills is derived from their importance in daily activities. Included in this chapter are procedures for (a) determining the value of a group of coins, (b) counting change, (c) decimal notation for money, and (d) consumer skills. A more in-depth list of problem types appears in the Instructional Sequence and Assessment Chart (see Figure 17.1).

Determining the Value of a Group of Coins

Preskills for determining the value of a group of coins includes the ability to identify and tell the value of individual coins and knowledge of the 5, 10, and 25 count-by series.

Students are usually taught to identify coins in the first grade. This is a fairly simple preskill to teach since many students will already be able to recognize several coins. A format similar to that used in symbol identification would be presented in which the teacher initially models and tests the name of a coin and then models and tests its value: "This is a nickel. What is this? . . . A nickel is worth 5¢. How much is a nickel worth? . . ." For this task, the teacher can use either real coins or pictures of coins.

The penny and nickel should be introduced first. After students can label and state their values, dimes can be introduced, followed by quarters. Note that the coins are introduced cumulatively, which implies that students must be able to discriminate the new coin from previously introduced coins before the teacher can present a new example.

The preskill for counting groups of similar coins is knowledge of the respective count-by series. Once students have learned the count-by series, they have little trouble applying the skill to coin counting. In presenting counting groups of similar coins for the first time, the teacher indicates the value of the coin and the models counting. For example, "Here is a group of nickels. Each nickel is worth 5¢. To find out how many cents this group of nickels equals, I count by 5s. My turn." The teacher then counts by 5 as he or she touches each coin. After modeling, the teacher tests students on counting several sets of like coins. Worksheet exercises like the one in Figure 17.3 should follow the oral presentation.

Problems in which students determine the value of a set of mixed coins are usually introduced in second grade and contain just two or three coins. In later grades, the number of coins to be counted increases. We recommend a two-step strategy: *(a)* grouping like coins together and *(b)* starting with the

Figure 17.1 Instructional Sequence and Assessment Chart

Grade Level	Problem Type	Performance Indicator
2a	Value of single coins	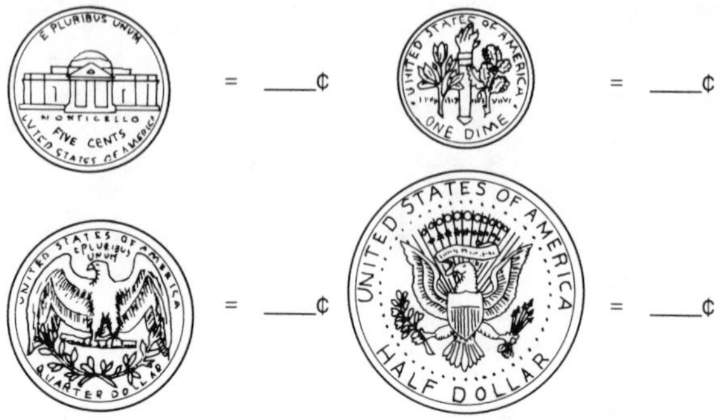
2b	Determining value of groups of like coins	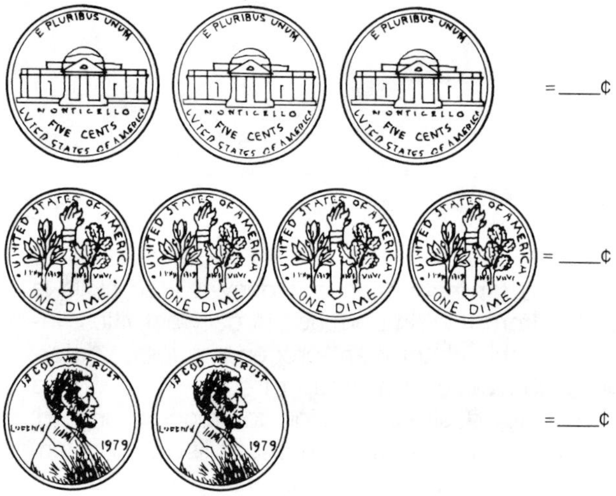
2c	Determining value of groups of different coins	

Figure 17.1 cont'd

Grade Level	Problem Type	Performance Indicator
3a	Consumer skills: Verifying change from less that $1.00	You bought a soda that costs 20¢. You give the clerk a half dollar. The clerk gives you this change. Is it correct?

You bought a soda that costs 27¢. You give the clerk 35¢. The clerk gives you this change. Is it correct?

Grade Level	Problem Type	Performance Indicator
3b	Consumer skills: Specifying change	Write the coins you would need to make 27¢. Write the coins you would need to make 79¢. Write the coins you would need to make 43¢.
3c	Decimal notation: Reading and writing dollar and cents notations under 10 dollars	Write four dollars & six cents _____ Write nine dollars & thirty cents _____ Write one dollar & five cents _____
4a	Decimal notation: Subtracting dollars and cents from whole dollar figures	$15.00 - 1.35 = 9.00 - 8.20 = 10.00 - 6.16 =
4b	Consumer skills: Adding and subtracting whole dollars and dollar and cents amounts	Jack had $6. He spent $3.25. How much does he have left? If you had $4 and you got $2.15 more, how much would you have? Jan buys a shirt for $2.85. She gives the clerk a $5 bill. How much change does she get back?
4c	Consumer skills: Determining cost of purchase for two groups of items	You buy 3 pencils for 15¢ each and 5 pencils for 10¢ each. How much do you spend? You buy 4 pens for 30¢ each and 2 erasers for 12¢ each. How much do you spend? You buy 5 pens for 15¢ each and 3 erasers for 8¢ each. How much do you spend?
4d	Consumer skills: How much can be bought with specified amount	Bill wants to buy pencils which cost 7¢ each. He has 2 dollar bills and a dime. How many pencils can he buy? Bill has 3 quarters. If spoons cost 5¢ each, how many spoons can he buy? Bill has 3 half dollars. If spoons cost 5¢ each, how many spoons can he buy?
4e	Consumer skills: Reading a price list	(see price list below)

Hamburger		Ice cream	
plain	35¢	cone	
cheese	50¢	small	40¢
bacon	70¢	large	60¢
fries add	20¢	sundae	
Soda		small	60¢
small	30¢	large	80¢
med.	40¢		
large	50¢		

Bill wants two hamburgers with cheese, one with fries, one without fries, a large soda, and two large ice cream cones. How much will all that cost?

Money   **437**

Figure 17.1 cont'd

Grade Level	Problem Type	Performance Indicator
5a	Consumer skills: Comparison shopping—unit cost	A 6 oz. package of rice made by ABC Company costs 96¢. A 5 oz. package made by the XYZ company costs 90¢. Which package of rice is the best buy? Tell why.

Figure 17.2 Skill Hierarchy

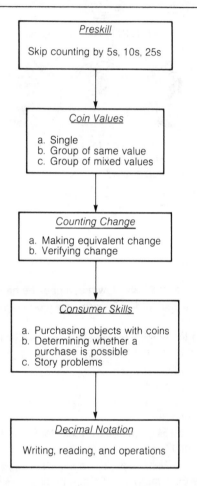

*Decimal notation is required for some advanced consumer skills.

A preskill for counting a group of unlike coins is addition facts in which 10, 5, or 1 is added to a two digit number ending in zero or 5 (e.g., 70 and 10 more is. . . . 70 and 5 more is. . . .).This preskill can be taught using a model-test procedure in which the teacher models several problems and tests students on a set of problems (e.g., 40 and 10 more, 40 and 5 more, 40 and 1 more, 45 and 5 more, 45 and 1 more, 80 and 5 more, 80 and 1 more, 20 and 10 more, 20 and 5 more). Facts in which 10 is added to a two digit number ending in 5 (35 + 10, 65 + 10) are particularly hard. They should not be introduced until the easier facts are mastered. Practice would be done daily for several weeks either orally or through worksheet exercises in which problems are written horizontally and there is some indication that students are not to realign numbers vertically but are to work each problem mentally.

To teach students to determine the value of a set of mixed coins, the teacher initially models by touching and counting the coins, and then tests, prompting students by telling the value of each coin. For example, let's say the teacher is having the students determine the value of a group including two quarters, three dimes and a nickel. The teacher says, pointing to the first quarter, "25."

"25 AND (pointing to next quarter) 25 MORE IS . . ."	"50"
"50 AND (pointing to the first dime) 10 MORE IS . . ."	"60"
"60 AND (pointing to next dime) 10 MORE IS . . ."	"70"
"70 AND (pointing to next dime) 10 MORE IS . . ."	"80"
"80 AND (pointing to nickel) 5 MORE IS . . ."	"85"

Counting Change

Three change-related skills are discussed in this section: (a) making equivalent change, which involves exchanging a group of smaller valued coins for a larger coin (e.g., two dimes and a nickel for a quarter) and (b) giving change when the amount to be given is specified, and (c) verifying the change received from a purchase.

coin worth the most and counting all like coins, then switching to the next highest coin in the group and counting by the value of that coin. For example, in counting two quarters, three dimes, and two nickels, students would begin counting the quarters (25, 50), switch to the dimes (60, 70, 80) and switch once more to the nickels (85, 90).

A strategy beginning with larger value coins is recommended over a strategy beginning with lower value coins since beginning with lower value coins results in a difficult counting sequence. For example, to count a quarter, dime, nickel, and two pennies, the student would count 1, 2, 7, 17, 42. Counting 25, 35, 40, 41, 42 is much easier.

Figure 17.3 Coin Counting Worksheet

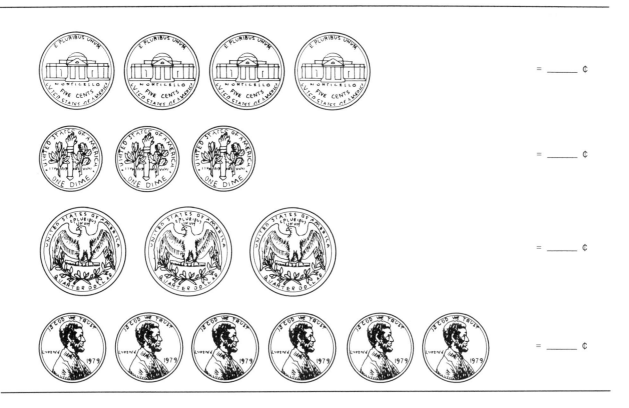

These skills would most likely be taught in third grade. The preskill is the ability to count groups of coins.

Making Equivalent Change

Giving equivalent change for a larger coin is not a complex skill to teach. However, two kinds of equivalent change exercises should be practiced. In the first type, the teacher has students first identify the value of a larger coin. Then the teacher has students determine the number of smaller value coins equal to the original coin. In this exercise, students are always counting like coins. In the second type of equivalent change problem, the students must count a set of different coins to determine whether or not a given amount of change is equivalent to the amount stated. Both types of exercises are illustrated in Figure 17.4.

Initially, coin equivalency problems would include pennies, nickels, dimes, and quarters (e.g., a quarter equals two dimes and a nickel). Larger values including dollar bills would be introduced later.

Worksheet exercises like Figure 17.5 present a different application of the equivalency skill. Students circle the appropriate more, less, or equal sign between two groups of coins. Initially, the teacher would lead the students through counting

the coins in each group. After counting the coins, the students would be instructed to write the value of each group above the group. If the values are equal, the students would be instructed to circle the equal sign. If the values of the groups are not equal, the students would circle the appropriate more or less sign.

Verifying Change

The easiest way of verifying change received is to begin at the price of the item(s) and then count the coins received as change, beginning with the coin of least value. Students would then compare the number ended with to the amount given to pay for the purchase (see Figure 17.6). For example, let's say a purchase of 36¢ is made and the student is given back four pennies and two nickels for a half-dollar. The student counts 37, 38, 39, 40, 45, 50. The student knows the change given is correct since she ends with 50¢, the value of the coin given to make the purchase. Initial examples should be relatively easy, including small numbers of coins. Later examples can include a greater number of coins. An example appropriate for the introduction of the skill might consist of payment of 40¢ for an object costing 36¢. To verify the change in this example, students need count only pennies: 37, 38,

Figure 17.4

Equivalent Change Exercise 1

TEACHER	**STUDENTS**
(Teacher uses real or pretend coins.)	

1. "I WANT TO FIND OUT HOW MANY NICKELS EQUAL ONE
   DIME. HOW MUCH IS A DIME WORTH?"   "10¢"
   "SO I COUNT NICKELS UNTIL I GET TO 10. WHAT DO I
   COUNT BY WHEN I COUNT NICKELS?"   "5"
   "STOP ME WHEN I GET TO 10. 5, 10 . . ."   Students say stop.
   "HOW MANY NICKELS DID I COUNT?"   "2"
   "SO HOW MANY NICKELS EQUAL ONE DIME?"   "2"
   Repeat step 1 with "HOW MANY PENNIES EQUAL ONE DIME?"

2. (Review of previously taught equivalencies.)
   "HOW MANY PENNIES IN A NICKEL?"   "5"
   "HOW MANY NICKELS IN A DIME?"   "2"
   "HOW MANY PENNIES IN A DIME?"   "10"

Equivalent Change Exercise 2

1. "I GAVE A MAN A QUARTER AND HE GAVE ME TWO DIMES
   AND A NICKEL. LET'S FIGURE OUT IF THESE COINS ARE
   WORTH THE SAME AS A QUARTER. HOW MUCH IS
   QUARTER WORTH?"   "25¢"
   "LET'S COUNT THE COINS AND SEE IF THEY'RE WORTH
   25¢. I'LL TOUCH, YOU COUNT."   "10, 20, 25"
   "ARE THOSE COINS WORTH 25¢?"   "Yes"

Figure 17.5

39, 40. A later example might involve payment of a dollar for an object costing 36¢ for which students would need to count pennies, dimes, and quarters: 37, 38, 39, 40, 50, 75, a dollar. Problems involving more than one dollar would be introduced last. Note that the same strategy applies to counting change from dollars. The student counts the change to determine if the object's cost plus the change equal the payment price. For example, if an object costing 37¢ is paid for with a $10 bill, the change counting would proceed as follows: 38, 39, 40, 50, 75, a dollar, 2, 3, 4, 5, 10 dollars. Again, practice would be provided in worksheet exercises and through hands-on activities in which students exchange facsimiles of coins.

Decimal Notation in Money

Money problems expressed in decimal notation typically are introduced in third grade. A problem states that a 39¢ toy is paid with a $5 bill and asks how much change should be given. The solution would be derived by subtracting 39¢ from $5 and expressed as $4.61. Specifying the exact coins would not be an appropriate response, unless the problem asked students to specify the change that would be given. Since many application problems call for an amount rather than the coins used to make change, the decimal notation for money should be introduced in the primary grades, even if general decimal instruction has not begun.

Fortunately, decimal notation for money is relatively safe to introduce before more comprehensive decimal instruction is taught. The students can be told that the two numbers to the right of the decimal stand for cents and that the numbers to the left of the decimal tell about dollars. A format for teaching students to read and write dollar figures expressed with decimal notation appears in Figure 17.7. Both parts of the format would be presented daily for 2–3 weeks. Six to eight examples should be included in each part.

Included in the format should be examples without dollars (e.g., $.45, $.30) and examples without cents (e.g., $5.00, $13.00). Students can be expected to have difficulty writing amounts between 1 and 9 cents because of the need to place a zero after the decimal: $7.03, $14.08. These examples, therefore, should not be introduced in the initial writing exercise, Concentrated practice on this type of example should be provided in later lessons. At that time, the teacher would explain simply by saying that there always needs to be two digits after the decimal when writing money figures. The teacher should then model that when the number of cents is below ten, a zero and then the digit for the number of cents are written.

Story problems with money expressed in decimal notation should be introduced when students are able to read and write decimal notation for money. A common story problem type, which deserves special attention, is illustrated below:

Jim bought a shirt for $3.62. He gave the clerk $10 bill. How much change will Jim receive?

Jill had $6. She was given $3.50 for working in the yard. How much money does she have now?

In these problems, a dollar amount is expressed without any cents after the decimal point. When working the problem, students must write the dollar amount with a decimal point and two zeroes. The critical skills of aligning the numbers according to the decimal point was discussed in Chaper 14. The teacher would model working several problems of this type before assigning students to work them.

Consumer Skills

Three consumer skills are discussed in this section. The first, a skill taught in second or third grade, involves teaching students to pay for purchases with coins. The second, a skill taught in third or fourth grade, involves teaching students to read price lists and menus. The third, a skill taught in fourth or fifth grade, involves teaching unit pricing to make comparisons when shopping.

Figure 17.6 Format for Verifying Change

TEACHER

STUDENTS

Write on board: 36¢ P P P P D Q Q

1. Point to P. "THIS STANDS FOR PENNY."
   Point to D. "THIS STANDS FOR DIME."
   Point to Q. "THIS STANDS FOR QUARTER."
   Point to each letter in random order and ask, "WHAT DOES THIS STAND FOR?"

2. Point to 36¢. "JOHN BOUGHT APPLES THAT COST 36¢. HE GAVE THE MAN A DOLLAR. WE'RE GOING TO COUNT THE CHANGE JOHN GOT AND SEE IF IT'S RIGHT. WE'LL COUNT FROM 36 AND SEE IF WE END WITH A DOLLAR." Point to pennies. "WHAT DO WE COUNT BY FOR THESE?"
   Point to dime. "WHAT DO WE COUNT BY FOR THIS?"
   Point to quarters. "WHAT DO WE COUNT BY FOR THESE?"

"1"
"10"

"25"

3. "LET'S COUNT THE CHANGE. START WITH 36— COUNT." Point to coins as students count.
   "DID WE END WITH A DOLLAR?"
   Repeat steps 2 and 3 with several more examples.

"37, 38, 39, 40, 50, 75, 100"
"Yes"

Figure 17.7 Format for Decimal Notation for Money

PART A: Reading Decimal Notation

<u>**TEACHER**</u>   <u>**STUDENTS**</u>

Write on board: $4.32

1. "HERE IS THE WAY TO WRITE DOLLARS AND
   CENTS." Point to the decimal point in $4.32. "THIS DOT
   IS A DECIMAL POINT. IT DIVIDES DOLLARS AND
   CENTS." Point to 4. "THIS TELLS US FOUR DOLLARS."
   Point to 32. "THESE TWO NUMBERS TELL US ABOUT
   CENTS. I'LL READ THE AMOUNT: FOUR DOLLARS
   AND THIRTY-TWO CENTS."

2. Write on board: $3.62
   "HOW MANY DOLLARS?"   "3"
   "HOW MANY CENTS?"   "62"
   "SAY THE WHOLE AMOUNT."   "$3.62"

   Repeat step 2 with $7.20, $.45,* $6.00, $.30*

PART B: Writing with Decimal Notation

Give students piece of lined paper.

1. "YOU'RE GOING TO WRITE MONEY AMOUNTS
   USING A DOLLAR SIGN AND A DECIMAL POINT."

2. "LISTEN, EIGHT DOLLARS AND THIRTY-TWO
   CENTS. SAY THAT."   "$8.32"
   "HOW MANY DOLLARS?"   "8"
   "WRITE A DOLLAR SIGN, THEN AN 8."

3. "EIGHT DOLLARS AND THIRTY-TWO CENTS.
   HOW MANY CENTS?"   "32"
   "WRITE A DECIMAL POINT ON THE LINE. THEN
   WRITE 32."

4. "WHAT AMOUNT DID YOU WRITE?"   "$8.32"
   Repeat steps 2-4 with these examples: $6.42, $.32, $4.10
   $7.00, $.57, $9.00.

*For examples with no dollars, the teacher should model the response on the first
day the format appears.

Making Purchases with Coins

When purchasing an item in a store, the student should use a strategy which allows her as quickly as possible to figure out the coins to give. We recommend that students begin counting with the largest value coins. For example, if a student has an assortment of coins and wants to buy something costing 28¢, the fastest way to count the exact amount would be to give a quarter and three pennies. This skill can be taught by using real coins or fascimiles of coins. The teacher presents the rule that "When

you count money to buy something, you start with the coins that are worth more." Next, the teacher models several examples and then tests. The format appears in Figure 17.8.

A mistake often made by students is inappropriately counting pennies for the value of the ones. For example, when counting out 38¢, students count out 30¢ using a quarter and a nickel and then put out eight pennies. One way to prompt students to use a nickel instead of a group of five pennies is to give students only four pennies with which to work. This procedure will force students to use nickels. As students become more adept at counting coins in an efficient manner, the teacher can give them more than four pennies. Often, students will not have the appropriate coins to allow them to count an exact amount. In these situations, students must count an amount that exceeds the purchase price.

Often, students will not have the appropriate coins to allow them to count an exact amount. In these situations, students must count an amount that exceeds the purchase price.

The format in Figure 17.9 teaches students to use the fewest coins to make a purchase. For example, with a purchase price of 69¢ and these coins—QQQDD—the coins that give a value closest to 69¢ are two quarters and two dimes; however,

using up the larger coins is much easier, in this case three quarters.

Counting Change

Counting change is usually done by a clerk. Because most cash registers display the amount of change to give, students need to be able to reach the amount using the fewest number of coins. Figure 17.10 gives a format for teaching that skill. The format is written just for coins. Adding dollar bills can be done using the identical format. The differences would be that whole dollars would be given and students wouldn't write letters for coins but rather numbers that represented the bills (e.g., 20, 10, 5 and 1). The same wording can be used. "Start

---

Figure 17.8 Format for Counting Coins to Reach an Exact Value

---

PART A: Structured Board Presentation

TEACHER

1. "TODAY YOU'RE GOING TO COUNT OUT MONEY AT YOUR SEATS. I'LL TELL YOU HOW MUCH SOMETHING COSTS AND YOU COUNT OUT THE MONEY TO BUY IT. WHEN YOU COUNT OUT MONEY TO BUY SOMETHING, START WITH THE COIN THAT'S WORTH MORE. IF I WANT TO BUY SOMETHING FOR 25¢, WOULD I USE 25 PENNIES OR 1 QUARTER?"
   "WHY?"

   "RIGHT, A QUARTER IS WORTH MORE THAN A PENNY. IF I WANT TO BUY SOMETHING THAT COSTS 20¢, WOULD I USE NICKELS OR DIMES?"
   "WHY?"

2. "MY TURN. I WANT TO BUY A BALLOON THAT COSTS 31¢. I START WITH A QUARTER: 25, 30, 31." Write Q   N   P on board.

3. "YOUR TURN." Pass out coins, either real or facsimilies. "A TOY CAR COSTS 28¢. START WITH THE COIN THAT'S WORTH THE MOST AND COUNT OUT 28¢."

   Monitor student responses.
   Repeat step 3 with several more examples.

STUDENTS

"1 quarter"
"A quarter is worth more than a penny"

"Dimes"
"A dime is worth more than a nickel"

Students should put out a quarter and three pennies.

Figure 17.9 Counting Coins When You Don't Have the Exact Amount

TEACHER	STUDENTS

1. "I'M GOING TO USE THE COINS I HAVE TO BUY SOMETHING THAT COSTS 56¢."
(Write 56¢. Below write QQQDDD.)
"THIS IS ALL THE MONEY I HAVE TO USE.
I START WITH THE COIN THAT HAS THE GREATEST VALUE. I GET AS CLOSE AS I CAN. IF I DON'T HAVE THE EXACT AMOUNT, I HAVE TO GIVE MORE. I'LL GET THE EXTRA MONEY BACK AS CHANGE. WATCH."
(Circle a coin each time you count.)
"25, 50, 75."
"I PAID MORE THAN 56¢, SO I'LL GET SOME CHANGE BACK."

2. "YOUR TURN. POINT TO PROBLEM 1 ON YOUR WORKSHEET." (1. 36¢ QDDN)
"START WITH THE COIN WORTH THE MOST. IF YOU DON'T HAVE EXACTLY 36¢, COUNT MORE THAN 36. CIRCLE THE COINS YOU'LL USE. RAISE YOUR HAND WHEN YOU'RE DONE."
(When most hands are raised) "TELL ME THE COINS YOU CIRCLED."

                                        "Q, D, N"

3. Repeat step 2 with these problems:
   2. 72¢ QDDDNNP
   3. 29¢ DDDNNPP

---

with the bill worth the most and see how close you can get. Then try the next largest bill." After students master change for coins and bills separately, mixed amounts can be presented. First tell the students to figure the bills. Check their answers. Then have them figure the coins and check their answers.

Reading Price Lists and Menus

Many price lists or menus utilize indentation systems to describe subcategories of a general group. Figure 17.11 includes a sample menu students might encounter in a fast food restaurant. Teachers should test students on reading various price lists and menus by asking students the price of various items. Teachers can then give students story problems such as: "Jerry has 2 dollars. He wants to buy a small hamburger, a large French fries and a small ice cream. Does he have enough money? If so, how much change will he receive?"

Teaching Unit Pricing

Unit pricing comparison shopping involves determining the relative cost of the same type of item when it appears in packages containing different quantities. For example, a 10 oz. bag of ABC soap costs 97¢ and an 8 oz. bag of XYZ soap costs 86¢. Which soap is a better buy? The teacher presents the rule: "To compare similar items in different size packages, we must divide to find the unit price." The teacher then models with several examples. For example, in comparing a 6 lb. package that costs 42¢ with a 5 lb. package that costs 40¢, the teacher points out that you must find the pound (the unit price) and illustrates how this can be done by dividing the total cost by the number of pounds: $42 \div 6 = 7$ and $40 \div 5 = 8$. Thus, the 6 lb. package is a better buy, since it costs a penny less per pound.

Figure 17.10 Counting Change

TEACHER	STUDENTS

1. Write on board: 73¢ Q
   D
   N
   P

   "WHEN YOU MAKE CHANGE, YOU HAVE TO
   FIGURE OUT WHAT COINS TO USE." (Point to
   each letter as you say) "I'M GOING TO FIGURE
   OUT HOW MANY QUARTERS, DIMES, NICKELS,
   AND PENNIES I USE TO MAKE 73¢. I START
   WITH THE COIN WORTH THE MOST—A
   QUARTER. I COUNT TO GET AS CLOSE AS I CAN
   TO 73: 25, 50. I COUNTED 2 TIMES. SO I WRITE
   THIS TO SHOW 2 QUARTERS." (Write QQ.)
   "NOW I COUNT DIMES. I'VE ALREADY GOT 50:
   60, 70. I COUNTED 2 TIMES, SO I WRITE DD
   FOR 2 DIMES. (Write DD.)
   NOW I TRY TO COUNT NICKELS. I ALREADY
   HAVE 70. I CAN'T COUNT ANY NICKELS. THE
   FIRST TIME I COUNT BY 5 I GET 75 AND
   THAT'S TOO BIG. I DON'T WRITE ANY N'S. NOW
   I COUNT PENNIES. I STILL HAVE 70: 71, 72, 73.
   I COUNTED 3 TIMES SO I WRITE PPP AFTER
   THE LAST D." (Write PPP.)
   "I'M DONE. THE ANSWER IS 2 QUARTERS, 2
   DIMES AND 3 PENNIES—THOSE COINS MAKE
   73¢. WATCH."
   (Point to each letter as you count: 25, 50, 60,
   70, 71, 72, 73)

2. "YOUR TURN."
   (Write this for problem 1: 48¢)
   "START WITH QUARTERS. GET AS CLOSE AS
   YOU CAN TO 48. RAISE YOUR HAND WHEN YOU
   KNOW HOW MANY QUARTERS." (When most
   hands are raised) "HOW MANY QUARTERS?"   "One"
   (Write one Q after 48¢.)
   "NOW FIGURE OUT HOW MANY DIMES TO GET
   AS CLOSE AS YOU CAN TO 48. REMEMBER
   YOU'VE ALREADY GOT 25 FROM THE
   QUARTER." (When most hands are raised) "HOW
   MANY NICKELS?"   "Zero" or "None"
   "ZERO NICKELS. IF YOU COUNT BY 5 EVEN ONE
   TIME YOU GET 50, AND THAT'S BIGGER THAN
   48. SO YOU DON'T WRITE ANYTHING. FIGURE
   OUT HOW MANY PENNIES YOU NEED TO GET TO
   48. REMEMBER YOU'VE ALREADY GOT 45."
   (When most hands are raised) "HOW MANY
   PENNIES?" (Write PPP after the last D.)   "Three"
   "LET'S SEE IF WE HAVE 48¢. START WITH THE
   Q AND COUNT THE COINS." (Count.)

3. Repeat step 2 with 55¢ and 82¢.

Figure 17.11

XYZ Fast Food Restaurant

Menu

Hamburgers		Ice Cream	
plain–small	$ .60	cones	
plain–large	$1.25	large	$.60
with cheese	add 10¢	small	$.50
French Fries		cups	
large	$ .60	large	$.50
small	$ .35	small	$.30

Application Items: Money

1. When counting a quarter, a dime, and two nickels, students count as specified below. Tell the probable cause of their errors. Specify what the teacher says to correct each student. (Assume students know the value of each coin.)

   Jill—25, 30, 35, 40
   Jim—5, 10, 20, 35

2. Tell the probable cause for each error below. Specify what the teacher says to correct each student.

   Jill had 5 dollars. She buys a pencil for 4 cents. How much money does she have left?

   Tom

   $$\begin{array}{r} {\overset{4}{\$\,5.00}} \\ -.04 \\ \hline \$4.06 \end{array}$$

   Ann

   $$\begin{array}{r} 5 \\ -4 \\ \hline 1 \end{array}$$

18 | Measurement

Customary and Metric Units

There are two basic measurement systems—the customary system, which is used in the United States and a few other countries, and the metric system, which is used in the majority of countries in the world.

The metric system has several advantages over the customary system. First, since the metric system uses the base 10 place value system, instruction in decimals directly relates to measurement skills. With customary units, different place value base systems are required for weight (16 ounces), length (12 inches, 3 feet), etc. Second, in the customary system there is no commonality among the units for various measurements, while there is commonality among the metric units. The prefixes in the metric system (milli, centi, deci, deka, hecto, kilo) are used in each area: length, weight, and capacity.

Table 18.1 includes the various customary and metric units for expressing length, weight, capacity and temperature. Note the orderliness of the metric system. The prefix in front of a unit tells the unit's relation to the base unit. At the same time, note how the various units in the customary system are so different from one another.

A conversion from customary to metric has begun in the United States. Since the conversion will take many years, and children in the United States growing up in the 1990s are likely to encounter both systems. Both the customary and the metric system will need to be taught. The question facing teachers is whether or not both systems should be taught simultaneously, and if not, which should be taught first. Unfortunately, there is no simple answer to this question. However, we have noticed that lower-performing students are likely to confuse facts from one system with the facts from another system if both systems are introduced concurrently. This information leads us to recommend that the two systems be taught independently of one another, preferably at different times during the year. Low-performing students should be familiar with common units from one system before the other system is introduced.

During the primary grades, measurement instruction is relatively simple. Common units and equivalencies are introduced, and students use tools to measure objects to the nearest whole unit. During the intermediate grades, measurement instruction becomes more complex as less commonly used units are introduced and more sophisticated uses of measuring tools are presented. While in the early grades students measured to the nearest whole unit, in later grades they are taught to measure partial units (e.g., 3 1/8 inches). Also in the intermediate grades, conversion problems are introduced in which students must convert a quantity expressed as one unit to a larger or smaller unit (5

447

Table 18.1 Metric and Customary Units for Measuring Length, Weight, and Capacity

Customary Units

Length	Weight	Capacity
12 inches = 1 foot	16 ounces = 1 pound	2 cups = 1 pint
3 feet = 1 yard	2,000 pounds = 1 ton	2 pints = 1 quart
5,280 feet = 1 mile		4 quarts = 1 gallon

Metric Units

Meaning of Prefix	Length	Weight	Capacity
thousandth	millimeter (mm)	milligram (mg)	milliliter (ml)
hundredth	centimeter (cm)	centigram (cg)	centiliter (cl)
tenth	decimeter (dm)	decigram (dg)	deciliter (dl)
whole	meter (m)	gram (g)	liter (l)
10 wholes	dekameter (dkm)	dekagram (dkg)	dekaliter (dkl)
100 wholes	hectometer (hm)	hectogram (hg)	hectoliter (hl)
1000 wholes	kilometer (km)	kilogram (kg)	kiloliter (kl)

Figure 18.1 Instructional Sequence and Assessment Chart

Grade Level	Problem Type	Performance Indicator
2a	Customary units: Length	_____ inches in a foot _____ feet in a yard About how long is a spoon? 6 inches 6 feet 6 yards About how tall is a person? 5 inches 5 feet 5 yards
2b	Customary units: Weight	_____ ounces in a pound _____ pounds in a ton About how much does a cat weigh? 8 ounces 8 pounds 8 tons About how much does a car weigh? 2 ounces 2 pounds 2 tons
2c	Customary units: Liquid capacity	_____ cups in a pint _____ pints in a quart _____ quarts in a gallon
3a	Metric units: Length	_____ centimeters in a meter About how long is a pen? 8 mm 8 cm 2 m 2 km About how long is a car? 2 mm 2 cm 2 m 2 km
3b	Metric units: Weight	_____ grams in a kilogram About how much does a pencil weigh? 75 mg 75 g 75 kg 75 cg About how much does a newborn baby weigh? 4 mg 4 g 4 kg 4 cg

Figure 18.1 cont'd

Grade Level	Problem Type	Performance Indicator

3c — Metric units: Capacity

_____ milliliters in a liter

How much water can we put in a baby bottle?
250 ml   250 dl   250 l   250 kl

How much milk would a basketball hold?
3 ml   3 dl   3 l   3 kl

3d — Customary units: Length (tool)— measure to nearest half-inch

How long is the line?

_____

Circle the correct answer:
2 inches   2 1/2 inches
3 inches   3 1/2 inches

3e — Customary units: Length (tool)— using a ruler to the nearest fourth-inch

How long is the line?

_____

3 inches   2 3/4 inches
3 1/4 inches   2 1/4 inches

4a — Customary units: Length conversions—inches, feet, yards

4 feet = _____ inches
2 yards = _____ feet
36 inches = _____ feet

4b — Customary units: Length (tool)— using a ruler to the nearest eighth-inch

Make an X over 2 1/4
Make an R over 1 1/2
Make a T over 2 3/8
Make a B over 2 1/4

4c — Customary units: Operations— regrouping required

Circle the correct answer.
 4 feet 5 inches
+3 feet 8 inches
‾‾‾‾‾‾‾‾‾‾‾‾‾‾‾‾‾
 8 feet 3 inches
 8 feet 1 inch
 7 feet 3 inches

Circle the correct answer
 3 weeks 4 days
-1 week   6 days
‾‾‾‾‾‾‾‾‾‾‾‾‾‾‾‾‾
 1 week 8 days
 2 weeks 8 days
 1 week 5 days

4d — Customary units: Area—volume

What is the area of a room 8 feet long and 10 feet wide?

_____

What is the volume of a box 6 inches long, 8 inches wide and 4 inches high?

_____

Figure 18.1 cont'd

Grade Level	Problem Type	Performance Indicator
4e	Customary units: Story problems—renaming	Jill wants to make ribbons 6 inches long. How many feet of material will she need to make 8 ribbons? Jill is 6 feet 2 inches. Her sister is 4 feet 10 inches. How much taller is Jill?
5a	Metric equivalencies—less common units	Circle the answer. A kilogram equals: 1 gm 10 gm 100 gm 1,000 gm A hectogram equals: 1 gm 10 gm 100 gm 1,000 gm A dekaliter equals: 1 l 10 l 100 l 1,000 l A milliliter equals: a tenth of a liter a hundredth of a liter a thousandth of a liter A centigram equals: a tenth of a gram a hundredth of a gram a thousandth of a gram A decimeter equals: a tenth of a meter a hundredth of a meter a thousandth of a meter
5-6	Metric conversions	20 meters = _____ centimeters 5000 centigrams = _____ grams 500 kilometers = _____ meters 3.6 meters = _____ centimeters 46 grams = _____ kilogram 2.7 liters = _____ deciliters

meters = 500 centimeters). Finally, operations and story problems involving measurement facts are presented.

A sequence of major skills appears in the Instructional Sequence and Assessment Chart in Figure 18.1. Though not all possible items for customary and metric units are included, each type of item appears with at least one of the two systems of units.

Introducing the Concept

Teachers working with beginning level kindergarten or first grade students who have had no previous experience with measurement should demonstrate with concrete objects how to use consistent units as standards in measurement. Length can be introduced first. To illustrate measurement of length before students are taught about abstract concepts of inches and feet, the teacher can present an exercise in which students measure the lengths of various strips using paper clips as the measurement standard. The teacher first demonstrates by laying the clips along the edge of the paper and determining that the paper is "x clips long." For example, this slip of paper is three clips long:

Following the demonstration, students are given the opportunity to determine the lengths of several strips of paper using paper clips.

This exercise serves two purposes. First, it introduces students to the concept of measuring a specific attribute, like length. Secondly, the exercise provides the opportunity to demonstrate how the units used for measurement are equivalent. The paper clips used in measuring length are always the same size.

Teachers can introduce weight measurement in the same way with a balance scale. First, the teacher demonstrates how the scale works. This is done by showing students that the weights on both sides of the scale are the same when the trays of the scale are the same height. Similarly, the teacher must show that when the weights are not the same, the side that is pushed down is heavier. Following the demonstration with a balance scale, the teacher introduces students to standard weights against which they will measure various objects. For example, blocks that weigh an ounce can be used as the measuring standard against which other objects can be measured.

For liquid capacity, the teacher sets out a number of empty cups, presents a water-filled container whose capacity is to be measured, and pours the contents into the cups, one at a time. The teacher then asks how many cups of water the container holds. Because of the potential mess involved in pouring liquids, this activity is best done as a teacher demonstration only.

Primary Grades

Introducing Common Units and Equivalencies

During the primary grades, students learn the more common units and their equivalencies:

Length
customary—inch, foot, yard
metric—centimeter, meter, kilometer

Weight
customary—ounces, pounds
metric—gram, kilogram

Capacity (liquid)
customary—pint, quart, gallon
metric—milliliter, liter

The basic pattern in introducing units follows a five-step procedure. The teacher does the following:

1. Tells the function of the specific unit; e.g., "Inches tell how long something is. We use inches to measure objects that are not very big. Feet also tell how long something is. We use feet to measure objects that are pretty big."

2. Illustrates the unit; e.g., the teacher draws lines on the board, "This line is an inch long." For demonstrating weight, the teacher might give students blocks weighing an ounce or a pound.
3. Demonstrates how to use measuring tools, measuring to the nearest whole unit.
4. Presents application exercise in which the students determine which unit to use to measure an object; e.g., "What unit would we use to tell how long a piece of paper is? What unit would we use to tell how long the chalkboard is?"
5. Presents the equivalency fact; e.g., "12 inches equals one foot."

Application exercises (step 4) and equivalencies (step 5) should incorporate review of previously introduced units from all areas. For example, assume students have learned inch, foot, ounce, pound, and pint. Here is a representative set of questions that might be asked: "What unit would we use to tell how tall a person is? What unit would we use to tell how much a person weighs? What unit would we use to tell how much a letter weighs? What unit would we use to tell how long a pencil is?"

Equivalency review might include these questions: "How many ounces in a pound? How many inches in a foot? How many pints in a quart?" Review can be provided daily in worksheet exercises. A sample worksheet appears in Figure 18.2.

In addition to worksheet exercises, the teacher should incorporate measuring tasks into daily activities. Scales, thermometers, rulers, and liquid containers should be readily accessible. Students should be encouraged to apply measuring skills with concrete objects.

The sequence and rate of instruction of measurement facts and skills must be carefully controlled. New information is introduced cumulatively. That is, a new piece of information is not introduced until mastery of prior skills and information is demonstrated. Also, review of prior information is incorporated into tasks that introduce new skills. The length units, inch and foot, are usually introduced first. Several weeks later, ounces and pounds might be introduced, and several weeks after that pints and quarts.

When the students demonstrate mastery of these smaller units, larger units (yard, ton, gallon) can be introduced. A new set of units would be introduced only after students have mastered all the previous sets.

If a school district teaches both metric and customary units, common customary units should probably be introduced first. The common metric

Figure 18.2 Measurement Review Worksheet

Circle or fill in the answer.

1. A pencil is about 6 _____ long.	feet	pounds	inches	pints
2. A cat weighs about 8 _____.	feet	pounds	inches	pints
3. A woman is about 5 _____ tall.	feet	pounds	inches	pints
4. He drinks a _____ of milk every day.	foot	pound	inch	pint
5. How many inches in a foot?	_____
6. How many feet in a yard?	_____
7. How many ounces in a pound?	_____
8. How many pints in a quart?	_____
9. About how many pounds does a dog weigh?	2	20	200
10. About how many feet high is a door?	8	80	800

units (gram, kilogram, centimeter, meter, kilometer, liter) can be introduced next. The same five steps outlined on page 451 would be used. The key teaching behavior, regardless of which system is being taught, is providing the students with adequate practice to facilitate mastery.

Measuring Tools

Calibrated measurement instruments include rulers, scales, thermometers, and speedometers. Every calibrated instrument is divided into segments representing specific quantities. The easiest type of instrument to read is one in which each line represents one unit. For example, on most thermometers each line represents 1 degree, likewise, on many bathroom scales each line designates 1 pound. Often instruments only label some of the lines that stand for quantities:

Those instruments require students to figure out what the unmarked lines represent before they are able to read them. Instruments like the ruler and scales found in grocery stores contain lines that represent fractions of a unit (e.g., 1/4 inch, 1/8 pound).

In the early primary grades students learn to measure length to the nearest inch (or centimeter) and weight to the nearest pound (or kilogram). In the late primary and intermediate grades, students learn to measure more precisely.

Measuring length with a ruler might be introduced first. The teacher explains that the numbers on the ruler indicate how many inches from the end of the ruler to the line corresponding to that nu-

meral. The teacher then models using the ruler to measure several lines or objects, pointing out the need to properly align the front end of the ruler and the beginning of the line or object being measured. Finally, the teacher has the students use the ruler themselves. In order to make initial instruction more manageable, the teacher can give students worksheets with lines of various lengths (to the nearest inch).

For weight, the students put the object on the scale and read the number closest to the pointer. For capacity, the students fill the container with water, pour the water into a calibrated flask, and read the number closest to the water level. When teaching students to use measuring tools on which a line represents each unit but the relative value of each line is not shown:

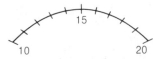

the teacher models how to count from the last given unit to the target unit. In the example below, the teacher models counting from 25, touching and counting each line—25, 26, 27, 28—to the quantity. A discussion on measuring to the nearest fraction of an inch appears later in this chapter.

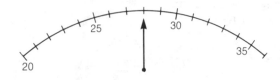

Intermediate Grades

During the intermediate grades, the teacher follows these steps:

1. Presents and reviews all equivalencies
2. Teaches students more sophisticated uses of measuring tools (e.g., measuring to nearest 1/8 of an inch)
3. Teaches students to convert units to larger or smaller units
4. Presents measurement operations and story problems

To review previously introduced customary equivalencies, the teacher might prepare a handout, like the one in Figure 18.3, with the standard equivalencies written on it. Students who did not already know them would be asked to memorize these standard equivalencies. For students who have difficulty, the teacher can present verbal exercises to review the material.

Exercises in which students identify the most appropriate unit to measure various objects (step 4 on page 451) would follow the memorization exercise. A similar procedure should be used to review more common metric units as well.

Metric Equivalencies

In fifth or sixth grade, after decimals have been taught, exercises designed to teach students about the structure of the metric system should be presented. Figure 18.4 includes a format for teaching students the prefixes for the metric system. In Parts A and B, the teacher merely presents the meaning of the prefixes. The prefixes for units less than 1—milli, centi, deci—are presented in Part A. Note that the teacher must emphasize the *th* ending of the word equivalents so that students will note they are fractions and pronounce them correctly. In Part B, the teacher presents the prefixes, indicating units greater than 1: deka, hecto, and kilo. Depending on the level of students, a week or more of practice may be required to teach the meanings of these prefixes. The teacher would not go on to Part C, however, until the students demonstrate knowledge of all the metric prefixes.

Part C teaches students to use their knowledge of metric prefixes to tell the value of metric units. For example, the teacher models, "Since milli means a thousand*th*, milligram refers to a thousandth of a gram." Part D is a worksheet exercise in which students must find and circle the numerical representation of a specific metric unit. For example, a worksheet problem may ask for the amount that equals a centimeter, giving the following choices: 100 meters, .01 meter, .10 meter. Note that the ability to read decimal numbers is a prerequisite for

this task. Daily worksheet exercises would continue for several weeks.

Abbreviations for metric units should also be introduced in a worksheet exercise. Teachers should not take for granted that students will be able to decode abbreviations. Several lessons should be devoted to teaching metric abbreviations.

Converting Units

This section deals with problems in which students must convert a quantity expressed as one unit into an equal quantity expressed in terms of a larger or smaller unit; for example, 3 feet can be converted to 36 inches, 2 meters to 200 centimeters.[1]

The preskill for conversion problems is knowledge of equivalencies. Students cannot convert 5 kilograms to grams unless they know the number of grams in 1 kilogram. Conversion problems should not be presented until students know equivalencies.

There are three basic steps in any conversion problem: (a) determining whether the "new" unit is larger or smaller than the original unit, (b) determining what multiple the larger unit is in relation to the smaller unit, and (c) multiplying when converting to a smaller unit or dividing when converting to a larger unit. These steps are illustrated in Figure 18.5. Note the steps are basically the same for problems with customary units.

CONVERTING METRIC UNITS Early intermediate grade teachers should limit examples to conversions with small quantities of common units (e.g., 5 meters = _____ centimeters). In the late intermediate grades, teachers can present the conversion strategy with larger numbers. Below is a description of the procedure for teaching conversion with metric units. Before the metric conversion strategy is introduced, students should know the equivalencies between metric units, be able to read and write mixed decimals and decimal numbers, and be able to multiply or divide by multiples of 10 by moving the decimal point to the right or the left. When dividing, the decimal point is moved to the left. For example, when dividing by 10, the decimal point is moved one place to the left (75 ÷ 10 = 7.5); by 100, two places (75 ÷ 100 = .75); by 1000, three places to the left (75 ÷ 1000 = .075). When multiplying, the decimal point is moved to the right. Instructions for teaching

---

[1] This section does not deal with converting quantities from standard to metric units or vice versa (e.g., 1 meter = 39 inches). Such exercises would be taught by showing students how to use conversion tables.

Figure 18.3

Length	Weight	Capacity
12 inches = 1 foot	16 ounces = 1 pound	2 cups = 1 pint
3 feet = 1 yard	2,000 pounds = 1 ton	2 pints = 1 quart
5,280 feet = 1 mile		4 quarts = 1 gallon

Figure 18.4 Format for Metric Prefixes

Day	Part A Prefixes for Less Than 1 Problems	Part B Prefixes for More Than 1 Problems	Part C Structured Board Presentation Problems	Part D Structured Worksheet Problems	Part E Supervised Practice Problems	Part F Independent Practice Problems
1-3	1					
4-6		1				
7-8			8			
9-10				4	4	
11-Till accurate					8	8

PART A: Prefixes for Less Than 1

TEACHER

Write on board:

milli—thousandth of
centi—hundredth of
deci—tenth of
one whole
deka
hecto
kilo

1. "THESE ARE PREFIXES USED IN THE METRIC SYSTEM. THEY TELL US HOW MUCH OF THE BASE UNIT WE HAVE."

2. Point to milli, centi, deci. "THESE PREFIXES SAY THERE IS LESS THAN ONE WHOLE. WHAT DO THESE PREFIXES TELL?"
   Point to deka, hecto, kilo. "THESE PREFIXES SAY THERE IS MORE THAN ONE WHOLE. WHAT DO THESE PREFIXES SAY?"

3. Point to milli. "THIS SAYS MILLI. WHAT DOES IT SAY?"
   "MILLI MEANS A THOUSANDTH OF. WHAT DOES MILLI MEAN?"
   Repeat step 3 with centi and deci.

4. "LET'S READ ALL THESE PREFIXES AND READ WHAT THEY MEAN." Point to milli, centi, deci.

5. Erase the words thousandth of, hundredth of, tenth of.
   Point to milli. "WHAT IS THIS PREFIX?"
   "WHAT DOES MILLI MEAN?"
   Point to centi. "WHAT IS THIS PREFIX?"
   "WHAT DOES CENTI MEAN?"
   Point to deci. "WHAT IS THIS PREFIX?"
   "WHAT DOES DECI MEAN?"
   Point to the three prefixes in random order until students identify all three correctly.

STUDENTS

"There is less than one whole."

"There is more than one whole."

"Milli"

"A thousandth of"

"Milli"
"A thousandth of"
"Centi"
"A hundredth of"
"Deci"
"A tenth of"

Figure 18.4 cont'd

PART B: Introducing Prefixes (More Than One Whole)

TEACHER   **STUDENTS**

Write on board:

milli
centi
deci
one whole
deka—ten wholes
hecto—one hundred wholes
kilo—one thousand wholes

1. "WHAT DOES MILLI MEAN?"	"A thousandth of"
"WHAT DOES CENTI MEAN?"	"A hundredth of"
"WHAT DOES DECI MEAN?"	"A tenth of"

2. "LET'S READ THE PREFIXES THAT TELL ABOUT MORE THAN A WHOLE." Point to deka. "THIS SAYS DEKA. WHAT DOES IT SAY?"   "Deka"
"WHAT DOES DEKA MEAN?"   "10 wholes"
Point to hecto. "THIS SAYS HECTO. WHAT DOES IT SAY?"   "Hecto"
"WHAT DOES HECTO MEAN?"   "100 wholes"
Point to kilo. "THIS SAYS KILO. WHAT DOES IT SAY?"   "Kilo"
"WHAT DOES KILO MEAN?"   "1,000 wholes"
Erase the words: ten wholes, hundred wholes, thousand wholes.

3. Point to deka. "WHAT DOES THIS SAY?"   "Deka"
"WHAT DOES DEKA MEAN?"   "10 wholes"
Repeat step 3 with hecto and kilo.

4. "NOW LET'S TELL WHAT ALL THE PREFIXES MEAN." Point to milli. "WHAT IS THIS PREFIX?
"WHAT DOES IT MEAN?" Pause, signal. Repeat the question in step 4 for all prefixes, presenting them in random order; give individual turns.

PART C: Structured Board Presentation

1. "WHAT DOES KILO MEAN?"   "1000 wholes"

2. "KILO MEANS 1000 WHOLES. SO KILOMETER MEANS 1000 METERS. WHAT DOES KILOMETER MEAN?"   "1000 meters"
"YES, A KILOMETER EQUALS 1000 METERS. SAY THAT."   "A kilometer equals 1000 meters."
Repeat steps 1 and 2 with millimeter, hectogram, centigram.

3. "WHAT DOES DECILITER MEAN?" Pause.   "A tenth of a liter"

    TO CORRECT: "WHAT DOES DECI MEAN?"
                Repeat step 3.

Repeat step 3 with:
dekaliter—10 liter
centigram—a hundredth of a gram
kiloliter—hundred liters
dekagram—10 grams
centiliter—hundredth of a liter

Figure 18.4 cont'd

PART D: Structured Worksheet

a. a kilogram equals

    1,000 grams   .001 gram   100 grams

b. a millimeter equals

    1,000 meters   .001 meters   .01 meters

c. a centigram equals

    100 grams   .001 grams   .01 grams

d. a hectoliter equals

    .01 liters   .1 liters   10 liters   100 liters

1. "LOOK AT PROBLEM a. YOU HAVE TO CIRCLE
   WHAT A KILOGRAM EQUALS. WHAT DOES KILO
   MEAN?"   "A thousand wholes"
   "SO WHAT DOES A KILOGRAM EQUAL?"   "A thousand grams"

2. "CIRCLE THE ANSWER."
   Repeat steps 1 and 2 with several examples.

---

multiplying decimals by multiples of 10 appear on pages 394–396 of Chapter 14. A similar exercise would be used to teach students to divide by multiples of 10.

Before beginning conversion exercises, the teacher should give students worksheets like the one in Figure 18.6 designed to provide practice in discriminating dividing and multiplying by various multiples of 10. The discussion in Chapter 14 on multiplying decimals by multiples of 10 specifies example types to include in worksheet exercises. Students may require several weeks of practice to develop mastery. In some multiplication problems, students should have to add one or more zeroes (e.g., $100 \times 3.5 = .035$). In some division problems, a zero should have to be added in front of the original digits (e.g., $3.5 \div 100 = .035$). Such examples are difficult and require modeling.

A format for presenting the conversion strategy appears in Figure 18.7. As mentioned earlier, this format assumes that students have been previously taught the metric equivalencies (e.g., when asked what a hectogram equals, they will say 100 grams). If students have not developed mastery in the preskills, they will find the conversion exercises quite difficult and frustrating. The format contains four parts. Parts A and B teach important component skills. Part A teaches students to determine whether they are changing the original unit to a bigger or smaller unit. Part B presents the rules, "When we change to a bigger unit, we divide; when we change to a smaller unit, we multiply." Part B concludes with an exercise in which the teacher writes sets of units on the board, such as

centigram ———→ gram

and leads the students in determining the appropriate operation.

For gram ———→ milligram, the teacher might say "We're changing to milligram, which is a smaller unit than gram. So we multiply." For meter ———→ kilometer, "We're changing to kilometer, which is a bigger unit than meter. So we divide." Teachers raised in the United States may find that learning these rules themselves requires a good deal of practice due to their unfamiliarity with metrics.

Part C is a structured board presentation in which the teacher presents all the steps in the conversion strategy. After the students determine whether to multiply or divide, the teacher leads them through deriving the number by which to multiply or divide. "There are 100 centigrams in a gram, so we divide by 100." Finally, the teacher demonstrates moving the decimal as a quick way of multiplying or dividing by multiples of 10. For example, determining how many grams 2,135 centigrams equal requires division since the new unit is bigger. Students divide by 100 since there are 100 centigrams in a gram. Thus, the decimal point is moved two places to the left, giving an answer of 21.35 grams.

Part D is a structured worksheet exercise. Note the many lessons in which the structured worksheet exercise is presented. Because this exercise incorporates several difficult component skills, a great amount of practice is necessary to develop mastery.

Four example selection guidelines are important:

Figure 18.5 Steps in Basic Conversion Problems

	Problem a	Problem b	Problem c	Problem d
Determine whether the new quantity is a bigger (higher order) or smaller (lower order) unit.	48 inches = _____ feet Change inches to feet. Feet is a bigger unit.	3 pounds = _____ ounces Change pounds to ounces. Ounces is a smaller unit.	5 kilograms = _____ grams Change kilograms to grams. Grams is a smaller unit.	300 centimeters = _____ meters. Change centimeters to meters. Meter is a bigger unit.
Determine difference between units.	12 inches in a foot	16 ounces in a pound	1,000 kilograms in a gram	100 centimeters in a meter
Multiply if changing to a smaller unit. Divide if changing to a bigger unit.	Since change is to a bigger unit, division is called for. 48 inches ÷ 12 = 4 feet	Since change is to a smaller unit, multiplication is called for. 3 pounds × 16 = 48 ounces	Since change is to a smaller unit, multiplication is called for. 5 kilograms × 1000 = 5,000 grams	Since change is to a bigger unit, division is called for 300 centimeters ÷ 100 = 3 centimeters

Figure 18.6

a. 37 × 100 = _____	b. 4 ÷ 1000 = _____	c. 53.2 × 100 = _____	d. 7.04 × 10 = _____
e. 4.8 × 1000 = _____	f. 28.5 ÷ 10 = _____	g. 72 × 1000 = _____	h. .37 × 100 = _____
i. 7 ÷ 100 = _____	j. .37 × 100 = _____	k. 5.43 × 10 = _____	l. .4 × 1000 = _____
m. 37 ÷ 10 = _____	n. 4.2 ÷ 10 = _____	o. 72 ÷ 10 = _____	p. 38 ÷ 10 = _____
q. .52 × 100 = _____	r. 4.8 ÷ 1000 = _____	s. 400 ÷ 1000 = _____	t. 52 ÷ 100 = _____

1. In all problems, one of the units should be a base unit. The base units are gram, meter, or liter.
2. In half of the problems, the students should convert a unit to a larger unit; while in the other half, the students should convert to a smaller unit.
3. In half of the problems, the quantity of original units should be a whole number; while in the other half, the quantity should be a decimal or mixed number.
4. The amount the student multiplies or divides by should vary from problem to problem: 10 in one problem, 1,000 in the next, 100 in the next, and so on.

An example of an appropriate set of problems, following the guidelines, appears below. The answers are in parentheses.

142 centigrams = _____ grams (1.42)
9.8 grams   = _____ milligrams (9,800)
35 centigrams = _____ grams (.35)
20 hectograms = _____ grams (2,000)
4.35 grams   = _____ milligrams (4,350)

Note that the examples shown in the format in Figure 18.7 all refer to grams. The next day's unit might refer to liters or meters. In each lesson, a different type of unit is used.

CONVERTING CUSTOMARY UNITS Teaching students to convert quantities from one unit to another unit is more difficult in the customary system than in the metric system for three specific reasons. First, whereas with metric conversions the students always multiply or divide by a multiple of 10, in conversion problems with customary units, the number to multiply or divide by varies from problem to problem; converting inches to feet requires division by 12, and converting feet to yards requires division by 3.

A second reason for increased difficulty involves the procedures used when the converted unit is not a multiple of the original unit. In the customary system, the answer must be expressed in terms of a mixed number with two different units (e.g., 7 feet = 2 yards, 1 foot).

A final reason why customary conversions are more difficult is that conversions are sometimes made to a unit two or more steps removed. In the metric system the original unit is simply multiplied or divided by 10, 100, or 1000. In the customary system, a dual conversion is required. For example, to convert yards to inches the student must first convert yards to feet and then feet to inches, first multiplying by 3, then by 12.

The sequence for introducing conversion problems with customary units should be carefully controlled with easier problems introduced first. The three basic types of conversion problems in the customary system are illustrated below:

1. Converting a quantity of a specified unit into a quantity of the next larger or smaller unit; examples involve whole numbers only:
   28 days equal _____ weeks
   6 feet equal _____ yards
   24 inches equal _____ feet
   4 weeks equal _____ days
   2 yards equal _____ feet
   2 feet equal _____ inches
2. Converting a unit into a mixed number (and vice versa) containing the next largest or smallest quantity:
   27 inches equal _____ feet _____ inches
   19 ounces equal _____ pounds _____ ounces
   13 days equal _____ weeks _____ days
   2 feet 3 inches equal _____ inches
   1 pound 3 ounces equal _____ ounces
3. Converting a unit into a unit twice removed:
   2 yards equal _____ inches
   2 quarts equal _____ cups
   72 inches equal _____ yards
   16 cups equal _____ quarts

Figure 18.7 Format for Metric Conversions

Day	Part A Relative Sizes of Units Problems	Part B Determining Appropriate Operations Problems	Part C Structured Board Presentation Problems	Part D Structured Worksheet Problems	Part E Supervised Practice Problems	Part F Independent Practice Problems
1-3	6					
4-6	4 (step 5 only)	6				
7		6	4			
8-12		2	6	4		
12-Till accurate					8	
Till fluent						8

PART A: Relative Sizes of Units

Write on board:

milligram	centigram	decigram	gram	dekagram	hectogram	kilogram
$\frac{1}{1000}$ gm	$\frac{1}{100}$ gm	$\frac{1}{10}$ gm	1 gm	10 gm	100 gm	1000 gm

1. "THESE ARE THE METRIC UNITS FOR MEASURING WEIGHT. MILLIGRAM IS A THOUSANDTH OF A GRAM. IT IS THE SMALLEST UNIT. WHAT IS THE SMALLEST UNIT?"   "Milligram"

   "KILOGRAM IS A THOUSAND WHOLE GRAMS. IT IS THE BIGGEST UNIT. WHAT IS THE BIGGEST UNIT?"   "Kilogram"

2. Start at gram and point to the left. "IF WE MOVE THIS WAY, WE'RE CHANGING TO A SMALLER UNIT." Point to the right. "IF WE MOVE THIS WAY, WE'RE CHANGING TO A BIGGER UNIT."

3. Point to the left. "WHICH WAY AM I CHANGING?"   "To a smaller unit"
   Point to the right. "WHICH WAY AM I CHANGING?"   "To a bigger unit"

4. Point to centigram. "IF WE HAVE CENTIGRAMS AND WE WANT TO CHANGE TO GRAMS, WHICH WAY ARE WE CHANGING?" Pause, signal.   "To a bigger unit"

   Repeat step 4 with grams to kilograms, grams to milligrams, hectograms to grams, kilograms to grams, grams to decigrams.

5. Erase the board. "I WANT TO CHANGE CENTIGRAMS TO GRAMS. WHAT DOES A CENTIGRAM EQUAL?"   "A hundredth of a gram"
   "WHEN I CHANGE CENTIGRAMS TO GRAMS, WHICH WAY ARE WE CHANGING?" Pause, signal.   "To a bigger unit"

   Repeat step 5 with same examples as in step 4.

PART B: Determining Appropriate Operations

1. "HERE ARE TWO IMPORTANT RULES:
   WHEN WE CHANGE TO A BIGGER UNIT, WE DIVIDE. SAY THAT."   "When we change to a bigger unit, we divide."

   "WHEN WE CHANGE TO A SMALLER UNIT, WE MULTIPLY. SAY THAT."   "When we change to a smaller unit, we multiply."

Figure 18.7 cont'd

TEACHER

2. "WHAT DO WE DO WHEN WE CHANGE TO A
   BIGGER UNIT?"
   "WHAT DO WE DO WHEN WE CHANGE TO A
   SMALLER UNIT?"

"Divide"

"Multiply"

3. Write on board: gram to centigram. "WHEN WE
   CHANGE FROM GRAMS TO CENTIGRAMS, WHICH
   WAY ARE WE CHANGING?" Pause, signal.
   "DO WE MULTIPLY OR DIVIDE WHEN WE
   CHANGE FROM GRAMS TO CENTIGRAMS?" Pause,
   signal.

"To a smaller unit"

"Multiply"

    TO CORRECT: "IF WE HAVE GRAMS AND WE
              CHANGE TO CENTIGRAMS, WHICH
              WAY ARE WE CHANGING? IF WE
              CHANGE TO A SMALLER UNIT
              WHAT DO WE DO?"

    Repeat step 3 with these examples: g to kg, g to mg,
hg to g, kg to g, g to dg.

PART C: Structured Board Presentation

Write on board:

    350 centigrams = _____ grams

1. "THIS PROBLEM SAYS, 350 CENTIGRAMS EQUALS
   HOW MANY GRAMS? WE'RE CHANGING CENTI-
   GRAMS TO GRAMS. WHAT ARE WE DOING?"

"Changing centigrams to grams"

2. "ARE WE CHANGING TO A BIGGER OR SMALLER
   UNIT?" Pause, signal.

"Bigger"

3. "WE'RE CHANGING TO A BIGGER UNIT, SO DO
   WE MULTIPLY OR DIVIDE?"
   "YES, WHEN WE CHANGE TO A BIGGER UNIT,
   WE DIVIDE."

"Divide"

4. "HOW MANY CENTIGRAMS IN EACH GRAM?"
   "SO WE DIVIDE BY 100. LET'S DIVIDE BY MOVING
   THE DECIMAL. WHEN WE DIVIDE BY 100, WHAT
   DO WE DO TO THE DECIMAL?"

"100"

"Move it to the left 2 places"

5. Write 350 next to grams. "IF I MOVE THE DECIMAL
   POINT TWO PLACES TO THE LEFT, WHERE WILL
   IT BE?"

"Between the 3 and 5"

Write on board: 350 centigrams = 3.50 grams

6. "READ THE PROBLEM NOW."

"350 cg = 3.50 g"

    Repeat steps 1–5 with these problems:

    314 grams = _____ milligrams
       (Move decimal point 3 places to right.)
    315 grams = _____ kilograms
       (Move decimal point 3 places to left.)
    7 centigrams = _____ grams
       (Move decimal point 2 places to left.)
    18 kilograms = _____ grams
       (Move decimal point 3 places to right.)
    30 meters = _____ decimeters
       (Move decimal point 1 place to right.)

Figure 18.7 cont'd

PART D: Structured Worksheet

TEACHER	**STUDENTS**

a. 232 centiliters equal _____ liters

1. "READ PROBLEM a. ARE YOU CHANGING TO A
   BIGGER OR SMALLER UNIT?" Pause, signal.   "Bigger"

2. "SO DO YOU MULTIPLY OR DIVIDE?" Pause, signal.   "Divide"

3. "WHAT DO YOU DIVIDE BY?"   "100"
   "WHICH WAY DO YOU MOVE THE DECIMAL
   POINT?"   "To the left"
   "HOW MANY PLACES DO YOU MOVE IT?"   "Two"

4. "WRITE THE ANSWER."   Students write 2.32.
   "READ THE PROBLEM."   "232 centiliters equals 2.32
                                                     liters."

Repeat steps 1-4 with remaining problems.

Figure 18.8 Format for Converting to Mixed Numbers

PART A: Structured Worksheet

TEACHER	**STUDENTS**

Write on board:

a. 27 inches = _____ feet _____ inches
b. 32 days = _____ weeks _____ days
c. 28 eggs = _____ dozen _____ eggs
d. 7 feet = _____ yards _____ feet

1. "READ PROBLEM a."   "27 inches = _____ feet _____
                                                    inches."
   "IN THIS PROBLEM YOU HAVE TO CHANGE 27
   INCHES TO FEET AND INCHES."

2. "TO WORK THIS PROBLEM, FIRST YOU FIND OUT
   HOW MANY FEET ARE IN 27 INCHES, THEN YOU
   SEE HOW MANY INCHES ARE LEFT OVER."

3. "ARE WE CHANGING TO A BIGGER OR SMALLER
   UNIT?" Pause, signal.   "Bigger"
   "SO DO WE MULTIPLY OR DIVIDE?"   "Divide"

4. "HOW MANY INCHES ARE IN 1 FOOT?"   "12"
   "SO WE DIVIDE BY 12."

5. "12 GOES INTO 27 HOW MANY TIMES?" Pause, signal. "2"
   "THERE ARE 2 FEET IN 27 INCHES. WRITE 2 IN
   FRONT OF THE WORD FEET."
   "DO YOU HAVE SOME INCHES LEFT OVER?"   "Yes"
   "YOU USED 24 INCHES. SUBTRACT 24 FROM 27
   AND SEE HOW MANY YOU HAVE LEFT." Pause.
   "HOW MANY INCHES LEFT?"   "3"
   "WRITE 3 IN FRONT OF THE WORD INCHES. SO
   27 INCHES EQUALS WHAT?"   "2 feet, 3 inches"

Repeat steps 1-5 for remaining problems.

Figure 18.9 Format for Converting from Mixed Numbers

PART A: Structured Worksheet

TEACHER

Write on board:

a. 3 feet 4 inches = _____ inches

b. 2 weeks 3 days = _____ days

c. 2 pounds 3 ounces = _____ ounces

d. 3 gallons 1 quart = _____ quarts

1. "READ PROBLEM a. THIS PROBLEM ASKS US TO
   CHANGE 3 FEET 4 INCHES INTO INCHES IN ALL.
   FIRST WE'LL FIND HOW MANY INCHES IN 3 FEET.
   THEN WE'LL ADD IT TO 4 INCHES."
   Write in. + over first problem.

   in.+
   3 feet 4 inches = _____ inches
   "WHAT DO WE DO FIRST?"
   "THEN WHAT DO WE DO?"

2. "LET'S CHANGE 3 FEET TO INCHES. ARE WE
   CHANGING TO A BIGGER OR SMALLER UNIT?"
   "SO WHAT DO WE DO?"

3. "HOW MANY INCHES IN A FOOT?"
   "SO YOU'LL MULTIPLY BY 12. EVERYBODY, HOW
   MANY INCHES IN 3 FEET?"
   "CROSS OUT 3 FEET AND WRITE 36 ABOVE IT."

4. "NOW WHAT DO WE DO?"

5. "HOW MANY INCHES IN ALL? WRITE IT IN FRONT
   OF INCHES."

6. "READ THE PROBLEM."

STUDENTS

"Find how many inches in 3 feet."
"Add 4 inches"

"Smaller"
"Multiply"

"12"

"36"

"Add it to 4 inches"

Students write 40.

"3 feet 4 inches equal 40 inches"

The preskill for presenting conversion problems with customary units is knowledge of equivalents and of multiplication and division facts. Since measurement conversion tasks are usually introduced before students can divide by two digit numbers, the teacher may choose to teach the students to count by 12s. Knowing this count-by series will help students in converting inches to feet and in determining dozens.

The format for introducing the first type of customary conversion problems—problems in which a unit is converted evenly into the next larger or smaller unit—would be basically the same as that for converting metric units (see Figure 18.7). The teacher would have students (a) tell whether they are changing to a bigger or smaller unit, (b) tell whether they multiply or divide, and (c) tell by what number they multiply or divide. "We want to find how many ounces in 6 pounds. We're changing to a smaller unit so we multiply. There are 16 ounces in a pound, so we multiply by 16."

The format for problems in which the conversion results in a remainder (e.g., 27 inches equal 2 feet 3 inches) is the same as for the previous type of problem except the teacher must explain what to do with the remainder. For example, in solving the problem 27 inches = _____ feet, after the students determine that 27 must be divided by 12, the teacher points out that since 12 goes into 27 with a remainder, the remainder tells the number of inches left. A structured worksheet presentation for converting from smaller to larger units when there is a remainder appears in Figure 18.8.

The format for converting a mixed quantity to a lower unit appears in Figure 18.9. When converting 2 feet 11 inches to inches, the teacher has the students cross out the 2 and write 24, the number of inches, above it. Then they add that quantity, 24 inches, to the 11 inches to end with 35 inches.

Problems in which students must convert to a unit twice removed are quite difficult (e.g., 2 yards = _____ inches). The strategy we recommend involves having the students translate the quantity unit by unit. For example, in converting 2 yards to inches, the student would first convert 2 yards to 6 feet, then 6 feet to 72 inches.

Operations

This section deals with addition, subtraction, multiplication, and division operations with measurement units. As with most measurement-related skills, performing operations with customary units is more difficult than performing operations with metric units. The differences arise in problems requiring renaming. Since the metric system uses a base 10 place value system, renaming presents no problems. Students merely apply the renaming skills they learned previously in decimal instruction. However, when working with customary units, there is no consistent base from which to work. The base for ounces is 16; for inches, 12; for feet, 3; etc. So students must be taught to use these bases rather than the base 10.

Addition and subtraction problems with measurement units are usually introduced in fourth or fifth grade. The operations cause little difficulty in measurement problems that do not involve renaming:

```
  6 lb 4 oz      6 lb 4 oz      6 lb 4 oz
 +1 lb 1 oz     -1 lb 1 oz     ×      2
 ─────────      ─────────      ─────────
  7 lb 5 oz      5 lb 3 oz     12 lb 8 oz

   3 lb 2 oz      6.4 kg         6.4 kg
 2)6 lb 4 oz     +1.1 kg        -1.1 kg
                 ───────        ───────
                  7.5 kg         5.3 kg

   6.4 kg          3.2 kg
 ×    2         2)6.4 kg
 ───────
  12.8 kg
```

Problems that do require renaming, on the other hand, are quite difficult:

```
 4   18         1                4    14
 8̶ lb 2̶ oz      3 weeks 4 days   8̶ ft 2̶ in
-3 lb 4 oz     +1 week  5 days   -2 ft 8 in
 ─────────     ──────────────    ─────────
 1 lb 14 oz     5 weeks 9̶ days   2 ft 6 in
                         2
```

A preskill for renaming problems is converting units, which was discussed previously. When working an addition problem, the teacher instructs students to always start working with the smaller unit. The difficult part of addition problems occurs after students have derived a sum which includes enough of the smaller unit to form a larger unit. In the problem

```
 3 ft  8 in
+2 ft  6 in
───────────
       14 in =
```

the students add 8 and 6 to end with 14 inches, which is more than 1 foot. The student must carry 1 to the feet column, cross out the 14, and write 2 to represent the remaining inches:

```
     1
 3 ft 8 in
+2 ft 6 in
──────────
    1̶4̶
     2
```

The teacher leads students through sets of problems, renaming them when they must carry: "Remember, we're adding inches. How many inches a foot? Yes, 12 inches in a foot. So if we have 12 or more inches in the inches column, we must carry a foot to the feet column."

Figure 18.10 illustrates a format for presenting addition problems with renaming. The key in teaching the operations with customary units is teaching students *when* to rename and *what numbers* to use. Part A of the structured board presentation focuses on when renaming is appropriate. Part B provides practice in renaming with the appropriate numbers. Examples would include problems that require renaming and problems that do not require renaming. The example in the format includes weight units; similar exercises would be done with length and capacity units.

After students can rename a variety of units when adding, they are given problems with subtraction. The difficult aspect of subtraction problems lies in renaming the minuend. For example, to work the problem

```
 8 lb 4 oz
-3 lb 8 oz
──────────
```

the students must rename 8 pounds 4 ounces, borrowing a pound from 8 pounds, leaving 7 pounds, and increasing the ounces by 16 ounces (a pound) so there are 20 ounces:

```
 7    20
 8̶ lb 4̶ oz
-3 lb 8 oz
──────────
```

We recommend that teachers introduce this skill by first presenting problems in which a mixed unit is subtracted from a whole unit. Following are examples of such problems:

```
  3 ft         8 lb
-1 ft 4 in    -2 lb 5 oz
──────────    ──────────
```

Figure 18.10 Format for Renaming Customary Units

PART A: Discrimination Practice

TEACHER	STUDENTS

a. 3 lbs _____ oz
   +2 lbs _____ oz
   _____ oz

1. "FIRST, WE ADD THE OUNCES; THEN WE ADD
   THE POUNDS. HOW MANY OUNCES IN A POUND?"   "16"
   "THAT MEANS THAT IF WE END UP W˜ ˜H 16 OR
   MORE OUNCES, WE HAVE TO RENAM˜

2. "I'LL WRITE NUMBERS FOR OUNCES. TELL ME
   IF WE HAVE TO RENAME."

3. Write 7 and 5 in the blanks.
   "WHAT'S THE ANSWER FOR OUNCES?"   "12"
   "DO WE HAVE TO RENAME 12 OUNCES AS
   POUNDS?"   "No"
   Repeat step 3 with 9 + 9, 9 + 5, 8 + 9, 8 + 8, 9 + 6.

PART B: Structured Worksheet

Give students worksheet with 8-10 problems such as these:

a. 5 lb 9 oz   b. 4 lb 2 oz
   +3 lb 9 oz   +3 lb 11 oz

1. "TOUCH PROBLEM a. READ THE PROBLEM."

2. "WE START ADDING OUNCES."

3. "WHAT IS 9 + 9?"   "18"
   "WRITE 18 UNDER THE LINE."

4. "HOW MANY OUNCES IN A POUND?"   "16"

5. "DO WE RENAME 18 OUNCES AS POUNDS?"   "Yes"

6. "CROSS OUT 18 AND WRITE A 1 OVER THE
   POUNDS COLUMN."

7. "WE HAD 18 OUNCES. WE PUT A POUND IN THE
   POUNDS COLUMN. HOW MANY OUNCES DID WE
   TAKE FROM 18 OUNCES WHEN WE RENAMED?"   "16"

   TO CORRECT: "A POUND HAS 16 OUNCES."

8. "WE HAD 18 OUNCES; WE MOVED 16 OUNCES.
   HOW MANY OUNCES ARE LEFT?"   "2"
   "WRITE 2 UNDER THE OUNCES."

9. "NOW ADD THE POUNDS. HOW MANY POUNDS?"   "9"

10. "READ THE WHOLE ANSWER."   "9 pounds 2 ounces"

The teacher leads students through working these problems, pointing out the need to rename and how to rename: "We must borrow a foot from 3 feet. I'll cross out 3 feet and write 2. I borrowed a foot from 3 feet. How many inches in a foot? . . . So I write 12 in the inches column." After several days practice, the difficult problems, in which two mixed numbers are involved, can be presented. An example of a structured worksheet part of a format for subtrac-tion problems with renaming appears in Figure 18.11.

Multiplication and division problems requiring renaming with measurement units are quite difficult. A strategy for working multiplication problems involves teaching the students to first multiply each unit. For example, in the problem

$$5 \text{ ft } 7 \text{ in}$$
$$\times \quad 4$$

Figure 18.11 Format for Subtraction with Renaming

PART A: Structured Worksheet

TEACHER	**STUDENTS**
Write on board:	
5 lb 2 oz	
-2 lb 9 oz	
1. "READ THE PROBLEM."	"5 lb 2 oz minus 2 lb 9 oz"
2. "CAN YOU START WITH 2 OUNCES AND SUB-TRACT 9 OUNCES?"	"No"
3. "YOU MUST RENAME. CROSS OUT 5 POUNDS AND WRITE 4."	
4. "WE BORROWED A POUND. HOW MANY OUNCES IN A POUND?"	"16"
5. "WRITE 16+ IN FRONT OF THE 2 OUNCES."	
6. "HOW MANY OUNCES DO WE START WITH NOW?"	"18"
7. "CROSS OUT 16 + 2 AND WRITE 18 ABOVE IT."	
8. "AND WHAT DOES 18 - 9 EQUAL?"	"9"
"SO HOW MANY OUNCES DO YOU END UP WITH?"	"9"
"WRITE IT."	
9. "HOW MANY POUNDS DO YOU END UP WITH?"	"2"
"WRITE IT."	
10. "WHAT'S THE ANSWER?"	"2 lb 9 oz"

---

the students first multiply 4×7 inches then 4×5 feet, writing the products for each:

$$\begin{array}{r} 5 \text{ ft} \quad 7 \text{ in} \\ \times \qquad 4 \\ \hline 20 \text{ ft} \quad 28 \text{ in} \end{array}$$

After the products are written for each unit, the students rename, converting the smaller quantity and adding:

$$\begin{array}{r} 5 \text{ ft} \quad 7 \text{ in} \\ \times \qquad 4 \\ \hline 20 \text{ ft} \quad 28 \text{ in} \\ 2 \text{ ft} \quad 4 \text{ in} \\ \hline 22 \text{ ft} \quad 4 \text{ in} \end{array}$$

Division problems, on the other hand, require a unique strategy. The students rewrite the quantity in terms of its lower units before working the problem. For example, in dividing 3 pounds 4 ounces by 2, we suggest converting 3 pounds 4 ounces to 52 ounces, dividing 52 by 2, which equals 26 ounces, then converting the 26 ounces to 1 pound 10 ounces.

Story Problems

Story problems involving measurement units can be introduced as soon as students have learned to work operations. The strategies are the same as outlined in the problem-solving chapter. Below are examples of story problems:

Division

a. James has 2 feet of ribbon. He wants to make kites. Each kite needs 4 inches of ribbon. How many kites can James make?

Subtraction

b. Tonia weighed 8 pounds, 4 ounces when she was born. Three months later, she weighed 11 pounds, 7 ounces. How much weight did she gain in those 3 months?

Multi-step

c. Bill's plant is 4 feet tall. If it grows 3 inches a year for 5 years, how tall will it be?

Teachers should present about five problems daily for at least several weeks. In the first lesson a new type of story problem appears, the teacher leads the students through the problems. Division problems such as the one illustrated above will be particularly difficult and should receive extra emphasis. Examples should include a mix of the new problem type and previously introduced types.

Measurement **465**

Figure 18.12 Recommended Set of Rulers

a. Marked to the nearest half of an inch

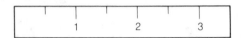

b. Marked to the nearest quarter of an inch

c. Marked to the nearest eighth of an inch

d. Marked to the nearest sixteenth of an inch (standard rulers)

Measuring Tools

During the early primary grades, students are taught to read calibrated measuring tools to the nearest unit. In later primary grades, students are taught to read fractional parts of units. We will discuss a procedure for teaching students to read rulers used in the customary system. Once students can read rulers, they should have little difficulty transferring these reading skills to other tools such as scales and measuring cups.

Rulers in the customary system are usually calibrated to allow measurement to the closest sixteenth of an inch. Because the different marks on the rulers tend to confuse students, a systematic approach should be taken in teaching students to measure the various fractional parts of an inch. We recommend preparing a set of rulers. In the first ruler, each inch would be divided into halves. In the second ruler, each inch would be divided into fourths. In the third and fourth rulers, each inch would be divided respectively, into eighths and sixteenths of an inch. Figure 18.12 illustrates the four rulers. A preskill for reading these tools is the ability to read and write mixed fractions.

A ruler in which an inch is divided into a greater number of parts is introduced only after students have demonstrated mastery in using the preceding ruler in the series.

A simple model-test procedure can be used to teach students to read units to the nearest half-inch. The teacher points out that since the line between the numbers divides the inch into two equal parts, each line represents a half-inch. The same procedure would be used to introduce rulers divided into fourths. The teacher points out that since there are four parts between each inch, each inch is divided into fourths. The teacher then models and tests, reading the ruler starting at the 1/4 inch mark: "1/4, 2/4, 3/4, 1, 1 1/4, 1 2/4, 1 3/4, 2" etc. Note that the teacher would *not* initially have the students read 2/4 as 1/2. The teacher then presents an exercise in which she points to a line on the ruler and has students determine how far it is from the front end of the ruler.

When students can identify the lengths represented by various lines, the teacher can present an exercise to teach that the line which indicates 2/4 of an inch also is the line which indicates 1/2 of an inch. The teacher explains that the line is in the middle of the inch and so divides it into halves. The teacher explains further that when using a ruler, the length is always reported with the smallest numerical denominator. Therefore, instead of saying a line is 3 2/4 inches, the line is said to be 3 1/2 inches. A practice exercise in which the teacher has the students find the lines on the ruler that represent various distances would follow the explanation (e.g., Find the line on the ruler that shows 4 1/2 inches. Find the line that shows 2 1/4 inches, etc.). Practice can be provided in worksheet exercises like the one in Figure 18.13.

Figure 18.13 Worksheet Exercise for Determining Length

Make an X over the line which indicates 3 3/4 inches.
Make an R over the line which indicates 2 1/2 inches.
Make an S over the line which indicates 5/8 of an inch.
Make a B over the line which indicates 2 3/8 inches.

Rulers in which each inch is divided into eighths are introduced when students (a) can use rulers in which each inch is divided into fourths and (b) have learned fraction equivalency skills. Students should have had enough practice rewriting 6/8 as 3/4, 4/8 as 1/2, and 2/8 as 1/4 so that they can make these conversions with ease. The teacher introduces the ruler containing eighths by pointing out that since each inch is divided into eight parts, the lines tell about eighths of an inch. The teacher then has students read the lines on the ruler: "1/8, 2/8, 3/8, 4/8, 5/8, 6/8, 7/8, 1, 1 1/8," etc.

After several days, the teacher presents exercises teaching students to express 2/8, 4/8, and 6/8 as 1/4, 1/2, and 3/4, respectively. The teacher reminds students that length is always reported with fractions expressed in their simplest, smallest possible terms and models and tests the various equivalencies.

The same basic procedure would be followed for introducing rulers in which each inch is divided into sixteenths. These rulers would not be introduced, however, until students were very fluent in using the ruler divided into eighths. Daily practice over a long period is needed to develop student fluency in these skills.

Research

Research on procedures for teaching measurement (time, money, length, weight) is extremely limited.

Because money skills are such important survival skills, much of the research on instructional procedures has been done with handicapped students. For the most part, these studies demonstrated the feasibility of teaching money skills rather than comparisons of alternative instructional strategies (Trace, Cuvo, & Criswell, 1977; Bellamy & Buttars, 1975).

Research on other measurement topics, such as length, tends to be descriptive, focusing on developmental trends rather than instructional practices. For example, Bailey (1974) found that about two-thirds of the group of 7 year old children tested exhibited transitivity; i.e., they could use a measuring stick to determine the relative length of two other sticks. For example, the students would hold stick C next to stick A, then next to stick B, and then make a statement about the relative lengths of A and B. A much more difficult task (only 3% of the students responded correctly) involved statements concerning the relative length of paths that varied in two dimensions, e.g., one was 3/5 units and the other, 4/7 units. Students would say that 4/7 was longer than 3/5 because 4/7 had more pieces; or they would say 3/5 was longer than 4/7 because 3/5 had longer pieces. While studies of this type serve an important function—identifying common student confusions—unfortunately, the researchers provided little guidance in how to design instruction procedures that would overcome those confusions.

Application Items: Measurement

1. Write a format for introducing the unit, yard. Assume students have previously learned inches and feet, ounces and pounds. Include all five steps discussed on page 451. For step 4 write six questions.

2. Below are errors made by students on conversion tasks. Tell the probable cause and specify a remediation procedure.

   Ann

   6 feet = <u>75</u> inches

   $$\begin{array}{r} \overset{1}{}\overset{2}{} \\ \times\ 6 \\ \hline 75 \end{array}$$

   Janet

   6 feet = <u>60</u> inches

   $$\begin{array}{r} 10 \\ \times\ 6 \\ \hline 60 \end{array}$$

   Tim

   9 yards = <u>3</u> feet

   $3\overline{)9}$

3. A student says the x is over the line which shows 1 3/4 inches. Specify the wording in the correction made by the teacher.

4. Specify the wording in the correction to be made by the teacher.

   $$\begin{array}{r} 1\ \text{foot}\ 7\ \text{inches} \\ +\qquad 8\ \text{inches} \\ \hline 2\ \text{feet}\ 5\ \text{inches} \end{array}$$

5. For each error tell the probable cause and specify what the teacher says to correct.

   Jim

   148 meters equal _____ km $148 \div 1000 = 1.48$

   Tina

   148 meters equal _____ km $148 \times 1000 = 148,000$

6. Write a structured worksheet presentation to lead students through working this problem.

   348 centimeters = how many meters?

19 Mathematics Study Skills: Graphs, Charts, Maps, and Statistics

An understanding of mathematics is often required to comprehend material from other content areas such as science, social studies, or health. Mathematics in content area material often appears in the form of graphs, charts, maps, and statistics. For example, a health text might contain graphs illustrating changes in the occurrence of lung cancer and changes in the percentage of women who smoke. Questions at the end of the unit could then ask students to give the percentage of changes in smoking and in the occurrence of lung cancer from 1968 to 1978. Or a chart in a science text might give the size, distance from the sun, mass, etc., for the planets in our solar system. A map in a history book might show the principal towns in colonial America, and a question may require students to determine how far apart they were. Obviously, students who lack specific mathematics study skills would find these items difficult. Therefore, mathematics study skills should be included in any comprehensive mathematics instructional program. Mathematics study skills discussed in this chapter include reading and interpreting graphs, reading charts, interpreting maps, and interpreting and determining statistical figures. The instructional Assessment Chart in Figure 19.2 lists specific problem types discussed in the chapter.

Graphs

A graph is a drawing or picture representation of a relationship between two or more sets of numbers. Figure 19.3 includes examples of the various types of graphs students will encounter in the elementary grades. Note that there are four main types: pictographs and bar, line, and circle graphs.

Graphs are typically introduced during late third or early fourth grade. The first type of graph introduced is usually the pictograph, followed by bar, line, and circle graph, respectively.

Two major factors determine the difficulty of interpreting line and bar graphs: (a) the amount of information on the graph and (b) the need for inferring or estimating amounts. Graphs become more complex as they show more than one set of relationships. For example, a simple line graph may show the performance of one student on a series of tasks. A more complex line graph would show the performance of several students all on the same graph with separate lines representing each student. In reading a graph with more than one set of information, the student must be able to use the key to determine which line refers to which student. Graphs with two sets of information are illustrated in Figure 19.4.

Figure 19.1 Skill Hierarchy

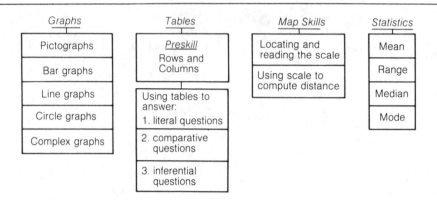

Figure 19.2 Instructional Sequence and Assessment Chart

Grade Level	Problem Type	Performance Indicator
3a	Interpreting line graphs	

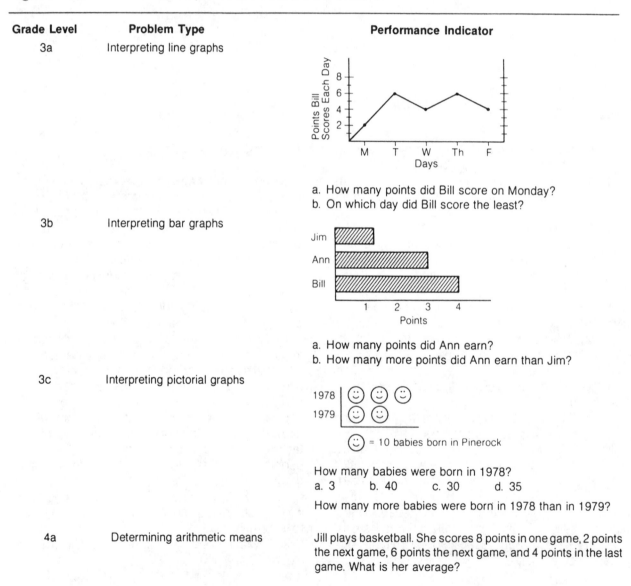

a. How many points did Bill score on Monday?
b. On which day did Bill score the least?

3b	Interpreting bar graphs	

a. How many points did Ann earn?
b. How many more points did Ann earn than Jim?

3c	Interpreting pictorial graphs	

1978
1979

= 10 babies born in Pinerock

How many babies were born in 1978?
a. 3   b. 40   c. 30   d. 35

How many more babies were born in 1978 than in 1979?

4a	Determining arithmetic means	Jill plays basketball. She scores 8 points in one game, 2 points the next game, 6 points the next game, and 4 points in the last game. What is her average?

Figure 19.2 cont'd

Grade Level	Problem Type	Performance Indicator

4b — Interpreting map legends (simple application with whole numbers)

If A is 2 inches from B on the map, how much is the distance in miles between A and B?

5a — Interpreting complex graphs with one variable—bar graph

How many points did Ann score?
a. 15   b. 19   c. 17   d. 20

How many points did Bill score?
a. 20   b. 15   c. 19   d. 16

5b — —line graph

How many points did Ann score on Wednesday?
a. 20   b. 22   c. 28   d. 25

How many points did Ann score on Monday?
a. 15   b. 10   c. 9   d. 12

5c — —pictograph

= 10 babies

How many babies were born in 1959?
a. 30   b. 3   c. 40   d. 35

5d — Interpreting tables

Players on Taft High School Basketball Team

Name	born	height	weight
Jill Hernandez	1948	5'7"	134
Tammy Smith	1950	5'4"	128
Jackie Wilson	1946	5'2"	140
Tanya Jones	1948	5'8"	132

a. Who is the heaviest player on the team?
b. How much heavier is Tanya than Tammy?
c. How much younger is Tammy than Jill?

Figure 19.2 cont'd

Grade Level	Problem Type	Performance Indicator

6a Reading Timetables

		Bus A	Bus B	Bus C	Bus D
Lv.	downtown	9:09	9:18	9:36	9:47
Ar.	25th St.	9:14	9:23	9:41	9:52
Ar.	34th St	9:18	9:26	9:44	9:55
Ar.	41st St.	9:21	9:29	9:47	9:58
Ar.	49th St.	9:24	9:32	9:49	10:00
Ar.	62nd St.	9:31	9:39	9:56	10:07

a. When will Bus C arrive at 41st Street?

b. How long does it take Bus B to get from 34th street to 62nd street?

c. What time would you leave downtown if you wanted to be at 62nd street just before ten o'clock?

6b Interpreting complex graphs with two sets of information—bar graph

a. How many hours of school work did Bill do in February?

b. In which month did Bill do more school work than housework?

6c —line graph

a. On which days did Jill run more than Mary?

b. How many miles did Jill run on Wednesday?

6d Calculating statistics (range, median, mode)

Mrs. James gave a test to the 9 students in her class. The marks are written below:

Ann	23	Monica	41
Cathy	18	Naomi	35
David	41	Paul	41
James	23	Sarah	42
		Tom	38

a. What is the range?

b. What is the median?

c. What is the mode?

472 Skills and Concepts

Figure 19.2 cont'd

Grade Level	Problem Type	Performance Indicator
6e	Interpreting map legends (complex applications with fractions)	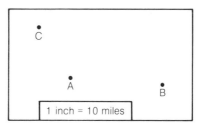

a. If city C is 2 1/2 inches from city B on the map, how far apart are cities C and B?

Figure 19.3   Simple Graphs

---

1. Bar Graphs
   a. horizontal

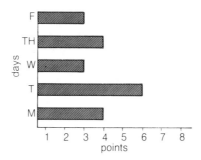

   b. vertical

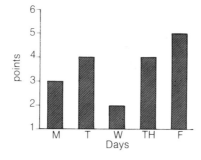

2. Line Graph

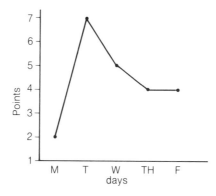

Figure 19.3 cont'd

3. Pictograph

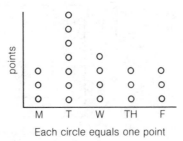

Each circle equals one point

4. Circle Graph

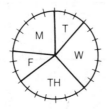

Figure 19.4 Complex Graphs

---

1. Bar Graph
   (double)

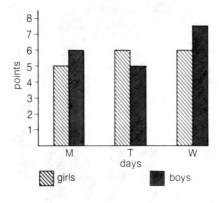

2. Line Graph

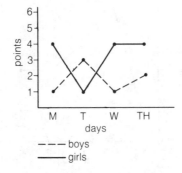

Figure 19.5 Graphs Requiring Estimation

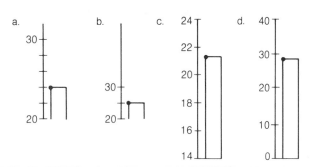

Graphs also become more complex as students must infer the amount indicated. Figure 19.5 includes excerpts from four graphs. In examples a and b, the end of the bar is directly across from a mark which has no number next to it. The students must infer the number represented by the mark. In example a, there are five spaces between 20 and 30. Thus, each space represents a quantity of 2. In example b, there are two spaces between 20 and 30; thus, each space must represent 5.

Graphs become even more difficult to read when the end of the bar is not directly across from a mark, as in examples c and d in Figure 19.5. To determine the value, the students must mentally divide the space into equivalent units so that the point corresponds to a unit. In example c, the closest units are 20 and 22. The point is approximately 1/2 of the unit, so the value of the point is 1/2 of 2, or 1. Thus, the intersection point is about 21. Example d is significantly more difficult since there is a greater difference between the numbered spaces, and the intersection does not fall at a halfway mark. To make the estimation, students must mentally divide the space into 10 equivalent units and then make an estimate.

Pictorial graphs become more difficult when (a) each picture stands for a quantity other than one (for example, a pictograph in which each graph represents five units is more difficult than a pictograph in which each picture represents one unit) and (b) when fractional parts of a picture are shown. For example, let's say each smiling face represents 100 students and this picture is shown:

The student must determine the quantity the last picture represents by computing one-half of a hundred. Even more difficult would be an example in which a partial representation greater or less than one-half is shown:

In such an instance, the student must estimate the fraction of the unit shown and then figure out the quantity it represents. In the above example, about 1/4 of the face is shown; 1/4 of 100 is 25.

The sequence for introducing various types of graphs should be carefully coordinated with number reading and fraction skills so that students have mastered all component skills before needing them to read graphs. Simple graphs are introduced first. Just one difficulty factor would be introduced at a time as more difficult graphs are introduced.

The teaching procedure involves the teacher's modeling how to find information on the graph using a given question. For example, let's say a bar graph shows the number of points Sarah scored in basketball games during recess each day. A question is, "How many points did Sarah score on Tuesday?" The teacher first points out what the numbers stand for: "These numbers tell us the points Sarah scored." The teacher next points out what the letters under each bar would stand for: "This M stand for Monday. This T stands for Tuesday . . .," etc. Finally, the teacher models how to determine how many points Sarah scored on a given day. "To find how many points Sarah scored on Tuesday, I move my finger to the T. Then I move my finger up until the top of the bar. Finally, I move my finger to the numeral across from the top of the bar. It's a 6, so the graph tells us that Sarah scored 6 points on Tuesday." The same basic procedure is used when more com- plex graphs are used. The teacher points out the various information shown on the graph and then models how to get information to answer specific questions.

A variety of literal questions should be included in examples. Literal questions ask for the amount at a particular time (e.g., How many points did Sarah score on Monday?) or the particular time on which a specified quantity was given (e.g., On what day did Sarah score 8 points?). Questions calling for comparisons should gradually be included and come to represent a greater proportion of the total questions (e.g., How many more points did Sarah score on Monday than Tuesday? On which day did she score the most points? On which day did she score the fewest points?).

Tables or Charts

A table or chart, like a graph, specifies the relationship among sets of numbers. Reading tables and charts is frequently necessary in adult life: time schedules for buses, trains, and airplanes; financial charts dealing with income taxes, loan rates, eligibility for benefits; instructions for recipes, medicines, and so on.

A preskill for using tables is an understanding of the concepts of row and column. Teachers can explain the terms in this way, "The lines of information going down the page are called columns. The lines of information going across the page are called rows."

The procedure for teaching students to read charts and tables would follow a model-test sequence for the various parts of the table, i.e., title, rows, columns. The teacher first points out the title of the table and discusses its intent. The teacher then points out the heading in each column, discussing the type of information found under each heading. After leading students through interpreting the headings, the teacher would point out how the students read across the row. Lastly, the teacher models the strategy for locating information by looking for the intersection of rows and columns.

The teacher must carefully design questions that require the students to use the table. During the early intermediate grades, these questions should be literal or comparative. A literal question is one that can be answered by simply referring to the chart (e.g., "What time does bus 834 arrive at 145th Street?"). A comparative question, on the other hand, asks the students to tell the difference between two pieces of information (e.g., "How many minutes between when bus 837 and 849 arrive at 135th Street?").

During the late intermediate grades, inferential questions should be introduced. An inferential question is one in which the information on the chart is used in conjunction with other information to answer a question (e.g., "During snowy weather which bus would you take if you wanted to arrive at 125th

Street at 5:35 PM?"). The chart would show two buses, one arriving at 5:34 and one arriving at 5:25. The student would have to infer that since buses travel slower on snowy days, taking the 5:25 bus would be better.

Figure 19.6 contains a format for introducing time schedules. Part A is a structured exercise in which the teacher models and tests how to locate information on the table. To do this the teacher should put a reproduction of the table on the blackboard or use an overhead projector to ensure that all students can see. Students should also have a copy of the table so they can practice finding information from the table at their seats. Following Part A, students should be given worksheets containing a table and set of relevant questions to complete under teacher supervision. One or two tables would be presented daily for several weeks.

Note that in the example presented in the format, reading a bus schedule, students must first find the row containing the location of the bus stop, then look across the row for the appropriate time, and finally go up that column to find the bus they must take. Locating a row or column in a bus time schedule differs from locating information in a table where students must locate the intersection of a row and column. For example, in the following table, if students were to find the distance Springfield is from Salem, students would find the row for Springfield, find the column that is headed Salem and then look for the intersection to find the distance. Students should be given a variety of tables to work from.

	Portland	Albany	Salem
Eugene	118	30	62
Springfield	123	35	67
Creswell	132	44	76

Maps

There are many skills involved in reading a map. However, our discussion deals only with the mathematics skills directly involved in map reading, e.g., computing the distance between two points on a map.

The difficulty of computing distances on a map is affected by two factors:

1. The presence of fractional numbers. If the distance between two points is 1 1/4 inches and the scale says 1 inch equals 20 miles, the student must multiply 1 1/4 times 20:

$$1\frac{1}{4} \times 20 = \frac{5}{4} \times 20 = \frac{100}{4} = 25 \text{ or}$$

$$(1 \times 20) + (\frac{1}{4} \times 20)$$

2. The relative size of the numbers. Determining the distance between two points is more difficult when each inch represents 500 miles rather than 5 miles.

The preskills for simple map problems include measuring with a ruler to the nearest inch (or centimeter) and knowing multiplication facts. For more complex map problems students must also be able to measure to the nearest fractional part of an inch and multiply a whole number and mixed fraction.

The teaching application involves modeling and prompting students in applying these three component skills:

1. Locating and reading the scale
2. Measuring the distance between two points on a map
3. Multiplying the distance by the scale value

Initially, map problems should involve questions in which no fractional parts of a unit are involved. Fractional parts of a unit should be introduced only after multiplying fractions has been taught.

Statistics

The four basic statistical concepts introduced in the elementary grades are range, mean (or average), mode, and median.

The *range* refers to the difference between the smallest and largest number in a set. For example,

the distances that girls in Mr. Adams' class can throw the shotput are: 32 ft, 29 ft, 41 ft, 18 ft, 27 ft, and 42 ft. The range would be computed by subtracting 18 ft, the lowest score, from 42 ft, the highest score: 42 − 18 = 24. The range would be 24 ft.

The *mean*, the most commonly used statistic, is computed by adding a group of numbers and dividing the sum by how many numbers were added. For example the mean of the numbers 24, 26, 20, and 30 is computed by adding these numbers and then dividing the sum 100, by 4; the mean (100 ÷ 4) is 25.

The *median* denotes the middle measurement of a set that has been arranged in order of magnitude. For example, a teacher gives a test to a class of nine students and then lists the marks in order, from lowest to highest: 64, 70, 70, 70, 78, 92, 94, 94, 98. The median would be the score that comes in the middle, 78. Four students scored less than 78, and four scored more than 78. The median is relatively easy to figure with an odd number of scores. If there are 17 scores, the median would be the ninth number, eight numbers would be smaller and eight larger. For 13, the seventh number is the median; six are smaller and six are larger. The median is somewhat difficult to compute for an even number of scores. The teacher must average the middle two numbers. For example, if eight students score 13, 17, 19, 20, 24, 28, 31, 37, the median would be computed by figuring the average of the middle two numbers:

$$\frac{20 + 24}{2} = \frac{44}{2}$$

The median equals 22.

The mode denotes the most frequently occurring value in a collection of values. For example, in

Figure 19.6 Format for Reading Time Schedules

PART A: Structured Worksheet

TEACHER

Write on board or use overhead projector:

Bus Time Schedule

Locations	Bus 287	Bus 124
23rd St.	2:15	3:44
37th St.	2:25	3:54
45th St.	3:05	4:02
64th St.	3:34	4:31
76th St.	3:48	5:06

STUDENTS

Figure 19.6 cont'd

TEACHER   **STUDENTS**

1. "THIS IS PART OF A BUS TIME SCHEDULE. IT
   TELLS US WHEN BUSES ARRIVE AT DIFFERENT
   PLACES."

2. "REMEMBER THE LINES OF INFORMATION
   GOING DOWN THE PAGE ARE CALLED COLUMNS.
   TOUCH THE HEADING FOR THE FIRST COLUMN.
   READ IT."   "Locations"
   "UNDER THIS HEADING ARE ALL THE PLACES
   THAT THE BUSES STOP. THEY STOP AT 23RD ST.,
   37TH ST., 45TH ST., 64TH ST., AND 76TH ST. TOUCH
   THE HEADING FOR THE NEXT COLUMN. READ IT."   "Bus 287"
   "THAT IS THE NUMBER OF A BUS. UNDER THIS
   HEADING ARE ALL THE TIMES BUS 287 WILL
   ARRIVE AT DIFFERENT BUS STOPS. WHAT
   TIME DOES BUS 287 STOP AT 23RD ST.?" Pause, signal.   "2:15"
   Repeat question with remaining locations. Repeat step
   2 with bus 124.

3. Point to the time schedule. "LET'S SAY THAT WE
   WANT TO FIND OUT WHAT BUS STOPS AT 45TH
   STREET AROUND 4:00. FIRST, I FIND 45TH STREET;
   THEN I GO ACROSS UNTIL I FIND A TIME CLOSE
   TO 4 PM. LAST I GO UP THE COLUMN TO FIND
   THE BUS NUMBER. THE BUS I WOULD TAKE TO
   GO TO 45TH STREET AT ABOUT 4:00 WOULD BE
   BUS 124 SINCE IT STOPS AT 45TH STREET AT 4:02."

4. "NOW IT'S YOUR TURN. FIND THE BUS THAT
   STOPS AT 76TH STREET AT ABOUT 3:45. FIRST
   FIND THE ROW FOR 76TH STREET. NOW FIND THE
   TIME YOU WANT—CLOSE TO 3:45." Pause. "WHAT
   IS THE NUMBER OF THE BUS?"   "287"
   "WHAT BUS WOULD YOU TAKE ON 76TH STREET
   AT ABOUT 3:45?"   "Bus 287"
   Repeat steps 3 and 4 with several questions.
   a. How long does it take to get from 23rd street to 45th
      street on bus 124?
   b. How long does it take to get from 45th street to 76th
      street on bus 287?
   c. When does bus 287 arrive at 67th street?
   d. When does bus 124 arrive at 45th street?

looking at the student's performance on the tests in the preceding paragraph, we note that one student scored 84, three scored 70, one scored 78, one scored 92, two scored 94, and one scored 98. The score which occurred most often, 70, is the mode.

Statistical concepts should be introduced cumulatively, beginning with the mean, which is the most common statistic. When students have demonstrated mastery in computing the mean, the teacher can introduce the range since computing the range is relatively easy and is unlikely to be confused with the mean. The median should be introduced third, and mode last, since it is the least

frequently used. The mean is usually introduced in fourth or fifth grade.

Teaching Procedure

A similar teaching procedure can be used to teach mean, median, range, and mode. The teacher defines the term, models how to figure out the particular statistic, and then leads the students through working several problems.

Sets of problems should contain cumulative review. After each new statistical concept is introduced, the teacher should present exercises in which the students apply all the statistical concepts introduced to date. For example, if range and mean had been taught previously and the median had just been introduced, the teacher should present an exercise in which the students are required to compute all three statistics (range, mean, and median). Since the teaching procedure is similar for all the statistics, we have included a format only for mean, the most difficult and commonly used statistic (see Figure 19.7). This format demonstrates the mechanics of determining the mean. The teacher presents two steps: (a) add the numbers and (b) divide the sum by how many numbers were added. When presenting the format, examples should be prepared initially so that the mean will be a whole number; i.e., the sum of the quantities must be a multiple of the divisor. A problem in which the sum is 24 and the divisor is 5 would be inappropriate initially, since 24 is not a multiple of 5. After this format has been presented for several days, a demonstration illustrating the concept of mean with a balance bar may be presented.

$$2 + 5 + 7 + 10 = 24, \ 24 \div 4 = 6$$

Next the teacher places a fulcrum under position 6 and shows that the bar balances. The teacher summarizes by saying that the mean (6) is the center that balances the numbers on both sides.

Figure 19.7 Format for Computation Strategy (the Mean)

Day	Part A Structured Board Presentation Problems	Part B Structured Worksheet Problems	Part C Supervised Practice Problems	Part D Independent Practice Problems
1	3			
2-4	2	4		
5-6		1	3-6	
8-Till accurate			4-8	
When students reach 90% accuracy				4-8

PART A: Structured Board Presentation

TEACHER

1. "LISTEN: BEN GOT 4 POINTS ON MONDAY, 7 POINTS ON TUESDAY, 3 POINTS ON WEDNESDAY, AND 6 POINTS ON THURSDAY." Write 4, 7, 3, 6. "WE WANT TO FIGURE THE AVERAGE NUMBER OF POINTS BEN GOT EACH DAY. WHAT DO WE WANT TO FIGURE OUT?"

2. "HERE'S HOW WE FIGURE THE AVERAGE. FIRST WE ADD, THEN DIVIDE THE SUM BY HOW MANY NUMBERS WE ADDED. FIRST WE ADD, THEN WHAT DO WE DO?"

3. "FIRST WE ADD." Write on board:

   4
   7
   3
   +6

   "WHAT IS THE SUM OF 4, 7, 3, AND 6?" Pause.

STUDENTS

"The average number of points Ben got each day"

"Divide the sum by how many numbers we added"

"20"

Figure 19.7 cont'd
TEACHER
STUDENTS

4. "THE SUM IS 20. WE ADDED. NOW WE DIVIDE
   BY HOW MANY NUMBERS WE ADDED." Point to 4,
   7, 3, and 6 as you say, "WE ADDED 1, 2, 3, 4 NUMBERS."

5. "WE ADDED 4 NUMBERS, SO WE DIVIDE 4 INTO
   20. WHAT DO WE DIVIDE?"   "4 into 20"
   "HOW MANY TIMES DOES 4 GO INTO 20?"   "5"
   "YES, BEN'S AVERAGE IS 5 POINTS EACH DAY.
   WHAT IS BEN'S AVERAGE?"   "5 points each day"
   "DID BEN SCORE EXACTLY 5 POINTS EVERY DAY?"   "No"
   "5 POINTS A DAY IS HIS AVERAGE."
   Repeat steps 1 - 5 with these examples:
   Jill scored the following points in each game: 6, 8, 9, 5, 0,
   10, 4.
   Tom ran these numbers of miles each day: 3, 1, 1, 7, 0, 0.

PART B: Structured Worksheet

Give students worksheets with several problems like this:

Jack ran 5 miles on Monday, 2 miles on Tuesday, 4 miles
on Wednesday, 0 miles on Thursday, and 9 miles on Friday.
What is the average number of miles he ran each day?

□ _____ _____ _____

1. "READ THE PROBLEM. WHAT DOES THE PROB-   "The average number of miles he
   LEM ASK FOR?"   ran each day"

2. "WHAT DO WE DO FIRST TO FIGURE THE   "Add the miles"
   AVERAGE?"
   "ADD ALL THE MILES." Pause. "HOW MANY MILES
   DID HE RUN ALTOGETHER?"   "20"

3. "WHAT DO WE DO AFTER WE FIND THE SUM?"   "Divide by how many numbers
                                                      we added"
                                                      "5"
4. "HOW MANY NUMBERS DID WE ADD?" Pause, signal.
   "SAY THE DIVISION PROBLEM."   "5 goes into 20"
   "HOW MANY TIMES DOES 5 GO INTO 20?"   "4"
   "WRITE THE NUMERAL IN THE BOX."

5. "NOW WE HAVE TO WRITE IN THE WORDS. READ   "What is the average number of
   THE LAST SENTENCE."   miles he ran each day?"
   "SO THE WORDS WE PUT IN THE ANSWER ARE
   MILES EACH DAY. WHAT ARE THE WORDS THAT
   GO IN THE ANSWER?"   "Miles each day"
   "WHAT IS THE ANSWER? SAY THE WHOLE
   ANSWER."   "4 miles each day"
   "WRITE THE WORDS."

   Repeat steps 1-5 with remaining problems.

Application Items: Study Skills

1. For each pair of questions below tell which is more difficult and why.

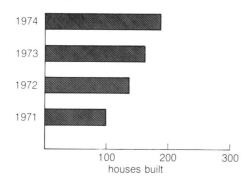

houses built

Pair one
   a. How many houses were built in 1974?
   b. How many houses were built in 1972?

Pair two
   a. How many more houses were built in 1974 than 1971?
   b. How many more houses were built in 1973 than 1972?

2. Below are two errors made by students on the problem specified. Tell the cause of each error. Specify the remediation procedure.

Jill played in 5 basketball games.
She scored 25 points in the first game, 15 points in the second game, 17 points in the third game, 21 points in the fourth game and 22 points in her last game.
What was her average?

Alex
$$\begin{array}{r} 25 \\ 15 \\ 17 \\ 21 \\ +22 \\ \hline 100 \end{array}$$

Jill
$$\begin{array}{r} 25 \\ 15 \\ 17 \\ 21 \\ +22 \\ \hline 99 \end{array}$$
$$\begin{array}{r} 19.8 \\ 5\overline{)99} \\ \underline{5} \\ 49 \\ \underline{45} \\ 40 \end{array}$$

Ramon
$$\begin{array}{r} 25 \\ 15 \\ 17 \\ 21 \\ +22 \\ \hline 100 \end{array}$$
$$\begin{array}{r} 200 \\ 5\overline{)100} \end{array}$$

3. Tell the component skills a student must have mastered to work the following problem. (*Note:* A is 1 3/4 inches from B)

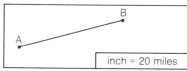

inch = 20 miles

How far from city A to city B?

20 Geometry

As Schminke, Maeterns, and Arnold (1978) have noted, "Geometry is the study of special relationships. It is that branch of mathematics concerned with observations, construction, and description of shapes, and with location of points in one-, two-, or three-dimensional space." In this chapter we present a brief look at teaching geometry. We deal with information and skills students will need to pass competency tests. There is much more to teaching geometry. For an more in-depth overview of the myriad activities in geometry teaching, see *Teaching the Child Mathematics* (C.W. Schminke et al., 1978) and *Elementary Mathematics Methods* (Jerman & Beardslee, 1978)

The geometry objectives discussed in this chapter fall into three major categories:

1. Identifying and defining various figures and concepts
2. Measuring area of a figure, e.g., determining perimeter, area, circumference
3. Constructing figures using an instrument such as a compass or protractor

Skill Hierarchy

The specific skills to be taught can be found in Figure 20.1, the Instructional Sequence and Assessment Chart.

Teaching Procedures

Next to each objective in the Instructional Sequence and Assessment Chart are one, two, or three asterisks. These asterisks indicate the teaching procedure required for the specific skill. One asterisk indicates that the objective falls in the class of identifying and defining geometric figures and concepts. Specific teaching procedures for skills for this area appear on pages 482–86. Two asterisks next to an objective indicate that the objective falls in the class of measuring geometric figures. Procedures for measuring geometric figures appear on pages 489–90. Three asterisks next to an objective indicate that the objective falls in the class of constructing geometric figures. Procedures for constructing geometric figures appear on page 490.

Identifying and Defining Geometric Figures and Concepts

Table 20.1 lists most figures and relationships taught in the elementary grades.

The table shows the relationship between various figures and concepts. It is not intended to imply an order for introducing skills. A suggested order for introducing skills appears in the Instructional Sequence and Assessment Chart.

Figure 20.1 Instructional Sequence and Assessment Chart

Grade Level	Problem Type	Performance Indicator
1a	Identify circle.*	Mark each circle with X. 
1b	Identify rectangle.*	Mark each rectangle with X. 
1c	Identify triangle.*	Mark each triangle with X. 
1d	Identify square.*	Mark each square with X. 
1e	Identify interior of closed figure.*	Tell me when I touch the interior of this figure. 
1f	Identify exterior of closed figure.*	Tell me when I touch the exterior of this figure.
2a	Identify cube.*	Mark each cube with X. 
2b	Identify sphere.*	Mark each sphere with X. 
2c	Identify cone.*	Mark each cone with X. 
2d	Identify the diameter of a circle.*	What is a diameter? Put X on each line that is the diameter of a circle. 
2e	Draw a line segment.***	Draw the line segment CD.
3a	Measure perimeter.**	Find the perimeter of this square. 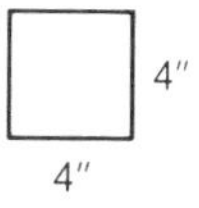

Figure 20.1 cont'd

Grade Level	Problem Type	Performance Indicator
3b	Measure area of rectangle or square.**	Find the area of this rectangle.
3c	Identify pyramid.*	Mark each pyramid with X.
3d	Identify cylinder.*	Mark each cylinder with X.
4a	Define/identify radius.*	What is the radius of a circle? Mark each line that is a radius with X.
4b	Using a compass, construct a circle when given a radius.***	Draw a circle that has a radius of 2 inches. Use a compass.
4c	Label angles.*	For each example write the name of each angle.
4d	Define degree/measure angles using protractor.**	Measure each of the following angles.
4e	Construct angles using a protractor.***	Construct the following angles. 90° _____ 45° _____
4f	Define/identify right angle.*	What is a right angle? Circle each right angle.
4g	Define/identify acute angle.*	What is an acute angle? Circle each acute angle.
4h	Define/identify obtuse angle.*	What is an obtuse angle? Circle each obtuse angle.

Figure 20.1 cont'd

Grade Level	Problem Type	Performance Indicator
4i	Define/identify right triangle.*	What is a right triangle? Circle each right triangle.
4j	Define/identify equilateral triangle.*	What is an equilateral triangle? Circle each equilateral triangle.
4k	Define/identify isosceles triangle.*	What is an isosceles triangle? Circle each isoceles triangle.
4l	Define/identify scalene triangle.*	What is a scalene triangle? Circle each scalene triangle.
4m	Identify the following polygons:* pentagon hexagon octagon	Draw a P over the pentagon. Draw an H over the hexagon. Draw an O over the octagon.
4n	Measure the volume of a cube.**	What is the volume of a figure that is 5 inches long, 3 inches wide, and 6 inches high?
5a	Identify parallel lines.*	Circle each group of parallel lines.
5b	Identify perpendicular lines.*	Circle each group of perpendicular lines.
5c	Identify a parallelogram.*	Circle each parallelogram.

Teaching students to identify new figures and concepts is simply a form of vocabulary teaching. Therefore, the procedures discussed in Chapter 4 on vocabulary are applicable here. Three basic methods of vocabulary instruction are outlined in that chapter: (a) examples only, (b) synonyms, and (c) definitions. The examples-only method is used to present vocabulary terms and concepts that cannot be readily explained by using a synonym or definition. In teaching a term through examples, the teacher constructs a set of examples, half of which are examples of the term (positive instances) and half of which are examples of a similar but different term (noninstances). The set must be carefully de-signed to show the range of positive instances and rule out possible misinterpretations. For example, when ovals are introduced, a variety of ovals should be presented to demonstrate the range of figures called ovals:

Noninstances should include circles so that the students will not consider circles as ovals. As the examples are presented, the teacher points to each example saying, "This is an oval" or "This is not an oval" then tests the students by asking, "Is this an oval?"

Table 20.1 Elementary Level Figures and Relationships

1. *Open Figures*
    a. *Line Segment*—the shortest distance between two points (*Note*: A line extends infinitely in space in two directions).

    b. *Ray*—a line beginning at a point and extending infinitely into space

    c. *Angle*—formed by two rays both of which have the same end point which is called the vertex

    (1) *Right angle*—measures 90°

    (2) *Acute angle*—measures more than 0° and less than 90°

    (3) *Obtuse angle*—measures more than 90° and less than 180°

    (4) *Straight angle*—measures 180°

2. *Closed Figures*
    a. *Polygons*—simple (no crossed lines) closed figures bound by line segments
       (1) *Triangles*—three-sided figures
          (a) Equilateral—all sides measure the same length
          (b) Right—contains one right angle
          (c) Isosceles—two sides of equal length
          (d) Scalene—no two sides are of the same length
       (2) *Quadrilateral*—four-sided figures
          (a) Rectangle—four right angles, two pairs of sides with equal lengths
          (b) Square—four equal sides, four right angles
          (c) Parallelogram— two pairs of parallel lines

          (d) Rhombus—parallelogram having two adjacent sides congruent

          (e) Trapezoid—no right angles, one pair of nonparallel lines

       (3) *Additional Polygons*
          (a) Pentagon—five-sided figure
          (b) Hexagon—six-sided figure
          (c) Septagon—seven-sided figure
          (d) Octagon—eight-sided figure
    b. *Curved Figures*
       (1) *Ovals*

       (2) *Circles*

Table 20.1 cont'd

    (a) Center—midpoint of circle
    (b) Radius—line segment extending from midpoint to edge
    (c) Diameter—line which divides the circle in half

3. *Identification of Dimensional Shapes*

    a. *Cube*

    b. *Pyramid*

    c. *Cone*

    d. *Cylinder*

    e. *Sphere*

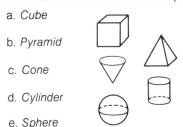

4. *Line Relationships*
    a. *Perpendicular lines*—lines that intersect to form a 90° angle
    b. *Parallel lines*—lines that exist besides each other without intersecting

5. *Figure Relationships*
    a. *Similarity*—having the same shape
    b. *Congruence*—having the same shape and size
    c. *Symmetry*—a figure can be folded along a line and the two parts coincide

---

The presentation of examples and nonexamples has been shown to be an effective way of teaching geometric concepts. In a study done by Petty and Jansson (1987), students in one group were taught to identify various geometric shapes using a rational sequence of examples and nonexamples, while students in the other group were given definitions of shapes in a traditional basal-style of instruction. Not surprisingly, students who were given the systematic sequence of instruction using examples and nonexamples performed significantly higher on measures of concept attainment than those who experienced the more traditional instruction.

Teaching vocabulary through synonyms involves explaining a new term by using a word or phrase already known to the students. For example, the word *interior* may be explained as meaning "inside". Teaching vocabulary through definitions, on the other hand, involves using a longer explanation. For example, a pentagon may be defined as a closed figure having five straight sides. Following either a synonym or definition, the teacher presents a set of positive and negative examples asking, "Is this a _____ ?"

The synonym or definition selected need not meet all the requirements of a formal definition of the concept. A teacher may initially choose a simplified definition that is not technically correct but will help the students master the concept (e.g., a rectangle has four sides and four square corners). More sophisticated definitions can be used in later grades.

Whether the concept is best taught through examples only, definition, or synonym, the teaching format consists of the same parts. The format in Figure 20.2 illustrates the basic identification/definition teaching procedure. In Part A, the teacher first models several examples (in examples only) or models and tests the synonym or definition. The teacher then tests students orally on a set of instances and noninstances of the concept. Part B is a worksheet exercise in which students must use the information they have just learned. For example, after modeling and testing the definition of a parallelogram and testing students on several positive and negative examples of parallelograms, the teacher has students complete a worksheet requiring them to circle all examples of parallelograms.

Worksheets should contain two distinct sections—one section testing application of the new definition and one section testing students on concepts taught previously. This cumulative review serves two important functions. First, it helps prevent students from forgetting taught earlier concepts. Second, it helps provide the discrimination practice needed when similar figures are presented. Note that student performance on the review sections of the worksheets should determine when a new concept can be introduced. Generally, new in-

Figure 20.2 Format for Identification/Definition—Triangle

Day	Part A Structured Board Problems	Part B Less Structured Worksheet Problems	Part C Independent Practice Problems
1-2	1		
3	1	1	
4-Till accurate			1

PART A: Structured Board Presentation

TEACHER   **STUDENTS**

1. "LISTEN TO THIS DEFINITION: A TRIANGLE IS
   A CLOSED FIGURE THAT HAS THREE STRAIGHT
   SIDES. HOW MANY SIDES DOES A TRIANGLE
   HAVE?"   "3"

2. "I'M GONG TO POINT TO SOME FIGURES, YOU
   TELL ME IF THEY ARE TRIANGLES."

   Point to   △

   "IS THIS A TRIANGLE?"   "Yes"
   "HOW DO YOU KNOW?"   "It has three sides."
   Point to the following figures in the sequence shown.

   ◁ △ ▽ □ ◣ ○ ▭ ◹

PART B: Less Structured Worksheet

a. Draw a circle around each triangle.

   △ ○ ▭ △ ○ ◁ ◸ ◤ ◹ △ ▽ ○

b. Write the letter R over each rectangle.
   Write the letter S over each square.
   Write the letter T over each triangle.
   Write the letter C over each circle.

   △ ▫ ○ ○ ◺ ▭ ▭ ○ □ ▯ ⌐

1. "LOOK AT PROBLEM a ON YOUR WORKSHEET.
   READ THE DIRECTIONS."   "Draw a circle around each
                                                                  triangle."

2. "TOUCH THE FIRST FIGURE. IS THAT A
   TRIANGLE?"   "Yes"
   "SO WHAT ARE YOU GOING TO DO?"   "Draw a circle around it."
   "DO IT."

3. "TOUCH THE NEXT FIGURE. IS THAT A
   TRIANGLE?"   "No"
   "SO WHAT ARE YOU GOING TO DO?"   "Nothing"

4. Have students complete the worksheet by themselves.

formation should not be introduced until students can demonstrate mastery on previously introduced information. In addition to worksheet review, extra practice should be incorporated into the classroom routine in the form of games and displays.

One way for students to practice identifying figures is to use flash cards. In flash card practice, the figure is drawn on one side of a flash card and the label of that figure on the other side. Students study the cards and then take turns asking each other to identify the terms.

Measuring

During the elementary grades, students are taught to measure (a) the perimeter of polygons, (b) the radius and diameter of a circle, (c) the area of a rectangle and square, (d) the volume of a cube, and (e) the number of degrees in an angle.

Recommendations regarding when to introduce each measurement skill can be found by consulting the Instructional Sequence and Assessment Chart in Figure 20.1.

The perimeter of a polygon is the sum of the length of each of its sides. The radius of a circle is the distance between the midpoint of the circle and the edge of the circle:

The diameter is a line running from one side of the circle to the opposite side through the midpoint:

In teaching the students to figure the perimeter of a closed figure, the teacher defines *perimeter* and models how to compute it. The same procedure would be used in measuring the radius and diameter of a circle.

Area refers to the relative surface occupied by a plane figure. In teaching students to figure the area of a rectangle or square, the teacher first presents an exercise showing how a rectangle may be divided into square inches by making horizontal and vertical lines at inch intervals:

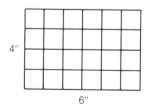

The teacher points out the meaning of the term *square inch*. After presenting several illustrations, the teacher gives a rule for determining the area—multiply the length times the width—and demonstrates its application, figuring out the area of several rectangles and squares. The teacher emphasizes the need to express the answer in terms of square units (square inch, square foot, etc.). A final exercise involves the students' having to determine the perimeter and area of a rectangle or square. A sample worksheet exercise appears in Figure 20.3. The purpose of the worksheet exercise is to provide students with the practice needed to discriminate these two similar measurements.

Figure 20.3 Sample Measuring Worksheet

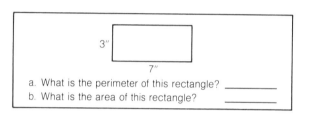
a. What is the perimeter of this rectangle? _____
b. What is the area of this rectangle? _____

Volume refers to a number indicating the amount of space inside a figure. A procedure similar to that described for teaching the area of a rectangle would be used to teach students to determine the volume of a cube. The teacher first demonstrates how a cube may be divided into inch cubes. The teacher then models and tests finding the volume of a cube—multiplying the length times the width times the height—emphasizing the need to express the answers in terms of cubic inches.

Teaching students to figure the number of degrees in an angle requires teaching them to use a protractor. The teacher models how to align (a) the base of the protractor and the base of the angle and (b) the vertex (point of the angle) with the center of the protractor base.

The second step requires deciding which row of numbers to read. As indicated in Figure 20.4, protractors have two rows of numerals. If the baseline of the angle points to the right:

the lower numbers are read. If the baseline of the angle points to the left:

the top numbers are read.

The third step involves determining the number of degrees by noting the places at which the ray and the protractor intersect. In Figure 20.4, the intersection is at 70. Thus, the angle is 70°.

Figure 20.4

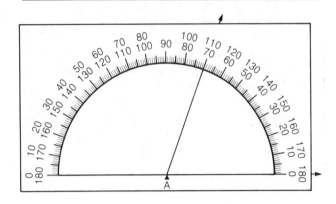

Constructing Figures

Constructing figures requires the use of tools such as a ruler, compass, and protractor. In order to teach students to use such tools to construct or measure geometric figures, teachers must provide a clear model as well as sufficient, structured practice. The practice gives the teacher an opportunity to give feedback to as many students as possible. In modeling the use of a compass, for example, the teacher should emphasize the need to keep the compass upright when drawing a circle, not letting it slant. The teacher can then demonstrate how circles can be drawn the "wrong way" as well as show how to correctly use the instrument.

Summary

The brief overview of geometry in this chapter discussed teaching simple concepts and computations. Our purpose was to suggest teaching methods that will help students develop only the most minimal competencies in this area. A fuller array of activities for teaching geometry appears in the books cited at the beginning of the chapter.

Appendix A

Direct Instruction Mathematics: A Longitudinal Evaluation of Low-Income Elementary School Students

Russell Gersten and Doug Carnine
University of Oregon

The recent National Assessment of Educational Progress (1979) found that at all grade levels, in all components of mathematics (concepts, problem solving, computation), students from disadvantaged urban areas performed at a lower level than their peers in other areas of the country. The National Institute of Education (Cohen, Koehler, Datta, & Timpane 1980, p. 1) concluded, "These differences have not come about recently and have shown little sign of dissipating over time."

The purpose of this paper is to describe an instructional model, the Direct Instruction model, that has been effective in teaching mathematics to disadvantaged students. The first section of the paper describes the methodology and presents an overview of the research conducted. The final section discusses more general implications of the findings for improving classroom practices. Issues to be addressed include training and supervision of teachers, use of paraprofessionals in the classroom, criteria for selection or adaptation of curricula for low-SES students, and methods for assessing student progress.

Direct Instruction mathematics: an overview

Although in recent years the term "direct instruction" has been used in a multitude of ways, in this paper it refers to a comprehensive educational model involving (a) a specific curriculum, (b) a specific way of teaching (rapidly paced small-group instruction), (c) a specified model of inservice education, and (d) a system for monitoring both student and teacher performance. It is a synthesis of learning theory, behavioral technology, and Engelmann's principles of instructional de-

sign (Becker & Carnine 1980; Engelmann & Carnine 1982).

The major principle behind the Direct Instruction model is deceptively simple: Virtually all children can learn mathematics if (a) lessons are designed so that students can readily understand what is being presented, (b) adequate practice with corrective feedback is provided, and (c) progress through the curriculum is assessed regularly.

The Distar materials used with the model were designed for structured small-group teaching situations. The classroom schedule is arranged so that each student receives at least 30 minutes a day of intensive small-group instruction with a teacher or trained paraprofessional aide. A more detailed discussion of materials and instructional strategies appears in Silbert, Carnine, and Stein (1981). There are some similarities with adaptations of basal math series for effective urban education, such as those described by Good and Grouws (1979) and Nagel and McLevie (1981).

Distar Arithmetic I and II and a modified version of III by Engelmann and Carnine (1972, 1975, 1976) *explicitly* teach students rules and strategies for solving problems and performing arithmetic computations. To teach these rules, strategies, and concepts efficiently, teachers demonstrate, prompt, and test students on each step of a new skill before expecting the students to work independently. In Direct Instruction, rules for solving word story problems or performing difficult computations (e.g., two-digit divisor problems) are explicitly taught, modeled, and then practiced and reviewed. Nothing is left to chance; children are not asked to infer rules or generalizations. For example, in

The Elementary School Journal
Volume 84, Number 4

teaching strategies for solving word story problems, children ask two questions to determine which operation to carry out. In answering the first question, students decide whether the problem entails multiple, equivalent-sized groups. If so, the problem calls for multiplication or division. Problems with unequal-sized groups require addition or subtraction. The second question asks whether the total is given in the problem. When the total is given in problems with equivalent-sized groups, students divide; conversely, when the total is not given, students multiply. A similar strategy is taught for discriminating addition from subtraction problems.

The curriculum also calls for considerable practice with corrective feedback. Teachers and aides are trained to provide immediate corrective feedback to student responses and to model correct problem-solving strategies if a student is confused. Principles of mastery learning are adhered to; groups do not go on to the next lesson until mastery (i.e., 85%–95% accuracy) is reached on the previous one.

An essential component of Direct Instruction is continual assessment both of student progress through the program and of teacher performance. Students are given individually administered criterion-referenced tests (by a tester other than the classroom teacher) on material covered during the preceding 2 months. Scores on these tests are used to determine whether a child (or group) needs remediation and whether individual students need to be placed in either a more accelerated or slower-paced group. Teachers and aides are observed weekly and given specific feedback. They then follow concrete remediation strategies for improving their teaching techniques (for more details, see Meyer, Gersten, & Gutkin 1983; Morimitsu 1979). The Direct Instruction approach toward teaching mathematics was evaluated in the context of Project Follow Through. The next section describes Follow Through and the results of the mathematics portion of the Follow Through evaluation.

The nature of Follow Through and the questions posed in the evaluation

Since 1968 the federally funded Follow Through Project has served as a research laboratory for the development and implementation of innovative teaching practices in schools serving low-income students. Over 180 school districts have been involved in Follow Through, ranging from rural areas such as Flippin, Arkansas, to the Rosebud Sioux Indian reservation in South Dakota, to inner-city districts in Philadelphia, New York, and Los Angeles. Each school district was aligned with a sponsor—a university or educational laboratory representing a specific model of education. The range of educational philosophies and models included in Follow Through was as diverse as the children served. They ranged from Piagetian-derived approaches to open classroom models, psychodynamic approaches, and several models based on discovery learning, as well as three approaches with a behavioral orientation.

Two sets of research questions were addressed in the independent evaluation conducted by Abt Associates (Stebbins 1976; Stebbins, St. Pierre, Proper, Anderson, & Cerva 1977), for the U.S. Office of Education (commonly called the Abt Report). The first set are methodologically intricate: Do children involved in the Direct Instruction Follow Through mathematics program for 3 years (first through third grade) or 4 years (Kindergarten through third grade) perform significantly higher on the mathematics subtests of the Metropolitan Achievement Test (Durost, Bixler, Wrightstone, Prescott, & Balow 1971) than (*a*) demographically similar students in local comparison groups and (*b*) children in other Follow Through programs?

In contrast, the second question asked was relatively simple and down to earth: Can low-income students taught with a Direct Instruction math program for 4 years perform at a level comparable to their middle-class peers?

We will also address a few questions supplemental to the Abt evaluation: Are there traces of the effects 2–3 years after the intervention is completed? What effect does the program have on those children entering Kindergarten or first grade with low academic skills, as measured by IQ tests and the Wide Range Achievement

Test (Jastak & Jastak 1965)? These questions were explored through a variety of quasi-experimental designs.

Results of the national Follow Through evaluation

It is important to note that Follow Through was not only one of the largest and most expensive social experiments ever conducted (McDaniels 1975) but also one of the most controversial (see Bereiter & Kurland 1981–82; Haney 1977; House, Glass, McLean, & Walker 1978). The methodological intricacies of the Follow Through evaluation go well beyond the scope of this article. However, some of the issues raised concerning the "fairness" of the measures used in the Follow Through evaluation are unpersuasive when the target is mathematics instruction. Both the affective instruments in the battery (the Coopersmith [1967] Self-Concept Inventory and the Intellectual Achievement Responsibility Scale [IARS] [Crandall, Katkowsky, & Crandall 1965]) and the reading and language subtests of the Metropolitan Achievement Test (Durost et al. 1971) have been criticized as being too narrow in scope (e.g., House et al. 1978; McLean 1978). However, there is considerably less controversy concerning either the content validity or the reliability of the math problem-solving and math computation subtests of the elementary form of the Metropolitan Achievement Test (see Bereiter & Kurland 1981–82; Wolf 1978), even though these tests do not necessarily assess a child's ability to devise unique solutions to complex mathematical problems.

The Abt Report attempted to examine the effectiveness of the nine major Follow Through sponsors by using a longitudinal design with replications across sites and across two cohorts of children. For each of these sponsors, six to 10 representative sites were selected for intensive study.

Since random assignment of children to treatment was deemed politically unfeasible, a quasi-experimental design (Campbell & Stanley 1966) was utilized; for each Follow Through site chosen, a roughly equivalent local "comparison group" was selected by the Stanford Research Institute. Demographic information was collected on all Follow Through and comparison children on the following variables (which were later used as covariates): family income, ethnicity, mother's education, primary language spoken at home, and academic entry skills.

The nature of math instruction in either the Follow Through or comparison classrooms was *not* measured in a systematic fashion. It is highly unlikely that Direct Instruction methods were used in the comparison classrooms. However, Stallings's (1975) observations of a small subsample of schools indicated that Direct Instruction classrooms could be correctly discriminated from comparison classrooms and other Follow Through classrooms over 90% of the time on the basis of observable variables, such as type of questions teachers asked during math lessons, amount of small-group instruction, and how teachers responded to student errors.

Outcomes measures. All students in the Follow Through and comparison classrooms were tested upon entry into the program on the arithmetic subtest of the Wide Range Achievement Test (Jastak & Jastak 1965). Children were tested at the end of Grades 1, 2, and 3 on the Metropolitan Achievement Test (MAT). The math problem-solving and math computation sections of the MAT are generally considered reliable (with coefficients over .85) and valid subtests; the validity of the math concepts subtest is more open to question (Bereiter & Kurland 1981–82; Buros 1978; Wolf 1978).

Two affective measures, the Coopersmith Self-Concept Inventory and IARS, were utilized as supplemental measures. The reliabilities of these tests are appreciably lower than the MAT—.69 for Coopersmith, .55 for IARS (House et al. 1978)—though many would argue they are reliable enough to be utilized in evaluations of mean group performance (Cook & Campbell 1979; Wisler, Burns, & Iwamoto 1978). In any case, their role was primarily supplemental.

Comparisons with local and "pooled" comparison groups. For each site selected for the national longitudinal evaluation sample (Stebbins et al. 1977), an analysis of covariance (with multiple covariates) was conducted on each of the math subtests of the MAT, as well as the total math composite.

An effect was considered significant if the result was statistically significant and the magnitude of the treatment effect was at least .25 SD pooled. (This procedure eliminated the possibility of finding effects that were statistically significant but not large enough to be considered educationally meaningful.)

Using the entire non-Follow Through control sample (with sample sizes of approximately 1,000 depending on the variable) and the entire set of demographic variables, a "predicted" or "expected" score was derived for each site using a multiple regression level. If a site's performance on a subtest significantly deviated from this predicted score, the effect was tallied. (Even if the local comparison group was less disadvantaged than the Follow Through sample; leading to possibly biased results, the estimate based on the large "pooled" non-Follow Through sample was unlikely to be biased.)

The authors of the Abt evaluation presented what is essentially a "box score" for each of the nine major educational models. The performance of Follow Through students was compared with (a) students in a local comparison group and (b) an "expected" score based on the demographic characteristics of the Follow Through students. For each sponsor, a box score or net percentage was derived in the following fashion: Net Percentage of Significant Outcomes = [(Number of Positive Effects − Number of Negative Effects)/Total Number of Effects] × 100.

Percentages of significant outcomes are presented in table 1 for each math

subtest—computation, problem solving, concepts, and the total math composite.[1]

The highest incidence of significant positive effects is in math computation, where 66% of the effects are both statistically and educationally significant. On math problem solving, 55% of the effects for Direct Instruction are positive. Thirty-seven percent of the effects for Direct Instruction are positive in math concepts. The results indicate that the Direct Instruction model produced consistently positive effects in both basic skills and higher-order skills in a variety of sites for two cohorts of children. Performance of students in the Direct Instruction model is superior to that of students in the other eight approaches in all domains of mathematics.

Normative performance. The mean standard score in total math on the elementary level of the Metropolitan Achievement Test for each Follow Through sponsor, converted to a percentile, is reported in figure 1. The dark horizontal line near the top (at 50) represents national median performance. The shaded horizontal line at the bottom represents mean performance for students in low-income minority schools according to recent Department of Education evaluations (Ozenne et al. 1976) and the study of low-income students in comparison schools (Molitor, Watkin, Napior, & Proper 1977). Each box represents .25 SD. Children in the Direct Instruction Follow Through program are performing within two percentile points of the national median and over 1 SD above the typical level for children in low-income minority schools. These children perform at a significantly

TABLE 1. Net Percentage of Statistically and Educationally Significant Outcomes Favoring Follow Through Students on the Metropolitan Achievement Test

Approach (and Sponsor)	Math Computation	Math Problem Solving	Math Concepts	Total Math
Direct Instruction (University of Oregon)	+59	+50	+32	+47
Behavior analysis (University of Kansas)	+38	−12	− 4	+ 8
Parent education (University of Florida)	+ 4	0	− 8	0
Bilingual (Southwest Educational Development Lab)	+13	+ 6	+25	+19
Child centered, responsive education (Far West Lab)	+ 6	0	0	0
Child development, psychodynamic (Bank Street)	− 8	− 8	− 8	−17
Language experience (TEEM) (University of Arizona)	+ 7	−13	−20	−20
Piagetian (High Scope Foundation)	− 6	−11	−11	−17
Open education (Educational Development Center)	−20	−10	−15	−20

higher level than children in the other Follow Through models. Stebbins (1976, pp. 168–69) states, "The Direct Instruction Model is specific in stating that children participating in the Follow Through program are expected to, on the average, perform at the same level as their middle-class peers by the end of third grade. This goal has largely been achieved."

Effects of Direct Instruction on self-concept. People unfamiliar with Direct Instruction or behavioral approaches were surprised by the finding that children taught with these procedures reported higher self-concept and more sense of responsibility for their academic successes and failures than children taught with approaches (such as Bank Street and Educational Development Center) whose explicit goal was to build up the self-concept of students in the program through psychodynamic methods. The results of

the three self-concept measures are presented in table 2.[2] Direct Instruction is among the three highest-ranked models on all measures. While it is true that the Coopersmith Self-Esteem Inventory and the IARS measures have less than ideal reliability for individual assessment, their reliability is adequate for research involving large samples (Cook & Campbell 1979; Nunnally 1978; Wisler et al. 1978). Trends that are replicated with thousands of children in eight sites over two cohorts of children would appear to be more than a chance finding. Scheirer and Kraut (1979) discuss other replications of this finding.

Results of the University of Oregon evaluation

Replication across time. In their recent work on quasi-experiments, Cook and Campbell (1979) indicate that, no matter how well designed, quasi-experiments

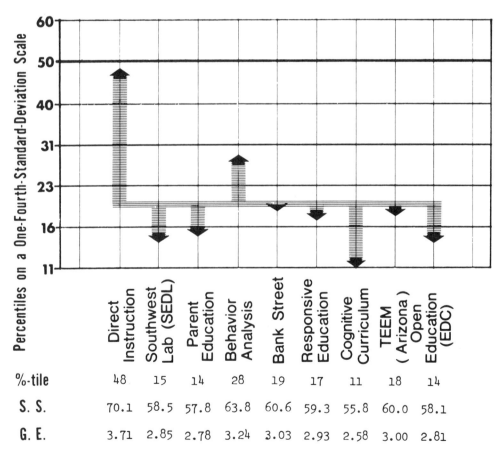

%-tile	48	15	14	28	19	17	11	18	14
S. S.	70.1	58.5	57.8	63.8	60.6	59.3	55.8	60.0	58.1
G. E.	3.71	2.85	2.78	3.24	3.03	2.93	2.58	3.00	2.81

Grade equivalent for 50th percentile is 3.75

FIG. 1.—Median standard scores, percentiles, and grade equivalents for the nine major Follow Through sponsors on the total math subtest of the Metropolitan Achievement Test.

TABLE 2. Net Percentage of Statistically and Educationally Significant Outcomes on Affective Measures

Approach	No. of Sites	Coopersmith Self-Esteem		IARS −		IARS +	
		%	Rank	%	Rank	%	Rank
Direct Instruction	16	+18	3	+21	2	+21	1
Behavior analysis	13	+24	1	+30	1	− 9	6
Parent education	12	+ 5	4.5	+19	3	+14	2
Southwest Lab	8	+21	2	0	4	0	4
Cognitive curriculum	9	0	7	−13	6	0	4
Responsive education	16	+ 4	6	− 8	5	0	4
Bank Street	12	+ 5	4.5	−17	7	−11	7
Open education (EDC)	10	− 6	8	−19	8	−18	8
TEEM (Arizona)	15	−12	9	−23	9	−23	9

cannot rule out rival hypotheses; therefore, replication is essential. The nature of Follow Through allowed for extensive replications across time—that is, replications of effects over seven to nine cohorts of children at the same site. For each of the 11 Direct Instruction projects, students were pretested (on entry) on the Wide Range Achievement Test (WRAT) and posttested (at the end of third grade) on both the WRAT and the MAT. These data allowed for an intensive examination of stability of effects across cohorts. The results (Gersten 1981) indicate strong replication of effects over six to eight cohorts of children. For 10 of the 11 projects, mean scores for low-income students on both the MAT and WRAT are consistently at, above, or within .25 SD units of the national norm level. All 11 sites were recently validated by the Joint Dissemination Review Panel of the National Institute of Education and Department of Education as demonstrating consistent, significant evidence of effectiveness in mathematics. As effects are replicated over six to eight cohorts of children, with a variety of teachers, supervisors, and consultants, it becomes increasingly clear that the effects are a result of the components of the educational model rather than other factors.

The low-IQ study. This study explored the hypothesis that, with appropriate educational programming, all students— regardless of entry skill level or IQ—can make roughly comparable yearly gains in mathematics achievement. To explore this hypothesis, yearly total math scores on the MAT were analyzed to explore whether there was a significant interaction between the child's IQ at entry (measured by the Slosson Intelligence Test [Slosson 1963]) and yearly growth on the total math subtest of the MAT. A 6×3 mixed analysis of variance was performed with one between-subjects factor (IQ level at entry) and one within-subjects factor (year of test) (Gersten, Becker, Heiry, & White, in press). No significant interaction was found between entry IQ and yearly achievement scores, despite the large sample size of 2,100 and consequent high statistical power. Those entering with low IQ scores tended to begin and end with lower MAT scores than their peers, *but they still maintained the same average growth rate of 1.0 grade-equivalent units a year.* These analyses appear to indicate that, when the curriculum is broken down into small steps and students are taught in small groups based on skill level, virtually all children, not just the upper half, can progress at a reasonable rate without the need for special education or remediation services.

Later effects of Direct Instruction. In 1975 and 1976, an attempt was made to ascertain whether the effects of the mathematics program were enduring. Fifth and sixth graders at seven sites were tested on all subtests of the intermediate level of the MAT. Scores were contrasted with the performance of local comparison children, using analysis of covariance techniques with SES, parent education, rate, and primary home language as covariates. Analyses were performed on math problem solving, concepts, computation, and total math. The results indicated consistent, significant, positive findings in the area of math problem solving, weaker but significant effects in concepts, and null effects in computation. It appears that students retain some of the general problem-solving strategies taught in Distar arithmetic programs and use them in the fifth- and sixth-grade material they encounter. However, once graduated from the program after third grade, they are *not* learning the new computational skills in multiplication, division, measurement, and other new areas that should be taught in the intermediate grades. Details of the study are reported in Becker and Gersten (1982).

Conclusions and implications

The data presented above indicate that low-income primary-grade students who received the full 3- or 4-year Direct Instruction mathematics program tended to perform significantly better in all mathematic subtests of the Metropolitan Achievement Test than students who received other approaches, whether experimental or traditional. Direct Instruction Follow Through students achieved at a level much higher than is typical for students with similar demographic characteristics (see, e.g., NAEP 1979; Ozenne et al. 1976); in fact, their mean performance was at a level comparable to their middle-income peers.

What the data do not tell the reader is exactly what implications this study has for improving mathematics instruction in the primary grades. In this section, we will offer our speculations.

The Direct Instruction mathematics program can be broken down into three components. Each is likely to have contributed to the positive effects. The first component is organization of the classroom to maximize the amount of time students are actively engaged in mathematics activities at a high success level. Stallings's (1975) observational study of Follow Through classrooms indicated that students in Direct Instruction classrooms did spend more time engaged in math instruction than students in traditional classrooms and all but one other Follow Through Model (behavior analysis). The second component is the teacher performance variables that are part of the model and the focus of in-service training, such as techniques for procuring high student accuracy rate, systematic use of praise, and strategies for correcting errors that children make. The third component is the principles behind the curriculum developed and used in the program.

The academic learning time component is a recurrent issue in recent teacher effectiveness studies. The amount of time students are observed to be engaged actively in academic activities consistently correlates with student academic gain, both in compensatory education settings (Cooley & Leinhardt 1980; Rosenshine 1976; Stallings 1975) and regular education settings (Fisher, Berliner, Filby, Marliave, Cahen, & Dishaw 1980).

One way academic engaged time was increased in Direct Instruction Follow Through classrooms was to teach math in small groups of six to 10 pupils at all grade levels. In a naturalistic study of six classrooms, Good and Beckerman (1978) found that small-group instruction with a teacher provided the highest percentage of time on task for students—82%. Peterson, Janicki, and Swing (1981) also found that maximal learning in math occurred for low performers when students were taught in small groups.

In many of the Follow Through sites, the math program was taught by trained paraprofessional aides, while the teacher worked on reading and language. The use of paraprofessional aides as teachers (rather than classroom helpers or tutors) is unprecedented. This required extensive in-service training. The scripted Distar lessons facilitated the process. The advantage was that children could be taught math (as well as reading and language) in what appears to be an optimal-size group of five to 10 students at approximately the same current skill level. A long-term benefit of this procedure was that it led some of the paraprofessionals to pursue professional careers in education.

Research on the second component demonstrates that the proper use of various Direct Instruction teaching techniques enhances learner performance in mathematics: academically oriented feedback (Good & Beckerman 1978), appropriate correction of student errors (Carnine 1980; Siegel 1977), rapid pacing of tasks (Carnine 1976), and provision of signals to encourage group participation (Cowart, Carnine, & Becker 1976). Moreover, research indicates that the training of teachers in appropriate procedures for correction of student errors (Siegel 1977) and in cuing and pacing of lessons (Carnine & Fink 1978) is necessary if the techniques are to be used properly. For example, Siegel (1977) reported that, after training, teachers who were initially "low correction" implementers (i.e., rarely used correction procedures) actually surpassed their higher-performing peers who did not receive training. Moreover, students in the classes of the "low correction" teachers who underwent training outperformed students of initially higher-performing teachers who were not trained. A naturalistic study conducted in an urban Direct Instruction Follow Through setting (Gersten, Carnine, & Williams 1982) indicated that classrooms in which teachers (a) corrected student errors at a rate of at least 80%, (b) paced lessons at a rapid rate, and (c) procured mean student accuracy of 80% or higher during lessons, gained more on standardized achievement measures than students whose teachers were not performing at that level. These findings suggest that the Follow Through scores at the end of third grade may have resulted in part from teacher training on Direct Instruction teaching techniques.

The relative importance of the curriculum compared with other variables (degree of teacher implementation, amount of academic engaged time, and use of criterion-referenced assessment systems) has not been rigorously investigated. Yet an interesting perspective on this question emerges if one reexamines the data in table 1. It is clear that both the behavior analysis and the Direct Instruction models are effective in teaching skills in math computation, with 55% and 66% of significant outcomes, respectively. In the higher-order conceptual operations, the Direct Instruction model also produces significant gains: 55% for problem solving and 37% for concepts. Behavior analysis, on the other hand, produces negative values of −13% and −5%. Both behavior analysis and Direct Instruction utilize principles of extensive academic engaged time and reinforcement (Stallings 1975) and

consistent monitoring of student performance (Becker, Engelmann, Carnine, & Rhine 1981; Ramp & Rhine 1981); yet the behavior analysis model utilizes the mathematics curriculum currently used in the school district, whereas Direct Instruction classrooms use the Distar arithmetic series, which is based on the explicit teaching of general case strategies for cognitive skills. Thus, there is some evidence suggesting that, when amount of engaged time is kept relatively constant, learning higher-order cognitive skills is enhanced by a well-designed curriculum that explicitly tries to teach them.

Darch, Carnine, and Gersten's (1983) research is a first step in this direction. They examined the relative effects of (a) mastery learning and (b) type of curriculum on the achievement of fourth-grade students in solving math word problems. Half the students received instruction using traditional basal curriculum; the other half used a Direct Instruction curriculum. Each sample was further subdivided so that half received a fixed number of lessons on the material, and half received additional practice lessons if they did reach mastery on the material. They found that the additional practice did nothing to enhance the performance of students taught with traditional materials. Even with up to eight additional "practice" lessons to ensure mastery, their performance was no different than the students who had the fixed number of lessons. (Their mean scores, at the 60% level, were far from mastery, whereas the mean for Direct Instruction groups was in the 90%–95% range.)

The research of Good and Grouws (1979) in fourth-grade mathematics also tends to support the importance of a well-designed curriculum. Teachers were trained to adapt their teaching of traditional basal arithmetic texts by incorporating the following features of Direct Instruction: (a) systematic sequencing of skills and strategies, (b) daily review and practice of previously learned material, and (c) explicit teacher modeling and explanation of problem-solving strategies. Classes taught by teachers trained in these techniques gained significantly more than comparison classes (where the basal texts were taught in a conventional fashion).

The key principles of Direct Instruction curriculum design are (*a*) making each step in the problem-solving process explicit in the early stages of instruction, (*b*) beginning instruction in a highly structured context and then systematically moving the learner to unstructured applications, and (*c*) teaching general case strategies for working a wide range of complex problems. The importance of teaching explicit general case strategies is illustrated in two recent studies, one on teaching a multiplication algorithm (Carnine 1980) and one on teaching fact relations (Carnine & Stein 1981). Engelmann and Carnine (1982) and Stevenson (1975) give additional research and an elaboration of the instructional design procedures.

The advantages of improved mathematics instructional methods like Direct Instruction or the Good and Grouws (1979) method are numerous. Schools *can* respond to public criticism of current levels of mathematics achievement by providing a foundation in basic mathematical operations and problem-solving strategies for virtually all students. When mathematics foundations are taught more efficiently, time becomes available for intensive work on problem solving and, for students who are interested, topics in higher-level mathematics.

These possibilities must be tempered by caution in generalizing our results to other less disadvantaged learners, grades other than the primary grades, and activities other than those covered in standardized achievement tests.[3] However, demonstration of the capability of thousands of low-income minority children to succeed in mathematics gives some basis for optimism in more far-reaching efforts to improve mathematics instruction.

Notes

The authors wish to thank Paul Williams and Peter Sharpe for their assistance in the data analyses, and Bill White, Harriet Kandelmann, and Craig Darch for feedback on an earlier version of this manuscript.

1. In many of the communities, the comparison (non-Follow Through) students were less disadvantaged than the Follow Through students. To remedy this problem, all comparisons involving noncomparable control groups (differing by more than .5 SD on any demographic covariate) were considered untrustworthy and "grayed out" (deleted from the analysis). This was done because covariance adjustments tend systematically to *under*adjust for the more disadvantaged group (usually the Follow Through children). Because of the underadjustments, truly positive treatment effects may yield nonsignificant *F* ratios. Our analysis differs from Abt's in that the "gray out" rules have been revised in the following fashion. If there is a discrepancy of over .5 SD units between Follow Through and comparison group on a covariate favoring the comparison group and the analysis of covariance indicates a positive effect for Follow Through, the result is *not* grayed out. Campbell and Erlebacher (1970) clearly indicate that the covariance adjustment should handicap the Follow Through sample; if the Follow Through children—with this handicap—still significantly outperform the comparison children, there is clear evidence of a strong effect. (For further discussion, see Becker [1978].)

2. The Abt results on affective measures differ somewhat from earlier results obtained by Stallings and Kaskowitz (1974). Stallings and Kaskowitz found that the Direct Instruction and behavior analysis students did well on the IARS−, but not IARS+. However, this finding *was not replicated* in the larger Abt evaluation, as can be seen in table 2 of this paper. Considering the small sample size in Stallings' third-grade study (often only two or three sites per model) versus the larger Abt sample (usually 10–18 sites per model), we believe the Abt findings to be more reliable.

3. There is some evidence suggesting that Direct Instruction can also be successful with middle-income students. Guthrie (1977) reported that Direct Instruction was the only Follow Through model to have consistent effects for both low- and middle-income children enrolled in Follow Through. On the MAT computation subtest, the mean grade-level performance for the 321 non-low-income students who were enrolled in Direct Instruction classrooms was 4.76, almost a full year ahead of the national norm, corresponding to the 83d percentile. The mean for the concepts subtest was 4.42 (corresponding to the 68th percentile), and 4.26 for problem solving (75th percentile). Since no non-low-income comparison groups were available, the results must be considered merely exploratory. A study by Adamson (1976) with a control group also illustrates the potentiality of Direct Instruction with above-average students. (The students had an average IQ of 111.) The Distar program was compared with Developing Mathematical Processes (DMP), which "relies heavily on perceptual activities, discovery, and open-ended questions with a manipulative approach utilizing measurement" (p. 70). She found that Distar stu-

dents were able to transfer from a previously taught form of computation, whereas the DMP students were largely unable to do so. She also reported that Distar worked equally well with both cooperative and noncooperative students, whereas DMP tended to work mainly with the cooperative students. "In the Distar program the child is not given the choice not to learn, and therefore he learns" (p. 75).

References

Adamson, G. Mathematics achievement between first-grade students using developing mathematical processes and DISTAR arithmetic mathematics instruction (Doctoral dissertation, Brigham Young University, 1975). *Dissertation Abstracts International,* 1976, **36,** 4211A. (University Microfilms No. 76-683).

Becker, W. C. The national evaluation of Follow Through: behavior-theory-based programs came out on top. *Education and Urban Society,* 1978, **10,** 431–458.

Becker, W. C., & Carnine, D. W. Direct Instruction: an effective approach to education intervention with disadvantaged and low-performers. In B. Lahey & A. Kazkin (Eds.), *Advances in child clinical psychology.* Vol. **3.** New York: Plenum, 1980.

Becker, W. C., & Gersten, R. A follow-up of Follow Through: meta-analysis of the later effects of the Direct Instruction model. *American Educational Research Journal,* 1982, **19,** 75–93.

Becker, W. C.; Engelmann, S.; Carnine, D. W.; & Rhine, W. R. The Direct Instruction model. In W. R. Rhine (Ed.), *Encouraging change in America's schools: a decade of experimentation.* New York: Academic Press, 1981.

Bereiter, C., & Kurland, M. Were some Follow Through models more effective than others? *Interchange,* 1981–82, **12,** 1–22.

Buros, O. *Eighth mental measurements yearbook.* Highland Park, N.J.: Gryphon, 1978.

Campbell, D. T., & Erlebacher, A. How regression artifacts in quasi-experimental evaluations in compensatory education tend to underestimate effects. In J. Hellmuth (Ed.), *Disadvantaged child: compensatory education—a national debate.* Vol. **3.** New York: Brunner/Mazel, 1970.

Campbell, D. T., & Stanley, J. *Experimental and quasi-experimental designs for research.* Chicago: Rand McNally, 1966.

Carnine, D. Effects of two teacher presentation rates on off-task behavior, answering correctly, and participation. *Journal of Applied Behavior Analysis,* 1976, **9,** 199–206.

Carnine, D. W. Preteaching versus concurrent teaching of the component skills of a multiplication algorithm. *Journal of Research in Mathematics Education,* 1980, **11,** 375–378.

Carnine, D. W., & Fink, W. T. Increasing the rate of question-asking and use of signals in Direct Instruction trainees. *Journal of Applied Behavior Analysis,* 1978, **11,** 34–56.

Carnine, D., & Stein, M. Organizational strategies and practice procedures for teaching basic facts. *Journal of Research in Mathematics Education,* 1981, **12,** 65–69.

Cohen, M.; Koehler, V.; Datta, L.; & Timpane, M. Instructionally effective schools: research area plan. Unpublished manuscript, National Institute of Education, 1980.

Cook, T. D., & Campbell, D. T. *Quasi-experimentation: design and analysis for field settings.* Chicago: Rand McNally, 1979.

Cooley, W. W., & Leinhardt, G. The instructional dimensions study. *Education Evaluation and Policy Analysis,* 1980, **2,** 7–25.

Coopersmith, S. *The antecedents of self-esteem.* San Francisco: W. H. Freeman, 1967.

Cowart, J. B.; Carnine, D.; & Becker, W. C. The effects of signals on child behaviors during Distar instruction. In *Analysis of achievement data on six cohorts of low-income children from 20 school districts in the University of Oregon Direct Instruction Follow Through model* (Technical Report 76-1, Appendix A). Eugene: University of Oregon, 1976.

Crandall, V. C.; Katkowsky, W.; & Crandall, V. J. Children's beliefs in their own control of reinforcements in intellectual-academic achievement situations. *Child Development,* 1965, **36,** 91–109.

Darch, C.; Carnine, D.; & Gersten, R. Instructional approaches and level of practice in fourth-grade math problem solving. Paper presented at the annual meeting of the American Educational Research Association, Montreal, April 1983.

Durost, W. N.; Bixler, H.; Wrightstone, J.; Prescott, G.; & Balow, I. *Metropolitan Achievement Test.* New York: Harcourt Brace Jovanovich, 1971.

Engelmann, S. E., & Carnine, D. W. *Distar arithmetic III.* Chicago: Science Research Associates, 1972.

Engelmann, S. E., & Carnine, D. W. *Distar arithmetic I* (2d ed.). Chicago: Science Research Associates, 1975.

Engelmann, S. E., & Carnine, D. W. *Distar arithmetic II* (2d ed.). Chicago: Science Research Associates, 1976.

Engelmann, S., & Carnine, D. W. *Theory of instruction.* New York: Irvington, 1982.

Fisher, C. W.; Berliner, D. C.; Filby, N. N.; Marliave, R.; Cahen, L. S.; & Dishaw, M. M. Teaching behaviors, academic learning time, and student achievement: an overview. In C. Denham & A. Lieberman (Eds.), *Time to learn.* Washington, D.C.: USOE/ National Institute of Education, 1980.

Gersten, R. Final reports to Joint Dissemination Review Panel, National Institute of Education, for Direct Instruction Follow Through projects. In *Education programs that work: a* catalog of exemplary programs approved by the Joint Dissemination Review Panel (8th ed.). Washington, D.C.: Department of Education, National Diffusion Network Division, 1981.

Gersten, R.; Becker, W. C.; Heiry, T. J.; & White, W. A. Entry IQ and yearly academic growth of children in Direct Instruction programs: a longitudinal study of low SES children. Educational Evaluation and Policy Analysis, in press.

Gersten, R.; Carnine, D.; & Williams, P. Measuring implementation of a structural educational approach: an observational approach. Educational Evaluation and Policy Analysis, 1982, 4, 67–79.

Good, T. L., & Beckerman, T. M. Time on task: a naturalistic study in sixth-grade classrooms. Elementary School Journal, 1978, 78, 193–201.

Good, T., & Grouws, D. The Missouri Mathematics Effectiveness Project. Journal of Educational Psychology, 1979, 71, 355–362.

Guthrie, J. T. Research views—Follow Through: a compensatory education experiment. Reading Teacher, 1977, 3, 240–244.

Haney, W. A technical history of the national Follow Through evaluation. Cambridge, Mass.: Huron Institute, August 1977.

House, E. R.; Glass, G. V.; McLean, L. D.; & Walker, D. F. No simple answer: critique of the "Follow Through" evaluation. Harvard Educational Review, 1978, 28, 128–160.

Jastak, J. F., & Jastak, S. R. The Wide Range Achievement Test. Wilmington, Del.: Guidance Associates of Delaware, 1965.

McDaniels, G. L. The evaluation of Follow Through. Educational Researcher, 1975, 4, 7–11.

McLean, L. D. Evaluation of early childhood education: no simple answer to the right questions. Paper presented at the conference entitled "Nature, Nurture, and School Achievement." York University, Toronto, May 1978.

Meyer, L. A.; Gersten, R. M.; & Gutkin, J. Direct Instruction: a Project Follow Through success story in an inner-city school. Elementary School Journal, 1983, 84, 241–252.

Molitor, J.; Watkin, N.; Napior, D.; & Proper, E. C. Education as experimentation: the non-Follow Through study. Cambridge, Mass.: Abt, 1977.

Morimitsu, C. Supervision of Direct Instruction. Unpublished manuscript, University of Oregon, 1979.

Nagel, T., & McLevie, J. Status Report 1 on the progress of implementing the Achievement Goals Program in San Diego schools. San Diego: Board of Education, 1981.

National Assessment of Educational Progress. Mathematical knowledge and skills. Washington, D.C.: National Institute of Education, August 1979. (ERIC Document Reproduc-

tion Service No. ED 176 964)

Nunnally, J. Psychometric theory (2d ed.). New York: McGraw-Hill, 1978.

Ozenne, D., et al. Annual evaluation report on programs administered by the U.S. Office of Education, fiscal year 1975. Washington, D.C.: Capital Publications, Educational Resources Division, 1976.

Peterson, P. L.; Janicki, T. C.; & Swing, S. R. Ability × treatment interactions effects on children's learning in large-group and small-group approaches. American Educational Research Journal, 1981, 18, 453–473.

Ramp, E. A., & Rhine, W. R. Behavior analysis model. In W. R. Rhine (Ed.), Encouraging change in America's schools: a decade of experimentation. New York: Academic Press, 1981.

Rosenshine, B. Classroom instruction. In N. L. Gage (Ed.), Psychology of teaching. Seventy-seventh yearbook of the National Society for the Study of Education. Chicago: National Society for the Study of Education, 1976.

Scheirer, M. A., & Kraut, R. E. Increasing educational achievement via self-concept change. Review of Educational Research, 1979, 49, 131–150.

Siegel, M. A. Teacher behavior and curriculum packages: implications for research and teacher education. In L. J. Rubin (Ed.), Handbook of curriculum. New York: Allyn & Bacon, 1977.

Silbert, J.; Carnine, D.; & Stein, M. Direct Instruction mathematics. Chicago: Merrill, 1981.

Slosson, R. L. Slosson Intelligence Test. East Aurora, N.Y.: Slosson Educational Publications, 1963.

Stallings, J. Implementation and child effects of teaching practices in Follow Through classrooms. Monographs of the Society for Research in Child Development, 1975, 40(7–8, Serial No. 163).

Stallings, J., & Kaskowitz, D. Follow-through classroom observation evaluation, 1972–73. Menlo Park, Calif.: Stanford Research Institute, 1974.

Stebbins, L. B. (Ed.). Education as experimentation: a planned variation model. Vol. 3A. Cambridge, Mass.: Abt, 1976.

Stebbins, L. B.; St. Pierre, R. G.; Proper, E. C.; Anderson, R. B.; & Cerva, T. R. Education as experimentation: a planned variation model. Vols. 4A, 4C. An evaluation of Follow Through. Cambridge, Mass.: Abt, 1977.

Stevenson, H. W. Learning and cognition. In J. N. Payne (Ed.), Mathematics learning in early childhood. Reston, Va.: National Council of Teachers in Mathematics, 1975.

Wisler, C.; Burns, J.; & Iwamoto, D. Follow Through: a response to the critique by House, Glass, McLean, and Walker. Harvard Educational Review, 1978, 48, 171–185.

Wolf, R. Review of Metropolitan Achievement Test. In O. K. Buros (Ed.), The sixth mental measurements yearbook. Highland Park, N.J.: Gryphon, 1978.

References

Abt Associates. *Education as experimentation: A planned variation model* (Vol. 3A). Cambridge, MA.: Abt Associates, 1976.

Abt Associates. *Education as experimentation: A planned variation model* (Vol. 4B). Cambridge, MA.: Abt Associates, 1977.

Aiken, Lewis R., Jr. Verbal factors and mathematics learning: A review of research. *Journal for Research in Mathematics Education*, 1971, *2*, 304–313.

Aiken, L. R. Language factors in learning mathematics. *Review of Educational Research*, 1971, *42*, 359–385.

Alberto, P. A. & Troutman, A. C. *Applied behavior analysis for teachers.* (3rd Ed.) Columbus, OH: Merrill Publishing Co., 1990.

Alessi, G. J. *Effects of Hutchings' "low stress" algorithms on children's addition scores under varying conditions of token economy reinforcement and problem difficulty.* University of Maryland Arithmetic Center Monograph #10, 1974.

Ashcraft, M. H. Is it farfetched that some of us remember our arithmetic facts? *Journal for Research in Mathematics Education*, 1985, *16* (2), 99–105.

Ashcraft, M. H., & Furman, B. A. Mental addition in third, fourth, and sixth graders. *Journal of Experimental Child Psychology*, 1982, *33*, 216–234.

Ashlock, R. B. Teaching the basic facts: Three classes of activities. *The Arithmetic Teacher*, 1971, *18*, 359.

Ashlock, R. B., & Herman, W. L. *Current research in elementary school mathematics.* New York: Macmillan, 1970.

Bailey, T. G. Linear measurement in the elementary school. *The Arithmetic Teacher*, 1974, *21*, 520–525.

Ballew, H., & Cunningham, J. W. Diagnosing strengths and weaknesses of sixth-grade students in solving word problems. *Journal for Research in Mathematics Education*, 1982, *13*, 202–210.

Balow, B. The long term effect of remedial reading instruction. *The Reading Teacher*, 1965, *18*, 581–586.

Balow, I. H. Reading and computation ability as determinants of problem solving in arithmetic. *Journal of Educational Research*, 1964, *11*, 18–22.

Bana, J. P. & Nelson, D. Some effects in nonverbal mathematical problems. *The Alberta Journal of Educational Research*, 1977, *23*, 268–279.

Baroody, A. J. Mastery of basic number combinations: Internalization of relationships or facts. *Journal for Research Mathematics Education*, 1985, *16* (2), 83–98.

Baroody, A. J. The development of counting strategies for single digit addition. *Journal for Research in Mathematics Education*, 1987, *18* (2), 141–157.

Baroody, A. J. & Ginsburg, H. P. The effects of instruction on children's understanding of the equals sign. *The Elementary School Journal*, 1983, *84* (2), 199–212.

Barr, D. C. A comparison of three methods of introducing two-digit numeration. *Journal for Research in Mathematics Education*, 1978, *9*, 33–43.

Bassler, O. C., Beers, M. I., & Richardson, L. Comparison of two instructional strategies for teaching the solution of verbal problems. *Journal for Research in Mathematics Education*, 1975, *6*, 171–177.

Bean, J. E. Arithmetic understanding of elementary school teachers. *Elementary School Journal*, 1959, *59*, 447–450.

Becker, W. C., Engelmann, S., & Carnine, D. W. The direct instruction model. In R. Rhine (Ed.), *Encouraging change in America's schools: A decade of experimentation.* New York: Academic Press, in press.

Becker, W. C. *Applied psychology for teachers.* Chicago, IL: Science Research Associates, 1986.

Beentjes, J., & Jonker, V. Inconsistency in addition and subtraction strategies. *Journal of Experimental Education*, 1987, *56*, 4–7.

Begle, E. *Critical variables in mathematics education.* Washington, D.C.: National Council of Teachers of Mathematics, 1979.

Behr, M. J., Washsmuth, I., Post, J. R., & Lesh, R. Order and equivalence of rational numbers: A clinical teaching experiment. *Journal for Research in Mathematics Education*, 1984, *15* (5), 323–341.

Bellamy, T., & Buttars, K. L. Teaching trainable level retarded students to count money: Toward personal independence through academic instruction. *Education and Training of the Mentally Retarded*, 1975, *10*, 18–25.

Blankenship, C., & Lovitt, T. Story problems: Merely confusing or downright befuddling? *Journal for Research in Mathematics Education*, 1976, *7*, 290–298.

Bloom, B. S. *Human characteristics and school learning.* New York: McGraw-Hill, 1976.

Bolster, L. C., Crown, W., et al. *Scott, Foresman Mathematics.* Glenview, Ill: Scott, Foresman Publishing Co., Inc., 1985.

Brophy, J. E., & Evertson, C. M. *Learning from teaching: A developmental perspective.* Boston: Allyn & Bacon, 1976.

Brownell, W. A. The effects of practicing a complex arithmetical skill upon proficiency in its constituent skills. *Journal of Educational Research*, 1953, *44*, 65–81.

Brownell, W. & Carper, D. V. Learning the multiplication combinations. *Duke University Studies in Education*, 1943, *7*, 1–177.

Brownell, W. A., Doty, R. A., & Rein, W. C. *Arithmetic in grades 1 and 2: A critical summary of new and previously reported research.* Durham, N.C.: Duke University Press, 1941.

Burton, W. H. *The guidance of learning activities: A summary of the principles of teaching based upon the growth of the learner.* New York: Appleton-Century-Crofts, 1952.

Cacha, F. B. Subtraction: Regrouping with flexibility. *The Arithmetic Teacher*, 1975, *22*, 402–404.

Callahan, L. G. & Glennon, V. J. *Elementary school mathematics: A guide to current research.* Washington, D. C.: Association for Supervision and Curriculum Development, 1977.

Carnine, D. W. *Comparing a Distar and a practice only treatment in teaching three fraction skills.* Follow Through Technical Report, University of Oregon, 1976.

Carnine, D. W. Preteaching versus concurrent teaching of the component skills of a multiplication algorithm. *Journal for Research in Mathematics Education*, 1980, *11* (5), 375–378.

Carnine, D. W., & Engelmann, S. *Corrective mathematics.* Chicago: Science Research Associates, 1981.

Carnine, D., & Silbert, J. *Direct instruction reading.* (2nd ed.) Columbus, OH: Merrill, 1990.

Carnine, D. W., & Stein, M. Organizational strategies and practice procedures for teaching basic facts. *Journal for Research in Mathematics Education*, 1981, *12* (1), 65–69.

Carpenter, T. P., Coburn, T. G., Reys, R. E., & Wilson, J. W. Note from national assessment: Word problems. *The Arithmetic Teacher*, 1976, *23*, 389–393.

Carpenter, T., Coburn, T., Reys, R., Wilson, J., & Corbitt, J. *Results from the first mathematics assessment of the national assessment of educational progress.* Reston, VA.: National Council of Teachers of Mathematics, 1978.

Carpenter, T. P., Corbitt, M. K., Kepner, H. S., Jr., Lindquist, M. M., & Reys, R. E. Solving verbal problems: Results and implications from national assessment. *The Arithmetic Teacher*, 1980, *28* (1), 8–12.

Carpenter, T. P., & Moser, J. M. The acquisition of addition and subtraction concepts in grades one through three. *Journal for Research in Mathematics Education*, 1984, *15* (3), 179–202.

Clark, C. M, Gage, N. L, Marx, R. W., Peterson, P. L., Stayrook, N. G., & Winnie, P. H. *A factorially designed experiment on teacher structuring, soliciting, and reacting. Final report.* Stanford, CA: Center for Research and Development in Teaching (ERIC Document Reproduction Service No. ED 134 591), 1976.

Cook, C. J., & Dossey, J. A. Basic fact thinking strategies for multiplication—revisited. *Journal for Research in Mathematics Education*, 1982, *13* (3), 163–171.

Damus, M. E. How to teach verbal problems. *School Science and Mathematics*, 1970, *70*, 121–138.

Davis, E. J. Suggestions for teaching the basic facts of arithmetic. In M. N. Suydam & R. E. Reys (Eds.), *Developing computational skills: 1978 yearbook.* Reston, VA.: National Council of Teachers of Mathematics, 1978.

Days, H. C., Wheatley, G. H., & Kuhn, G. Problem structure, cognitive level, and problem-solving performance. *Journal for Research in Mathematics Education*, 1979, *10*, 35–146.

Dilley, C., Rucker, W., & Jackson, A. *Elementary mathematics, Level II, Teacher's guide.* Boston, MA: Heath, 1975.

Dilley, C. A., Rucker, W. E., & Jackson, A. E. *Heath Elementary Mathematics.* Lexington, MA: Heath, 1975.

Divincenzo, R. M. Clustering operations: A more efficient alternative for teaching common fraction operations. *School Science and Mathematics*, 1979, 328–332.

Edge, D., & Ashlock, R. B. Using multiple embodiments of place value concepts. *Alberta Journal of Educational Research*, 1982, *28* (3), 276–279.

Elementary School Mathematics Committee. If you don't know how their children think, how can you help them? *The Arithmetic Teacher*, 1975, 580–585.

Engelmann, S. *Conceptual learning.* San Rafael, CA: Dimensions Publishing Co., 1969.

Engelmann, S. E., & Carnine, D. W. *Cognitive learning: A direct instruction perspective.* Chicago: Science Research Association, 1982.

Engelmann, S. E., & Carnine, D. W. *Distar arithmetic I* (2nd ed.). Chicago: Science Research Associates, 1975.

Engelmann, S., & Osborn, J. *Distar language I.* Chicago: Science Research Associates, 1976.

Engelmann, S., & Osborn, J. *Distar language II.* Chicago: Science Research Associates, 1977.

Fleischner, J. E., Nuzum, M. B., & Marzola, E. S. Devising an instructional program to teach arithmetic problem-solving skills to students with learning disabilities. *Journal of Learning Disabilities*, 1987, *20*, 214–217.

Fuson, K. C., & Brinker, K. J. The comparative effectiveness of microcomputers and flash cards in the drill and practice of basic math facts. *Journal for Research in Mathematics Education*, 1985, *16* (3), 225–232.

Gilmary, S. Transfer effects of reading remediation to arithmetic computation when intelligence is controlled and all other school factors are eliminated. *The Arithmetic Teacher*, 1967, *14*, 17–20.

Glennon, V. J. A study in needed redirection in the preparation of teachers of arithmetic. *The Mathematics Teacher*, 1949, *42*, 386–396.

Goodstein, H. A., Bessant, H., Thibodeau, G., Vitello, S., & Vlahakos, I. The effect of three variables on the verbal problem solving of educable mentally handicapped children. *American Journal of Mental Deficiency*, 1972, *76*, 702–709.

Grossnickle, F. E., & Perry, L.M. Division with common fraction and decimal divisors. *School Science and Mathematics*, 1985, *85* (7), 556–565.

Guthrie, J. T. Follow Through: A compensation education experiment. *The Reading Teacher*, 1977, *31* (2), 240–244.

Hiebert, J. The position of the unknown set and children's solutions of verbal arithmetic problems. *Journal for Research in Mathematics Education*, 1982, *13*, 341–349.

Houlihan, D. M., & Ginsburg, H. P. The addition methods of first and second grade children. *Journal of Research in Mathematics Education*, 1981, *12* (2), 95–106.

House, Glass, McLean, & Walker. No simple answer: Critique of the Follow Through evaluation. *Harvard Educational Review*, 1978, *48*, 128–160.

Howard, D. P. The needs and problems of socially disadvantaged children as perceived by students and teachers. *Exceptional Children*, 1968, *34*, 327–335.

Hunicutt, C. W., & Iverson, W. J. *Research in the three R's*. New York: Harper, 1958.

Husen, T. (Ed.). *International study of achievement in mathematics: A comparison of twelve countries* (Vols. 1 & 2). New York: John Wiley & Sons, 1967.

Hutchings, L. Low-stress subtraction. *The Arithmetic Teacher*, 1975, *22*, 228–232.

Jackson, M. B., & Phillips, E. R. Vocabulary instruction in ratio and proportion for seventh graders. *Journal for Research in Mathematics Education*, 1983, *14* (4), 337–343.

Jerman, M., & Beardslee, E. *Elementary mathematics methods*. New York: McGraw-Hill, 1978.

Jerman, M. Individualized instruction in problem solving in elementary school mathematics. *Journal for Research in Mathematics Education*, 1973, *4*, 6–19.

Jerman, M. E. & Mirman, S. Linguistic and computational variables in problem solving in elementary mathematics. *Educational Studies in Mathematics*, 1974, *5*, 317–362.

Jerman, M., & Rees, R. Predicting the relative difficulty of verbal arithmetic problems. *Educational Studies in Mathematics*, 1972, *4*, 306–323.

Jerman, M., & Sanford, M. Linguistic and computational variables in problem solving in elementary mathematics. *Educational Studies in Mathematics*, 1974, *5*, 317–62.

Jerons, S. M. & Peck, D. M. Missing addend problems. *School Science and Mathematics*, 1976, *76*, 647–661.

Jones, E. D., Krouse, J., Feorene, D., & Saferstein, C. A. A comparison of concurrent and sequential instruction of four types of verbal math problems. *Remedial and Special Education*, 1985, *6* (5), 25–31.

Kameenui, E., Chadwick, J., & Carnine, D. W. Preteaching versus concurrent teaching of the component skills of a subtraction algorithm to skill deficient second graders: A component analysis of direction instruction. *The Exceptional Child*, 1986, *33* (2), 103–115.

Kameenui, E., Carnine, D., Darch, C., & Stein, M. Two approaches to the development phase of mathematics instruction. *Elementary School Journal*, 1986, *86* (5), 633–650.

Kameenui, E. J., Griffin, C. C., & Hytner, G. P. *An analysis of word problem solving instruction in two basal mathematics series and editions*. Unpublished manuscript, Purdue University, Lafayette, IN, 1988.

Kelly, B., Gersten, R., & Carnine, D. Student error patterns as a function of curriculum design: Teaching fraction to learning disabled and remedial high school students. *Journal of Learning Disabilities*, in press.

Kenney, R. A. Mathematical understandings of elementary school teachers. *The Arithmetic Teacher*, 1965, *12*, 431–442.

Kleinfeld, J. Effective teachers of Eskimo and Indian students. *School Review*, 1975, *11*, 301–344.

Knifong, J. D., & Holtan, B. An analysis of children's written solutions to word problems. *Journal for Research in Mathematics Education*, 1976, *7*, 106–112.

Knifong, J. D., & Holtan, B. D. A search for reading difficulties among erred word problems. *Journal for Research in Mathematics Education*, 1977, *8*, 227–230.

Knifong, J. D., & Holtan, B. D. Computational requirements of standardized word problem tests. *Journal for Research in Mathematics Education*, 1980, *11*, 3–9.

Kratzer, R. O., & Willoughby, S. S. A comparison of initially teaching division employing the distributive and Greenwood algorithms with the aid of a manipulative material. *Journal for Research in Mathematics Education*, 1973, *4*, 197–204.

Lankford, F. G. What can a teacher learn about a pupil's thinking through oral interviews? *The Arithmetic Teacher*, 1974, *21*, 26–32.

Lindquist, M., Carpenter, T. P., Silver, E. A., & Matthews, W. The Third National Mathematics Assessment: Results and implications for elementary and middle schools. *Arithmetic Teacher*, 1983, *31* (4), 14–19.

Lindvall, C. M. & Ibarra, C. B. Incorrect procedures used by primary grade pupils in solving open addition and subtraction sentences. *Journal for Research in Mathematics Education*, 1980, 11, 50–61.

Lindvall, C., Mauritz, I , & Gibbons, C. *An analysis of incorrect procedures used by primary grade pupils in solving open addition and subtraction sentences*. Paper presented at the annual meeting of the American Educational Research Association, Toronto, Canada, March 1978. Pittsburgh: Learning Research and Development Center, University of Pittsburgh, 1978.

Linville, W. J. Syntax, vocabulary and the verbal arithmetic problem. *School Science and Mathematics*, 1976, *76*, 152–157.

Loftus, E. F., & Suppes, P. Structural variables that determine problem-solving difficulty in computer-assisted instruction. *Journal of Educational Psychology*, 1972, *63*, 531–542.

McDaniels, G. Follow Through yields new evidence of school effects. Education Daily, 1975, *5*.

McGinty, R. L., VanBeynen, J., & Zalewski, D. Do our mathematics textbooks reflect what we preach? *School Science and Mathematics*, 1986, *86*, 591–596.

Murray, J. The relative difficulty of the basic number facts. *Studies in Arithmetic* (Vol. 10). London: University of London Press, 1939.

Muth, K. D. Solving arithmetic word problems: Role of reading and computational skills. *Journal of Educational Psychology*, 1984, *76*, 205–210.

Nibbelink, W. H., Stockdale, S. R., Hoover, H. D., & Mangru, M. Problem solving in the elementary grades: Textbook practices and achievement trends over the past thirty years. *Arithmetic Teacher*, 1987, *35*, 34–37.

Nichols, E. D., Fennell, F. M., Anderson, P. A., Floutney, F., et al. *Holt Mathematics*. New York: Holt Publishing Co., Inc., 1985.

O'Daffer, P. G., Fleenor, C. R., et al. *Addison-Wesley Mathematics*. Menlo Park, CA: Addison-Wesley Publishing Co., 1985.

Overman, J. R. An experimental study of the effect of the method of instruction on transfer of training in arithmetic. *Elementary School Journal*, 1930, *31*, 183–190.

Pace, A. Understanding and the ability to solve problems. *The Arithmetic Teacher*, 1961, *8*, 226–233.

Paine, S. C. Structuring classrooms for success: A direct instruction approach. Eugene, OR: University of Oregon, 1980.

Peck, D. M., & Jencks, S. M. Conceptual issues in the teaching and learning of fractions. *Journal for Research on Mathematics Education*, 1981, *12* (5), 339–348.

Pellegrino, J. W., & Goldman, S. R. Information processing and elementary mathematics. *Journal of Learning Disabilities*, 1987, *20* (1), 23–32.

Petty, O. S., & Jansson, L. C. Sequencing examples and nonexamples to facilitate concept attainment. *Journal for Research in Mathematics Education*, 1987, *18* (2), 112–125.

Pincus, M., Coonan, M., Glasser, H., Levy, L., Morgenstern, F., & Shapiro, H. If you don't know how children think, how can you help them? *The Arithmetic Teacher*, 1975, *22*, 580–585.

Poyla, G. *How to solve it.* New York: Doubleday, 1957.

Rathmell, E. C. The effects of multibase grouping and early or late introductions of base representations on the mastery learning of base and place value numeration in grade one. Doctoral dissertation, University of Michigan. *Dissertation Abstracts International*, 1973, *33* 6071A. (University Microfilms No. 73–11, 237), 1972.

Resnick, L. What do we mean by meaningful learning? Paper presented at the National Convention of the American Education Research Association, 1980.

Rieth, H. J., Polsgrove, L., & Semmel, M. I. Relationship between instructional time and academic achievement: Implications for research and practice. *Education Unlimited,* 1979.

Rosenshine, B. Classroom instruction. In N.E. Gage (Ed.), *The psychology of teaching methods.* Seventy-fifth yearbook of the National Society for the Study of Education. Chicago: University of Chicago Press, 1976.

Rosenshine, B. Content, time and direct instruction. In P. L. Peterson & H. J. Wahlberg (Eds.), *Research on teaching: Concepts, findings, and implications.* Berkeley, CA.: McCutchan, 1979.

Rosenshine, B., & Berliner, D. C. Academic engaged time. *British Journal of Teacher Education*, 1978, *4*, 3–16.

Rosenthal, D. J. A. & Resnick, L. B. Children's solution processes in arithmetic word problems. *Journal of Educational Psychology*, 1974, *66*, 817–825.

Rucker, W. E., Dilley, C. A., & Lowry, D. A. *Heath Mathematics*, Lexington, MA.: Heath Publishing Co., Inc., 1987.

Sauls, C., & Beeson, B. F. The relationship of finger counting to certain pupil factors. *Journal of Educational Research*, 1976, *70*, 81–83.

Schminke, C., Maeterns, N., & Arnold, W. *Teaching the child mathematics.* New York: Holt, 1978.

Scott, L. Children's concept of scale and subtraction of fractions. *The Arithmetic Teacher*, 1962, *9*, 115–118.

Secada, W. G., Fuscon, K. C., & Hall J. W. The transition from counting-all to counting-on in addition. *Journal of Research in Mathematics Education*, 1983, *14* (1), 47–57.

Sedlak, R. A. Performance of good and poor problem solvers on arithmetic word problems presented in a modified cloze format. *Journal of Educational Research*, 1974, *67*, 467–471.

Smith, R. F. Diagnosis of pupil performance on place value tasks. *The Arithmetic Teacher*, 1973, *20*, 403–408.

Soar, R. S. Teacher-pupil interaction. In *A new look at progressive education* (yearbook). Washington, D.C.: Association for Supervision and Curriculum Development, 1972.

Spradlin, E. E., Cotter, V. W., Stevens, C., & Friedman, M. Performance of mentally retarded children on pre-arithmetic tasks. *American Journal of Mental Deficiency*, 1974, *78*, (4), 397–403.

Staats, A. W., Brewer, B. A., & Gross, M. C. Learning and cognitive development: Representative samples, cumulative hierarchical learning and counting learning mediated by verbal-response chains. *Monographs of the Society for Research in Child Development*, 1970, *35* (Serial No. 141).

Stallings, J. Implementation and child effects of teaching practices in Follow-Through classrooms. *Monographs of the Society for Research in Child Development*, 1975, *40*, (7–8) (Serial No. 163).

Stebbins, L., Proper, E., St. Pierre, R., & Cerva, T. *Education as experimentation. A planned variation model* (Vol. 4). Cambridge, MA: Abt Associates, 1977.

Steinberg, R. M. Instruction on derived facts strategies in addition and subtraction. *Journal for Research in Mathematics Education*, 1985, *16* (5), 337–355.

Suydam, M. N., & Dessart, D. J. *Classroom ideas from research on computational skills.* Reston, VA: National Council of Teachers of Mathematics, 1976.

Suydam, M. N., & Reys, R. E. (Eds.). *Developing computational skills: 1978 yearbook.* Reston, VA.: National Council of Teachers of Mathematics, 1978.

Thibodeau, G. P. Manipulation of numerical presentation in verbal problems and its effect on verbal problem solving among EMH children. *Education and Training of the Mentally Retarded*, 1974, *9*, 9–14.

Thornton, C. A. Emphasizing thinking strategies in basic fact instruction. *Journal for Research in Mathematics Education*, 1978, *9*, 214–227.

Trace, M. W., Cuvo, A. J., & Criswell, J. L. Teaching coin equivalence to the mentally retarded. *Journal of Applied Behavior Analysis*, 1977, *10* (1), 85–92.

Underhill, R. G. *Teaching elementary school mathematics* (3rd ed.). Columbus, OH: Merrill, 1981.

Vanderlinde, L. F. Does the study of quantitative vocabulary improve problem solving? *The Elementary School Journal*, 1964, *65*, 143–152.

Weaver, J. F. A crucial problem in the preparation of elementary school teachers. *Elementary School Journal*, 1956, *56*, 255–261.

Wheatley, G., & Wheatley, C. How shall we teach column addition? Some evidence. *The Arithmetic Teacher*, 1978, *24*, 18–19.

Wheeler, L. J., & McNutt, G. The effect of syntax on low-achieving students' abilities to solve mathematical word problems. *The Journal of Special Education*, 1983, *17*, 309–315.

Wilson, J. The role of structure in verbal problem solving. *The Arithmetic Teacher*, 1967, *14*, 486–496.

Wolters, M.A.D. The part-whole schema and arithmetical problems. *Educational Studies in Mathematics*, 1983, *14*, 127–138.

Index